BIOLOGICAL STAINS

A Handbook on the
Nature and Uses of the
Dyes Employed in
the Biological Laboratory

SEVENTH EDITION

BALTIMORE, MARYLAND · 1961

BIOLOGICAL STAINS

by H. J. Conn

prepared with the collaboration of various members of the Biological Stain Commission

Revised with the assistance of

E. H. Stotz, V. M. Emmel
and Mary A. Darrow

with two chapters on Histochemical Reagents by

R. D. Lillie and G. G. Glenner respectively

THE WILLIAMS & WILKINS COMPANY

COMPOSED AND PRINTED AT THE

WAVERLY PRESS, INC.

BALTIMORE, MD., U.S.A.

PREFACE

The current edition follows the precedent of previous ones in gradually extending the scope of the book and increasing its accuracy. This edition even more than heretofore, has had the cooperation of other members of the Biological Stain Commission, and for this the author is grateful. Special thanks are due to H. A. Davenport, Louis Gershenfeld, E. K. Kline, R. D. Lillie and the late S. I. Kornhauser for their assistance, and particularly to Mary A. Darrow, V. M. Emmel, and Elmer H. Stotz for their active participation in the preparation of the manuscript of this seventh edition.

Special attention should be called to two new chapters on histochemical reagents which have been contributed by two of the collaborators: one on diazonium salts by R. D. Lillie, and one on tetrazolium compounds by G. G. Glenner. These two chapters expand the scope of the book considerably.

Appendix II, dealing with methods of testing stains for certification, has been carefully brought up to date by three members of the Commission's Rochester laboratory: V. M. Emmel, Mary A. Darrow, and Nicholas Parente. The average reader of this book may seldom have occasion to refer to this appendix, but it is called to the user's attention because some of the methods included are of value in general laboratory usage. For other procedures it should be noticed that numerous page references are given throughout this book to methods described in the second edition of the Commission's other book, *Staining Procedures* (Williams & Wilkins Co., 1960).

The general objects of this book have not been changed since the first edition appeared in 1925. As they were well stated in the preface to that book it is here repeated.

Geneva, N. Y.

H. J. Conn

v

PREFACE TO FIRST EDITION

When microscopists first began, in the sixties and seventies, to use stains, the demand for dyes for this purpose was naturally too small to justify a special source of supply. They therefore had to make use of textile dyes, which were then very crude and were not constant in their composition. After a number of years, however, the demand for biological stains grew and a special commercial source of supply for them first appeared in Germany. This was the Dr. G. Grübler and Co. This company did not manufacture the dyes, as used commonly to be thought in other countries; but on the other hand it cannot be denied that its founder made a distinct contribution to science in making the first effort to secure constancy and reliability in dyes intended solely for the use of the microscopist. It is supposed that he tested dyes under the microscope himself, and if a batch proved satisfactory in his experience bought a supply large enough for a number of years, bottled it under his own label and sold it to biologists. There is no question but that in this way the biologist was furnished with a much more reliable line of stains than if he had been obliged to buy directly from the dye manufacturers; but it was an empirical method of standardization and there was nothing to prevent different batches of some dye secured by this company from varying considerably in their composition. Such upon investigation has proved to be the case.

Although a great service was done to biologists by this company in the latter part of the nineteenth century, such methods of standardization are not in keeping with modern scientific knowledge. A recent cooperative undertaking has therefore been organized in America to put the standardization of stains upon a scientific basis. This undertaking started after the war had caused a shortage of stains, with the object of securing a reliable supply when the foreign sources were unavailable. It has since been widened in scope; and now that the foreign products are again available, the purpose of the work is to effect a scientific standardization of stains whether derived from foreign or domestic sources. As a matter of fact, so far only domestic samples have been considered. This has not been because of any prejudice against foreign stains, but because of practical difficulties; it is, in brief, difficult to test each batch before it is put on the market when the concern handling it is in Europe.

The organization through which this work is being carried on is known as the Commission on Standardization of Biological Stains. It was organized in 1922 under the auspices of the National Research Council and is still affiliated with it, although now no longer a part of the larger body. It is in effect a coordinating committee representing the American Chemical Society, the American Society of Bacteriologists, the Society of American Zoologists, the Botanical Society of America, the American Association of Pathologists and Bacteriologists and the American Association of Anatomists. It has a membership of about sixty biologists, members of the various societies just mentioned, who assist in the examination and testing of stains, each in those particular lines of technic with which he is especially familiar. It has secured the cooperation of chemists, dye manufacturers and stain dealers, so as to be sure that the needs of biologists can be reflected immediately in the supply of stains on the market. Its affairs are managed by an executive committee of five members, the present members of which represent bacteriology, botany, dye chemistry, pathology and zoology, respectively. This executive committee has undertaken the preparation of this book. The authorship of the book has been assumed by the chairman of the committee, however, in order to fix the responsibility and to make bibliographic references to it simpler than in the case of plural authorship; but the assistance of the other committee members in the work has been so great that they may be considered practically co-authors of the book. The chairman of the committee, therefore, wishes to take this occasion to acknowledge the invaluable assistance given by these other members. Without their cooperation such an undertaking would have been impossible.

The chief object of the book is to present in logical form the information which has been accumulating in the hands of the Commission since it was organized. It is neither a treatise on dye chemistry nor one on microscopy, although it contains information in both fields. It is an effort to present in a form acceptable to biologists the principles of dye chemistry so far as they have a bearing on biological stains; and to discuss the suitability of the different dyes for various biological purposes, presenting data partly original and partly drawn from the literature. The subject matter is realized to be incomplete, particularly that part of it which deals with the biological uses of dyes. An effort has been made to list the most important present uses of stains, and of the obsolete uses to mention those of historical significance; but it is realized that there must be many omissions. It is hoped that readers of the book will cooperate by calling to the author's attention places where the treatment of any subject seems inadequate.

H. J. Conn, *Chairman,*
Commission on Standardization
of Biological Stains.

Geneva, N. Y., 1925

TABLE OF CONTENTS

                                                                                                PAGE
Preface..   v
Chapter I. Uses and standardization of biological stains.......................   1
Chapter II. The general nature of dyes and their classification..............   15
Chapter III. The mechanism of staining.......................................   34
Chapter IV. The spectrophotometric and chromatographic analysis of dyes....   41
Chapter V. Nitro and azo dyes..   52
   1. Nitroso dyes...   52
   2. Nitro dyes...   53
   3. The azo group...   56
      Mono-azo dyes..   57
      Dis-azo and poly-azo dyes..   73
Chapter VI. The quinone-imine dyes..   90
   1. The indamins..   91
   2. The indophenols...   91
   3. The thiazins..   93
   4. The oxazins...   106
   5. The azins...   115
      Amino-azins or eurhodins...   115
      Safranins..   118
      Indulins...   124
Chapter VII. The phenyl methane dyes..   126
   1. Diphenyl methane derivatives...   128
   2. Triphenyl methane derivatives..   129
      Diamino triphenyl methanes...   130
      Triamino triphenyl methanes (rosanilins)...........................   136
      Hydroxy triphenyl methanes (rosolic acids).........................   161
   3. Diphenyl-naphthyl methane derivatives...................................   163
Chapter VIII. The xanthene dyes...   165
   1. The pyronins..   165
   2. The rhodamines..   168
   3. Fluoran derivatives (eosins)...   171
   4. Phenolphthalein and the sulfonphthaleins...............................   185
   5. Acridine dyes...   194
Chapter IX. Miscellaneous dyes and pigments...................................   199
   1. The anthraquinone group..   199
   2. Thiazole dyes...   204
   3. Quinoline dyes..   206
   4. Phthalocyanine dyes..   207
   5. Mineral pigments..   207
   6. Silver proteinates..   209
Chapter X. Diazonium and tetrazonium salts....................................   210

Chapter XI. Tetrazolium salts... 230
  1. Monotetrazolium salts... 231
  2. Ditetrazolium salts... 233
Chapter XII. Natural dyes.. 236
  1. Saffron.. 236
  2. The indigo group... 237
  3. Berberine... 238
  4. Cochineal products... 238
  5. Orcein and litmus.. 241
  6. Brazilin and hematoxylin... 243
Chapter XIII. Neutral stains.. 250
  1. Ehrlich's "tri-acid stain".. 252
  2. Thiazin cosinates.. 253
  3. Other compound stains... 259
Appendix I. Tables relating to stains....................................... 261
Appendix II. Methods for testing biological stains.......................... 276
Bibliography... 316
Index.. 340

I

USES AND STANDARDIZATION OF BIOLOGICAL STAINS

WHAT ARE STAINS?

A question frequently asked is, "what are biological stains and how do they differ from dyes?" The answer is simply that they *are* dyes, but are adapted for very special purposes. The manufacturer thinks of two classes of dyes, those intended for general purposes and those specially adapted for biological use. To him the "biologicals" are a class in themselves, notable chiefly because of the care with which they must be manufactured and the necessity of having them agree with rigid specifications so that they will be satisfactory for the delicate procedures in which they are employed. To the biologist, however, there are several classes of products included among the "biologicals" and not all of them are stains; there are medicinal dyes, bacteriostatic agents, and indicators, which are not truly stains but are put in the same group by the manufacturer. Strictly speaking, however, a biological stain is a dye used for making microscopic objects more clearly visible than they would be unstained. Such a dye may also serve for textile purposes as well; but usually a special grade is needed for biological use The same statement is equally true (perhaps more so) of medicinals and indicators; and since chemically they are all very similar they are all considered in this book. Chief stress, however, is laid on those which are employed primarily as stains.

THE HISTORY OF STAINING

Considering how dependent microscopists are today upon the use of stains, it is hard to realize that much important work had been done with the microscope before the use of stains was attempted. Although natural dyes such as carmine and indigo were well known in the early days of the microscope, their use in staining microscopic preparations does not seem to have become common till about 1850; and aniline dyes were not put on

1

the market until 1856. Yet anyone who has studied the history of biology must realize that many discoveries had been made with the microscope before this period.

It is safe to say, nevertheless, that the use of stains revolutionized microscopic technic. The early microscopists were able to make much progress without stains because of their painstaking diligence. The work without stains must have been extremely difficult, and it is hard on reading some of the old publications to believe that some of the minute structures described were actually seen. Few users of the microscope today would be likely to have either the patience or the eyesight to do the work described in those early days. The fact that the microscope is now being used successfully in the hands of so many students who would not think of comparing themselves with the pioneers in microscopy is due to the use of stains more than to any other factor—although, of course, no one can deny that modern improvements in the microscope have also played a part of great importance.

As a matter of fact, a revolution of a different sort, which has no relation to staining, is in progress at the present time. The last two decades have brought out more radical changes in microscope design than have been seen for the greater part of a century. These include not only the electron microscope, but also various applicitions of X-ray, phase contrast, reflecting optics, and fluorescence of chemicals (fluorochromes) which are not colored in ordinary light. What will be the outcome of such radical departures is still impossible to predict. One might almost assume that the use of improved types of microscopes would eventually eliminate the need of stains to render objects more easily visible—were it not for the equally rapid development in histochemistry, in which field dyes or similar reagents are apt to be needed for a long time to come.

The present is hardly the place to go into the history of staining in any detail; it has been adequately treated elsewhere. Gierke (1884) was the first to discuss the subject, and presented a fairly detailed account of the early uses of biological stains, as they were understood at that time in Germany, and brought the subject on which he wrote up to the date. Conn (1933, 1948) has presented a rather more cursory review on staining history, up to modern times, based on a study of moderately recent publications without making any search through old texts. Such a search has been made however, by Lewis (1942) who has presented the most thorough review of the beginnings of staining that has yet appeared, and shows that its origin can be traced way back to Leeuwenhoek, the "father of the microscope," and the first scientist to see bacteria.

Histological technic, as we know it today, seems to have become fairly well understood about 1860, and it embraced the use of certain natural dyes, notably carmine, but also indigo, madder, saffron and phytolacca. This rapid development of the subject followed a paper by Gerlach (1858) in which he particularly called attention to importance of staining (with carmine) in histology. It is not certain whether or not Gerlach thought he had originated the idea; but it is clear that he was hailed as the father of staining by many of his contemporaries, particularly in Germany. Careful students of the subject, however, like Gierke, took pains to explain that though Gerlach had established (eingefürt) staining technic, the actual use of dyes in microscopic work preceded him. Gierke cites Göppert and Cohn (1849) as the earliest users of biological stains. Subsequently, however, the introduction of stains into microscopic work has been ascribed to Ehrenberg (1838); then to Hill (1770); while now Lewis (1942) quotes from a letter written by Leeuwenhoek to the Royal Society in 1714 (published 1719) in which he mentions staining sections of muscle fibers in saffron to increase the visibility of the particles as viewed under one of his high power lenses.

One can never be certain how long any particular individual will remain credited with being the "first" to do something; but it is difficult to see how the use of dyes in microscopy can precede the invention of Leeuwenhoek's microscopes.

Following the work of the pioneers in staining the development of the subject was rapid, particularly after hematoxylin had been introduced by Waldeyer (1863) and more successfully by Böhmer (1865), aniline dyes by Beneke (1862) and alcohol differentiation by Böttcher (1869).

Gierke (1884), in his historical discussion of staining, says that the history up to his day was divided into three periods, each occupying a decade. The first decade, the fifties, was characterized by a few important but unrelated discoveries which ended in the work of Gerlach—each investigator follwed up accidental observations on the staining powers of carmine and the other well known dyes of those days. After Gerlach's work, the development of the technic in the sixties was more rapid and depended less upon chance success by the individual investigator; the effort was made to use similarly all the dyes and metallic colors then available. The next decade would have had much less left to develop in this line if it had not been that by this time the great variety of aniline dyes was available and microscopists were constantly finding new uses for them. Gierke wondered if there would be any opportunity for equal development during the 10 years to follow his paper.

That development did not stop in his day is well known. Scarcely a year has passed without the introduction of some new staining technic of considerable importance. Sometimes dyes hitherto unknown to the biologist have been shown to be valuable in bringing out some particular structure; at other times new combinations of dyes have proved of special value for other purposes; while by other investigators it has been shown that old methods used with modern refinements of apparatus and technic, may bring out details not dreamed of by the early histologists.

USES OF STAINS

Only a brief summary of the uses of stains is given here. More detailed citations are given under the discussion of the individual dyes throughout this book. Certain very general texts of the subject are also useful; among those which have proved most valuable sources of the information given in these pages are: Mann (1902), Ehrlich (1910), Krause (1926–1927), Lee (1950, and earlier editions), McClung (1950 and earlier editions).

Animal Microtechnic. Although the earliest uses of stains were botanical, modern histological technic was first developed on zoological material. As a result the first extensive use of stains was in animal histology. It is still true that there are many more staining procedures developed in animal histology than in plant histology, and that many more dyes are thus employed in the former field than in the latter.

In animal histology one thinks first of the *general tissue stains*. These involve the use of one, two, and occasionally three dyes in staining sections of general animal tissue designed primarily to differentiate nuclei from cytoplasm of cells and to permit distinctions between the various types of tissue. Best known of these are the various procedures calling for hematoxylin, sometimes alone and sometimes with a counterstain, such as eosin Y, Congo red, or safranin; the hematoxylin-eosin combination is in such general use that it is commonly referred to as the "H-E stain." Although these hematoxylin procedures have received many modern refinements, they date back to the 19th century and still bear the names of Heidenhain, Delafield, and Mayer, men who did their chief work in the eighties and nineties. Also included among the general tissue stains are various combinations of basic dyes such as crystal violet, methylene blue or one of the azures, with some contrasting acid dye such as eosin Y; the former to stain the nuclei, the latter, the cytoplasm of the cells.

Somewhat more specialized in their application are the *connective tissue stains*. The distinction between them and the general tissue stains is more or less arbitrary, particularly because some procedures that bring out connective tissue and elastin to good advantage are also fine general tissue stains. The grouping can, however, be made in a rough way and for practical purposes is rather convenient. Of special note among the connective tissue stains is a triple-staining procedure proposed by Mallory, which in its original form called for the dyes, aniline blue, orange G, and acid fuchsin; its important feature is mordanting in phosphotungstic acid before applying the final staining fluid. It has been variously modified in recent years and the variants are usually called modifications of the "Mallory aniline blue connective tissue stain," although some of them omit the aniline blue entirely. Among connective tissue stains are also included a variety of double, triple, and even quadruple stains of a miscellaneous nature, and the well known Mallory phosphotungstic acid hematoxylin method, in which such strong polychrome properties of the dye are developed that no counterstain is necessary to secure proper differentiation of tissue.

A third important group of methods in animal microtechnic includes those for *neurological staining*. These methods are very numerous and all highly specialized. Many of them (as is true of some methods for demon-strating connective tissue) are not actually dyeing procedures, but depend on the use of silver salts with which tissue elements are impregnated so that the desired structures are made visible when the salts are converted into metallic silver. As these silver methods do not involve dyes, no attention is given to them in the following pages. (They are, however, described in *Staining Procedures** Chapters 3–5.) This is not to say, however, that dyes are not used by neurologists in microtechnic; many such methods, as a matter of fact, do call for dyes, either with or without impregnation of the tissue with metallic salts.

In addition to these three groups of procedures in animal histology, there are stains for other types of tissue and body fluids. Fats, for example, are stained by special oil soluble dyes, such as Sudan IV. Blood has its own special methods of staining, most of which depend on the use of compound stains, prepared by allowing eosin or a related dye to react upon a mixture of dyes of the methylene blue group; such compound dyes are also useful in staining bone marrow. Bone has its own special methods, many of which depend on the use of alizarin red S, which is particularly valuable by dem-onstrating bone in small specimens that have been cleared by treatment in alkali.

Histochemistry. Many of the above-mentioned specialized staining meth-ods may yield actual chemical information as to the nature of cell con-stituents, but were, in general, not designed to do so. Some theories of staining do postulate chemical affinities to explain differential staining; but they do not go very far in the matter, chiefly because stains are ordinarily applied to fixed tissue, whose chemical nature is realized to be very differ-ent from that which occurs in nature. The introduction, however, of rapid freezing methods is now enabling histochemists to avoid chemical fixation and is giving them material for study which is more nearly representative of natural conditions. Also their study of enzymes on the one hand, and their identification of the individual nucleic acis on the other are gradually giving them criteria to show which stains or other reagents are actually

* Conn, Darrow, and Emmel (1960).

specific for definite cytochemical ingredients. Especially important has become the use of the Schiff reagent (fuchsin-sulphurous acid), after some oxidizing agent, in the identification of mucopolysaccharides. Developments in histochemistry are now becoming so rapid that predictions are hard to make. The histochemical reagents of the future will probably be primarily chemicals other than dyes.

Plant Histology. A rough grouping of the most common plant histological methods can be made by recognizing general tissue stains and stains for woody tissue. This grouping is no more absolute, however, than the separation between general tissue stains and connective tissue stains in the zoological field. Probably the most frequently used dye in botanical microtechnic is hematoxylin, which is employed in a number of procedures either for general tissue or woody tissue. Another very valuable dye is safranin which is one of the best nuclear stains employed in botanical work; with a green or blue counterstain, very effective pictures are obtained.

Various combinations of stains have been employed for certain more highly specialized purposes, such as staining fungi in tissues, or for demonstrating pollen tubes in the style. For such purposes as this, numerous dyes have been called for, such as thionin, orange G, martius yellow, malachite green, acid fuchsin, methyl green, carmine, basic fuchsin, and lacmoid. It is nevertheless true, as stated above, that there is by no means such a variety of staining procedures in plant histology as in the zoological field.

Plant Cytology. Although the statement just made is true in the general histological field, it cannot be made in regard to cytology. The earliest cytological work was done with plant material, probably because of the greater ease with which rapidly dividing cells (meristematic tissue) can be obtained from plants than from animals. The result is a very considerable variety of procedures in plant cytology. Best known among them, undoubtedly, are: the variations of the hematoxylin methods; the Flemming triple stain, which calls for crystal violet, safranin, and orange G; and the acetocarmine method employed for fresh smears of anthers. There are numerous special combinations of crystal violet and of safranin, each with particular counterstains designed to bring out certain desired effects.

It is interesting to note that, although there are many dyes used in both plant and animal microtechnic, there are others that are important in one of these fields but not in the other. Thus carmine and safranin are preeminently botanical stains, methylene blue a very important zoological stain that is hardly ever employed by the botanist.

Microbiology. Another very important field in which biological stains are employed is the study of bacteria and related microorganisms such as fungi and protozoa. The dyes thus used are somewhat limited in number, methylene blue, crystal violet and basic fuchsin satisfying most of the bacteriologists' needs. It is very interesting, however, to note that these three dyes, which are pre-eminently bacteriological stains, are by far the largest sellers of any of the biologicals. This indicates that although the bacteriologist does not employ as many staining procedures as the worker in other fields, he is by far the most important customer, in point of quantity ordered, of any to whom the manufacturer supplies these products.

In microbiology dyes are used not only as stains but as constituents of culture media. They are thus employed either as indicators or for their bacteriostatic effects; sometimes they even serve in the differentiation of species.

A comparatively new field now is *bacterial cytology*. As in the case of histochemistry, development in this field has been made possible by improved methods of fixation. The conventional method of rendering bacterial cells stainable was merely to dry them on a slide, a process which distorts the cell and makes internal structure quite difficult to demonstrate. Such crude fixation methods are now being replaced, for all delicate work, with others that cause less distortion; and gradually bacterial cytology is being revealed. There are difficulties still to be surmounted; artifacts and true nuclear structures are sometimes difficult to tell apart, and misinterpretations are frequently made. Nevertheless, the field is being rapidly explored, and the subject of bacterial cytology is no longer so highly speculative as it was a comparatively few years ago.

Bacteriological staining methods (outside of cytology) can be divided into two groups: stains for bacteria in dried films; and stains for bacteria in tissue. The former consist of very simple procedures, ordinarily; about the most complicated of them is the Gram stain which calls for crystal violet and a counterstain; some species of bacteria taking the violet stain, others, the counterstain. The stains for bacteria in tissue are essentially histological methods, many of them very similar to those used for general animal tissue; their main purpose, however, is not the differentiation between different tissue elements but that between bacteria and the tissue in which they are located.

An important aspect of bacterial staining is the laboratory diagnosis of disease. In numerous diseases, of which tuberculosis and diphtheria are the most conspicuous examples, staining procedures play a prominent role in diagnosis; in the case of tuberculosis diagnosis, fluorescent dyes are proving their worth. So important is laboratory diagnosis that in spite of the smaller number of staining methods employed by the bacteriologist, he orders stains by the kilo while the zoologist may content himself with 10-gram bottles. This is the real reason why the bacteriologist is the chief customer of the biological stain company.

BIOLOGICAL STAINS IN TIME OF WAR

The last mentioned use of stains has made them a very important war commodity. The first World War proved this. Before that war practically all dyes had come from Germany, and no biological stains were considered reliable unless they bore the label of one particular German company. In 1914, the blockade of Germany prevented its dyes from going overseas and biologists in many other countries began to wonder where they would get fresh supplies of stains when the stocks of German dyes on hand at the beginning of hostilities were exhausted. In America this did not prove an immediate problem, for those stocks were quite large, partly in the hands of the users and partly in the storerooms of dealers, and if the demand had been only that of peacetime, probably the situation would not have become acute for several years. As soon as this country became involved in the war, however, the demand greatly increased. Every Army or Navy hospital had to have its laboratory; and because of the higher degree of medical care given the men than in any previous war, such hospitals and laboratories soon became quite numerous. The demand for stains, therefore, broke all previous precedents and the stock of German dyes available was no longer anywhere near enough for the demand. Laboratory technicians soon were forced to become familiar with American dyes—and they learned, in the hard way, that biological stains need standardization.

After that war the demand for stains seems to have decreased, although no actual figures are available. Then, gradually, during the next 20 years, the demand increased as new laboratories were started and new uses for stains proposed, but it did not reach a very high figure until 1939. Then almost simultaneously with the German invasion of Poland, the first marked increase in the demand (since the previous war) was noted. Just why the increase occurred then in America is hard to explain; but it is possible some users of dyes became panicky for fear that the coming of war would cause shortages in this field. No such shortage did develop, in America, at least; and it is well that it did not, for as soon as the U. S. Government, through Army, Navy, and lend-lease agencies, began ordering stains on the war basis, the increase in orders exceeded anything that had been previously thought possible. By 1943 the demand for stains was fully ten times that of 1939. It seems almost incredible to believe that any government in war should find it necessary to order any dye (even such a dye as crystal violet) by the thousands of bottles; and the fact that such orders were received again and again gives some idea as the number of field hospitals called for in modern warfare.

COMMERCIAL SOURCES OF STAINS

The early biologists naturally obtained their dyes from concerns whose primary business was supplying such products to the textile industry. This proved unsatisfactory because of the great variation in the dyes thus obtained, even though sold under the same name. To improve the situation, Dr. Weigert, in 1880, advised a Dr. Georg Grübler, a student of Ludwig and Dreschel at Leipzig, to concern himself with marketing aniline dyes especially to use in microscopy. Dr. Grübler, accordingly, founded a company (first registered as "Physiol.-chemisches Laboratorium, Dr. Georg Grübler"; subsequently known as "Dr. G. Grübler & Company") which originally dealt with stains and other physiologico-chemical preparations, but later specialized almost entirely in dyes.

In 1896 Dr. Grübler had to withdraw from this firm and a former partner of Dr. Grübler's named Schmid, became the proprietor. After retiring from this business, Dr Grübler started a laboratory of his own which continued for some time to supply Dr. G. Grübler & Company with certain products. This laboratory was subsequently incorporated in 1897 under the name of "Dr. G. Grübler's mikroskopisch-, chemisch-bacteriologisches Laboratorium," and was sold to Dr. Hollborn. The company thus founded subsequently became "Dr. K. Holborn & Söhne," and for a number of years continued its relations to the Grübler company. It did not, however, supply the latter company after 1921, but began marketing such products on its own account.

This matter is gone into in some detail because from 1921 till about 1945 there were two rival firms producing stains in Germany, the Dr. G. Grübler & Company and K. Hollborn & Sons; and the relationship between these two concerns is not generally understood. Each company made certain claims that are often interpreted as implying that it produced the only genuine Grübler stains. As a matter of fact, neither company manufactured dyes and the actual claims of the two companies were these: G. Grübler & Company claimed that they alone had the list of commercial sources from which Dr. Grübler obtained his dyes some 40 years previously and the standards set up by him at that time; K. Hollborn & Sons claimed that they were the only concern to produce the so-called "original Grübler preparations," these preparations being certain staining fluids and combinations of stains (e.g., the Giemsa stain) first developed in Dr. Grübler's private laboratory. It will be seen that these claims thus stated were not contradictory, but misunderstanding sometimes resulted from the advertisements published by the two companies.

The Grübler stains were pretty generally used throughout the world until about 1916–1918. The first World War changed the situation, because the temporary unavailability of German stains forced England and the United States to develop their own sources of stains. The second World War had an even greater effect on the situation; and some time either during the war or just after, the two above-mentioned German concerns seem to have gone out of business. There are still, however, "Grübler" stains produced in Germany and sold by agents in other countries, including the United States.

It required some time after the first World War before the biological stain production in other countries besides Germany could acquire the prestige formerly belonging to the productions of that country. At first perhaps, there was some reason for the unfavorable reputation attained by non-German stains. It naturally required some time for the concerns just then entering the field to learn to produce stains capable of giving the same results as those obtained by the German product. Eventually, however, American and British companies were able to put out stains of high quality and often even superior to those available before the war. In certain quarters the prestige of the German stains still worked to the discredit of the products of other countries; but before the second World War began, the resulting prejudice had just about come to an end in the United States. Although this prejudice has largely disappeared, special attention must be given here to the situation which existed in the United States and Canada, following the first World War, as it was this which led to the establishment of the Biological Stain Commission, the sponsor of this book.

MODERN STANDARDIZATION OF STAINS

The Biological Stain Commission is concerned with the inspection and standardization of stains, not with their manufacture, as is sometimes supposed. It was learned in 1920, while the post-war embargo on dyes was still in effect, that American scientists were being supplied with dyes from three or four different stain companies and that their products were not sufficiently uniform to be reliable. Accordingly, through the cooperation of the National Research Council of the United States and three or four American scientific societies, with temporary financial backing from the Chemical Foundation, the Commission on Standardization of Biological Stains (now known as the Biological Stain Commission) was established. The Commission is now an independent non-profit corporation, having representatives on its membership of eight American scientific societies with which it cooperates. The work of the Commission is two-fold. First, by cooperation of various biologists and chemists it gathers information concerning the nature of dyes as related to their use in microscopic technic; secondly, by working with the manufacturers and dealers it endeavors to see that the supply of stains available in America is of the highest possible quality as judged by their performance in actual laboratory use. The first of these purposes has inspired this book, which is now in its seventh edition, and at the same time has led to the publication by the Commission of a journal, *Stain Technology* and a laboratory manual, *Staining Procedures* (Conn, Darrow, and Emmel, 1960). The second object is being brought about by the plan of certifying stains.

The certification plan has been adopted because of the great difficulty of drawing up any chemical or physical standards to determine which stains are satisfactory and which are not. If such standards could be formulated, it would be possible to draw up specifications with which manufacturers of stains would be expected to comply.

Specifications. Drawing up specifications for biological stains has proved difficult. In many cases their chemistry is not entirely understood, and even when it is, their behavior in actual use is often dependent upon the amount and nature of impurities that may be present in only minute quantities. Since these impurities are sometimes beneficial and sometimes detrimental and their nature is often unknown, practical specifications are much more difficult to draw up than in the case of ordinary chemicals where a high degree of purity can be obtained and any impurity is undesirable.

Some 35 years ago the Stain Commission began trying to draw up specifications for some of the most commonly used stains. These specifications were published in the first edition of this book. They did not prove very useful, however, and of recent years no great attention has been given them. Much more workable specifications have since been secured, with the cooperation of the National Formulary Committee of the American Pharmaceutical Association.

In several recent editions of the National Formulary, published by the American Pharmaceutical Association, a section has been included in which formulae of staining solutions are given. Originally there was no agreement between these formulae and the ones recommended by the Stain Commission. Beginning in 1937, however, it was decided that the National Formulary Committee and the Commission on Standardization of Biological Stains should cooperate in this matter. As a result of this cooperation there have been several worth-while accomplishments:

1. Specifications of the most important stains now on the certification basis have been drawn up and have been published in recent editions of the National Formulary. These specifications are partly chemical and spectrophotometric, but also contain detailed statements as to how the stains should be tested as to their behavior for biological purposes and state the results to be expected from these tests. In every case it was intended that these specifications should harmonize with the tests as actually performed by the Stain Commission.

2. The formulae of staining solutions given in the National Formulary, in *Staining Procedures*, and in the *Manual of Microbiological Methods*, sponsored by the Society of American Bacteriologists, have been compared and studied critically with the object of publishing identical formulae in all three places.

3. Another result of this cooperation was to give the work of the Stain Commission more of an official standing than it had before. The Stain Commission was originally formed as an entirely unofficial organization and has never had any connection with any government organization. The specifications of the United States Pharmacopoeia and the National Formulary, however, do have official recognition. The publication of the

seventh and later editions of the Formulary, therefore, with its references to stains certified by the Commission, has resulted in their official adoption for many purposes throughout the United States. Most notable has been the adoption by the United States Armed Services in connection with purchases made by their procurement agencies. Inasmuch as the seventh edition of the National Formulary was published at about the time the United States entered the second World War, this proved a development of considerable significance.

4. It has been realized for some time that the specifications would be more satisfactory if they could eliminate statements that the dye under consideration should be satisfactory for such and such procedures. This has proved difficult because of lack of correlation between chemical and optical characteristics, on the one hand, and performance on the other. During recent years appreciation has been growing for the fact that this lack of correlation might be due to insufficient data; and that the only way to find out would be to collect the data. Accordingly the assay laboratory of the Stain Commission has been going over its collection of stain samples, some satisfactory and some unsatisfactory, to see if any agreement between the two types of specification can be found. It proves that such agreement is lacking in so many cases that specifications based on performance must still be included; but the data that are being collected are nevertheless proving distinctly valuable. They are showing better than ever before just what limits of variation in chemical and physical specifications are permissible; and as a result it is now possible to establish better definitions of and specifications for biological stains than ever before. Much of this new information is being incorporated into this edition of *Biological Stains*.

Standardization Procedures Now in Operation. This interrelation between the National Formulary specifications and the standardization methods of the Stain Commission makes these methods of considerable interest. It must be explained that the standardization procedures adopted by the Stain Commission have been entirely on the batch basis—that is, approval is not given to the entire product of any one company, but is extended to each individual batch that is put on the market. The reason for this is that the Commission has never felt willing to place reliance on chemical or optical tests. All the specifications that have been drawn up by the Stain Commission or by the National Formulary Committee have contained statements which mean essentially as follows: "The sample must prove satisfactory when tested by the following procedures: - - - - -". It is obvious that until it is known just how the results obtained in practical use correlate with chemical or optical properties, any tests depending upon performance must be carried out for each individual batch.

Commission Certified stains are now coming to be designated with the initials "C.C." following the name of the dye.

There is no need of listing here the tests actually employed by the Commission; they are given in an appendix of this book where they can be consulted by anyone who is interested. It must, however, be explained that these tests fall into two groups: chemical and optical on the one hand; tests for performance on the other. In interpreting results, greatest weight is given to the tests for performance. It happens not infrequently that a batch of some stain will prove to give perfectly satisfactory results in all the latter, but proves slightly low in dye content, or disagrees in some respect with optical characteristics called for in the specifications. The rule in the case of such a sample is to approve it on the basis of its performance in spite of the slight non-conformity in the case of chemical or optical characteristics.

Batches of dyes approved by the Commission are sold by the companies with a special label furnished by the Commission, known as the certification label. This label indicates the certification number of the batch and is not supposed to be employed for any batch other than that on which it is issued. A certification label on any bottle of stain means therefore, five things: (1) a sample of the batch bearing the label has been submitted to the Commission for testing and a portion of the sample is permanently on file; (2) the sample proves true to type, as judged by spectrophotometric tests; (3) its dye content is up to specification and is correctly indicated on the label; (4) it has been tested by experts in the procedures named on the label and has been found satisfactory by them; and lastly, (5) no other batch can be sold under the same certification number except by such a flagrant breach of confidence on the part of the company as to risk losing the good will of the Commission.

At the present time (1960), 57 stains have been put on the certification basis. These include all the most commonly used biological stains as well as a few in which the Stain Commission has become interested, although they are not so extensively employed in the laboratory as most of the others on the list.

There are, at the time this seventh edition goes to press, nine companies in the United States and one in Canada submitting their stains to the Commission for certification before putting them on the market. It must be realized, however, that no one of these concerns necessarily manufactures all the stains which it thus submits; but in the case of any stain which is manufactured elsewhere, the company takes responsibility for its performance as a biological stain on the basis of tests made to show its adequacy, and in many instances carries out a certain degree of purification or other processing before putting the stain on the market. One of these companies puts on the market every stain now on the certification list. Three other companies submit samples of over half the stains thus listed, while the other companies merely request certification of one or two dyes in which they specialize. No dyes have yet been certified by the Stain Commission submitted by any concern outside North America. The reason for this is because of the difficulty in handling the certification of stains on the batch basis with a concern that is located at a distance, doing business in this country only through agents who are not in direct touch with the actual manufacturers of the dyes.

Although this phase of the work of the Stain Commission is one of inspection, it has not brought about unpleasant relations with any manufacturer or dealer in stains. As a matter of fact, the hearty cooperation of the American stain companies has been obtained throughout; and without this cooperation much that has been accomplished in the way of standardization would have been impossible.

I I

THE GENERAL NATURE OF DYES AND THEIR CLASSIFICATION

Dyes are sometimes classed in two groups, the natural and the artificial. The former class is now of relatively smaller importance from the standpoint of the manufacturer and the textile dyer; for the artificial dyes far outnumber them and the advancement of science is gradually making it possible to produce many of the formerly natural dyes by artificial means (e.g., indigo, orcein). It just happens that one or two natural dyes, the derivatives of cochineal and logwood extract (see Chapter XII), are among the most valuable biological stains; but the natural dyes in general are so few in number than they can be practically disregarded in considering the general chemical nature of dyes.

Because the first artificial dyes were produced from aniline all of this class are often called "aniline dyes," although there are now a large number of them which bear no relation to this compound and are not derived from it. Therefore the term is now quite largely being replaced by the more correct expression "coal-tar dyes," since all of them are made by chemical transformations from one or more substances found in coal-tar.

Comparatively little is known concerning the chemistry of the natural dyes; but the synthetic dyes have been carefully studied and volumes have been written concerning their chemical composition and its relation to their behavior. Much of this is usually ignored by the biologist who employs dyes merely for staining microscopic objects. A familiarity with the general principles is useful, however, in helping him to employ stains scientifically. This is particularly true now that there is a growing tendency to use dyes in biological work as histochemical reagents, and the traditional staining procedures must often be reappraised as to their histochemical significance. The brief discussion that follows is intended to help the biologist to understand merely the fundamental principles of dye chemistry.

BENZENE

All coal-tar dyes are organic compounds of the aromatic series. In other words they may be considered as derivatives of the hydrocarbon, benzene, C_6H_6 , the formula for which is usually represented as

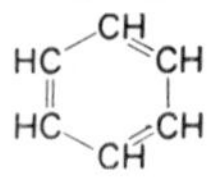

$$
\begin{array}{ccc}
 & \underset{\displaystyle CH}{} & \\
HC & & CH \\
\| & & | \\
HC & & CH \\
 & \underset{\displaystyle CH}{} &
\end{array}
$$

and is commonly written in the abbreviated form,

The double bonds in benzene are not fixed but oscillate between adjacent carbon atoms.

The importance of benzene in organic chemistry is because of the infinite number of ways in which it can combine with other radicals and elements, forming compounds of extreme complexity. If the elements in such compounds are combined in certain ways the substance is colored, and such colored compounds, after slight additional changes in the molecule, become dyes. In this resepct the colored benzene derivatives are unlike the colored pigments of simpler composition; many of the latter may show intense color, but do not act as dyes.

One type of substitution in the benzene ring is specially important in dye chemistry. Two atoms or groups having two valency bonds instead of one may also replace two hydrogen atoms, provided the replacement takes place simultaneously and the hydrogen atoms replaced are situated either in the ortho or in the para position to each other. Thus two oxygen atoms (which are bivalent) may replace two hydrogen atoms (which are monovalent) forming the compound known as quinone $C_6H_4O_2$, the formula for which is

$$
\begin{array}{ccc}
 & O & \\
 & \| & \\
 & C & \\
HC & & CH \\
\| & & \| \\
HC & & CH \\
 & C & \\
 & \| & \\
 & O &
\end{array}
$$

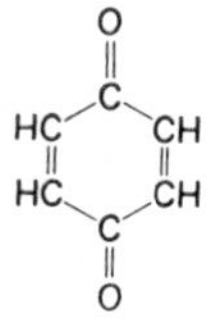

or as commonly written

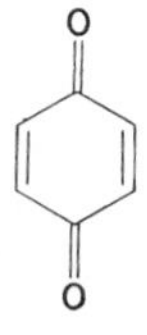

In printed formulae the quinone ring is sometimes abbreviated still further by omitting the double bonds within the ring. The substituent atoms or groups may or may not be alike, so long as both have two valency bonds entering into the combination. This type of substitution involves a rearranging of the double valency bonds in the benzene ring; and in compounds of this type, called quinoid compounds, the double bonds are supposed to be fixed, not mobile as in benzene. This change of the valency bonds takes place very readily in many dyes, and certain peculiarities of their behavior are explained by it; (see for example p. 187).

Three mono-substitution products of benzene are of importance in considering the structure of dyes, namely: toluene or methylbenzene, $C_6H_5 \cdot CH_3$; phenol, carbolic acid or phenylic acid, $C_6H_5 \cdot OH$; and aniline or phenyl amine, $C_6H_5 \cdot NH_2$. Their constitutional formulae are as follows:

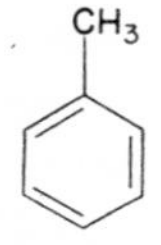

toluene 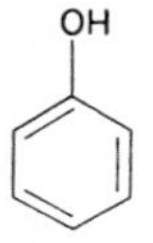   phenol 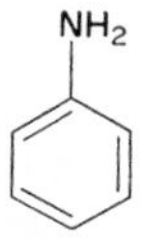   anilin

Two important di-substitution products are xylene or dimethyl benzene $C_6H_4 \cdot (CH_3)_2$, and toluidine, $C_6H_4 \cdot CH_3 \cdot NH_2$. Both of these occur in the above mentioned three isomeric forms, as shown below for xylene:

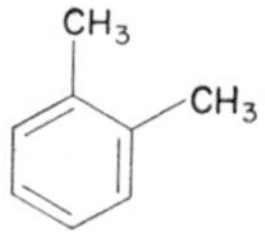

ortho-xylene 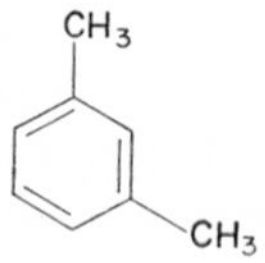   meta-xylene    para-xylene

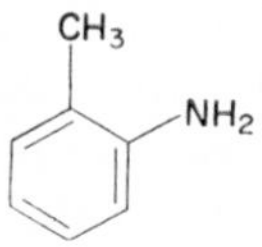

ortho-toluidine

RELATION OF MOLECULAR STRUCTURE TO COLOR

Although there is still much to learn as to the explanation of color in terms of structural formulae, it is now well known that certain definite atomic groupings (known as *chromophores*) are associated with color. The fundamental groupings involved in these chromophores are C=C, C=O, C=S, C=N, N=N, N=O, and NO_2 ; and the more of these that occur in the same compound the more pronounced the color. It will be noticed that the quinone ring, as pictured above, contains the following chromophore grouping in duplicate $=C—C=C—C=$. Quinone, itself, is in fact colored, and the quinone ring is one of the most important chromophores known, all compounds containing it showing intense color.

Although the situation is not completely understood, physical chemistry offers theories as to why some compounds are colored. We know that color is caused by selective absorption of certain wave lengths of light, so that the light transmitted by or reflected from a given substance lacks these particular wave lengths of the visible spectrum and accordingly appears colored. Such a substance, in other words, acts as if it were a prism or grating provided with a screen to block off certain parts of the spectrum in which the refracted light is normally transmitted. Conceivably the chromophores confer upon the molecule properties of just this sort, acting possibly as a system of resonators tuned to vibrate at the same rate as the waves to be absorbed. The theory cannot be discussed here in any detail; but it should be pointed out that valence electrons under certain circumstances confer resonance on a given compound. The unsaturated compounds, such as those containing the double bonds of the chromophores, show a special tendency toward resonance; and it is a fact that as the general degree of unsaturation and complexity of a compound increases, the spectral absorption tends to pass from ultraviolet toward infrared, that is, the color transmitted (or reflected) changes from yellow through reds to blues.

The benzene compounds containing chromophore radicals are known as chromogens. A chromogen, however, although it is colored, is not a dye, in that it possesses no affinity for fibers or tissues. It may coat them, but only mechanically, and it will be easily removed by mechanical processes; that is, it will not "take." (See, however, the discussion of fat stains, p. 57.) In order for a substance to be a dye, it must contain in addition to the chromophore group, a group which imparts to the compound the property of electrolytic dissociation. Such auxiliary groups are known as auxochromes. They may slightly alter the shade of the dye, but are not the cause of the color. Their function is to furnish salt-forming properties to the compound. Certain chromophoric groups have also slight auxochromatic properties.

To illustrate these different types of groups, let us take a typical example. The nitro group ($—NO_2$) is a chromophore. When three of these groups displace three hydrogen atoms in a benzene molecule, we have the compound trinitrobenzene, which is yellow. It is not a dye, however, but is a chromogen. It is insoluble in water, and is neither an acid nor a base; that is, it does not dissociate electrolytically and consequently cannot form salts with either alkalies or acids. If, however, one more hydrogen atom is replaced, this time with the hydroxyl group (—OH), which is an auxochrome, the resulting compound,

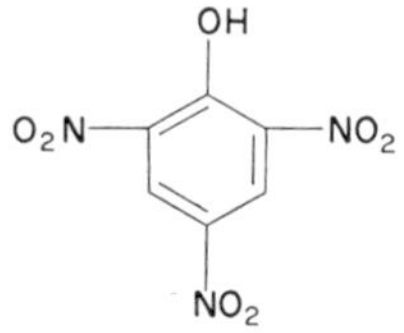

is an acid, capable of electrolytic dissociation and of forming salts with alkalies. It is the familiar substance picric acid, and is a yellow dye.

It will thus be seen that the color of picric acid is due to the chromophoric nitro groups, and that its dyeing properties are due to the auxochromic hydroxyl group. If the nitro groups be reduced to amino groups (—NH$_2$), which are not chromophores, the resulting compound is colorless and hence is not a dye.

Summing up, we arrive at the definition of a dye as an organic compound which contains chromophoric and auxochromic groups attached to benzene rings, the color being attributable to the chromophores and the dyeing property to the salt-forming auxochromes.

ACID AND BASIC DYES

There has sometimes been misunderstanding among biologists as to the meaning of the terms "acid dyes" and "basic dyes." It was sometimes assumed that the terms refer to the H-ion concentration of the dye solutions. Nothing could be further from the truth. The distinction actually depends on whether the significant part of the dye is anionic or cationic, and bears no direct relation to the reaction of any solution of the dye. As a matter of fact, the most strongly anionic or *acid* dyes, like eosin Y, regularly form salts with metallic ions and the basicity of the metallic cation determines the reaction of the solution, e.g., the solution of the sodium salt of eosin is basic in reaction. Similarly the reaction of solutions of salts of strongly basic dyes is ordinarily determined by their anion—usually the chloride ion.

As the auxochromes are the salt forming groups of dyes, it is ordinarily the nature of the auxochrome present that determines in which of these two classes a dye belongs.

Some auxochromes are basic, e.g., the amino group (—NH$_2$), while others are acidic, e.g., the carboxyl group (—COOH). The amino group owes its basic character (which it transmits to the whole molecule) to the ability of its nitrogen atom to become pentavalent by the addition of the elements of water (or of an acid), just as in the case of ammonia; thus:

$$H\!-\!N\!\!\begin{array}{c}H\\H\end{array} + O\!=\!\begin{array}{c}H\\H\end{array} = H\!-\!N\!\!\begin{array}{c}H\\OH\end{array} \quad \text{and} \quad H\!-\!N\!\!\begin{array}{c}H\\H\end{array} + H\!-\!Cl = H\!-\!N\!\!\begin{array}{c}H\\Cl\end{array}$$

ammonia   water   ammonium   ammonia   hydro-   ammonium
              hydroxide   chloric   chloride
                                       acid gas

$$R\!-\!N\!\!\begin{array}{c}H\\H\end{array} + O\!=\!\begin{array}{c}H\\H\end{array} = R\!-\!N\!\!\begin{array}{c}H\\OH\end{array} \quad \text{and} \quad R\!-\!N\!\!\begin{array}{c}H\\H\end{array} + H\!-\!Cl = R\!-\!N\!\!\begin{array}{c}H\\Cl\end{array}$$

amine   water   hypothetical   amine   hydro-   amine
             organic am-   chloric   hydro-
             monium base   acid gas   chloride

In other words, the NH_2 group yields hydroxyl ions and enables the compound to ionize and to act as a cation in forming salts; such a dye is a basic dye.

The carboxyl group (—COOH), on the other hand, is acidic, as it can furnish hydrogen ions by electrolytic dissociation. Many of the most important acid dyes contain this group, but since they are usually manufactured as sodium salts, the characteristic group in these dyes is —COONa. Other acid dyes contain the weaker auxochrome group —OH, and form salts as R—ONa.

The more basic or acidic groups in a compound, the stronger base or acid it becomes. If there is one of each, the basic character of the amino group predominates, but is weakened by the influence of the acidic group. The strength of both groups is also influenced by other groups or atoms in the compound; thus, for example, the chromophore —NO_2 , exerts an influence to make any hydroxyl group in the compound more strongly acidic, in other words to become more highly dissociated electrolytically. Moreover, alkylation has the effect of increasing the basicity of ammonium compounds.

One other group of atoms encountered in dye chemistry needs explanation, namely the sulfonic group, —SO_3H. It is a salt-forming group of strongly acidic character, in that it undergoes extensive electrolytic dissociation. This group, however, is only very feebly auxochromic. Its function is to render a dye soluble in water, or to change an otherwise basic dye into an acidic one, as in the case of the fuchsins, where the strong *basic fuchsins* are changed into the strongly acidic *acid fuchsins* merely by the introduction of sulfonic groups into the former. A compound which contains a chromophore group and a sulfonic group is not a dye, however, unless there is also present a true auxochrome group.

From this it can be understood what is meant by calling dyes either basic or acidic. Although the terms indicate the potentiality of the dye itself, they do not mean that the commercial products are actually bases or acids. They are ordinarily salts. An acid dye is a salt of a color acid—usually its sodium salt, but occasionally a salt of potassium, calcium or ammonium. A basic dye is a salt of a color base—usually a chloride, but sometimes a sulfate or acetate. (The oil-soluble dyes present an exception to this statement; see p. 57.) The terms *anionic* and *cationic dyes* would be more suitable, and they are coming to be increasingly employed. Basic dyes are sometimes available as free bases, in which case the name is ordinarily followed by the word "base." Thus "basic fuchsin" means the salt of fuchsin with some colorless acid (e.g., hydrochloric) while "fuchsin base" indicates the color base of this dye, not combined with any acid.

THE CHROMOPHORES

As stated above, every dye contains at least one group of atoms known as a chromophore, which is regarded as being responsible for the colored properties of the compounds in which it occurs. Some of these chromophores have a basic character, others acid. There are only a comparatively small number of them which enter into the usual biological stains, and only these need be considered here. They are as follows:

BASIC CHROMOPHORES

1. The *azo group*, —N=N— is found in all azo dyes, of which methyl orange and Bismarck brown are well known examples. In all these dyes, a benzene or naphthalene ring is attached to each nitrogen atom. All the dyes of this group may be looked upon as derivatives of azobenzene,

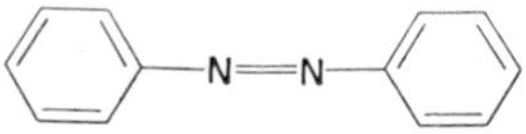

2. The *azin group*,

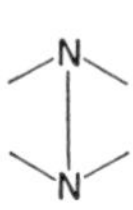

is found in phenazins, of which neutral red and the safranins are good representatives. The skeleton formula of a safranin is:

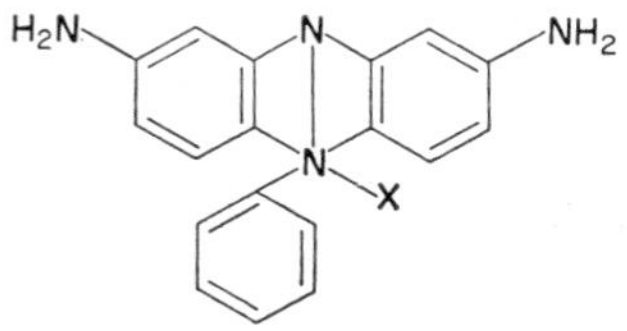

in which X represents the negative ion of a monobasic acid such as hydrochloric, acetic, nitric or sulfuric. This chromophore is capable of a variety of rearrangements of its valency bonds, as the bond between the two nitrogen atoms may disappear and the compound assume a quinoid structure, as for example the following grouping:

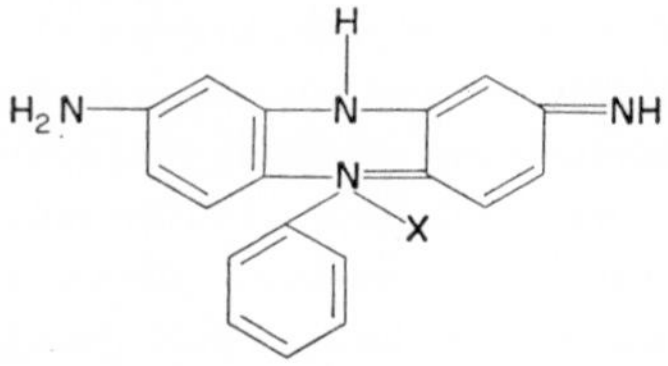

3. The *indamin group*, —N=, as observed in the indamins, thiazins, and so forth. Methylene blue is the best known representative of this group. In these dyes, two benzene rings are attached to the nitrogen atom, one of these being in the quinoid form and hence adding a second chromophore. The typical indamin formula is:

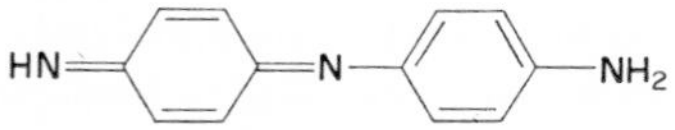

In the thiazins, such as methylene blue, the two benzene rings are further joined together by a sulfur atom, forming three closed rings of atoms. The simplest thiazin base would be:

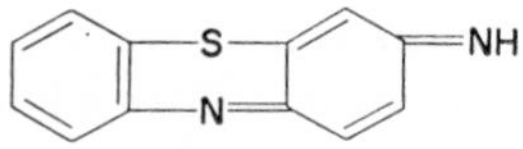

ACID CHROMOPHORES

1. The *nitro group*, —NO$_2$, as in picric acid
2. The *quinoid benzene ring*,

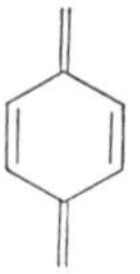

which occurs in a long series of dyes, such as the indamins above mentioned, the xanthenes and the di- and triphenyl methanes, which include many well known stains, such as rosolic acid, fuchsin, methyl green and the methyl violets. A typical triphenyl methane formula is that of pararosanilin base:

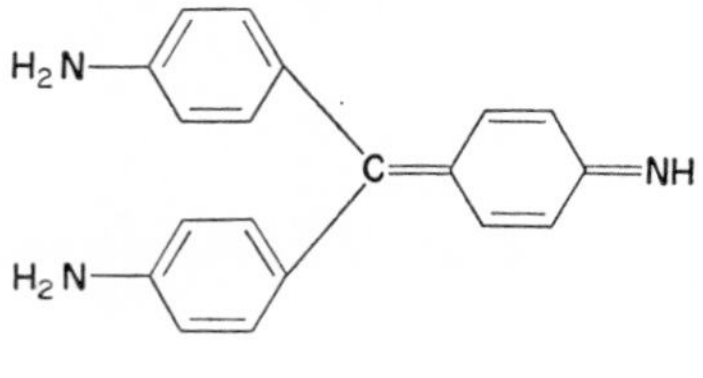

LEUCO COMPOUNDS

The different chromophores differ considerably from one another, but they all have one property in common. In the language of chemistry, they all have unsatisfied affinities for hydrogen; or in other words, they are all easily reducible, for combining with hydrogen is the opposite of oxidation and is, therefore, reduction. The nitro group may be reduced to an amino group; in the azin group the bond between the nitrogen atoms may break and two hydrogen atoms be taken on; while in the various chromophores with double bonds (such as the quinoid ring) the double bond may break and hydrogen atoms become attached to the valencies thus freed.

Now in every case this reduction destroys the chromophore group, and as a result the compound loses its color. In other words a dye retains its color only as long as its affinities for hydrogen are not completely satisfied. These colorless compounds are known as leuco compounds; thus fuchsin yields leuco fuchsin on reduction, and methylene blue reduces to leuco methylene blue. For example:

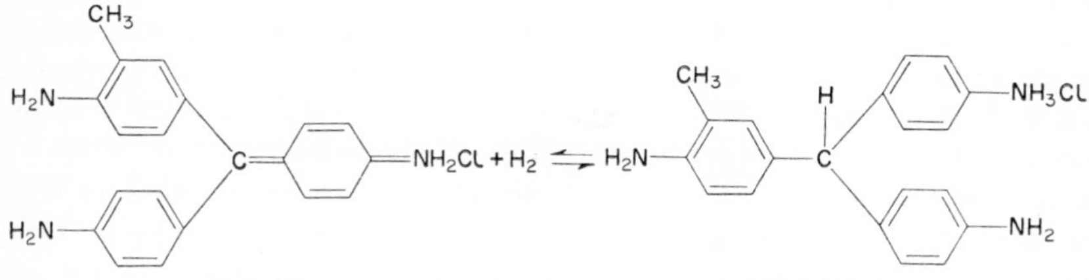

fuchsin   leuco fuchsin

Ordinarily this reaction is reversible under conditions favoring oxidation. It is of especial significance to the bacteriologist, as dyes can often be used as indicators of reduction.

Certain dyes form a still different type of leuco compound, often called a "leuco base." We have seen that the basic dyes ordinarily occur as salts of some colorless acid; now, in the case of certain dyes, notably the triphenyl methanes and xanthenes (Chapters VII and VIII), as soon as the acid radical is removed. the compound becomes colorless. This is because a re-arrangement of the atoms in the molecule takes place upon neutralization so as to give, not the true dye base, but a compound known as a carbinol (see pp. 126-7) in which the chromophore does not occur. Thus the theoretical base of fuchsin which should be obtained upon removal of the acid radical is:

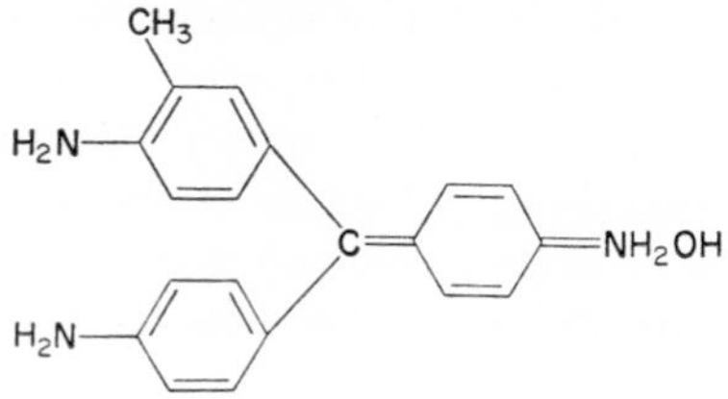

The compound actually formed, however, is the pseudo-base or carbinol:

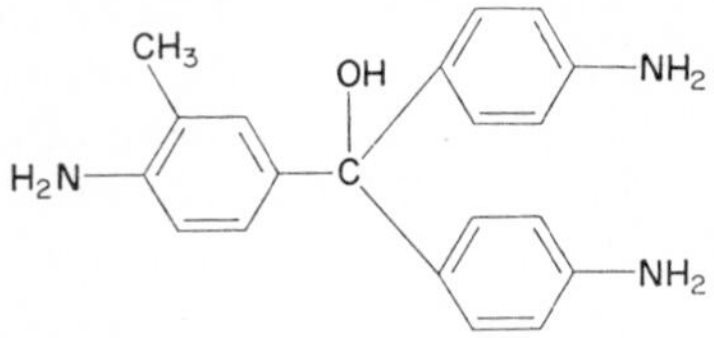

In this compound, it will be readily seen, there is no chromophore; hence it is colorless. These pseudo-bases are of little significance to the biologist, but they are of importance to the dye manufacturer as intermediates in the preparation of dyes.

In the case of many acid dyes, the chromophore is similarly broken by a rearrangement of the atoms which occurs on neutralization. This reaction is ordinarily very readily reversible and makes such dyes useful indicators of acidity. It is discussed more fully under acid fuchsin (p. 144) and phenol-phthalein (p. 186).

In the case of basic fuchsin, a still different type of leuco compound can be obtained, which has acquired considerable importance, both in cytology and in histochemistry. When this dye is reduced with sulfurous acid or a sulfite, a type of leuco fuchsin is produced which is known as Schiff's reagent, and has been used by chemists for many years as an indicator of the presence of aldehyde. Originally this reagent was thought to be no different from the leuco fuchsin referred to previously; but when its use as a histochemical reagent was first introduced it was noticed that the restored color, after contact with the aldehyde-like constituents of cells, was somewhat violet, rather than red (peak at 540 mμ vs. 560–570 mμ). This seemed to indicate that some other chemical change in the dye takes place in addition to its reduction. It is now believed that the sulfite radical combines with the reduced compound in some way; and the resulting compound, Schiff's reagent, is now generally called fuchsin-sulfurous acid, rather than leuco fuchsin. The importance of this reagent is being appreciated more and more, as histochemistry increases in significance; and it will be treated more fully elsewhere in this book.

CLASSIFICATION OF DYES

On the basis of the chromophore present the simple synthetic dyes are classified into several groups. If each of these groups were characterized by a single color or by a few closely related colors, dye chemistry would be a comparatively simple proposition. As a matter of fact a single chromophore may occur in dyes of practically all colors of the rainbow. It is ordinarily impossible to determine, *a priori*, from the chemical formula of a dye what particular color the compound may have; but there is, nevertheless, a certain general rule which correlates chemical formula with color. In any group of compounds, the simpler ones are converted into the more complex by substitution of radicals for hydrogen atoms. In the dyes the substituents are generally methyl or ethyl groups, or sometimes phenyl groups. Now the general rule is that the larger the number of hydrogen atoms that have been replaced by these groups the deeper the color. The tendency is for the color of the simplest dyes in any group of homologous compounds to be yellow, passing through red to violets and then blues and greens, as the homologs become higher through the introucdtion of successively larger numbers of methyl or other substituting groups. Thus the compound pararosanilin, which is very frequently sold as basic fucne ring, but without anmye, with an amino group attached to each benzehsin, is a triphenyl methan ethyl groups; thus:

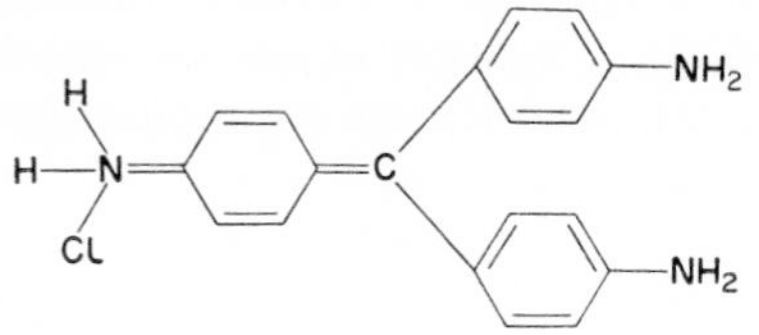

Rosanilin, which is similar in composition, but contains one methyl group attached to one of the benzene rings,

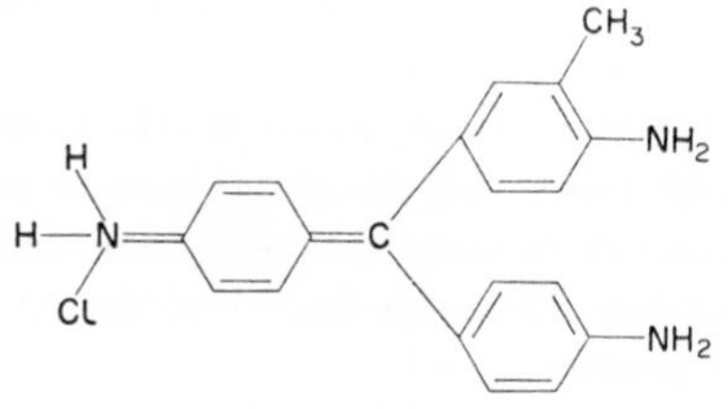

is a red very similar to pararosanilin but with less of a yellowish cast. Now another methyl group may be introduced into each of the other two benzene rings, and each one successively deepens the shade of red, so that the highest homolog of the series, new fuchsin:

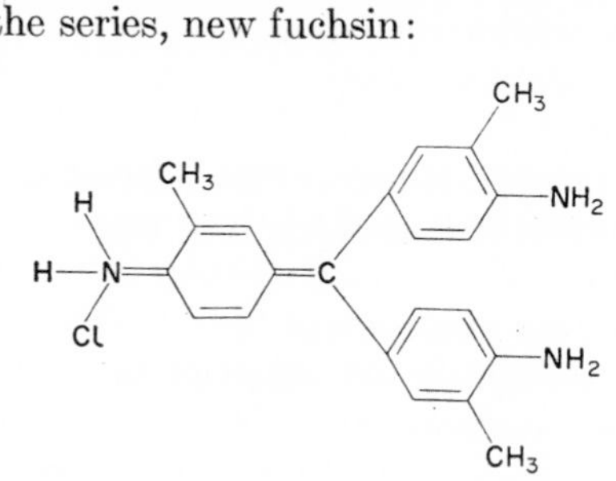

has a more bluish cast than any of the others. Thus basic fuchsins can vary considerably in their shade according to the proportions in which these four possible components may be mixed.

It is also possible in another way to deepen the color of pararosanilin still further, namely by introducing methyl groups into the amino radicals instead of directly on the benzene rings. Thus the methyl violets are obtained; and the more methyl groups introduced the bluer the violet, until when all six available hydrogen atoms are thus substituted, crystal violet, the deepest of them all, is obtained. By using three ethyl groups instead of methyl, Hofmann's violet or dahlia is formed, which is deeper in color than the trimethyl compound, due to the heavier groups introduced. If three phenyl groups (i.e., the benzene ring, C_6H_5—) are introduced instead of methyl or ethyl, the color is still further deepened, the resulting dye being spirit blue. Further, it is possible to introduce another methyl group into crystal violet, by addition of methyl iodide (or chloride) to one of the trivalent nitrogen atoms, whereby its valency is increased to five, and a green dye, methyl green, is produced:

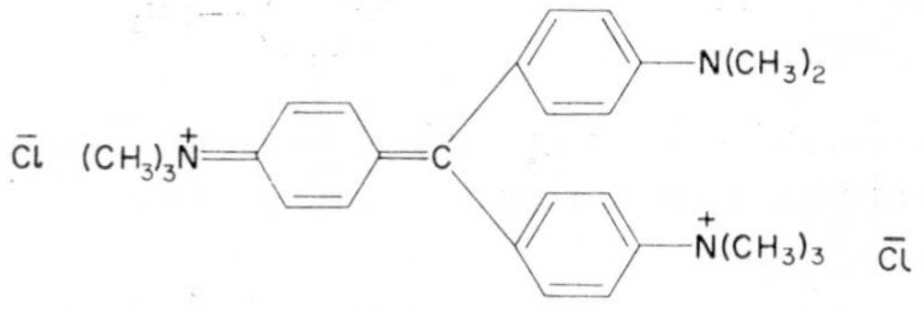

With these facts in mind it will be seen that the grouping of dyes as based upon these chromophores does not classify them in relation to their color. It is a useful classification, however, because it puts together those that have similar chemical structure. The important biological dyes, thus classified, fall into the following groups.

A. The nitroso dyes; e.g., *naphthol green B*
B. The nitro dyes; e.g., *picric acid*
C. The azo dyes; e.g., *methyl orange, Bismarck brown Y, orange G, Congo red, Sudan III and Sudan IV*
D. The quinone-imine group, including
    1. Indamins; e.g., *toluylene blue*
    2. The indophenols
    3. Thiazins; e.g., *thionin, toluidine blue, methylene blue*
    4. Oxazins; e.g., *brilliant cresyl blue, Nile blue*
    5. Azins, including
        a. Amino-azins; e.g., *neutral red*
        b. Safranins; e.g., *safranin O, magdala red*
        c. Indulins; e.g., *nigrosin*

E. The phenyl methane dyes, including
  1. Diphenyl methanes; e.g., *auramine O*
  2. Diamino triphenyl methanes; e.g., *malachite green, brilliant green, light green*
  3. Triamino triphenyl methanes; e.g., *basic fuchsin, acid fuchsin, methyl violet, gentian violet, methyl green, aniline blue*
  4. Hydroxy triphenyl methanes (rosolic acids); e.g., *aurin, red corallin*
  5. Diphenyl naphthyl methanes; e.g., *Victoria blue R*
F. The xanthene dyes, including
  1. Pyronins; e.g., *pyronin Y and B*
  2. Rhodamines; e.g., *rhodamine B*
  3. Fluoran derivatives; e.g., *eosins, erythrosin, rose bengal*
  4. Phenolphthalein and the sulphonphthaleins
  5. The acridine dyes; e.g., *acriflavine*
G. The anthraquinone dyes; e.g., *alizarin*
H. The thiazole dyes; e.g., *titan yellow*
I. The quinoline dyes; e.g., *pinacyanol*
J. The phthalocyanine dyes; e.g., *alcian blue*
K. The natural dyes; e.g., *indigo, hematoxylin, carmine.*

DYE NOMENCLATURE

Very little system has been used in naming dyes, and as a result their nomenclature is extremely confused. Until recently the manufacturer of a dye which he thought was new or which he wished the public to consider a new dye sold it under a new name which was not intended to give any clue as to the nature of the dye. If the manufacturer knew that the name was a mere synonym of one already in use he did not say so, for he wished to encourage the sale of his own product rather than that of some other dye maker. Accordingly it was often left for others, who were not financially interested, to work out the synonymy of the dyes; and the list of names that are found to apply to a single dye is sometimes amazing. Although the ethics of the dye industry are now greatly improved, the old synonyms still cause confusion.

With the dyes in general so unsystematically named, it is natural that the same confusion should reign in the nomenclature of biological stains. This confusion is very unfortunate, for it often misleads the biologist as to just what he is doing. For example, some histologist may have on hand a bottle of stain labeled dahlia and he may find it useful for some new technic, which he publishes; while another may propose for an entirely different technic the stain Hofmann's violet. Then a third laboratory worker may read both articles and wish to try both methods; so he accordingly orders both dahlia and Hofmann's violet. His dealer, who may be unacquainted with dyes, will very likely send him a bottle bearing each name, and the purchaser has no easy way of discovering that the two are identical; so he may continue for years to use the two stains for different purposes, misled by their labels and thinking them distinct. The manufacturers and dealers in stains sometimes used to encourage this confusion by their practice of taking care to have the label on the bottle agree with the name used in the customer's order, regardless of the usual name for the dye.

An attempt to relieve this confusion was made by the Commission on Standardization of Biological Stains (1923f) by publishing a list of biological stains with their best known synonyms. In each case one of the names was listed as a preferred designation. Sometimes general usage made it easy to select one name as the preferred one; but in other instances the selection was more or less arbitrary. This same list, with revisions in the way of additions and corrections, is given in the appendix of this book (p. 262–9; see p. 106 of first edition). A few new stains have been added to this list, but essentially it is the same as published in 1923. The chief changes have been in the list of synonyms, which has been revised to omit names that are obsolete and have no present meaning. With but one or two exceptions the preferred designations are still the same as in the first list.

DYE INDEXES

There have been two important indexes of dyes, one published in Germany (Schultz' Farbstofftabellen) the other in England (the Colour Index of the Society of Dyers and Colourists). Seven editions of the former appeared up to the time of the second World War, while only two editions have yet appeared of the latter. It was natural that the earliest efforts to index dyes should have been made in Germany as there was almost no dye industry outside that country until 1914; but the 1923 edition of Schultz was so much less complete than the Colour Index which came out the same year that there has been a recent tendency to follow the latter rather than the former. In the second edition of the present book, therefore, the Colour Index numbers of the various dyes were listed instead of the Schultz numbers.

The seventh Schultz index was as complete as the Colour Index, with an entirely new system of index numbers assigned to the dyes, agreeing neither with that in the other publication nor with earlier editions of Schultz. Considering how often it is desirable to refer to a dye by an index number, it is unfortunate that these numbers were not standardized in some way by international agreement. In the present edition of this book the Colour Index numbers (abbreviated C. I. No.) are used; but the Schultz numbers, included in previous editions, have been dropped.

During the early '50's a joint committee of the Society of Dyers and Colourists in England and the American Association of Textile Chemists and Colorists made a revision of the Colour Index with the hope of accomplishing the objective mentioned in the preceding paragraph. The compilers of the 1956 edition of this Index were fully aware of the confusion caused by frequent changes in index numbers, and accordingly adopted a five-figure system, with sufficient intervals between numbers in current use to provide for introductions of new dyes later without (so it is planned) having to re-number the old dyes. It is hoped that this system will secure uniformity. In the current edition of this book both old and new C. I. numbers are listed, as not all users may be familiar with the new ones. A table in the appendix lists both sets of numbers for purposes of comparison.

DYE SOLUBILITIES

Textile dyes are never of a high degree of purity. Some of the impurities are accidental; others are added intentionally so that dyers can obtain the desired shade without having to measure out dyes in very small quantities. Inasmuch as the early biological stains were textiles dyes without much, if any, modification, it is natural that some of them should also have been of low dye content, and also that different batches should have been of various degrees of purity. In general the present dyes are much more pure than those available before the war of 1914 to 1918. This makes it difficult to prepare stain solutions identical in strength with those prepared before that time.

There are two general types of stain formulae: in one a definite weight of dry dye is specified; in the other a certain volume of a saturated (generally alcoholic) solution of the dye. Each type of formula has its own possibilities of error; and to appreciate the problem it is necessary to understand certain facts in regard to the solubilities of dyes.

The error inherent in the first type of formula is plain at a glance. If two different staining solutions are made up containing 1 gm per 100 ml of dry methylene blue, and in one case the actual dye content of the dry stain is 90 percent, while in the other only 55 percent (a difference actually observed in samples at one time on the market), it is plain that the two solutions must differ greatly in their strength. For this reason an early recommenda-tion of the Commission (1923b) was that formulae of the second type be preferred, on the assumption that a saturated solution of a dye would more likely be of constant dye content than different lots of dry stain bought in the market.

This recommendation, however, was made without complete under-standing of the actual facts of the case. The amount of a dye that will go into solution in either water or alcohol depends upon the amount of mineral salts present. If a dye contains a large percentage of sodium chloride, for instance, a saturated solution will be of considerably lower actual dye con-tent than if the dye were free or nearly free from salt; the sodium chloride prevents the solvent from taking up as much of the dye as it would nor-mally. For this reason two staining solutions each containing 10 percent by volume of a saturated solution of the two methylene blues above mentioned would be quite different from each other in actual dye content, although possibly more nearly alike than if they had been prepared with identical weights of the dry stain.

As soon as the facts were fully understood the Commission (1933e) modified its recommendation. It is plain that the only way two stain solutions can be made identical, if different batches of stain are used, is to make them up on the basis of the weight of *actual dye* present in the stain samples employed. For some time now, all staining formulae recommended by the Commission have been put in such a form as to call for a definite weight of dye of a specified dye content—thus enabling the user to recognize any correction he has to make if he has a dye sample of different dye content. Many individual writers, however, especially writers of text books, have not followed this system. There are various reasons such a plan has not been generally adopted. The chief reason is that there is much variation in the dye content of individual batches, and it is obvious that the staining formulae cannot be generally put in the form recommended by the Commission unless the manufacturers print the actual dye content of the batch of stain on the container in which it is sold. Until about 1930 this was never done Since about that time, however, the Stain Commission has been issuing its' certification only when the dye content is printed on the label, except in instances where the necessary analytical methods are not available. This policy has gradually been changing the situation. At the present time almost all stains on the American market, except natural dyes, compound dyes like the blood stains, and a few complex dyes for which good analytical methods are still unavailable, are labeled as to their dye content. In all Commission publications (including *Stain Technology*) all formulae are given in terms of grams of Commission certified stains (unless the dye in question has never been certified), and as certification is now issued only on samples that vary within narrow limits, this amounts to recommending definite weights of actual dye. Gradually authors of papers published elsewhere are getting into the same habit; so the situation is much more satisfactory than a few decades ago.

In the present edition of this book there are listed, both under the individual dyes and in Table 4 in the Appendix, the solubilities of pure dyes in 95 percent alcohol and in water at 20° of the most commonly used stains. These data were originally published by Holmes (1927, 1928, 1929) and are based on determinations made by a cooperating laboratory of the U. S. Department of Agriculture. The author of these papers experienced considerable difficulty in obtaining the information given therein because of the strong effect of impurities upon the amount of dye capable of going into solution. The commercial samples of the dyes are rarely pure, and Holmes found it necessary to recrystallize each sample before determining solubility. This fact, therefore, must be taken into account in interpreting the figures. To obtain a solution of many dyes as strong as the figure given in the table, the dye sample employed must be strictly pure. As this is practically never true, the user of stains can rarely expect to make a saturated solution of the theoretically possible strength. These data nevertheless are useful in indicating the amount of stain to employ in order to obtain a saturated solution.

The data given in Table 5 were compiled in the hope of furnishing information of more practical value to users of stains than those published by Holmes; these were obtained through the courtesy of the American Pharmaceutical Association. In this table there are listed the solubilities of 50 samples representing 25 commercial certified stains. They are of interest in showing approximately how much deviation to expect between commercial samples of the same dye and about how nearly the solubilities of such samples approach those of the recrystallized dyes listed in Table 4. Frequently the data in Table 5 may prove of more assistance in determining how much dye to employ in making a saturated solution than those given in Table 4.

It would, of course, be still more useful if the solubilities in water and in alcohol of each batch could be printed on the label. Unfortunately, however, no practical method of furnishing this information to the manufacturers and of publishing it on the labels has yet been devised. One manufacturer, Edward Gurr (1959), does publish solubilities of some 40 of his ("michrome") stains; but he does not indicate the method used in analysis or tell whether more than one batch of each of his dyes was thus analyzed. In general, his figures fall within the range of those given in Table 5; those for methylene blue and aniline blue, however, are distinctly higher, that for the latter dye (50 percent in water) seeming unreasonably high. The determination of dye solubility is not a simple procedure, and most published figures must be accepted with considerable caution.

INFLUENCE OF IMPURITIES ON INTENSITY OF STAINING

Impurities present in any dye sample or in the solvent not only influence the solubility of the dye but may have a great effect on the intensity of staining. An impurity present may alter the H-ion concentration of the staining fluid; while acid dyes stain better in more acid solutions, and basic dyes in more alkaline solutions. If, moreover, the impurity is a mineral salt or the salt of an organic acid, it may have an effect on intensity of staining even if the reaction of the solution is not altered. Theories to explain these facts are discussed in Chapter III.

The practical lesson from this is that poor staining results with any dye sample are as often to be explained by the presence (or absence) of impurities in the dye, or in the water used as a solvent, as by some irregularity in the dye itself. In many instances the impurities normally present in some dye may be necessary to assure its proper behavior as a stain; and too great effort in the way of purification may be detrimental. This seems to have been unquestionably the case in respect to rose bengal. It has been found (Conn and Holmes, 1928) that a sample of the latter dye, too highly purified for good results if dissolved in distilled water, may stain satisfactorily in tap water containing a certain amount of calcium. It may well happen that the user of some dye which gives too weak staining can increase its intensity of action by adding some mineral salt to the staining solution or by altering the H-ion concentration with a buffer salt. In trying this experiment great caution must be employed, for large effects are sometimes produced by minute changes, and it is easy to bring about too weak staining on the one hand, or overstaining on the other if too much of any salt, acid, or base be added.

ASSAY METHODS

When the project of stain standardization was undertaken, in the early '20's, it was realized that reliable methods of assay were needed. They were so definitely lacking at that time that in the early certification work, primary stress was laid on performance of the batches tested; chemical and optical assay methods were at the start more or less incidental. This was regarded as an unsatisfactory and temporary expedient; but it was adopted because tests for performance were then regarded as more reliable than the assay methods then available.

These methods were crude. Dye content had to be determined by means of the rather tricky method of reduction with titanous chloride. This procedure depends on the fact that reducible radicals are present in almost all dyes, so that the dye strength of a sample can be determined by $TiCl_3$ titration, provided that: (1) the end point is sharp; (2) the molecular weight of the dye is known. These provisos make the method sometimes inapplicable. It often happens that the correlation is very poor between titration and colorimetric comparison of various samples of the same dye. As a result considerable research is often needed to establish a reliable assay method; nitrogen determinations or other more absolute procedures must be resorted to in order to establish a satisfactory norm for actual dye content determinations.

In addition to assay for dye content, the spectrophotometer was adopted quite early in the work for determining whether or not any sample was true to type. The original spectrophotometers (see Chapter IV) were visual instruments, and it was quite laborious to make accurate readings. The later introduction of photoelectric spectrophotometers has made for greater accuracy, but it has also necessitated some research before standards based on the new type of instrument were well established.

One advantage of the photoelectric instruments is the greater ease in obtaining with them a reading of the density at the peak of adsorption (D_p).

This has made it possible to use the spectrophotometer not only for determining the nature of the dye but for comparing the strength of various samples in cases where the titration method has proved inadequate.

The methods at present adopted in the Commission assay laboratory are given in the appendix of this book (pp. 276–315). Constant efforts are being made to improve the methods, and it is realized that they are much better than those adopted in the '20's. Nevertheless they are still unsatisfactory as methods for evaluating the performance of stains; and it is still necessary to continue the practice of testing them in actual use.

HISTOCHEMICAL REAGENTS

The possibility that dyes might some day serve as histochemical reagents was realized quite early. The well known fact that basic dyes have greater affinity for nuclear substance and acid dyes for cytoplasm, is enough to suggest this possibility to anyone; but for a long time the matter remained in the realms of theory, without much concrete fact on which methods could be based.

Undoubtedly the first real stimulus to histochemical technic came from Feulgen and Rossenbeck's application of the Schiff's reagent for aldehyde to cytological structures. (See p. 140). Feulgen was not unaware of what he had accomplished, as shown by the fact that he named the granules thus stained "nucleal" the terminal syllable indicating their supposedly aldehyde-like nature. That was about as far as one could go in those days; not until the various nucleic acids came to be recognized and localized in the cell could the specificity of the Feulgen reaction or the nature of the bodies stained by it be learned.

It was probably 10 years or more after Feulgen's work before the reaction named after him became well enough established so that the Stain Commission regarded it as a sufficiently important use for basic fuchsin to serve as one of the criteria of certification. It was realized that not all basic fuchsins were suitable for use in the technic; and for some time it seemed an unnecessary refinement to insist that a certified fuchsin should meet this requirement when the dye was so seldom used for the purpose. Now, however, the situation has changed greatly, thanks to the rapid development of histochemical technic, and no basic fuchsin unsatisfactory in the Feulgen procedure would be acceptable.

At present the efforts of histochemists are being directed toward finding other reagents that are specific for the same or other cytochemical features. Some of the reagents are dyes, others are not dyes but develop color in the presence of the chemicals with which they react. The proposal has been made to extend the principle of stain certification to cover some of these reagents but no definite plans to that effect have yet been made. Some of the most commonly used histochemical reagents are given in Chapters X and XI.

III

THE MECHANISM OF STAINING

There is to be found in the literature much discussion of the mechanism of staining. Most of this occurred at the '20's and '30's, and consisted of a somewhat heated controversy as to whether chemistry or physics explained the phenomena observed. Most of this controversy is now distinctly out of date, as it has become evident that physicochemical phenomena are involved which operate in the borderland between the more obviously physical and chemical reactions. Nevertheless a brief discussion of the earlier theories is useful even today as it helps interpret some aspects of tissue staining.

Theoretically the dyeing of textile fabrics and the staining of microscopic structures are the same. In one case only the gross effects are observed, in the other the microscopic details. Any theory, therefore, that will explain the details of microscopic staining will be fully adequate to account for dyeing in bulk.

It would seem at first thought that the dyes combine so firmly with the tissues stained by them that the phenomenon must be a chemical one; but the observed facts can be explained on a physical basis, and some observations are hard to explain if a chemical union between tissue and dye actually takes place. In a chemical union a new substance is formed which does not necessarily have the properties of either substance entering into its formation, and it is ordinarily impossible to recover the original substances by means of simple solvents. When tissue is stained there is no evidence of any new substance having been formed, the colored tissue merely taking on one of the characteristics of the dye (color) in addition to the properties which it originally possessed; it is, moreover, ordinarily possible to extract all or nearly all of the color by sufficiently long immersion in water, or by the fairly brief action of alcohol. Another observation which points against chemical action is that the tissue never removes the dye completely from solution, even though very dilute; whereas ordinary chemical reactions tend to continue until one of the components of the reaction is exhausted. Although these facts are not incompatible with chemical explanations, the original exponents of the physical theories regarded them as full refutation of the possibility of chemical action.

The original dispute concerning physical and chemical theories of stain action was based largely on *a priori* argument or on insufficiently understood evidence. The most recent publications on the subject do not try to differentiate between physical and chemical theories.

Physical Factors. There are three factors, all purely physical in nature, which together or separately may explain many, if not all, staining phenomena. In the first place, as nearly all substances stained are more or less porous, simple physical forces such as capillarity and osmosis can account for penetration of the dye into the interior of the tissue. In the second place, the action of *ad*sorption can account for many staining phenomena, even for much of the selective staining with which the biologist is familiar. In the third place, a dye may penetrate some cellular element by *ab*sorption, remaining there in a state of solid solution. Any one or all of these three forces may operate in any given instance. For a concise discussion of the physical explanations, especially the solution theory, see Holmes (1929b).

The absorption or solution theory is very simple and the action of some dyes on some kinds of cellular tissue in the presence of mineral salts suggests that this factor is important, at least in some instances. It is also supported by the fact that a dye causes the tissue to become the same color as the dye shows in solution, but not necessarily the same as it shows in its dry form. Dry fuchsin, for example, is green; its solution, however, is red, and so are tissues stained by it, no matter how completely they may be dried. It is nevertheless difficult to explain all staining phenomena, particularly differential staining, on the basis of solution.

Adsorption, on the other hand, furnishes a very satisfactory explanation even of much differential staining and by some authors it was once claimed that all staining phenomena might be accounted for in this way. The principle of selective adsorption is well known to physical chemists, whereby certain ions may be adsorbed by certain substances much more readily than by others. Equally well known is the fact that the rate of adsorption of any ion is strongly influenced by the presence of other ions in the solution, and that a specially strong influence is exerted by the reaction of the solution, in other words by the concentration of free hydrogen or hydroxyl ions in the fluid; the influence of the latter upon the adsorption of basic ions being exactly the opposite from its effect upon the adsorption of acid ions. Such principles as these may offer an explanation of such phenomena as the differential staining of different cellular elements, action of mordants, variations in rate of staining with changes in the salt content of the staining solution, and influence of H-ion concentration upon the color assumed by tissue when exposed to the action of both acid and basic dyes. Bayliss (1906) developed this particular phase of the physical theory into what he called an "electrical theory of staining." See also Parks and Bartlett (1935a and b).

It is not impossible that dyes may penetrate cells by mere sorption and diffusion, with precipitation inside the cells by acids or bases, or other chemical reagents present, thus preventing their extraction by simple solvents. Such a theory admits the possibility of chemical action without assuming an actual chemical union between the dye and tissue protein.

It is, however, frequently pointed out that there is no sharp distinction between chemistry and physics; and in such delicate reactions as those involved in staining, we may well be in the borderland between the two branches of science where it is impossible to say that a given phenomenon is purely physical or purely chemical. Nevertheless, there are certain chemical principles distinctly different from the physical ones just mentioned, that may well enter into the phenomenon of staining.

Chemical Factors. It is well known that some parts of the cell are acid in reaction, others alkaline; and it is evident that the former would tend to combine with the cations in solutions with which they come in contact, the latter with anions. Now, inasmuch as in certain dyes the color exists in the cation (basic dyes) and in others in the anion (acid dyes), it is natural to expect chemical combinations to take place between dye and tissue, depending upon the reaction of the latter. That the stained tissue does not present any characteristics to the eye not possessed by either tissue or dye before staining does not prove that no new substance has been formed, nor is this claim refuted by the fact that sufficiently long action by solvents removes the color. Alcohol and even water are not absolutely inert chemically and may withdraw the dye by chemical instead of physical action; the very length of time necessary to remove the color completely (sometimes so long as to allow bacterial decomposition of the tissue) indicates a rather strong union between dye and tissue. As to the fact that a tissue which has a strong affinity for some particular dye never withdraws that dye completely from a very dilute solution, one can point out instances where chemical reactions are known to take place and yet to stop before either component is exhausted. The failure to exhaust the dye completely from a surrounding solution may merely mean that an equilibrium has been reached; chemical action, moreover, is strongly indicated by the fact that in dilute solutions the tissues take up relatively larger quantities of the dye than in concentrated solution. Accordingly the observation that not all the dye is withdrawn from the solution is a poor argument against chemical action.

Furthermore, if adsorption is assumed to take place only at a specific site (i.e., at the COOH or NH_3 group), the physical and chemical concepts merge into one and cannot be distinguished from each other. It has been shown, for instance, that cells in which the COOH groups are blocked by the formation of methyl esters do not stain well with basic dyes. This observation is hard to explain on a purely physical basis; to explain it by adsorption requires the assumption that the phenomenon occurs only at a specific chemical site. Such an explanation comes quite close to assuming chemical action.

The fundamental principle involved in a chemical interpretation is that certain parts of animal or plant cells are acid in character and hence have an affinity for the basic dyes. The nuclei of the cells, or especially the chromatin within the nuclei, are assumed to be acid in character (due largely to their constitutent nucleic acid), and there is no question but that they have a strong affinity for basic dyes; while the cytoplasm has an affinity for acid dyes and is assumed to be basic in character. (See Stearn and Stearn, 1929–1930.)

This theory assumes that the acids and bases which go to make up body tissue are ordinarily amphoteric, capable of acting as bases in acid solutions and as acids in basic solutions, the H-ion concentration at which any such compound changes from an acid to a base in its action being known as its isoelectric point. It also assumes that these compounds, although insoluble, act as though they were electrolytes dissolved in any fluid in which they are immersed. Hence, on this assumption, such a compound acts as a base or as an acid in any staining solution according to whether its isoelectric point is below or above the H-ion concentration of that solution; in other words any cellular element takes a basic dye if the H-ion concentration of the staining solution is below its isoelectric point, an acid dye if it is above that point.

Now, exactly such a phenomenon as this is to be observed in staining any tissue. With very acid staining solutions even the nuclei take the acid dyes; if one employs successively a series of solutions of decreasing H-ion concentration, the affinity of the nuclei for the acid dyes rapidly becomes less; till at a fairly definite reaction, usually in the region of pH 4, they lose their affinity for acid dyes and take the basic dyes. In solutions near neutrality, therefore, the nuclei take basic dyes, the cytoplasm the acid dyes. Finally at a point considerably to the alkaline side of neutrality even the cytoplasm takes the basic dyes. Such an observation is interpreted to mean that the isoelectric point of the nuclei lies considerably to the acid side of neutrality, that of the cytoplasm considerably to the alkaline side. Now assuming that this interpretation is correct, it might be possible to determine the isoelectric points of different parts of the cell by staining at different reactions. This idea, however, has been distinctly discredited of recent years. For one thing, staining determinations of any protein must be made on fixed tissue; and the isoelectric point of a fixed protein may well be very different from that of the fresh material. Also, as Singer (1952) points out in his review of the factors which control staining, the position of the crossing point of the staining curves of acid and basic dyes is determined by various other factors, and does not definitely indicate the iso-electric point. He concludes, nevertheless, that although this point cannot be precisely defined by pH staining characteristics, it is possible to compare the curves of different proteins and to learn therefrom the *relative* position of their isoelectric points. Such results show that there is a definite tendency for cationic dyes to unite with anionic elements of the tissue, and *vice versa*.

These are not by any means the only chemical aspects of staining. It is difficult to explain wholly on the basis of various isoelectric points the fact that certain basic dyes have stronger affinities for certain parts of the nuclei than for others, and that of the various cytoplasmic structures outside the nucleus some are more readily stained by certain acid dyes and some by others. In the Flemming triple stain, for example, which employs the acid dye orange G and the two basic dyes safranin and gentian violet, with in-tervening alcoholic differentiation, it is possible to stain the chromatin with gentian violet and the rest of the nucleus with safranin. Before such a phenomenon as this can be explained on a purely chemical basis, it is ob-vious that we must have a much more detailed knowledge of histo- and cytochemistry than is yet available. The present tendency is to associate some of these phenomena with the different staining reactions of ribonucleic and deoxyribonucleic acids; but we still do not know the relative amounts of these two substances in various parts of the nucleus.

The weaknesses of purely chemical theories show up particularly in re-actions such as this triple stain. Besides the difficulty of accounting for the stronger affinity of certain portions of the nucleus for certain basic dyes and other portions of the nucleus for other basic dyes, there is the difficulty of explaining the action of solvents. The differential staining secured in the Flemming stain, and in fact in the majority of other similar procedures, is brought about not by the staining itself but by the action of solvents which extract some of the dyes more readily from certain portions of the cell than from others. In case a chemical union has taken place between the tissue and the dye, the alcohol or other solvent used must have the effect of breaking down the chemical compound formed between the tissue proteins and the dye molecule, or else it must actually dissolve out the compound in question. It is, however, difficult on the one hand to conceive of alcohol breaking down such a compound; while, on the other hand, if the compound formed is dissolved out of the tissue, it is hard to understand how restaining of de-colorized structures is possible.

It should also be remembered that the assumption of a definite isoelectric point for the protein of tissue is difficult to accept. A physical chemist de-fines this point as the reaction where the minimum dissociation occurs. Now a protein occurring in solid form can hardly be expected to dissociate, and accordingly it is a question whether it can properly be said to have an isoelectric point. It is, in short, difficult to conceive how an insoluble solid can behave as an electrolyte and take part in the reactions assumed for it.

One can, however, assume that differential staining indicates differences in chemical nature of the different parts of the cell without insisting that chemical factors alone, are involved. Even if the dye is actually taken up by a process of adsorption, and only chemical factors are involved, this process will be greatly influenced by the chemical nature of the different parts of the cell. Substances of an acid character would adsorb basic dyes more readily, and retain them in the adsorbed state more firmly than they would acid dyes, and substances of a basic character would adsorb acid more readily than basic dyes. Amphoteric substances are usually acid or basic in their prevailing character. Acid substances such as cell nuclei exert a decided chemical affinity for basic dyes and accordingly adsorb them readily. They have, however, inferior degrees of affinity for acid dyes and in order to obtain staining with such dyes it is only necessary to convert them into a favorable physical form for adsorption. Basic substances, on the other hand, such as cytoplasm, although ordinarily stained only by acid dyes, may be stained by basic dyes if the latter are employed in a favorable physical form. Favorable conditions for these unusual types of staining are obtained merely by altering the reaction of the staining solutions. Thus one does not have to assume chemical combination between dye and tissue in order to account for the different type of staining obtained in solutions of varying pH value.

Since the early '30's there has been no serious discussion as to the relative significance of physical and chemical factors; the difference does not now seem to be one of immense importance. All of the theories teach about the same practical lessons as to the type of dye to select for any particular purpose and as to the influence of salt content or H-ion concentration of staining solution or tissues upon the rate or intensity of staining. The user of biological stains should know enough about the various theories of their action to understand the influence of ionic concentration upon basic dyes on the one hand and acid dyes on the other; but realizing that the same phenomena can be explained by more than one theory, he can safely leave to the physical chemists all discussion of the mechanism involved. It should be realized that staining processes are of great complexity, so that both chemical and physical factors are necessary to explain them.

A good illustration of the modern way of treating the subject is the recent review paper by Singer (1952). In this paper the author mentions the various theories without showing special favor to any one of them, but gives his attention to the various controllable factors which influence staining of tissues. He points out that the extensive literature of the early part of this century on the theory of staining has brought out many facts of value relating to the interaction of dyes and tissue proteins, and that this interaction deserves further study, without theorizing as to whether it is chemical or physical. His paper is an excellent review of the information on this subject now available.

Histochemistry. It is interesting that now, when a purely chemical theory of staining is not generally accepted, specific instances of what seem to be definite chemical reactions between dyes (or related compounds) and tissue elements are becoming more numerous. The new science of histochemistry depends on the fact that some dyes, or uncolored chemicals which become colored under certain definite conditions, can be used as reagents for giving information as to the chemistry of cell constitutents.

As long ago as 1924 the classic work of Feulgen and his associates pointed the way to histochemistry in showing that certain parts of the nuclei of cells could restore the color to Schiff's reagent (fuchsin-sulphurous-acid) in much the same way as it could be restored in the test tube in the presence of aldehydes. Feulgen very logically assumed that he was demonstrating the presence of aldehyde-like substances in the nucleus and he called the phenomenon the "nucle*al* reaction." Although he probably had little conception of the field he was opening up, nevertheless this observation of his (but not necessarily his interpretation) did lead into modern histochemistry. Histochemical methods are now able to point out the cites of certain types of enzyme activity, to locate such compounds as 1,2-glycols in the cell, and to give valuable information as to the significance of ribonucleic acid in chromosomes. The subject has become too vast to discuss in this book; and the reader is referred to more authoritative reviews such as Lillie (1954), Davenport (1960), Lison (1953), and Pearse (1960), and Gomori (1952). All that needs to be said in this chapter is that these findings are coming to have an increasingly important bearing on the general theory of staining, and certainly indicate that chemical factors must be taken into account (in part, at least) in explaining the mechanism of staining.

IV

THE SPECTROPHOTOMETRIC AND CHRO-
MATOGRAPHIC ANALYSIS OF DYES

Chemical methods alone are inadequate in the analysis of many dyes. Not only is the detailed chemistry of some dyes obscure, but the reactions are often complicated by adulterating dyestuffs in such a manner as to preclude entire reliance on rigorous chemical methods. Often a slight change in the arrangement of atoms within the molecule will make a marked change in the nature of the dye, while such a minor change in structure is not always readily detected by chemical means alone. Hence the advisability of employing certain physico-chemical characteristics as displayed by the spectrophotometer in the study of dyes. So important is this study that a discussion of the principles involved is necessary here.

The absorption spectra obtained by the spectrophotometer are usually characteristic of any particular dye. Quantitative as well as qualitative data may be obtained by the spectrophotometer; and from the combined results nearly all dyes, even though differing from each other only in very minor particulars of chemical structure may be easily differentiated. This method is not only rapid but is also convenient.

The method depends upon the fact that any colored substance absorbs light of certain definite wave lengths and transmits or reflects the rest. The absorption spectrum is essentially the inverse of that which is reflected or transmitted. Therefore the color of light which reaches the eye after transmission through or reflection from a colored substance is complementary to the color of light absorbed by that substance. A violet dye, for example, appears that color because of its predominant absorption of greenish yellow light. The absorption maximum is quite characteristic of any dye; any two dyes having the same absorption curve (a somewhat rare occurrence) are of essentially the same color.

The wave length is ordinarily measured in millimicrons (mμ), or in Ångstrom units (Å); 1Å $= 0.1$ mμ. The visible spectrum begins at around

400 mμ in the violet and runs to about 750 mμ in the red. The wave lengths of the six most important colors, and their complementary colors are given in Table 1.

A variety of terms and units have come into common usage in connection with the practice of spectrophotometry and numerous symbols to represent them are employed. Since there is some confusion concerning the symbols used, the relationships between the various symbols and units and definitions of the terms most frequently encountered in the literature are given in Table 2.

The color of substances is ordinarily of complex origin, depending upon the absorption of light in varying degrees, over an extensive spectral range. Whereas the unaided eye is able to register only the composite effect, it is possible to resolve this effect into its component factors with the aid of a spectrophotometer. Although the eye is unable to distinguish between a violet dye and a suitable mixture of a red and a blue dye, the heterogeneous character of the mixture is readily apparent upon spectrophotometric examination. Pure dyes may have simple absorption spectra, in that their light absorption is all at one part of the spectrum, or they may be more complex, showing two or more points on the spectrum at each of which light is absorbed to greater extent than on either side of it. Thus even in the instance of pure products of identical color to the eye, the spectro-

TABLE 1

Spectrum

(Showing Complementary Colors)

Spectrum	Wave Lengths, mμ	Complementary Colors
Violet	400–430	Yellow
Blue	430–490	Yellow
Blue-green	490–510	Orange
		Red
Green	510–570	Purple
Yellow	570–600	Violet
		Blue
Orange	600–620	Blue-green
Red	620–750	Blue-green

TABLE 2

Relations between the Symbols and Units and Definitions of the Terms*

Symbols	Definitions
A	1. Ångstrom: also Å; 1/6438.4696 of the wave length of the Cd red line, or 10^{-8} cm = 0.1 mμ 2. Absorption: 1 − T
μ	Micron = 10^{-4} cm = 1000 mμ = 10,000 A
λ	1. Wave length: expressed in terms of Å or mμ (see 1, above) 2. Wave length of maximum absorption
I	Transmitted intensity; light transmitted by solute
I_o	Incident intensity; light transmitted by solvent
T	1. Transmission, transmittance and transmittancy: I/I_o 2. Percentage transmission: 100 × I/I_o
E	Extinction: also D or d; Log_{10} I_o/I, or −Log T
D	Density: also d or E; (see above)
c	Concentration of solution, gm per liter
d	Thickness of solution layer in cm. (Sometimes used to mean density)
k	Specific extinction coefficient: E/cd
ϵ	Molecular extinction coefficient: Mk, (M = molecular weight)

$I = I_o \cdot 10^{-kcd}$

$Log_0 I_o/I = kcd = E$

* For further discussion of this subject consult Brode (1943) and Gibb (1942).

photometer frequently reveals decided differences when the character of the light absorption is considered in detail.

While it may be necessary or advisable in some instances to determine absorption in the infrared or ultraviolet, the measurement of absorption within the visible spectrum, upon which color is dependent, is adequate for most purposes. The essential principle of operation of a typical spectro-photometer is best understood by considering first the principles of a visual instrument, although such instruments are now practically obsolete because of the greater efficiency of photoelectric measurements. These principles may be understood by reference to Fig. 1. Such instruments comprise essentially two beams of light from a common source, one to pass through a glass cell containing the sample to be examined, the other to pass through a

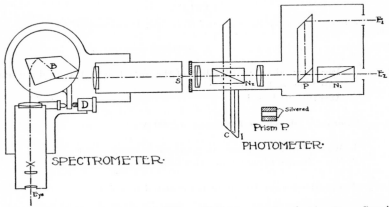

PHOTOMETER·

SPECTROMETER·

Fɪɢ. 1. Schematic diagram of Hilger-Nutting spectrophotometer. Specimen
holder with dye dissolved in a suitable solvent is placed at E_1 while a similar cell
with solvent alone is placed at E_2. Both are equally illuminated from the same
light source. Through the partially silvered prism, P, the upper and lower portion of
the photometer field is illuminated through the specimen while the central portion is
illuminated through solvent alone. This latter illumination may be varied by the
rotation of the analyzer, N_2, which is actuated by a graduated circle C, reading with
the index I. By this means the illumination of the several portions of the field is
maintained equal and absorption values read off of circle C. The spectrometer of
the constant deviation type serves to isolate particular portions of the spectrum by
means of a graduated drum D which through a screw actuates the prism table sup-
porting prism B.

similar cell containing solvent only; a photometer for adjusting the relative
intensity of the two beams; a spectrometer with prism and eyepiece arranged so that portions of the spectra of the light from the two beams are
observed juxtaposed in the field of the eyepiece. The spectrum of the beam
which has passed through the dye solution will be found deficient in those
portions which have been absorbed by the dye, and the degree of the deficiency at any position in the spectrum may be measured by determining
the degree to which the intensity of the light of the second spectrum must
be reduced in order to obtain an equal intensity in the two fields observed
by the eye.

The shutter of the eyepiece may be partially closed so that only a narrow
spectral range is visible; this allows the eye to concentrate on the matching
of two small fields, each of which appears uniform in color. The instrument
is provided with a screw drum, calibrated in wave lengths, by means of
which the prism may be rotated in such a manner as to bring light of any
desired wave length into the center of the field of vision.

This visual type of instrument, as explained above, is now rarely used,
having become obsolete on account of the greater efficiency of the photo-

electric cell in comparison with the eye. The eye is badly subject to fatigue after continuous use, and even at its best has low sensitivity at the violet end of the spectrum. The photoelectric cell, on the other hand, is not so subject to fatigue and can make readings over a longer wave length range— even into the ultraviolet, if special equipment for that purpose is provided. For these reasons more rapid readings can be made, and it is possible to obtain the exact point of maximum absorption much more quickly than with the eye. A photoelectric instrument such as the General Electric recording spectrophotometer, is even more automatic, as it has a motor-driven device that records even the most complicated absorption curve on a revolving drum in only a few minutes. A recording spectrophotometer, although it provides speed in determining a spectrum, is not essential for dyes because of their relatively simple absorption curves. Simple non-recording photoelectric instruments, such as the Beckman are ordinarily sufficient.

The optical principles of the Beckman are given in Fig. 2 and a photograph of an assembled instrument in Fig. 3. In theory, such an instrument merely replaces the eye with a photoelectric cell; but in actual practice the optical system is different. This is due to the fact that the photoelectric cell enables one to measure directly the intensity of the light by means of a potentiometer. With the eye as the recording agent, two beams of light are necessary, one passing through the unknown, the other through the solvent alone, plus an analyzer with which the intensity of the light can be varied until the two beams of light are equal in apparent strength. With the photoelectric cell, on the other hand, simultaneous inspection of two beams of light is not necessary, nor is the analyzer for reducing the light intensity needed; hence a single beam of light passing through the instrument is all that is needed, with resulting greater simplicity of the optical system. The chief bulk of a non-recording photoelectric spectrophotometer is occupied by a potentiometer to record the strength of the current generated by the photoelectric cell.

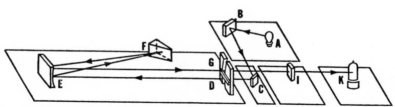

Fig. 2. Schematic optical diagram of Beckman model DU spectrophotometer

A. Light source
B. Condensing mirror
C. Diagonal mirror
D. Entrance slit
E. Collimating mirror
F. Quartz prism
G. Exit slit
I. Absorption cell
K. Photoelectric tube

FIG. 3. Photograph of an assembled Beckman model DU spectrophotometer

In measuring the complete visible absorption of a dye, a series of measurements is made over the portion of the spectrum in which any appreciable absorption may be noted. In doing this with such an instrument as the Beckman, one of the absorption cells is filled with the solvent alone, as a control, another with the dye dissolved in the same solvent, in quite dilute solution. Then, after checking the instrument as to its zero point the control cell is placed in the beam of light coming from the exit slit, the monochromator set to a point somewhat to one side of that part of the spectrum where absorption is expected, and a reading taken as to the intensity of the light reaching the phototube. Then a similar reading is taken with the unknown sample. The setting is then changed to a slightly different wave length, and new readings taken. In practice such readings are taken about every 5 mμ in the regions of slight absorption but at least every 1 mμ near the peak. The difference between the readings of the control and the unknown at any point indicates the absorption of light at that point. With the Beckman, four absorption tubes are provided, which allows for readings to be obtained one after the other with three different unknowns.

If measurements are carried out under suitable standardized conditions, the spectral position and the general form of the absorption curve are characteristic of the individual dye, while the magnitude of absorptive indices (the height of the curve) varies directly with the amount of dye present.

The absorption curves of dyes which are very closely related in structure are sometimes so similar as to be practically identical. In such instances the individual dyes may be recognized by means of quantitative determinations of the degree in which their absorption is modified under the influence of suitable variations in conditions.

The absorption curves of typical yellow, orange, red, violet, and blue dyes are recorded in Fig. 4. It will be noted that their maximum absorption in each case falls within the range of the complementary color (*cf.* Table 1). The great majority of dyes of these colors, in the usual solvents and under the usual conditions, show but one absorption band in the visible spectrum. The curves are seldom perfectly symmetrical, however, and usually give indications of localized secondary absorption in some portion of the band. It has been shown that this secondary absorption is due, in numerous instances, to a tautomeric form of the dye. It should never be accepted as evidence of the presence of a second dye unless it has been ascertained that it is not found with a pure sample of the dye under conditions of examination.

The absorption curve of a green dye is recorded in Fig. 5. It has a principal band in the orange and a secondary band in the violet. Both the absorption curve and the color of the dye could be matched closely by mixing a suitable blue and a yellow dye in the correct proportions. All green dyes absorb appreciable amounts of violet light as well as of red light.

In Fig. 6 is given the absorption curve of a dye mixture, together with the curves of the component dyes. The mixture is reported to have been marketed in good faith as asymmetrical dimethyl thionin, a dye which is intermediate in constitution and in color between thionin and methylene blue (see under azure A, on p. 97). The absorption curve plainly indicates the presence of two dyes, and suggests their probable identity. (It would be advisable to effect the separation of small amounts of both dyes, if their positive identification is desired.) The color of the mixture is very similar to that of dimethyl thionin. The absorption curve of that dye, however, is a simple and well defined curve resembling those of thionin and methylene blue, but occupying an intermediate position in the spectrum.

This illustration shows how valuable the spectrophotometric analysis may be in determining whether a given product is a simple dye or a mixture of two or more dyes. This fact, together with its use in determining the exact shade of any dye, makes it the most valuable test to apply to a stain, other than to determine by actual use whether the sample will prove satisfactory to the microscopist or not.

It should be remarked that the absorption curve of a dye is not necessarily the same in two different solvents. In the following pages aqueous solutions are to be understood unless some other solvent is specified.

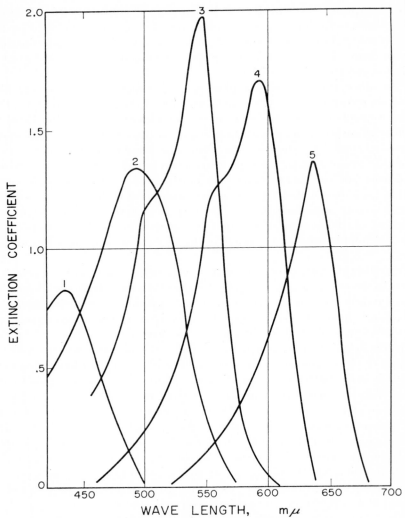

FIG. 4. Absorption curves of five dyes of different colors:
1. Tartrazine (yellow)
2. Orange G
3. Fuchsin (red)
4. Crystal violet
5. Neptune blue BG

CHROMATOGRAPHY

Recently more and more stress is coming to be laid on a different method of dye analysis known as chromatography. It has no real relation to spec-

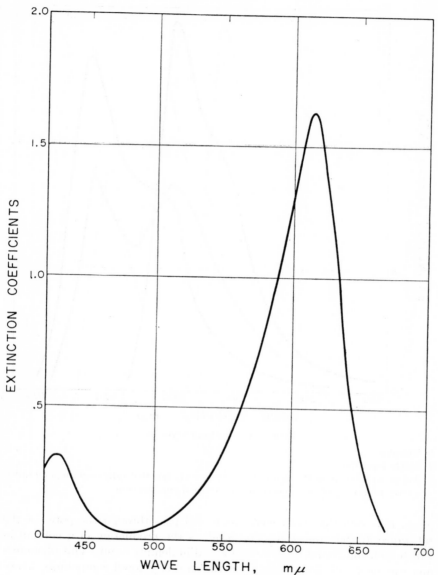

FIG. 5. Absorption curve of malachite green

trophotometry, but it is considered in this chapter because it also furnishes a means of separation and identification of dyes on the basis of differences in color that are not shown by simple visual comparison.

When two different chemicals are in solution together and are brought into contact with a porous substance in which capillary rise readily takes

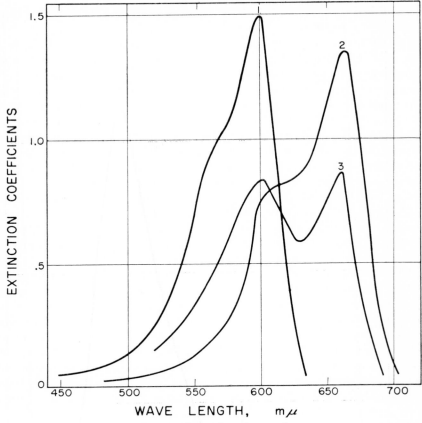

FIG. 6. Absorption curves of:

1. Thionin
2. Methylene blue
3. Apparent mixture of these two dyes, incorrectly labelled (although in good faith) a dye intermediate between them in chemical composition

place, it is rare that both compounds will pass through the pores of the substance at the same rate. The result is the production of a column in which each compound tends to be located in definite bands. This phenomenon was naturally first observed in the case of colored compounds; hence the name chromatography, although it is now used fully as much for uncolored as for colored compounds. Dyes lend themselves naturally to this method of analysis. The method is of value not only for showing the various bands of color that develop, but actually to isolate the individual constituents of the mixture, as the column can be cut into its various sections and the chemical there localized can be eluted by the proper reagent and thus obtained in pure form.

The method as originally developed called for a column of alumina in a glass tube, in which the bands are located at points determined by the differing degrees of adsorption taking place between the alumina and the different constituents of the mixture. A more recent development, known as paper partition chromatography, depends on a different principle, the relative solubility of different compounds in two solvents, together with the affinity of cellulose fibers for the solvents, which determines the rate of passage through the pores of the filter paper. The paper partition method has several advantages, among them the ease with which the chromatograms can be preserved and with which sections can be removed for extraction of the individual fractions. Simultaneous papers (Emery and Stotz, 1952; Christman and Trubey, 1952) have described the application of the technic to dye analysis; and at about the same time, Evans and Walls (1952) have shown the possibility of getting very similar chromatographic pictures by the use of filter paper electrophoresis.

A chromatographic strip obtained in this way from a mixture of dyes can be very striking. Emery and Stotz show that a mixture of three dyes (eosin Y, orange G, and erythrosin B) in a mixture of butanol and water, and allowed to diffuse from a spot at the top of a filter paper strip, develops five zones of color, one orange, one red, two pink and fluorescent, one fluorescent without color in ordinary illumination; of these five, the three fluorescent zones all come from eosin Y, the other two from orange G and erythrosin respectively. These authors, by cutting out the various zones have been able to isolate the individual dyes and to figure the concentration of each in the original mixture

This illustration is given merely to show the probable value of the method. Much more work must be done, before it can be used in routine dye analysis, and it is not likely to replace spectrophotometry; but, as shown by Emery and Stotz it can serve to reveal the identity of dyes in a mixture, even though one of them (in this case eosin Y) is present in such strength as to mask the others when analysis must depend on the spectrophotometer. Since the earlier publications there have been a number of reports on the paper and column chromatography of biological stains, and nearly all stains certified have been so analyzed in the Commission's laboratories. It is surprising to note how few of the commercial samples represent a single chemical species. Accordingly it is felt that chromatography has an important place in the control of manufacture and in the assay of biological stains.

V

NITRO AND AZO DYES

1. NITROSO DYES (QUINONE OXIMES)

The nitroso dyes are produced by the action of nitrous acid on phenolic compounds, according to the equation

$$\text{(OH benzene)} + HNO_2 = \text{(OH, NO benzene)} + H_2O$$

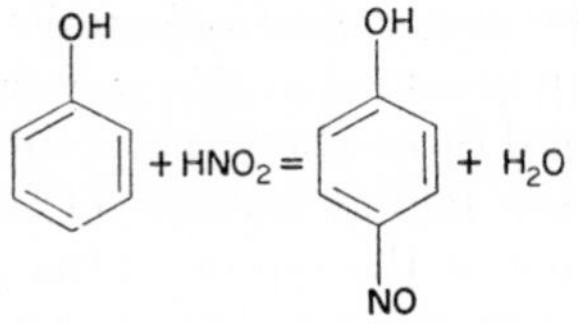

(nitrosophenol)

The fact, however, that the quinone oxime produced by the action of hydroxylamine on *p*-quinone according to the equation

$$\text{(O=quinone=O)} + NH_2OH = \text{(O=quinone=NOH)} + H_2O$$

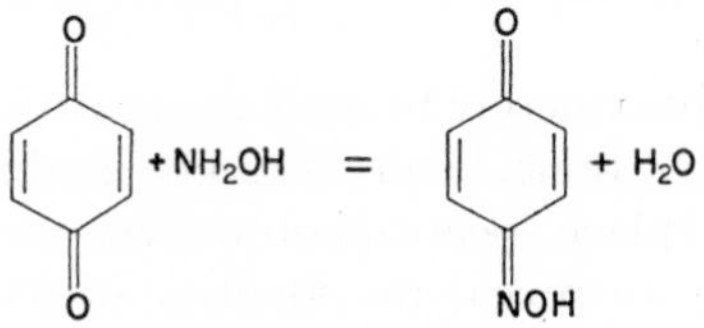

(quinone oxime)

is identical with the nitrosophenol produced as shown above, shows that in all probability the substances can react as quinone oximes, which better accounts for their behavior as dyeing agents since the quinone ring

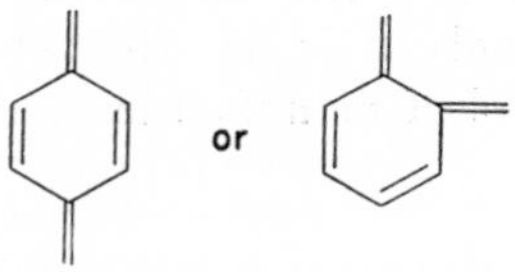

or

occurs frequently in other dyes as a chromophore (see page 22).

52

NAPHTHOL GREEN Y

C. I.* NO. 10005 (1 *ed.:* 2)

(C. I. Mordant Green 4)

Synonyms: *Fast printing green; Gambine*

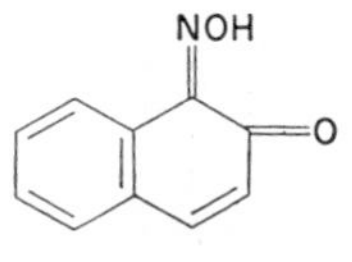

$C_{10}H_7NO_2$; mol. wt. 173.164

(*An acid dye*)

NAPHTHOL GREEN B

C. I. NO. 10200 (1 *ed.:* 5)

(C. I. Acid Green 1)

Synonyms: *Naphthol green; Green PL; Acid green O*

This dye probably has the formula:

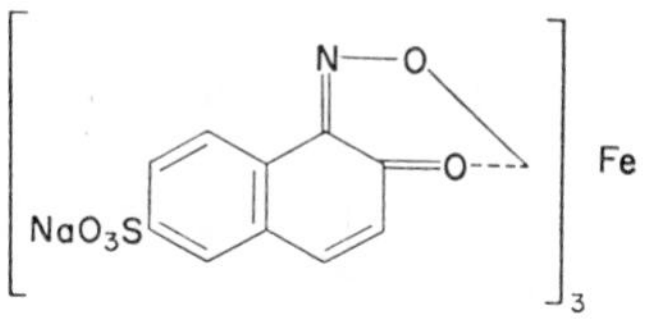

$C_{30}H_{15}N_3O_{15}S_3Na_3Fe$; mol. wt. 878.483

(*An acid dye*)

Some naphthol green, probably the second of the above two dyes, has been employed by Volkmann and Strauss (1934) as a component of a tissue stain, the other dyes used in combination with it being gentian violet and azocarmine G. Mollier (1938) calls for it in a quadruple tissue stain, with orcein, iron-hematoxylin, and azocarmine G.

For the technic of **Mollier's quadruple stain,** see *Staining Procedures*†, p. 57.

2. NITRO DYES

In this group the chromophore is —NO_2. The chromophore is of such a strongly acid character that the dyes of this group are all acid dyes.

---

* The abbreviation "C. I." stands for "Colour Index." The number immediately following is that of the current (2nd) edition; the one which follows is that of the first edition. The name of the dye given under the principal name is the preferred designation in the current Colour Index.

† Conn, Darrow, and Emmel (1960).

Picric acid is formed by the action of nitric acid on phenol, thus introducing three nitro groups:

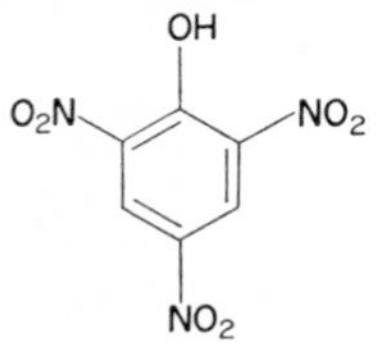

$C_6H_3N_3O_7$; mol. wt. 229.108

(An acid dye; absorption maximum about 360 in alcohol)[*]
Solubility at 26°C: in water 1.18%; in alcohol 8.96%

This compound forms salts by the dissociation of the —OH group, and the salts have considerable value as stains. Ammonium picrate is most commonly thus used.

According to Dehn and Ball (1917), picric acid also has an isomeric form

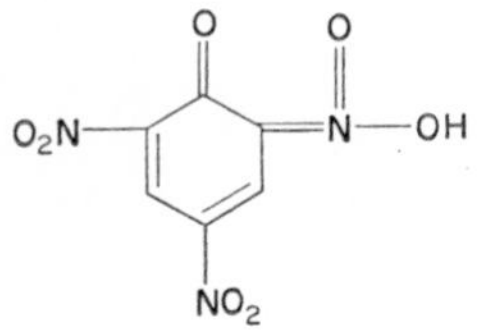

This orthoquinoid form occurs simultaneously with the benzenoid form, and changes in color of the compound may be explained by disturbance of the equilibrium between the two isomers. The quinoid isomer, with its —NOOH group, might well account for the strongly acid character of the compound.

Picric acid (or one of its salts) is quite extensively employed in contrast to acid fuchsin in the Van Gieson (1889) connective tissue stain (which was originally proposed for staining nervous tissue). It is also used as a general cytoplasmic stain in contrast to the basic dyes and to differentiate sections stained by hematoxylin. Wolf (1938) recommends it as a counterstain to crystal violet in the cytology of fungi; Astbury and Preston (1940) for staining cell walls of marine algae. It has further application as a fixative for tissues that are to be sectioned and as a slow decalcifying agent.

---

[*] When not otherwise specified, the absorption maximum is given for an aqueous solution.

Procedures Recommended by the Commission in Which This Stain Is Used*

Name of Procedure	Page Reference to *Staining Procedures*
Van Gieson's stain with iron hematoxylin......................	50
Picro aniline blue with Biebrich scarlet........................	62
Modified Gallego elastic tissue stain...........................	67
Schmorl's method for bone sections............................	145
Picro aniline blue with safranin for woody sections............	194
Goodpasture's stain for influenza bacilli in tissues.............	263-4
MacCallum's stain for influenza bacilli in tissues..............	262

* Under this heading are given references to procedures described in detail in *Staining Procedures*, edited by Conn, Darrow, and Emmel (1960).

MARTIUS YELLOW   C. I. NO. 10315 (1 *ed.:* 9)

(C. I. Acid Yellow 24)

Synonyms: *Manchester yellow; Naphthol yellow*

This dye is usually the sodium, or sometimes calcium or ammonium, salt of the following acid:

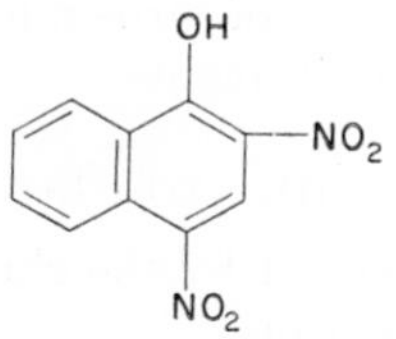

$C_{10}H_6N_2O_5$; mol. wt. 234.164

(An acid dye; absorption maximum about 445, [399, 379])
Solubility of sodium salt at 26°C: in water 4.57%; in alcohol 0.16%.
Solubility of calcium salt: in water 0.05%; in alcohol 1.90%

Martius yellow has been used by Pianese (1896) in combination with malachite green and acid fuchsin for studying cancer tissue; the same technic was applied to plant tissue by Müller (1912), and is now quite extensively used by plant pathologists in studying sections of tissue infected by fungi. It has been employed by Nebel (1931) in contrast to resorcin blue for staining pollen tubes in styles. Halbert (1935), by adding it to bacteriological media, finds that it favors the growth of *Escherichia coli*, but inhibits *Aerobacter aerogenes*. The dye is also used in preparing certain light filters used in photomicrography.

For technic of **Pianese III B Stain**, see *Staining Procedures*, p. 195.
For technic of **Lacmoid-martius-yellow stain for pollen tubes**, see Id. p. 198.

AURANTIA   C. I. NO. 10360 (1 *ed.*: 12)

Synonym: *Imperial yellow*

This dye is the ammonium salt of hexanitro-diphenylamine.

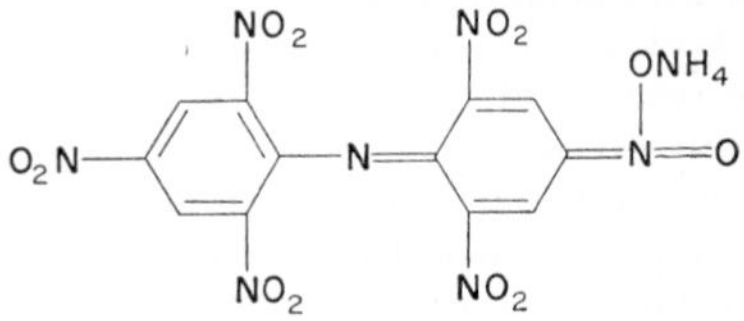

$C_{12}H_8N_8O_{12}$; mol. wt. 456.248

(An acid dye; absorption maximum about 425)
Solubility at 26°C: in water nil; in alcohol 0.33%

It is obsolete as a textile dye, although sometimes used as a photographic desensitizer. It is called for in combination with toluidine blue and acid fuchsin in the Champy-Kull technic for demonstrating certain cell constituents (mitochondria, etc.). It is very poisonous, frequently causing severe dermatitis.

Kassanis (1939) employes it in the Kull technic (i.e., with acid fuchsin and toluidine blue) for the study of virus infested plants. Favorsky (1939) uses it for inducing polyploidy in plants.

3. THE AZO GROUP

The azo dyes are characterized by the chromophore —N==N— joining benzene or naphthalene rings, thus:

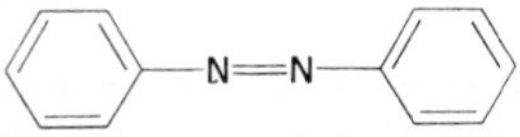

It is possible for the azo group to occur more than once in a molecule, forming the dis-azo dyes, thus:

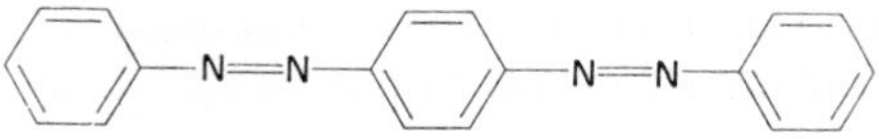

Similarly dyes with three or four azo groups are known. The azo chromophore is distinctly basic; but not sufficiently so to make the dyes basic when they contain hydroxyl groups. Those containing amino groups are of course, distinctly basic.

The position of the hydroxyl or amino group on a benzene ring in relation to the azo group is important. Ordinarily they are in the para position to each other, thus:

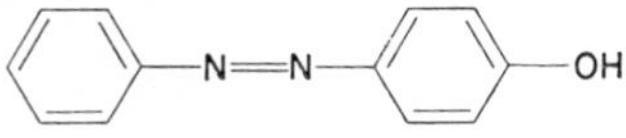

The ortho position is next frequently assumed; rarely the meta position. When the hydroxyl group assumes the ortho position the character of the compound is quite distinct from that of the para compounds. By a rearrangement of the atoms such a compound is sure to change to a quinoid form, thus:

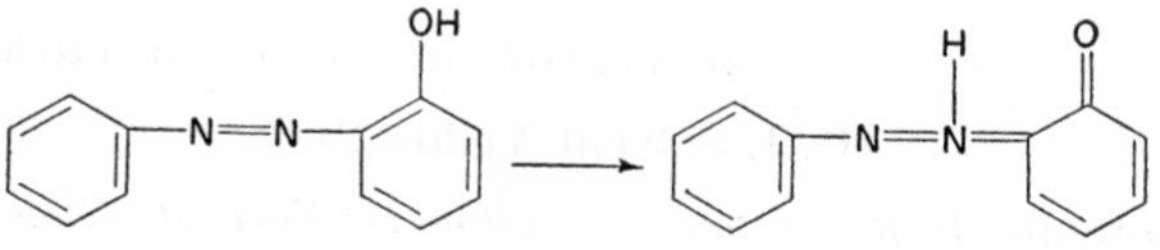

A compound of this latter structure cannot form salts and does not act as an ordinary dye. It does, however, prove to be soluble in oil and is able to color it by an apparently physical process. Hence the azo-ortho-phenols, or azo-beta-naphthols, like Sudan III and Sudan IV,

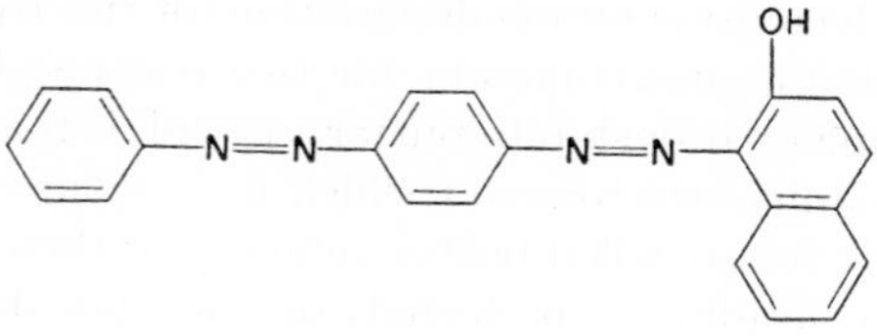

and

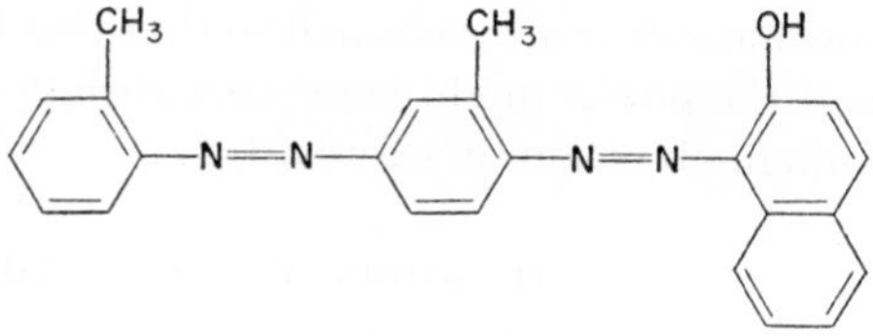

are important fat staining dyes.

A. MONO-AZO DYES

FAST YELLOW   C. I. NO. 13015 (1 ed.: 16)

(C. I. Acid Yellow 9)

Synonyms: *Fast yellow FY, G, S, BG, etc.; Acid yellow*

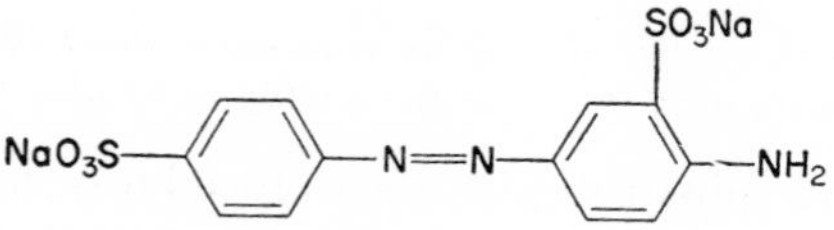

$C_{12}H_9N_3O_6S_2Na_2$; mol. wt. 401.342

(An acid dye; absorption maximum about 490 in acid solution)
Solubility at 26°C: in water 18.40%; in alcohol 0.24%

This dye is rarely used as a biological stain, but is called for by Schaffer for staining sections of bone, and by Unna in certain stain mixtures used in studying the phenomenon called by him chromolysis. Fast yellow G or GG is employed by Wallart and Houette (1934), together with hematoxylin and acid fuchsin, in a trichrome staining technic.

OIL YELLOW II   C. I. NO. 11020 (1 *ed.:* 19)

(C. I. Solvent Yellow 2)

Synonyms: *Butter yellow; Oil yellow D; Fast oil yellow B*

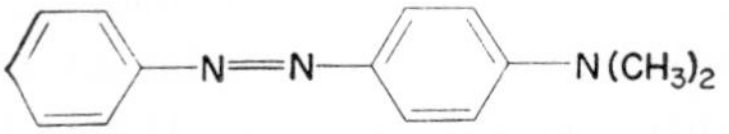

$C_{14}H_{15}N_3$; mol. wt. 225.284

Butter yellow is the most common designation for this dye in the biological literature. The name is unsatisfactory for two reasons; first, it sometimes falsely suggests some relationship to butter; second, it is ambiguous because C. I. No. 11160 (amino-azo-toluene) which is designated Solvent yellow 3 in the Colour Index is also called butter yellow. For these reasons the name given in the above heading is preferred; or one may definitely specify it by the chemical term, *p*-dimethyl-amino-azo-benzene.

It has not been used, apparently, as a stain, but has been considerably studied as a carcinogenic substance, so much so that fear has been expressed in some quarters that the public might come to associate cancer with butter and that this food might be thereby discredited.

CHRYSOIDIN Y   C. I. NO. 11270 (1 *ed.:* 20)

(C. I. Basic Orange 2)

Synonyms: *Brown salt R, Dark brown salt R*

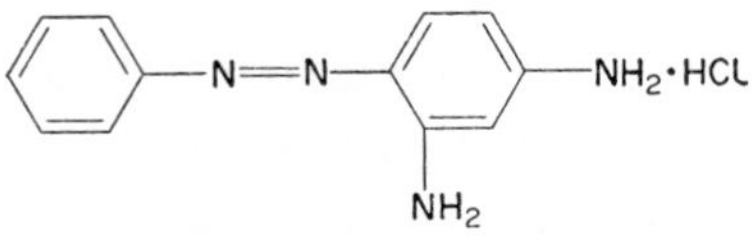

$C_{12}N_{13}N_4Cl$; mol. wt. 248.713

(A basic dye; absorption maximum about 461)
Solubility at 26°C: in water 0.86%; in alcohol 2.21%

This dye is a good substitute, in some procedures, for Bismarck brown. Like the latter, it is easily modified by heat, and boiling should be avoided in preparing solutions. Maheshwari and Wulff (1937) have employed it in the vital staining of pollen tubes; Lison (1938) for the vital staining of insects. Monné (1939) uses it to demonstrate the Golgi apparatus. Varco and Visscher (1941) include it among a series of dyes employed in the study of gastric secretion.

BENZENE-AZO-α-NAPHTHYLAMINE   C. I. NO. 11350

(C. I. Solvent Yellow 4)

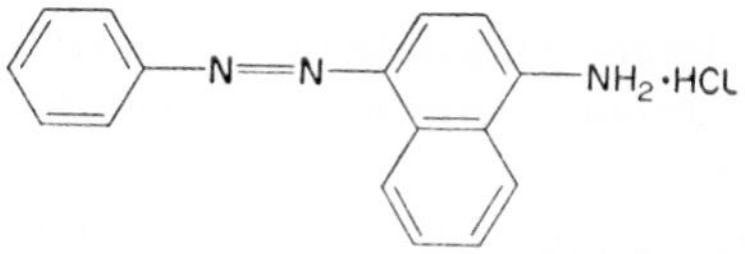

$C_{16}H_{14}N_3Cl$; mol. wt. 283.753

(Absorption maximum of hydrochloride 557.6 in alcohol)

A colored compound employed by Carter (1933) as a vital stain for protozoa (probably in the form of its hydrochloride) and given the abbreviated name "BAN." This product has apparently never been put on the market as a commercial dye; only its formula and chemical properties are known.

ORANGE G   C. I. NO. 16230 (1 *ed.:* 27)

(C. I. Acid Orange 10)

Synonym: *Wool orange 2G*

Slightly different grade: *Orange GG, GMP; Crystal orange GG*

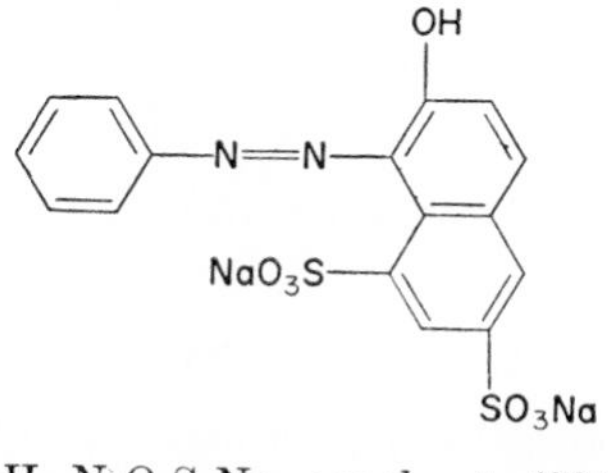

$C_{16}H_{10}N_2O_7S_2Na_2$; mol. wt. 452.382

(An acid dye; absorption maximum about 476–480)
Solubility at 26°C: in water 10.86%; in alcohol 0.22%

This dye is strongly acid because of the two sulfonic groups. It is one of the most valuable plasma stains in histological work. It has great use as a background stain for hematoxylin and other nuclear dyes in cytology. It is frequently employed, both by botanists and zoologists, as a cytoplasmic stain, together with the two nuclear dyes safranin and gentian violet in the Flemming triple stain. It is of importance to the pathologist for its use with aniline blue and acid fuchsin in the Mallory connective tissue stain; and is used in various other double and triple staining methods, such as that of Ehrlich-Biondi-Heidenhain, in which it is mixed with methyl green and acid fuchsin. The Ehrlich "triacid mixture," also a combination of these same three dyes, is used in staining blood. A further use is Bensley's "neutral gentian," a combination of orange G and gentian violet for staining the A and B cells in the islands of Langerhans. An important application is by Stoughton (1930), with thionin, for the differentiation of parasites in plant tissue; and perhaps even more important is its use by Papanicolaou (1941) in cancer cytology.

A spectrophotometric graph of this dye, compared with two other orange dyes, is given in Fig. 7, page 61.

Procedures Recommended by the Commission in Which This Stain Is Used

Name of Procedure	Page Reference to *Staining Procedures*
Mallory's aniline blue collagen stain..........................	52
Heidenhain's "Azan" modification...........................	53
Crossman's modification......................................	54
Acid alizarin blue modification.............................	55
Kornhauser's "Quad" stain...................................	58
An aldehyde fuchsin method for cell granules.................	172
With safranin and tannic acid for shoot apex.................	188
Stoughton's thionin and orange G for fungi in tissue..........	195
Newcomer's method for pollen tubes...........................	199
Flemming's triple stain......................................	213
Id., with iodine..	214
Feulgen stain, De Tomasi modification.......................	215

CHROMOTROPE 2R

c. i. no. 16570 (1 *ed.:* 29)

(C. I. Acid Red 29)

Synonyms: *Chromotrope N2R; Chromotrope blue 2R; Fast fuchsin G; XL Carmoisine 6R; Acid phloxine GR*

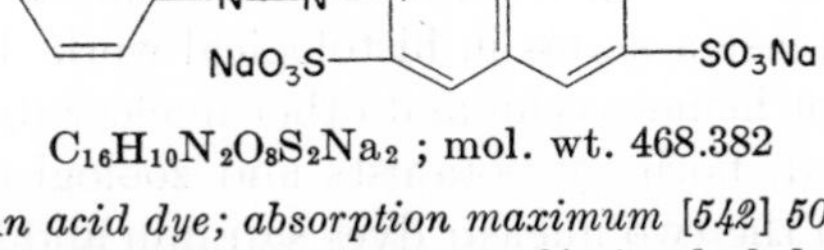

$C_{16}H_{10}N_2O_8S_2Na_2$; mol. wt. 468.382

(An acid dye; absorption maximum [542] 508)
Solubility at 26°C: in water 19.3%; in alcohol 0.17%

This dye has been employed by Lendrum (1935) as a counterstain to

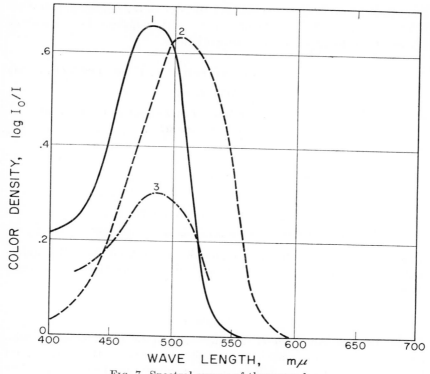

Fig. 7. Spectral curves of three azo dyes:
1. Orange G   2. Methyl orange   3. Orange II

celestin blue in animal histology. Lillie (1940) finds it is a fairly good substitute for "xylidine ponceau" in the Masson (1929) trichrome stain. Crossmon (1940) uses it in the selective staining of red blood cells in sections.

AZOPHLOXINE GA

c. i. no. 18050 (1 *ed.*: 31)

(C. I. Acid Red 1)

Synonyms: *Fast crimson GR; Amidonaphthol red G*

$C_{18}H_{13}N_3O_8S_2Na_2$; mol. wt. 509.434

(*An acid dye; absorption maxima 540, 502*)

Very little mention has been made of this dye in the biological literature but it has been called for by Dublin (1943) with "ponceau de xylidine" as one step of the Bodian stain in neuropathology.

SORBINE RED   C. I. NO. 14895 (1 *ed.*: 54)

(C. I. Acid Red 7)

Synonyms: *Azofuchsin 3B; Kiton red S; Eriorubine G; Azo acid red L; Azo rhodine 3G*

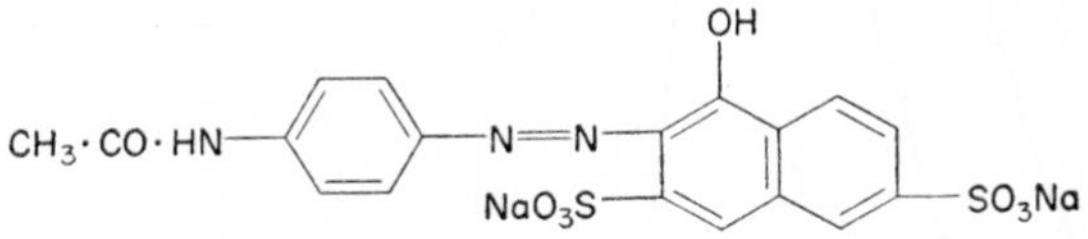

$$CH_3 \cdot CO \cdot HN \underset{NaO_3S}{\overset{OH}{\longrightarrow}} N{=}N \longrightarrow SO_3Na$$

$C_{18}H_{13}N_3O_8S_2Na_2$; mol. wt. 509.434

(An acid dye: absorption maximum about [545], *499)*

Lillie (1940) suggests this dye (under the name Azofuchsin 3B) among possible substitutes for "ponceau de xylidene" in the Masson trichrome technic.

AZO FUCHSIN

There is an occasional reference in histology to the use of an azo fuchsin. Such references are not sufficiently definite, however, as there are several different azo fuchsins. The following, for example, are recognized in the Colour Index:

Azo fuchsin 4G	C. I. No. 16570, C. I. Acid Red 29
Azo fuchsin	C. I. No. 17200, C. I. Acid Red 33
Azo fuchsin 3B	C. I. No. 14895, C. I. Acid Red 7
Azo fuchsin 6B	C. I. No. 18055, C. I. Acid Violet 7
Azo fuchsin B	C. I. No. 16550
Azo fuchsin G	C. I. No. 16540, C. I. Acid Red 31
Azo fuchsin 6B, GN or S	C. I. No. 16535

All of these acid mono-azo dyes are closely related chemically to orange G and Bordeaux red.

Of these, Lillie (1948) definitely specifies C. I. No. 16540 as a constituent of his naphthol blue black tissue stain.

AZO ACID BLUE B

C. I. NO. 16545 (1 *ed.*: 59)

There are various azo acid blues, with various shade designations attached to the names, but whose synonymy is somewhat confusing. They are mixtures; but an important constituent is regarded as being

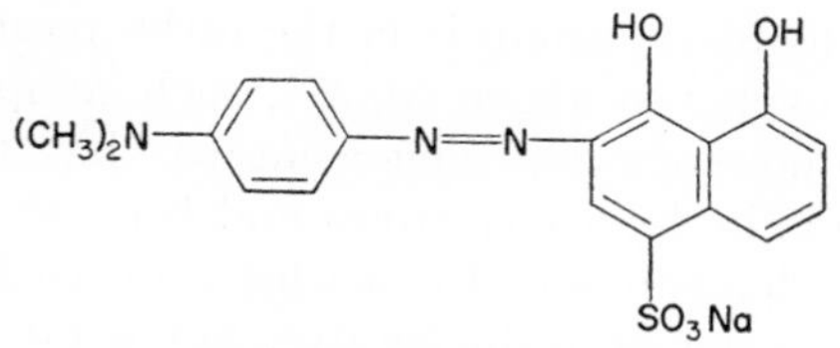

$C_{18}H_{16}N_3O_5SNa$; mol. wt. 409.395

(An acid dye)

Menner (1935) has called for this dye in a stain for nervous tissue. Otherwise there seem to be few, if any, references to it in the biological literature.

NITRAZINE   C. I. NO. 14890

Synonyms: *Nitrazine yellow; Delta dye indicator*

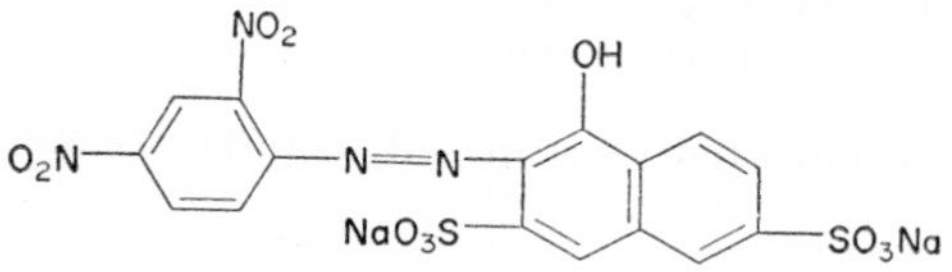

$C_{16}H_8N_4O_{11}S_2Na_2$; mol. wt. 542.382

(An acid dye)

This dye has been proposed as an indicator, having a pH range of 6.0 to 7.2. Its acid color is bright yellow, from which it passes through graygreen into its alkaline color, bright blue. This indicator can be used in the form of test strips, like litmus paper. It is more sensitive than litmus, however, and shows greater color contrast. Lillie (1940) finds it can replace xylidine ponceau in the Masson (1929) trichrome stain.

For technic of **Masson trichrome stain, Lillie modification,** see *Staining Procedures*, p. 72.

SUDAN II   C. I. NO. 12140 (1 ed.: 73)

(C. I. Solvent Orange 7)

Synonyms: *Oil scarlet; Fast oil orange II; Red B. Fat ponceau; Orange RR*

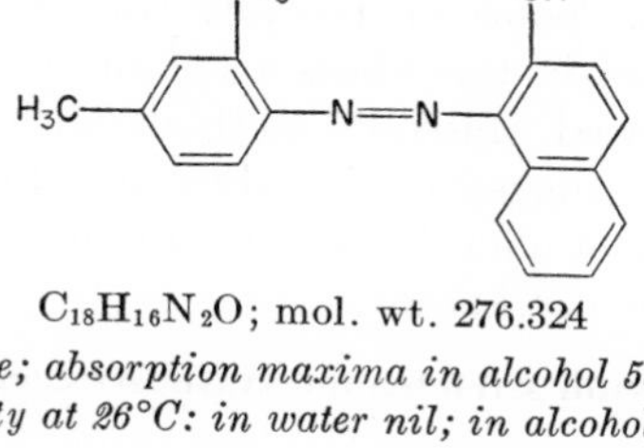

$C_{18}H_{16}N_2O$; mol. wt. 276.324

(An acid dye; absorption maxima in alcohol 531.5, 494.5)
Solubility at 26°C: in water nil; in alcohol 0.39%

In this dye the hydroxyl group is in the ortho position with respect to the azo group. As explained above (p. 57), such compounds show a tendency toward intramolecular rearrangement so that the hydrogen atom detaches itself from the hydroxyl group and becomes fixed to the neighboring nitrogen. Such a compound is neither acid nor basic and, not being able to form salts, is not an ordinary dye, but is fat soluble and has the power of coloring fat. Therefore, this compound, together with the following and several others of similar structure described below, are fat stains.

This fat stain has frequently been confused with oil red O because both were erroneously given in the first edition of the Colour Index as synonyms. Lillie (1944c) has tried both dyes in his supersaturated isopropanol technic, and finds Sudan II satisfactory, better in fact than Sudan III, although not so intense or yielding such a stable solution as oil red O, oil red 4B or Sudan red 4B. It is especially good as a fat stain for central nervous tissue, in combination with Weigert's technic for myelin. (See p. 76.)

For **Lillie's supersaturated isopropanol technic,** see *Staining Procedures*, p. 159.

PONCEAU 2R   C. I. NO. 16150 (1 *ed.:* 79)

(C. I. Acid Red 26)

Synonyms: *Ponceau R, RG, G, 4R, 2RE, NR, J, FR, GR; Scarlet R; Xylidine ponceau 3RS; Lake ponceau; Brilliant ponceau G; New ponceau 4R*

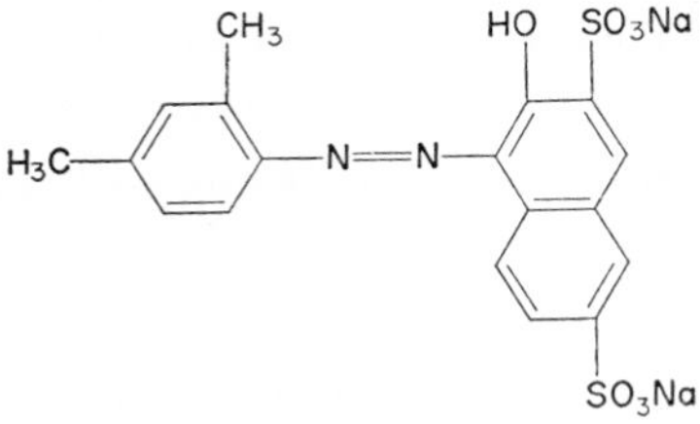

$C_{18}H_{14}N_2O_7S_2Na_2$; mol. wt. 480.434

(An acid dye; absorption maximum about [538] 499)

A dye called xylidine ponceau, possibly this one, has been used as an histological counterstain in the Masson technic (see Foot, 1933), and by others who have followed Masson's methods with certain modifications. Lillie (1940), however, suggests other dyes for this purpose which given better results. The exact identity of the French "ponceau de xylidine" employed by Masson is not known.

For the technic of **Masson's trichrome stain,** see *Staining Procedures*, p. 73–4.

OIL BROWN D C. I. NO. 12020 (1 *ed.*: 81)

(C. I. Solvent Brown 5)

Synonyms: *Sudan brown; Sudan brown AN; Fast oil brown S; Brilliant fat brown B; Fat brown III*

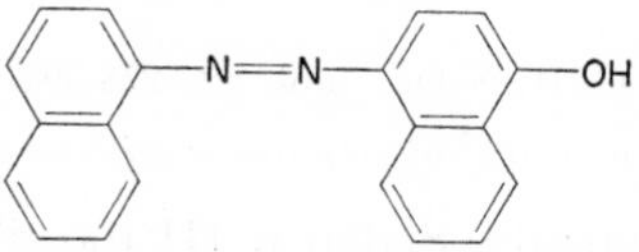

$C_{20}H_{14}N_2O$; mol. wt. 298.328

Lillie (1944c) recommends Sudan brown, Sudan brown 5B, and oil brown D as satisfactory fat stains in the supersaturated isopropanol technic. These dyes all undoubtedly represent shades of the above.

BORDEAUX RED C. I. NO. 16180 (1 *ed.*: 88)

(C. I. Acid Red 17)

Synonyms: *Fast red B, BN or P; Cerasin R; Archelline 2B; Azo-Bordeaux; Acid Bordeaux*

Various grades denoted: *Bordeaux B, BL, G, R, R extra*

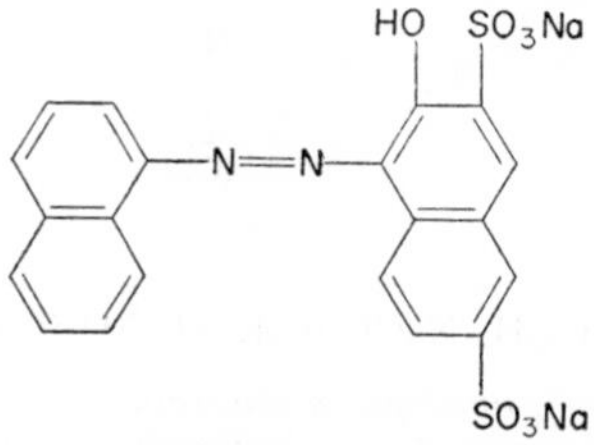

$C_{20}H_{12}N_2O_7S_2Na_2$; mol. wt. 502.438

(An acid dye; absorption maximum about 520)
Solubility at 26°C: in water 3.83%; in alcohol 0.19%

Bordeaux red is used as a cytoplasmic stain, as, for example, in aqueous solution when Heidenhain's hematoxylin is to be used immediately afterward as a nuclear stain. It has also been used with thionin and methyl green for staining sections, particularly of spleen, testis, and liver. Lillie (1940) finds it a fairly satisfactory substitute for xylidine ponceau in the Masson technic.

SUDAN R C. I. NO. 12150 (1 *ed.*: 113)

(C. I. Solvent Red 1)

Synonyms: *Brilliant fat scarlet B; Oil vermillion*

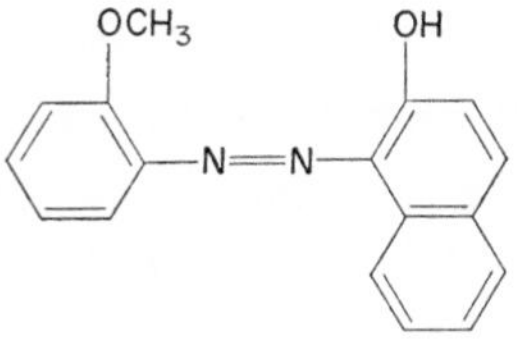

$C_{17}H_{14}N_2O_2$; mol. wt. 278.298

(A weakly acid dye; absorption maximum 569 [519.8])

Weichherz (1934) has used a Sudan R III (possibly this dye or possibly Sudan III) in connection with the Kahn reaction for the diagnosis of syphilis. It makes the reading of the tubes easier.

JANUS GREEN B

C. I. NO. 11050 (1 *ed.:* 133?*)

Synonyms: *Diazin green S; Union green B*

This is an azo dye having an azin as well as an azo chromophore group, and is thus related to the safranins. It is a compound of diethyl safranin with dimethyl aniline through an azo group.

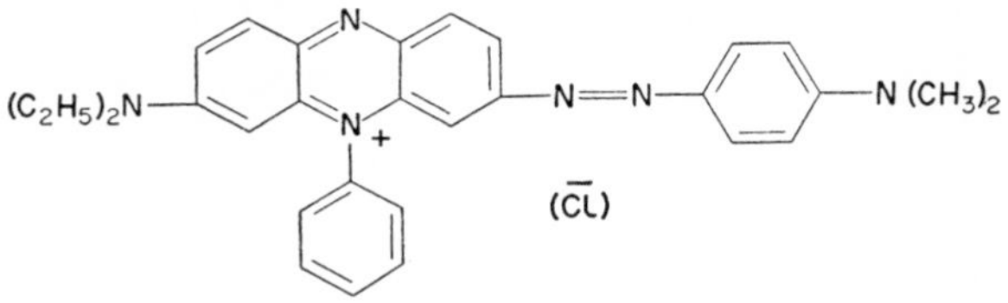

$C_{30}H_{31}N_6Cl$; mol. wt. 511.053

(A basic dye; absorption maximum about 610–623)
Solubility at 26°C: in water 5.18%; in alcohol 1.12%

Janus green is best known for its use in demonstrating mitochondria, stained *intra vitam*, according to the technic of Michaelis (1900), and as more recently developed by Cowdry, and by Bensley (1911). It is used supravitally with neutral red for blood; some, however prefer pinacyanole (see p. 207) for mitochondria in blood and blood-forming cells or lymphocytes. Faris (1924) has employed it with neutral red for sections of embryos, and has been employed in the vital staining of fungi and protozoa; also the supravital staining of blood (Sabin, 1929).

* In previous editions of this book, the C. I. Nos. 133 and 134 have been assigned respectively to Janus green B and the following dye, Janus black, although the formulae shown in the 1st edition of the Colour Index do not correspond to the commercially available products. The new C.I. numbers (11050 and 11825), however, do represent the dyes actually available and correspond to the formulae given here and on p. 68.

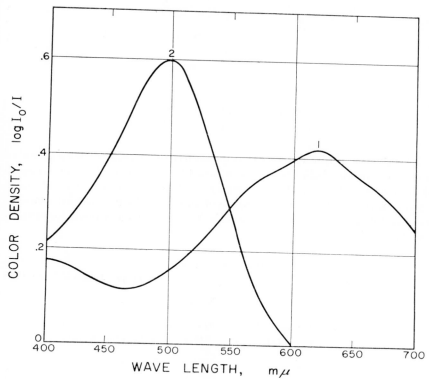

FIG. 8. Spectral curves of two azo dyes:
1. Janus green   2. Congo red

This dye is very toxic to fresh preparations. Various methods have been described to render it less so, by manipulation of commercial samples.

Soep (1927) proposes it in place of methylene blue for studying reductase production in milk.

A spectrophotometric curve of this dye is given in graph 1, Fig. 8, above. Like other green dyes, it has two absorption maxima, one in the violet and the other near the orange range.

For use in **Supravital staining of blood, see** *Staining Procedures*, p. 141.
For use in **Lillie modification of Ziehl-Neelsen technic,** see Id., p. 258.

JANUS BLACK

C. I. NO. 11825 (1 *ed.*: 134?*)

(C. I. Basic Black 2)

Synonym: *Diazine black*

* See footnote on p. 66.

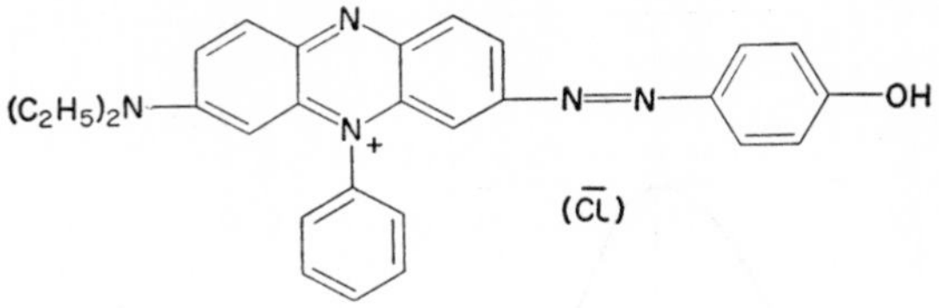

$C_{28}H_{26}N_5OCl$; mol. wt. 483.985

(*A basic dye*)

It will be seen from the above formula that this dye, like Janus green B, is an azo-safranin. It has rarely been called for in biology; but according to Maheshwari and Wulff (1937), Brestlavetz has employed it in vital staining pollen tubes. It was the existence of this dye which called attention to the possibility of using freshly diazotized safranin as a reagent for localizing phenols.

METANIL YELLOW

C. I. NO. 13065 (1 *ed.:* 138)

(C. I. Acid Yellow 36)

Synonyms: *Orange MNO or MN; Acid yellow R; Soluble yellow OL; Yellow M; Tropaeolin G*

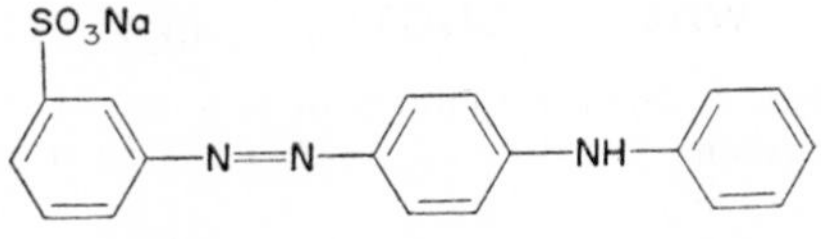

$C_{18}H_{14}N_3O_3SNa$; mol. wt. 375.379

(*An acid dye; absorption maximum 536 in hydrochloric acid solution*)
Solubility at 26°C: in water 5.36%; in alcohol 1.45%

In Masson's (1929) technic (see Foot, 1933) this dye is used as a connective tissue stain following hematoxylin and acid fuchsin.

For a technic adapted from Masson (1923), calling for **Mucicarmine with hematoxylin and metanil yellow,** see *Staining Procedures*, p. 36.

METHYL ORANGE

C. I. NO. 13025 (1 *ed.:* 142)

(C. I. Acid orange 52)

Synonyms: *Orange III; Helianthin; Gold orange MP; Tropaeolin D*

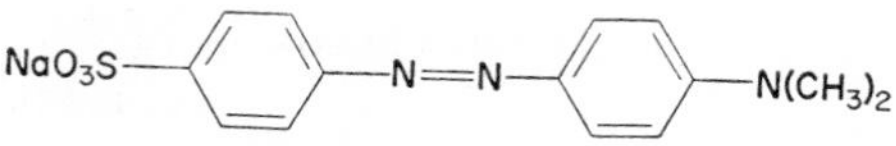

$C_{14}H_{14}N_3O_3SNa$; mol. wt. 327.339

(A weakly acid dye; absorption maximum 506–507 in acid solution)
Solubility at 26°C; in water 0.52%; in alcohol 0.08%

This dye has little use as a stain, but is widely employed as an indicator, as it is red in acid, and orange in alkaline solutions. Its chief value as an indicator is that it is sensitive to mineral acids without being affected by carbonates or most organic acids. It has been used as an indicator for cell sap by Pfeffer (see Krause, p. 2305), and occasionally as a counterstain in histology. Under the name of gold orange, it has been employed by Newcomer (1938) as a counterstain to crystal violet in staining pollen tubes.

A spectral curve of this dye, compared with orange II and orange G, is given in Fig. 7, p. 61.

PRONTOSIL

Synonym: *Prontosil red*

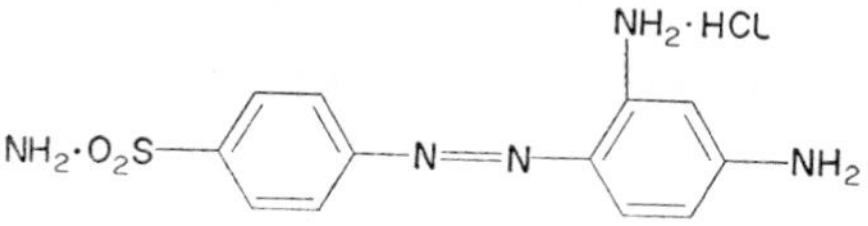

$C_{12}H_{14}N_5O_2SCl$; mol. wt. 327.795

This is a red substance employed principally as a therapeutic agent. It is essentially a basic dye in its chemical structure, although not used as a dye. It is referred to here only because it has been called for by Carter (1930) as a vital stain for insects and plants.

ORANGE IV   C. I. NO. 13080 (1 *ed.:* 143)

(C. I. Acid Orange 5)

Synonyms: *Orange N; Acid yellow D; Tropaeolin OO*

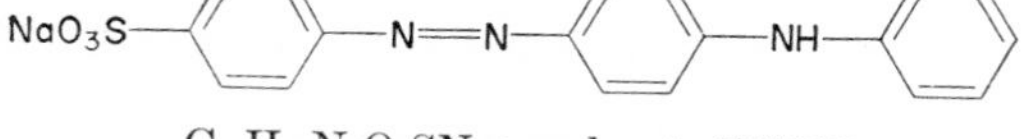

$C_{18}H_{14}N_3O_3SNa$; mol. wt. 375.379

(An acid dye; absorption maximum about 527 in acid solution)
Solubility at 26°C: in water 0.16%; in alcohol 0.2%

The only biological use of this dye seems to be occasionally as an indicator.

BRILLIANT YELLOW S
C. I. NO. 13085 (1 ed.: 144)

(C. I. Acid Yellow 16)

Synonyms: *Curcumine; Yellow WR*

$C_{18}H_{13}N_3O_6S_2Na_2$; mol. wt. 477.434

(An acid dye)

This dye is closely related to metanil yellow and orange IV, being manufactured by the sulfonation of the latter and containing one more sulfonic acid group. The exact position of the latter in the molecule is uncertain.

Margolena (1933b) has employed this dye in the Doglio (1932) technic, in which it is employed as a counterstain to carbol fuchsin in staining acid-fast bacteria. In Doglio's original paper the exact nature of the dye used is not specified, however, and at least two other dyes (C. I. Nos. 24890 and 13096) have been sold as brilliant yellow.

ORANGE I   C. I. NO. 14600 (1 ed.: 150)

(C. I. Acid Orange 20)

Synonyms: *Naphthol orange; Tropaeolin G or 000 No. 1*

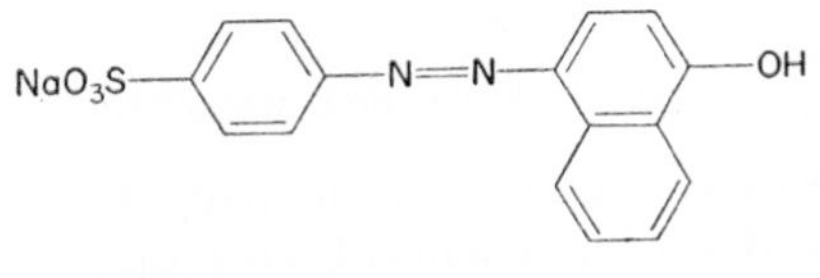

$C_{16}H_{11}N_2O_4SNa$; mol. wt. 350.327

(An acid dye; absorption maximum about 476)
Solubility at 26°C: in water 5.17%; in alcohol 0.64%

This is another dye which is turned red by excess of alkali and has therefore some use as an indicator. McLean and Ireland (1940) have employed it with malachite green for staining sections of roots or stems of plants.

ORANGE II   C. I. NO. 15510 (1 ed.: 151)

(C. I. Acid Orange 7)

Synonyms: *Gold orange; Orange A, P, or R; Acid orange II, Y or A; Orange extra; Mandarin G; Tropaeolin 000 No. 2*

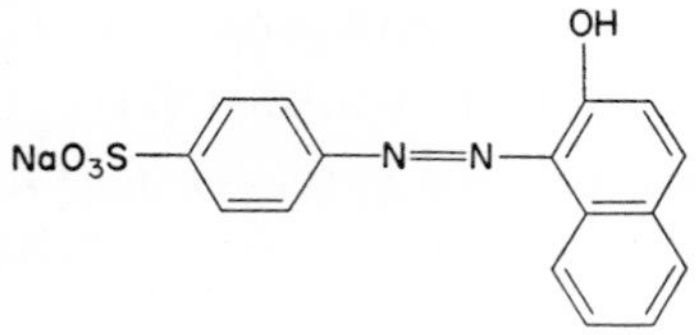

$C_{16}H_{11}N_2O_4SNa$; mol. wt. 350.327

(An acid dye; absorption maximum about 483–487)
Solubility at 26°C: in water 11.37%; in alcohol 0.15%

This dye, which differs from orange I only in the position of the hydroxyl group on the naphthalene radical, is similar to it in color and properties, but does not change color with changing reaction of its solution. This dye is rarely employed in microscopic work, and yet may be recommended as a valuable substitute for orange G when a stronger yellow is desired for contrast purposes. Thus French (1926b) used it in combination with eosin and azure C in a general tissue stain. It has been used by Bergonzini (1891) in place of orange G in the Ehrlich-Biondi stain; and by Ebbinghaus (1902) for staining keratin in sections of skin. Kalter (1943) includes it in a quadruple staining method, the other dyes in combination with it being fast green FCF, safranin O and crystal violet.

A spectral curve of this dye is given in graph 3, Fig. 7, p. 61.

NARCEIN   C. I. NO. 15511 (1 *ed.*: 152)

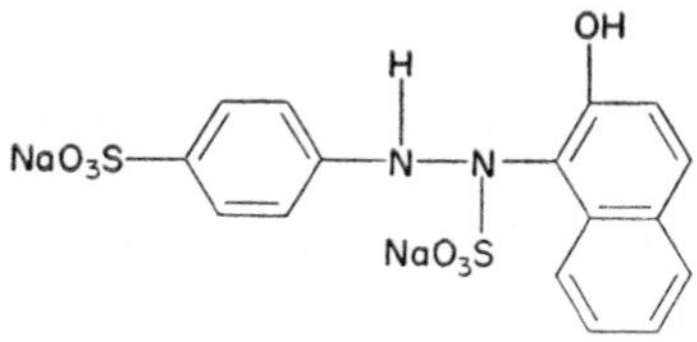

$C_{16}H_{12}N_2O_7S_2Na_2$; mol. wt. 454.398

(An acid dye)

Solubility at 26°C: in water 10.02%; in alcohol 0.06%

This dye is a derivative of orange II, prepared from the latter by treatment with sodium bisulfite. It is rarely used either as a textile dye or in microscopic technic. It has been called for by Ehrlich, however, in combination with pyronin and methyl green or methylene blue to form a neutral dye. It is no longer on the market, however.

AMARANTH   C. I. NO. 16185 (1 *ed.:* 184)

(C. I. Acid Red 27)

Synonyms: *Naphthol red S, C or O; Fast red; Bordeaux;*
Bordeaux SF; Victoria rubin O; Azo rubin; Wool red

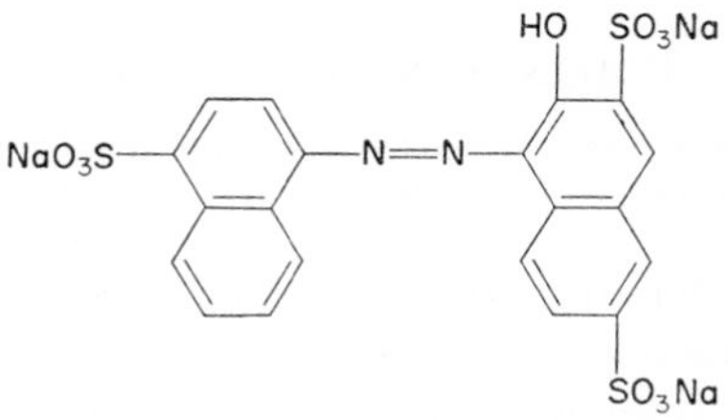

$C_{20}H_{11}N_2O_{10}S_3Na_3$; mol. wt. 604.493

(An acid dye; absorption maximum about 525)
Solubility at 26°C: in water 7.20%; in alcohol 0.01%

Amaranth is not a commonly used stain, but is of considerable importance as a food color. It has been used by Griesbach (1886) for staining axis
cylinders, by Chambers (1935) in staining cells in tissue culture; also by
Smith (1939) in color photomicrography.

METHYL RED   C. I. NO. 13020 (1 *ed.:* 211)

(C. I. Acid Red 2)

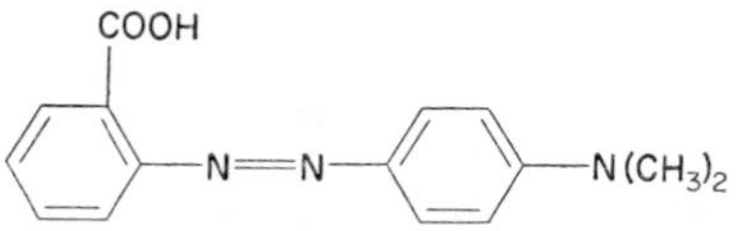

$C_{15}H_{15}N_3O_2$; mol. wt. 269.294

(A weakly acid dye; absorption maximum 530)

This dye has rarely been used for staining, but has long been employed
as an indicator. Its useful range is from pH 4.4 to pH 6.0 in which it changes
from red in acid solutions to yellow in basic. Although still of value for this
purpose it is coming to be replaced by certain of the sulfonphthalein indicators such as brom cresol green and chlor cresol green (see page 191),
which are more stable chemically and permit greater accuracy in reading.
The chief drawback to methyl red as an indicator is that it is easily reduced
with loss of color, and readings must be made very promptly after adding
it to the solution to avoid error due to this cause. Carter (1933) has recently
employed this dye in the vital staining of protozoa.

THIAZINE RED R

C. I. NO. 14780 (1 *ed.:* 225)

(C. I. Direct Red 45)

Synonyms: *Chlorazol pink Y; Rosophenine 10B*

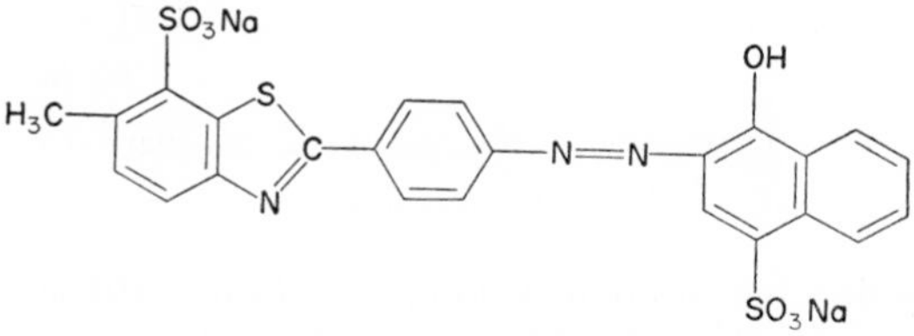

$C_{24}H_{15}N_3O_7S_3Na_2$; mol. wt. 599.576

(An acid dye; absorption maximum 505)

This dye has occasionally been used as a counterstain in animal histology. It was introduced by M. Heidenhain (1903). It is thought by some users to prove a satisfactory counterstain against hematoxylin for skeletal and cardiac muscle.

B. DIS-AZO AND POLY-AZO DYES

NAPHTHOL BLUE BLACK

C. I. NO. 20470 (1 *ed.:* 246)

(C. I. Acid Black 1)

Synonyms: *Pontacyl blue-black SX; Buffalo black NBR*

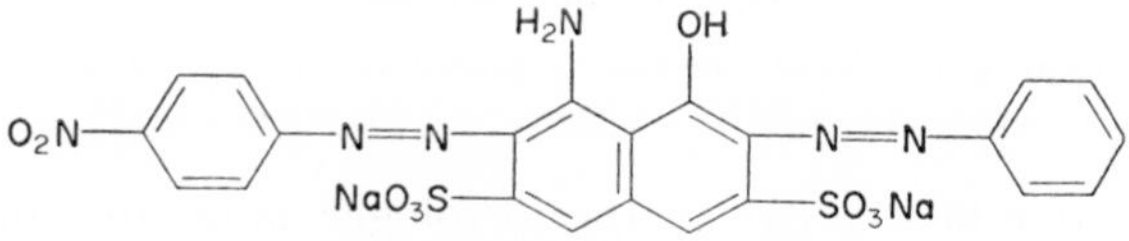

$C_{22}H_{14}N_6O_9S_2Na_2$; mol. wt. 616.506

(An acid dye)

This dye has rarely been mentioned for biological use; but is has been referred to by Lillie (1945c) as a stain for collagen. See *Staining Procedures* p. 59.

BRILLIANT CROCEINE

C. I. NO. 27290 (1 *ed.:* 252)

(C. I. Acid Red 73)

Synonym: *Croceine scarlet 3B, MOO*

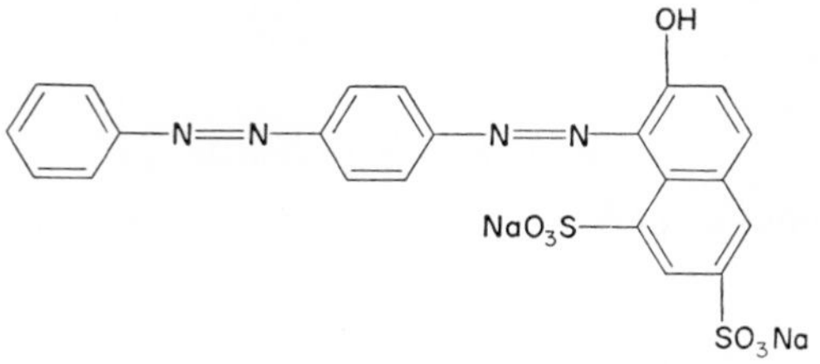

$C_{22}H_{14}N_4O_7 S_2Na_2$; mol. wt. 556.490

(*An acid dye*)

Brilliant croceine has been mentioned by Lillie (1945c) as a substitute for "xylidine ponceau" in the Masson triple stain.

SUDAN III   c. i. no. 26100 (1 *ed.*: 248)

(C. I. Solvent Red 23)

Synonyms: *Sudan G; Tony red; Scarlet B, fat soluble; Fat ponceau G; Oil red AS, O, B or 3B; Cerasin red*

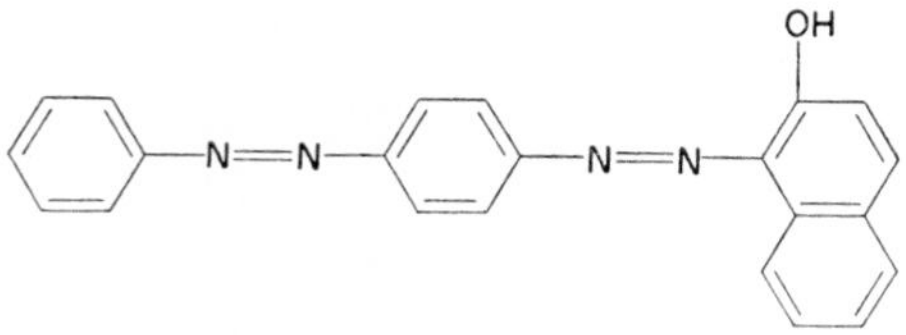

$C_{22}H_{16}N_4O$; mol. wt. 352.380

(*A weakly acid dye; absorption maximum in alcohol 508–510*)
Solubility at 26°C: in water nil; in alcohol 0.15%

The chief value of this dye to the histologist is because of the position of the hydroxyl group, which as explained above (pp. 57, 64) makes it oil soluble and hence a fat stain. It was introduced as a fat stain by Daddi in 1896. Herxheimer (1901) investigated this and several other fat stains, proposing formulae which are still used as the basis of modern procedures. It is also employed by botanists together with light green in the technic of Bugnon, for differentiating suberized and cutinized tissue in plants.

At one time Sudan III was the only important fat stain known except for OsO_4. More is now known in regard to fat soluble stains, thanks to the research of Michaelis (1901). It was he who showed the relation of this property of certain dyes to their lack of basic or acid character. He showed that new dyes with this property and of greater staining power might be built up synthetically by taking advantage of the fact that the azo group

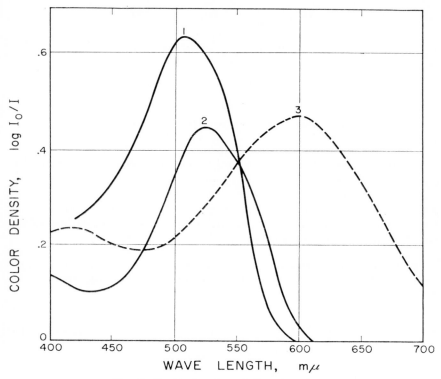

Fig. 9. Spectral curves of three azo dyes:

1. Sudan III   2. Sudan IV   3. Sudan black B

will attach itself in the ortho position if the para position is already occupied. In this way azo-ortho-phenols and beta-naphthols can be prepared, and they prove to be fat soluble. Michaelis suggested the following dye, which has now to a considerable extent replaced Sudan III.

Spectrophotometric graphs of Sudan III and Sudan IV are given in Fig. 9, above.

SUDAN IV   C. I. NO. 26105 (1 *ed.*: 258)

(C. I. Solvent Red 24)

Synonyms: *Scarlet red*; Oil red IV; Fat ponceau; Fat
Ponceau R or LB; Cerotin ponceau 3B*

* Various erroneous variations of this term, some wholly or partly in German (e.g., Scarlet R. Scharlach R, Scharlach red) occur in the literature and on labels. They may be corruptions of the brand name, Biebrich scarlet R, Med.

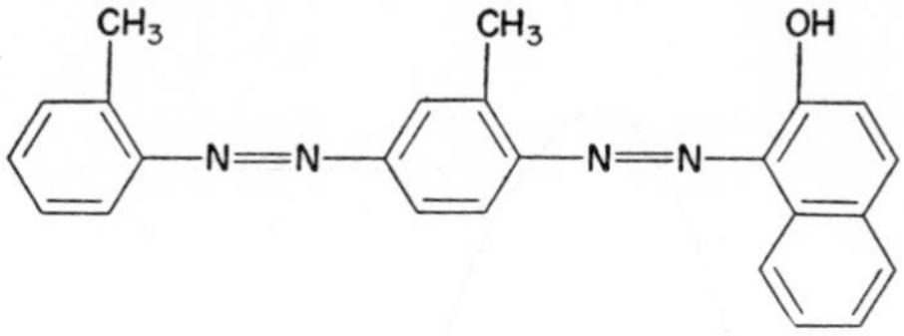

$C_{24}N_{20}N_4O$; mol. wt. 380.432

(A weakly acid dye; absorption maximum in alcohol 522–529)
Solubility at 26°C: in water nil; in alcohol 0.09%

This dis-azo naphthalene compound is similar to Sudan III except that it is a dimethyl derivative. This fact makes it a deeper, more intense stain; but having the hydroxyl group in the ortho position, it has similar physical properties and is fat soluble. Until recently it has been regarded as one of the best fat stains known; see, however, oil red O and oil red 4B, below, oil blue NA (p. 203) and Sudan black B, (p. 87).

For the technic of the **Herxheimer stain for fat** calling for the use of Sudan IV, see *Staining Procedures*, p. 153. For **Lillie's supersaturated isopropanol technic,** see p. 159.

SUDAN RED 7B   C. I. NO. 26050

(C. I. Solvent Red 1A)

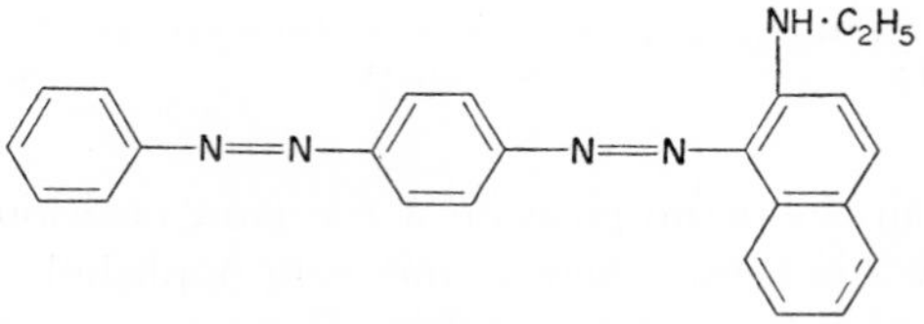

This dye has been employed by Barrolier and Suchowsky (1958) for staining fats to which it gives a brilliant slightly bluish-red color in frozen sections.

OIL RED O   C. I. NO. 26125

(C. I. Solvent Red 27)

As explained elsewhere, this dye has often been confused with Sudan II. It is, however, quite different in composition, more closely related to Sudan IV than to Sudan II. It consists of the following together with its isomers having the methyl groups in other positions:

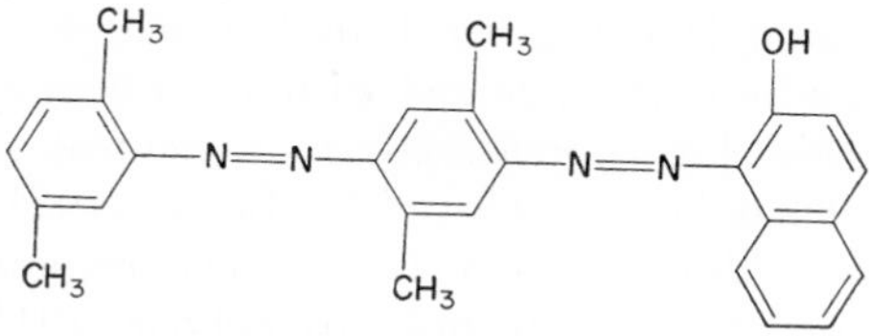

$C_{26}H_{24}N_4O$; mol. wt. 408.484

(*A weakly acid dye*)

Oil red O was recommended by French (1926) as a substitute for Sudan III, to be preferred because of its greater depth of color. Lillie (1944c) recommends it for this same reason, regarding it as one of the best fat stains known to him. It may be employed in the Herxheimer formula (an approximately 0.1 percent solution in equal parts of acetone and 70 percent alcohol), in the pyridine formula of Proescher (1927), or in Lillie's supersaturated isopropanol technic.

For **Proescher's oil-red-O-pyridin technic,** see *Staining Procedures,* p. 158.

For **Lillie's supersaturated isopropanol technic,** see *Staining Procedures,* p. 159.

OIL RED 4B

This is a dye of uncertain composition which is rarely referred to in the biological literature, but mentioned by Lillie (1944c) as one of the best fat stains to employ in the supersaturated isopropanol technic.

BIEBRICH SCARLET WATER SOLUBLE

C. I. NO. 26905 (1 *ed.:* 280)

(C. I. Acid Red 66)

Synonyms: *Croceine scarlet; Scarlet B, or EC; Ponceau B; Double scarlet BSF*

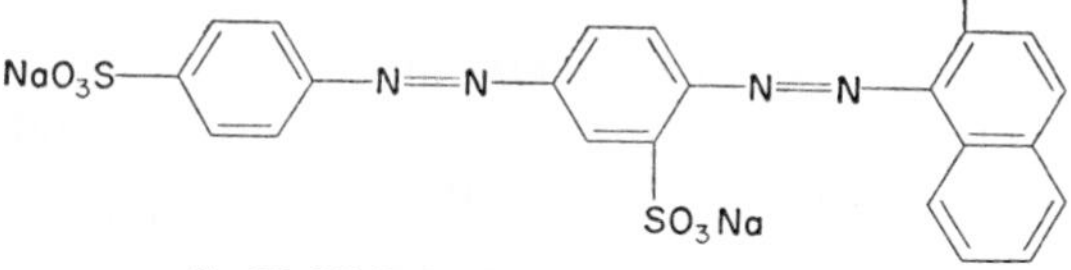

$C_{22}H_{14}N_4O_7S_2Na_2$; mol. wt. 556.490

(*An acid dye; absorption maximum about 503.5*)
Solubility at 26°C: in alcohol 0.05%

The chief biological application of this dye is for medicinal purposes, but it is occasionally used as a plasma stain, notably for tissues after staining with polychrome methylene blue or Unna's hematein. It has also been made use of by Paladino (1895) mixed with alum hematoxylin for double staining effect on histological material. In a neutral stain combination with ethyl violet, it has been employed by Bowie (1924) for staining the islets of Langerhans. More recently it has been recommended by Lillie (1940) in the Masson trichrome technic, by Schoor (1941) in combination with orange G and fast green FCF for staining vaginal smears; while McFarlane (1944) uses it in the modification of the Mallory stain which he terms "Picro-Mallory."

For use of **Biebrich scarlet with picro-aniline-blue,** or with **methyl blue,** see *Staining Procedures,* p. 62-3.

For technic of **Masson trichrome stain, Lillie modification,** see Id. p. 72.

PONCEAU S   C. I. NO. 27195 (1 *ed.:* 282)

Synonym: *Fast ponceau 2B*

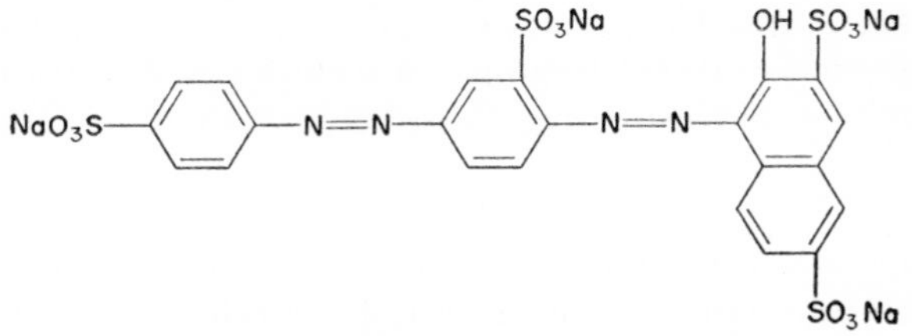

$C_{22}H_{12}N_4O_{13}S_4Na_4$; mol. wt. 760.600
(*An acid dye*)

Reference to this dye in biological literature shows a rather unusual history. It was mentioned quite early by Curtis (1905) who found it an improvement over acid fuchsin in the VanGieson stain. Little attention was paid to the suggestion, however, until fairly recently when the paper was discovered almost simultaneously by Ruth (1946) and Leach (1946) both of whom found the Curtis modification a useful one as it is less subject to fading.

ORSEILLIN BB

C. I. NO. 26670 (1 *ed.:* 284)

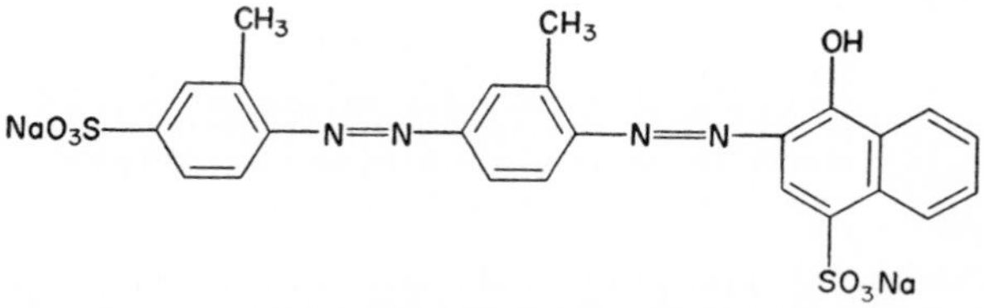

$C_{24}H_{18}N_4O_7S_2Na_2$; mol. wt. 584.542
(*An acid dye; absorption maximum 523*)

Cohen and Doak (1935) employed this dye in contrast to crystal violet for staining a mycorrhizal fungus on the roots of plants. Subsequently other authors including Alcorn and Yeager (1937), Keener (1951), have used it for staining other fungal parasites. Maneval (1941) lists it among several useful bacterial stains.

BISMARCK BROWN Y

C. I. NO. 21000 (1 *ed.*: 331)

(C. I. Basic Brown 1)

Synonyms: *Vesuvin; Phenylene brown; Manchester brown; Excelsior brown; Leather brown; Basic brown G, GX, or GXP*
Slightly different shade: *Bismarck brown G*

(A basic dye; absorption maximum 463. Solubility at 26°C: in water 1.36%; in alcohol 1.08%)

The various shades of Bismarck brown are mixtures of different compounds, the most important of which are salts of the following:

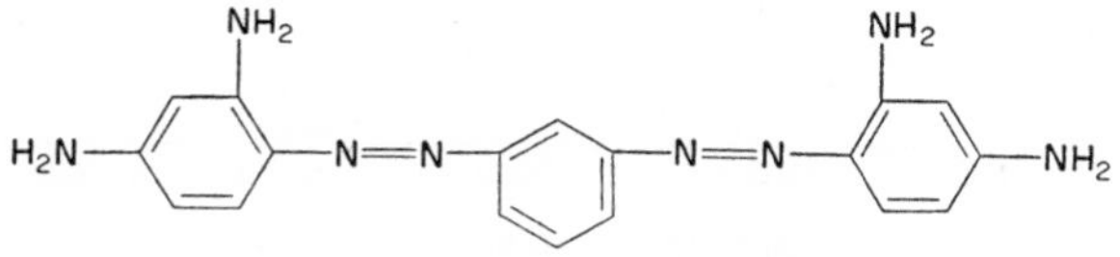

The dihydrochloride is $C_{18}H_{20}N_8Cl_2$; mol. wt. 419.318

This dye was formerly employed quite extensively as a contrast stain, but has now been replaced to some extent by others. It is still used, however, as a mucin stain, and is good for vital staining and for staining in bulk. It is employed in staining cellulose walls of plants in contrast to hematoxylin; and occasionally for staining bacteria in contrast to gentian violet in the Gram technic, to methyl or crystal violet in the Ljubinsky stain for diphtheria organisms, or to carbol-fuchsin for staining acid-fast bacteria. Blaydes (1939) points out that it stains more intensely if used in phenolic solution. It is included in the Papanicolaou (1941) technic for vaginal smears.

A caution to observe in connection with Bismarck brown is that solutions should not be boiled before using, because the composition of the dye is changed by heat.

A spectrophotometric curve of this dye is given in graph 1, Fig. 10.

For technic as **mucin and cartilage stain in contrast to methyl green,** see *Staining Procedures*, p. 33.
For technic of **Ljubinsky stain for diphtheria,** see Id., p. 234.

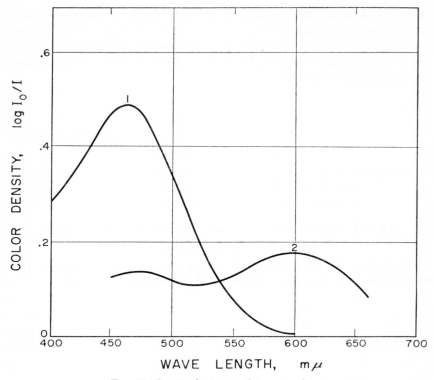

Fig. 10. Spectral curves of two azo dyes:
1. Bismarck brown Y   2. Chlorazol black E

BISMARCK BROWN R

c. i. no. 21010 (1 *ed.: 332*)

(C. I. Basic Brown 4)

Synonyms: *Bismarck brown GOOO 53A or 53B; Brown R, AT,
C or N; Manchester brown EE; Vesuvin NR, B, R;
Basic brown BR or BXN*

$C_{21}H_{26}N_8Cl_2$; mol. wt. 461.396

(*A basic dye. Solubility at 26°C: in water 1.10%, in alcohol 0.98%*)

This dye has not ordinarily been employed as a biological stain. One sample was submitted by a stain company by mistake, and it appeared to be a satisfactory substitute for Bismarck brown Y. Lillie (1945) specifies it as a good counterstain to oil blue NA.

CONGO RED   C. I. NO. 22120 (1 *ed.:* 370)

(C. I. Direct Red 28)

Synonyms: *Congo; Cotton red B or C; Direct red, C, R or Y*

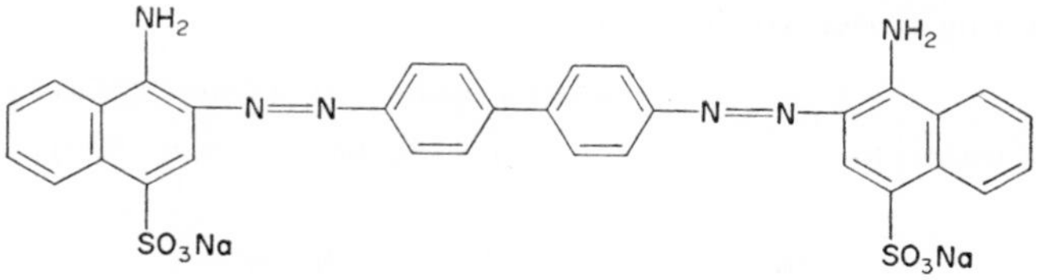

$C_{32}H_{22}N_6O_6S_2Na_2$; mol. wt. 696.670

(An acid dye; absorption maximum about 497)
Solubility at 26°C: in alcohol 0.19%

This dye is best known to the biologist as an indicator. The dye acid is blue, but its sodium salt is red. The red color of the salt is readily changed by weak acids into blue. Besides serving as an indicator, Congo red has certain histological uses, as for axis cylinders (Griesbach, 1886) for embryo sections (Schaffer, 1888), for staining elastic tissue (Matsuura, 1925), plant mucin, as a stain for Uredineae (Blackman, 1905) and as a general background stain in contrast to hematoxylin and other nuclear dyes. It has been used by Klebs (1886) as a reagent for cellulose. It proves useful as a negative stain for bacteria (Benians, 1916, Cumley, 1935, Maneval, 1934) and for staining protozoa (Merton, 1932) and yeasts (Gutstein, 1932). It has also been proposed as an elastin stain.

A spectrophotometric curve of this dye is given in graph 2, Fig. 8, p. 67.

For use of **Congo red with Mayer's hemalum,** see *Staining Procedures,* 42.
For use in **Bennhold's stain for amyloid,** see p. 38.

ERIE GARNET B

C. I. NO. 22145 (1 *ed.:* 375)

(C. I. Direct Red 10)

Synonyms: *Congo corinth G or GW; Corinth brown G; Cotton corinth G; Amanil garnet H; Direct garnet R; Buffalo garnet R; Direct violet C; Diamine Bordeaux CGN*

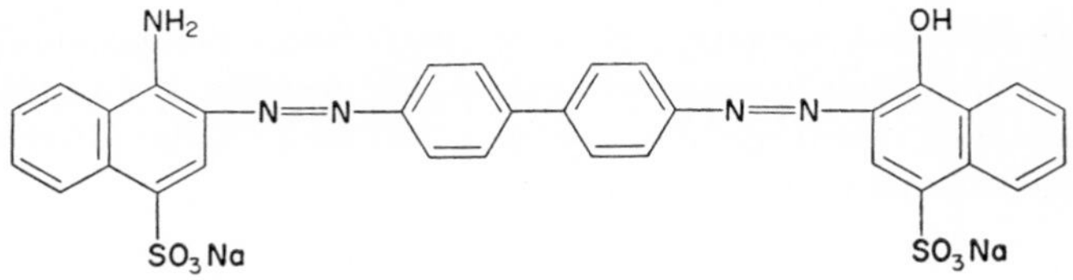

$C_{32}H_{21}N_5O_7S_2Na_2$; Mol. wt. 697.654

(An acid dye)

This dye has been employed by Geschickter (1930b), mixed with azure A, for staining frozen fresh tissue.

TRYPAN RED   C. I. NO. 22850 (1 *ed.*: 438)

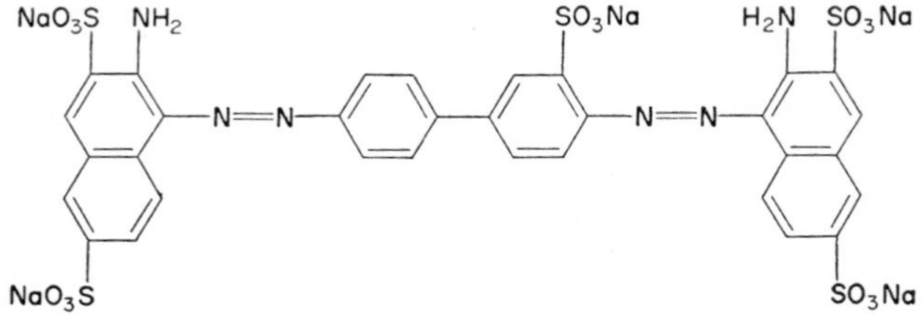

$C_{32}H_{19}N_6O_{15}S_5Na_5$; mol. wt. 1002.835

(An acid dye)

The chief use of this dye is as a vital stain. Varco and Vischer (1941), for instance, thus used it in studies of gastric secretion. As pointed out by Whitby (1942) this dye has an interesting history because it had very early application as a chemotherapeutic agent, and led ultimately to the discovery of the arsenicals.

BENZOPURPURIN 4B

c. i. no. 23500 (1 *ed.*: 448)

(C. I. Direct Red 2)

Synonyms: *Cotton red 4B; Dianil red 4B; Diamin red 4B; Sultan 4B; Direct red 4B*

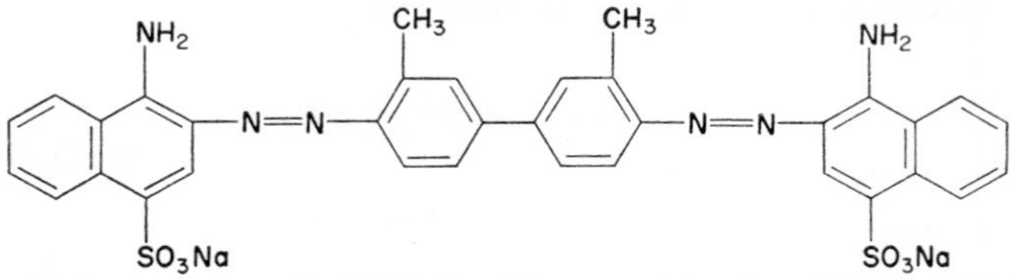

$C_{34}H_{26}N_6O_6S_2Na_2$; mol. wt. 724.722

(An acid dye; absorption maximum about 497)
Solubility at 26°C: in alcohol 0.13%

This dye has been employed by Zschokke (1888) as a plasma stain especially in contrast to hematoxylin, and by Ono (1934) for staining spirochaetes.

BRILLIANT PURPURIN R

C. I. NO. 23510 (1 *ed.:* 454)

(C. I. Direct Red 15)

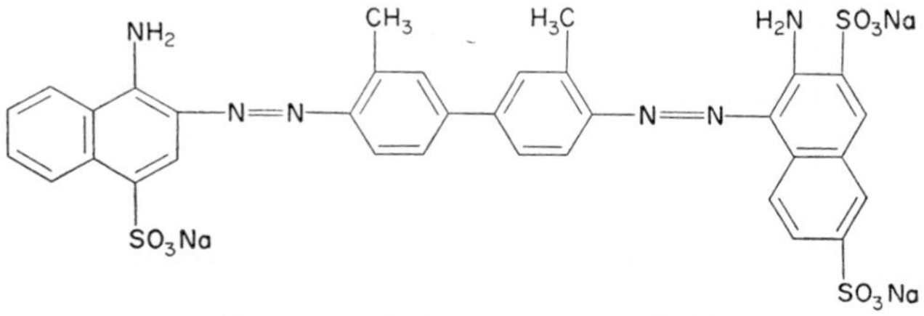

$C_{34}H_{25}N_6O_9S_3Na_3$; mol. wt. 826.777

(*An acid dye*)

Gutstein (1932) has employed a dye which he designates "brilliant purpur R" as a vital stain for yeasts. It probably is the above. Lillie (1948) included this dye, with azo fuchsin G and naphthol blue black, in a connective tissue stain.

VITAL RED   C. I. NO. 23570 (1 *ed.:* 456)

(C. I. Direct Red 34)

Synonyms: *Brilliant Congo R; Brilliant Congo red R; Acid Congo R; Azidine scarlet R; Brilliant vital red*

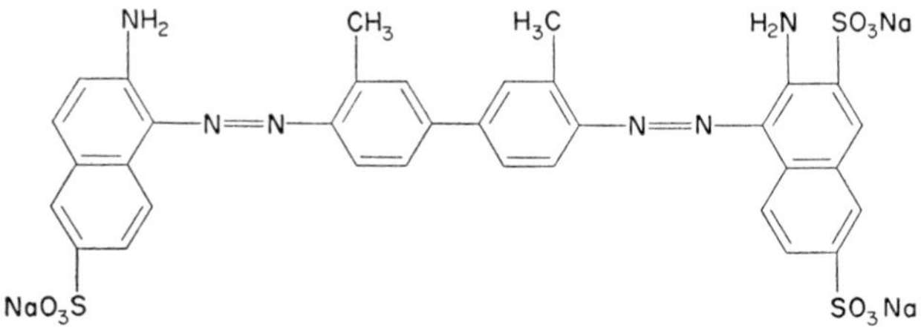

$C_{34}H_{25}N_6O_9S_3Na_3$; mol. wt. 826.777

(*An acid dye; absorption maximum about 498*)

This dye is a very important vital stain, much used by Evans. (See Dawson, Evans and Whipple, 1920.) Commercially it is better known under the name of brilliant Congo R. Difficulty was at first found in securing a satisfactory product, but it was overcome thanks to the cooperation of the Department of Agriculture, and a good vital red is now obtainable from stain dealers.

AZO BLUE   C. I. NO. 23680 (1 *ed.:* 463)

(C. I. Direct Violet 39)

Synonyms: *Benzoin blue R; Direct violet B*

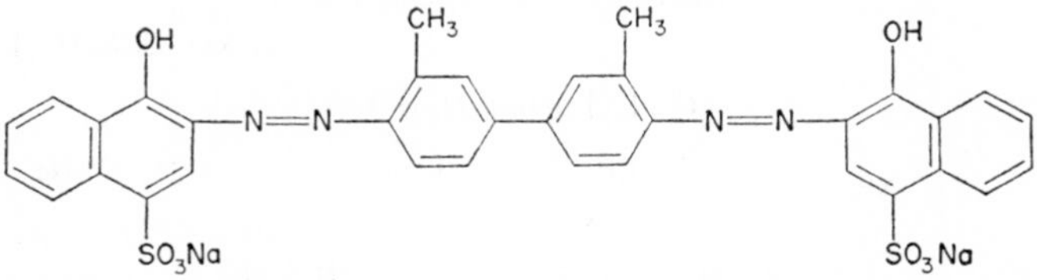

$C_{34}H_{24}N_4O_8S_2Na_2$; mol. wt. 726.690

(An acid dye; absorption maximum 560.5)

Monné (1935) has listed this dye among a series with which vital staining of protozoa has been secured. Butt, Bonynge and Joyce (1936) find that it can replace India ink in demonstrating capsules of bacteria. Broda (1939) uses it in the histochemical demonstration of magnesium.

DIANIL BLUE 2R

C. I. NO. 23690 (1 *ed.:* 465)

(C. I. Direct Blue 31)

Synonyms: *Direct steel blue BB; Benzo new blue 2B; Naphthamine brilliant blue 2R*

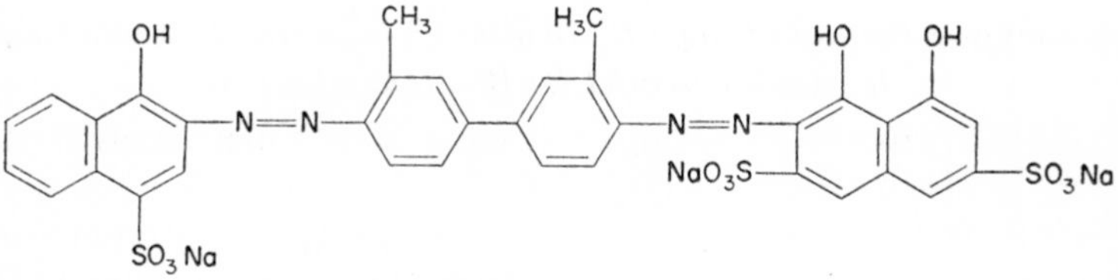

$C_{34}H_{23}N_4O_{12}S_3Na_3$; mol. wt. 844.745

(An acid dye; absorption maximum about 568)

This has been used as a vital stain by Corner and Hurni (1918); also by Sutter (1919), and Duran-Reynals (1937).

TRYPAN BLUE

C. I. NO. 23850 (1 *ed.:* 477)

(C. I. Direct Blue 14)

Synonyms: *Chlorazol blue 3B; Benzo blue 3B; Dianil blue H3G; Congo blue 3B; Naphthamine blue 3BX; Benzamine blue 3B; Azidine blue 3B; Niagara blue 3B*

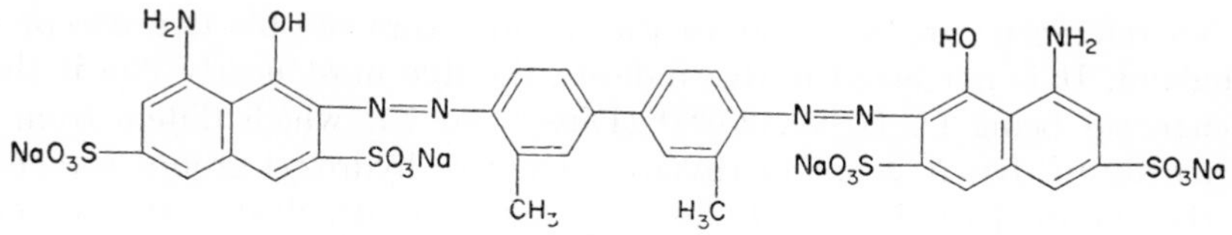

$C_{34}H_{24}N_6O_{14}S_4Na_4$; mol. wt. 960.832

(An acid dye)

This is a valuable vital stain. It is especially important because it is taken up by the reticulo-endothelial system. By injection into the circulatory system, it is employed for staining the uriniferous tubules; also for numerous other purposes in the vital staining of various kinds of tissue, from mammals, lower vertebrates and insects. It is used in chlamydospore agar for fungi.

EVANS BLUE

(C. I. Direct Blue 53)

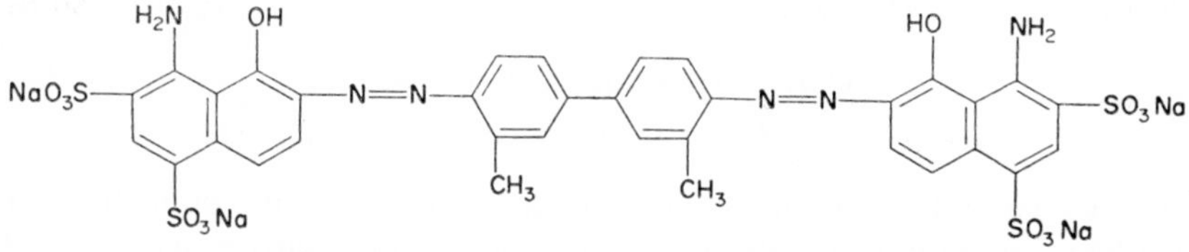

$C_{34}H_{24}N_6O_{14}S_4Na_4$; mol. wt. 960.832

(An acid dye)

The similarity between Trypan blue and Evans blue is evident by a glance at the two formulae. The latter, like the former, is employed as a vital stain. It has been thus employed in several rather varied applications: see Brunschwig, Schmitz and Jennings (1940), and Zahl and Waters (1941).

VITAL NEW RED

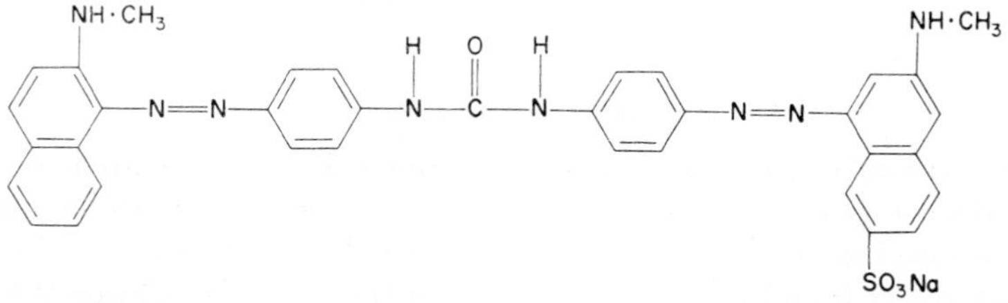

$C_{35}H_{28}N_8O_7S_2Na_2$; mol. wt. 782.752

(An acid dye)

No reference can be found to the manufacture of this dye except in England. It is not listed in dye indexes, the dye most nearly like it thus recognized being C. I. No. 25380 (Direct red 75) which differs from it primarily in that it is not methylated, has two hydroxyl groups attached to the naphthalene rings, and two sulfonic groups attached to the benzene rings. Vital new red has been called for in certain vital staining procedures, having been introduced for that purpose by Evans and Scott in 1921.

NIAGARA BLUE 4B

c. i. no. 24400 (1 *ed.*: 520)

(Direct Blue 15)

Synonyms: *Pontamine sky blue 5BX; Direct sky blue;
Benzo sky blue*

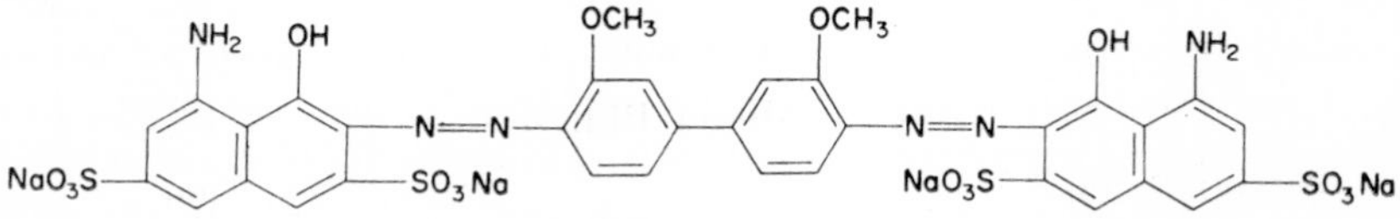

$C_{34}H_{24}N_6O_{16}S_4Na_4$; mol. wt. 992.832

(*An acid dye; absorption maxima about 634.2 and 589.5*)

Occasional references have been made to this dye in connection with histology for some time, although it has never come into general use. Recently Varrelman (1938) has employed it for demonstrating the vascular system of plants, taking advantage of its rise through stems which are stood in a solution of the dye. In the vital staining of skin or of tumors a pontamine sky blue has been recommended, which may be this dye or may be C. I. No. 24410, Direct blue 1, which has been sold under the name of pontamine sky blue 6BX (*Synonym:* Niagara sky blue 6B or Direct sky blue).

MARSHALL RED

HICKSON PURPLE

These are two new dyes of unknown composition, but stated to belong to the dis-azo group. They are discussed by Cannon (1941) as having been manufactured in the course of his study of chlorazol black E and of dyes of other colors found to be associated with that dye. He claims that they are valuable nuclear stains in general histology.

CHLORAZOL BLACK E

c. i. no. 30235 (1 *ed.*: 581)

(C. I. Direct Black 38)

Synonyms: *Pontamine black E, EX, or EXX; Erie black GXOO, B, BF;
Direct black MS, RL, E, GX, EE, 2V, F or A; Direct deep black
EW extra, E, EA, EAD extra; Renol black G*

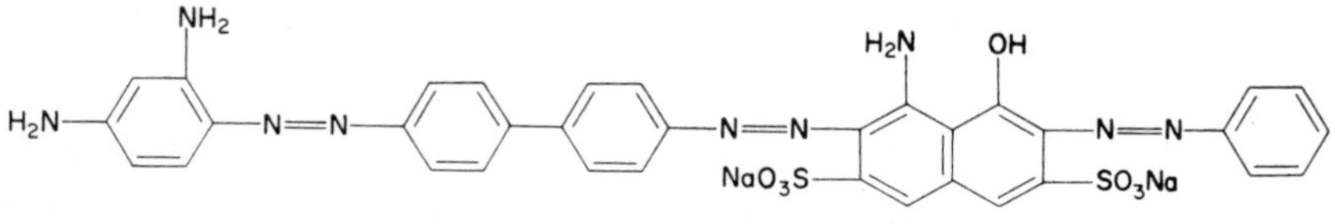

$C_{34}H_{25}N_9O_7S_2Na_2$; mol. wt. 781.738

(An acid dye: absorption maximum 598–602 in alcohol)

This dye was introduced into microscopic technic by Cannon (1937) who called attention to its use in general histology and cytology. It proves to be a valuable stain because it can be employed without mordanting or differentiation and gives a very sharp clear-cut picture both of nuclear and cytoplasmic structures. The black and gray tones it produces are well suited for photography.

For use as a **fat stain**, see *Staining Procedures*, p. 158.
For use as **general stain in plant histology**, see Id. p. 181.
For use as **plant cytological stain with aceto-carmine**, see Id. p. 206.

A spectral curve of this dye is given in graph 2, Fig. 10, p. 80. It will be noticed that the black color of the solution is indicated by partial absorption through the whole visual range, with only minor peaks at any wave length.

SUDAN BLACK B   c. i. no. 26150

(C. I. Solvent Black 3)

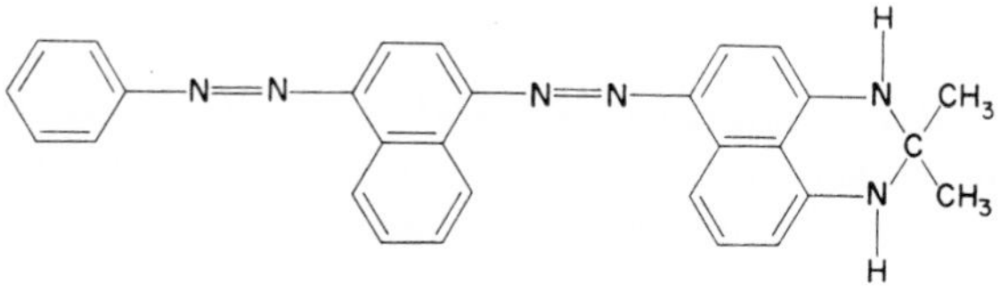

$C_{29}H_{24}N_6$; mol. wt. 456.530

(Absorption maximum 596–605)

This compound is one of the more recently developed fat stains. For a fat stain it has a rather unusual chemical structure, as it does not show the typical —OH group in the ortho (or beta) position. It was first prepared in Germany some time in the early '30's, and became available in France and England. Lison and Dagnelie (1935) proposed it as a myelin stain, but it was in England that its value as a stain for fats was first developed (Gerard, 1935). During the second World War it achieved general recognition for the purpose, both in Great Britain and in the United States. Hartman (1940) and later Burdon *et al.* (1942) found it valuable as a stain for bacterial fat. It has also been proposed for staining leucocyte granules and the Golgi apparatus.

Unfortunately just at the time when its value was most appreciated it went off the market entirely because of the war. It was not till after the close of the war that American manufacturers learned its formula and discovered how to make it.

A spectral curve of this dye is given in graph 3, Fig. 9, p. 75. Characteristic of a black dye is the fact that there is considerable light absorption even at the curve's minimum.

For use in **Burdon's method for Bacterial fat,** see *Staining Procedures,* p. 242.

ORANGE S

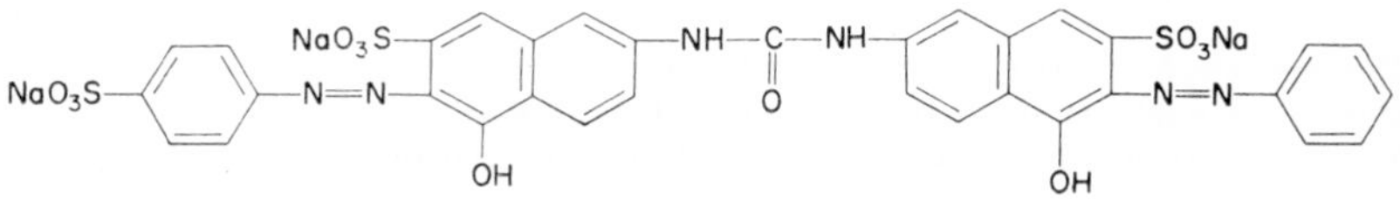

(*An acid dye*)

Occasional reference has been made to an orange S in the biological literature, which we are informed by the dye industry is probably of the above composition. It was proposed by DeGalantha (1936) in a mixture with alum hematoxylin for staining connective tissue and following Harris' hematoxylin for demonstrating amyloid.

VICTORIA GREEN G

This trisazo dye of unknown chemical composition was studied by Cannon (1941) in connection with other new azo dyes. He states it to have valuable properties as a nuclear stain in general histology.

Other azo dyes sometimes mentioned in connection with histology are:
Janus red; C. I. No. 26115 (1 *ed.:* 266)
Tropaeolin O; C. I. No. 14270 (1 *ed.:* 148). *Synonyms:* Chrysoin; Gold yellow; Acme yellow. C. I. Acid orange 6.
Tropaeolin Y; C. I. No. 14270 (See note).

Roccellin; C. I. No. 15620 (1 *ed.:* 176). *Synonyms:* Fast red A, AV, AL, BX, S or O; Cerasin; Rubidin; Cardinal Red. C. I. Acid red 88.

Crystal ponceau 6R; C.I. No. 16250 (1 *ed.:* 89) *Synonym:* Ponceau 6R. C. I. Acid red 44.

Carmine naptha; C. I. No. 11920 (1 *ed.:* 23). *Synonyms:* Sudan G; Oil yellow. C. I. Solvent orange 1.

Alizarin yellow GG; C. I. No. 14025 (1 *ed.:* 36). *Synonyms:* Anthracene yellow GG; Mordant yellow 2GT. C. I. Mordant yellow 1.

Chlorazol paper brown B. A dye put out by the Imperial Chemical Industries of Manchester, England. Proposed by Verdcourt (1947) for staining plant tissues.

Chrysoidin R.; C. I. No. 11320 (1 *ed.:* 21). *Synonyms:* Cotton orange; Cerotin orange. C. I. Basic Orange I.

Alizarin yellow R; C. I. No. 14030 (1 *ed.:* 40). *Synonyms:* Alizarin orange; Mordant yellow PN; Orange R; Anthracene yellow RN. C. I. Mordant orange 1.

Diamond flavine G; C. I. No. 14135 (1 *ed.:* 110). C. I. Mordant yellow 36.

Diamond black F; C. I. No. 26695 (1 *ed.:* 299). *Synonyms:* Salicin black D; Chrome black J or F. C. I. Mordant black 5.

Indole blue B or R; C. I. No. 12210 (1 *ed.:* 135). *Synonyms:* Indoine blue BB, R or BR; Safranin blue R; Janus blue G or R; Indophene blue; Basilene fast blue B. C. I. Basic blue 16.

Direct violet K, N or R; C. I. No. 22570 (1 *ed.:* 394). *Synonyms:* Chlorazol violet N; Pontamine violet N; Diamine violet N; Erie violet 3R. C. I. Direct violet 1.

V I

THE QUINONE-IMINE DYES

The dyes of the quinone-imine group contain two chromophore groups, the indamin group —N=, and the quinoid benzene ring

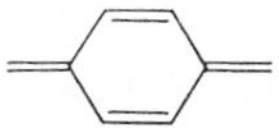

They are derivatives of the theoretical compound paraquinone-di-imine, which, if it existed in its free state, would have the formula

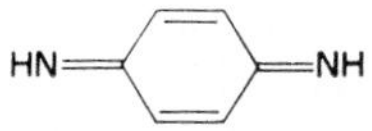

In the typical indamin formula one of the imine hydrogen atoms is replaced by a phenyl group, thus:

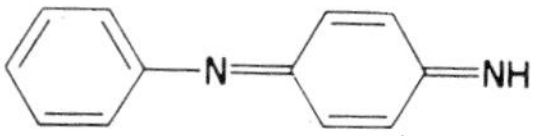

In the thiazins the introduction of a sulfur atom, attached to both the phenyl and the quinone groups, forms a third closed ring, as:

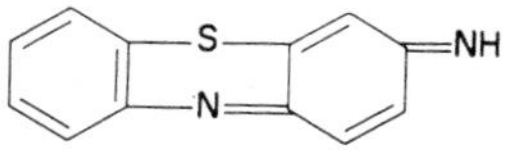

(*imino-thio-diphenylimine*)

In the oxazins an oxygen atom, and in the azins a nitrogen atom takes the place of the sulfur of the thiazins, thus:

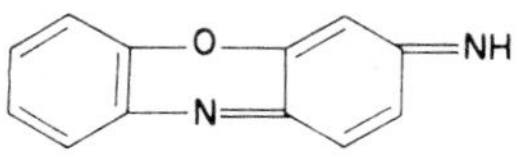

(*oxazin*) 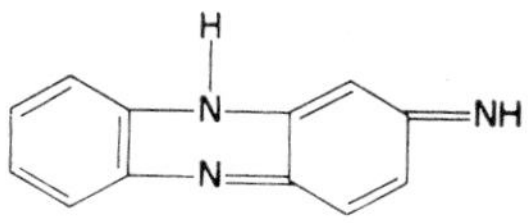   (*azin*)

1. THE INDAMINS

The indamin dyes are methylated amino derivatives of indamin. No dye in this group is a common biological stain. The following are occasionally mentioned, however, in connection with histology:

BINDSCHEDLER'S GREEN

C. I.* NO. 49405 (1 *ed.:* 819)

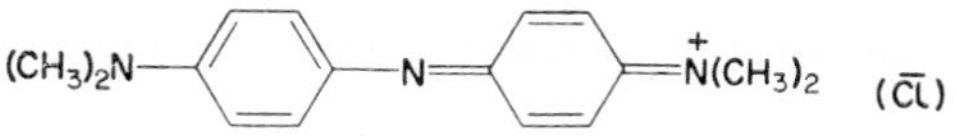

$C_{16}H_{20}N_3Cl$; mol. wt. 289.801

(A basic dye; typically of the above formula, but sometimes sold as the zinc double salt)

Bindschedler's green has occasional employment as an indicator of oxidation-reduction. It is reduced to the colorless *pp'*-tetra-methyldiamino-diphenylamine. Elliott and Baker (1935) subsequently employed it for this purpose in studying the metabolism of tumor tissue.

TOLUYLENE BLUE

C. I. NO. 49410 (1 *ed.:* 820)

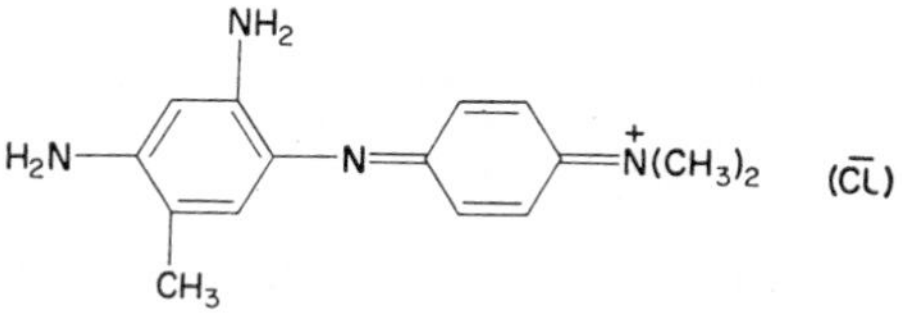

$C_{15}H_{19}N_4Cl$; mol. wt. 290.791

(A basic dye)

Like its homolog, Bindschedler's green, toluylene blue is readily reduced to a substituted diphenylamine; and accordingly it has similar indicator properties.

2. THE INDOPHENOLS

Closely related to the indamines is a small group of colored compounds known as indophenols, which do not readily form salts with mineral acids.

* The abbreviation "C. I." stands for "Colour Index." The number immediately following is that of the current (2nd) edition; the one which follows is that of the first edition. The name of the dye given under the principal name is the preferred designation in the current Colour Index.

The simplest compound of this group is indophenol (sometimes called benzenoneindophenol) and has the following structural formula.

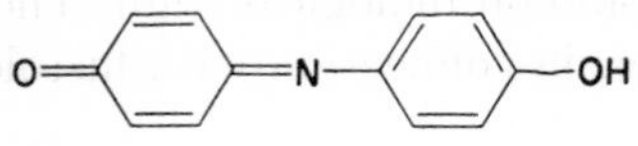

Various halogen substitution products of indophenol are known, and all have indicator value, showing an acid-base color change and a disappearance of color on reduction; some of them have been suggested to determine the virulence of the tubercle organism. The best known indicator of this series is:

2,6-DICHLOROINDOPHENOL

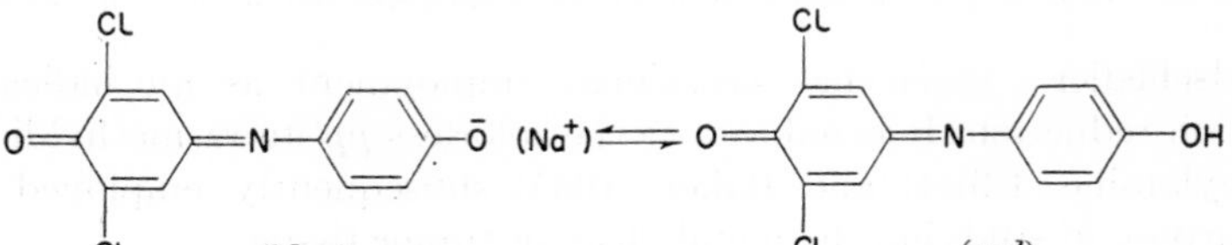

which on reduction becomes the following colorless compound:

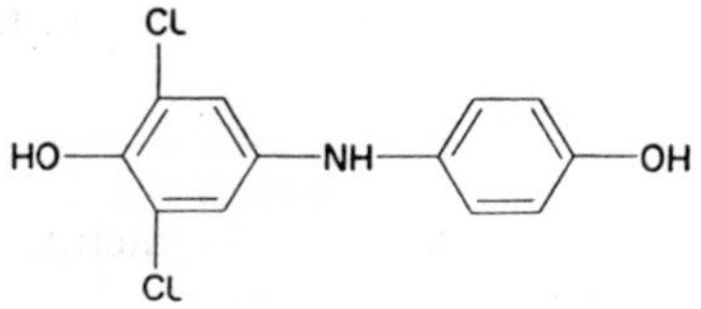

It will be seen that the type of color change shown by this indicator is very similar to that of litmus (see p. 243). Litmus is a non-synthetic product of unknown chemical composition; it is not believed to be related to the indophenols, in spite of its similar behavior as an acid-base and oxidation-reduction indicator.

There is only one other dye of this group that need be mentioned here.

INDOPHENOL BLUE

c. i. no. 49700 (1 ed.: 821)

Synonym: *Indophenol*

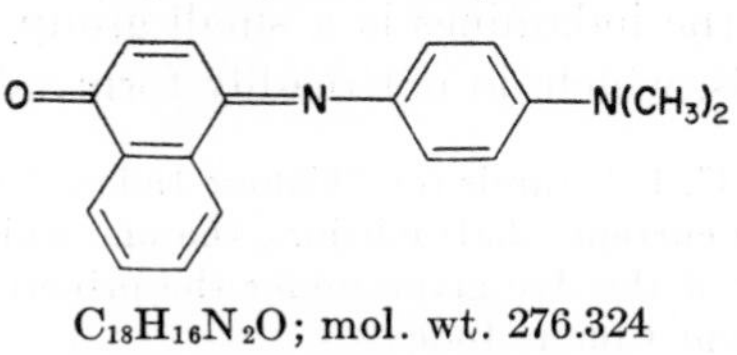

$C_{18}H_{16}N_2O$; mol. wt. 276.324

(*Absorption maximum in alcohol about 592*)

This compound is occasionally referred to in biological work. Herxheimer (1901), for example, employed a dye which he called indophenol (and which probably was indophenol blue), in saturated solution in 70 percent alcohol, as a fat stain. It is still sometimes used for the same purpose; see Black (1938), for instance.

3. THE THIAZINS

The thiazins constitute one of the most important groups of dyes from the standpoint of the biologist; while for textile dyeing the group contains but a small number of dyes of any importance. In these compounds, as mentioned above, the two benzene rings are further joined by a sulfur atom.

Considerable information is at hand concerning the spectrophotometric characteristics of the thiazins (Knapp, Emery and Stotz, 1950). From this information the absorption curves given in Figs. 11 and 12 have been derived for seven of the dyes in the group. Reference to these curves will be given under the individual dyes as discussed below.

THIONIN   C. I. NO. 52000 (1 ed.: 920)

Synonym: *Lauth's violet*

Thionin, having two amino groups, is a strongly basic dye. The exact structural formulae of this dye and its derivatives, as well as many others in which two benzene rings are similarly joined, are in some dispute. At least two types of formulae are possible for the thiazins and oxazins, as well as for the xanthene dyes (Chapter VIII). One type is known as the orthoquinoid, the other as the paraquinoid.

It is supposed (see p. 18) that when the quinoid ring is formed the two hydrogen atoms replaced by atoms or groups with double valency bonds may be either in the para or in the ortho position to each other. These facts make it possible for a thiazin or an oxazin to have either one or the other of the different structures represented by the following two formulae for the theoretical thionin base:

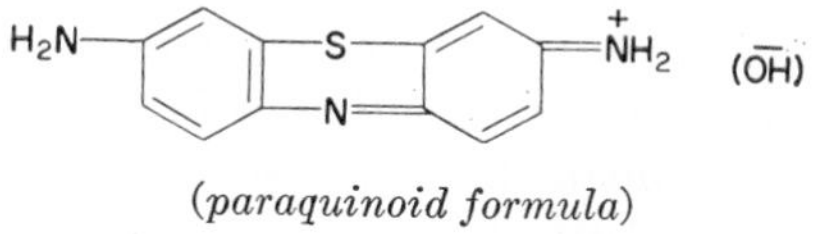

(*paraquinoid formula*)

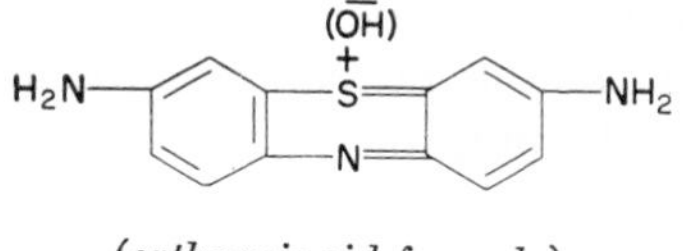

(*orthoquinoid formula*)

In the case of the paraquinoid formula the compound is an ammonium base of the type discussed on p. 20, which is capable of salt formation through its pentavalent nitrogen. In the case of the orthoquinoid formula the salt formation takes place through the tetravalent sulfur, the base being of the type known as a sulfonium base. There are arguments in favor of either formula, and from the standpoint of the biologist it does not matter which is preferred. Possibly both forms actually exist simultaneously. For the sake of uniformity the paraquinoid form will be shown in the following pages wherever possible; but with the understanding that the orthoquinoid form is equally permissible.

The dye, thionin, is a salt, generally a chloride, of the above-mentioned base; and on the assumption of paraquinoid structure, it has the following formula:

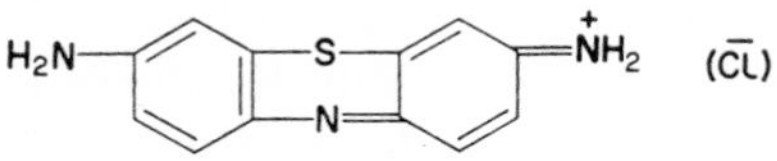

$C_{12}H_{10}N_3SCl$; mol. wt. 263.747

(*A basic dye; absorption maximum 598–599*)
Solubility at 26°C: in water 0.25%; in alcohol 0.25%

Thionin is violet in dilute solution, and has a very pronounced metachromatic effect, the colors in sections stained with it ranging from blue to reddish violet. A spectrophotometric graph of a typical sample of thionin is given in Fig. 11, p. 95 (curve 2).

It is no longer used as a textile dye, and is to be distinguished from thionin blue (C. I. No. 52025, C. I. Basic blue 25) which is known to the trade and has sometimes been furnished in place of the desired dye when thionin has been ordered. Thionin is an especially valuable dye for histological work on account of its metachromatic properties, that is, its ability to impart different colors to different histological or cytological structures. It is a very valuable chromatin and mucin stain, proving especially useful in staining the tissue of insects; and is recommended by Ehrlich because it stains amyloid blue but mast cells and mucin red. It is a useful vital stain; added to culture media, it serves to differentiate species of *Brucella*. Perhaps its greatest value at the present time is in the staining of frozen sections of fresh animal or human tissue, particularly in the study of tumors. It was also used by Frost (1916) for staining very young bacterial colonies in his "little plate" technic for counting bacteria. (Unfortunately Frost specified thionin blue in one of his papers, although the latter proves entirely unsatisfactory for the purpose.)

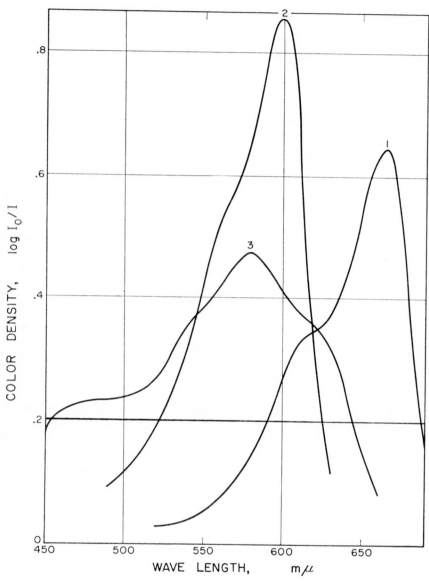

FIG. 11. Spectral curves of three thiazin dyes:

1. Methylene blue   2. Thionin   3. Methylene violet

Procedures Recommended by the Commission in Which This Stain Is Used*

Name of Procedure	Page Reference to *Staining Procedures*
Staining frozen sections..	47
Staining fixed tissue...	47
End point staining of Nissl granules...........................	94
Schmorl's method for staining bone sections...................	145
Stoughton's technic (with orange G) for fungi in plant tissue....	195

* Under this heading are given references to procedures described in detail in *Staining Procedures,* edited by Conn, Darrow, and Emmel (1960).

METHYLENE AZURE

C. I. NO. 52010 (1 *ed.:* 923)

This was first recognized as one of the components of polychrome methylene blue by Bernthsen (1885). It is now known to be a mixture, not a simple dye. Definite knowledge of its chemistry has been obtained by Kehrmann (1906), Bernthsen (1906) and MacNeal (1906, 1925). It is regarded as primarily a mixture of azure A and azure B, described below, compounds for which Bernthsen and MacNeal have given simple methods of preparation in relatively pure condition by the oxidation of methylene blue. Another oxidation product of methylene blue, described later by Holmes and French (1926), has been named azure C. Now that these three dyes, azures A, B and C are recognized, it would be most satisfactory if the name methylene azure could be dropped, and users specify the actual dye employed.

Azure I (Giemsa) is a trade name applied to a secret preparation which appears to be a somewhat variable mixture in which azure B predominates. Azure II (Giemsa) is an intentional mixture of azure I with an equal quantity of methylene blue. Products of these same names are now sold by various companies and they are certainly not all identical with the original Giemsa preparations. They all probably agree, however, in containing azure A and azure B as their chief constituents.

AZURE C

This dye is mono-methyl thionin:

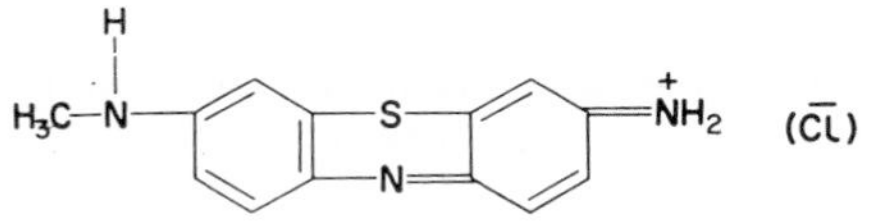

$C_{13}H_{12}N_3SCl$; mol. wt. 277.773

(A basic dye; absorption maximum 607–610)

Curve 4 in Fig. 12, p. 98, is a spectrophotometric graph of a typical sample of azure C.

It is not a textile dye, and up to the present has been manufactured only on a laboratory scale. A small lot, thus prepared, has been put on sale by one of the American stain companies. This dye, like the other azures described below, has up to the present been prepared only by the oxidation of methylene blue. If they should prove sufficiently valuable, a process of manufacture by direct synthesis could undoubtedly be developed. A product thus manufactured would probably be cheaper as well as purer than the present supply.

Azure C was recommended by French (1926b) with orange II and eosin as a tissue stain. Haynes (1926a) found it possible to obtain equally good results, however, with azure I (probably azure A) if the technic is slightly modified. Later (1927) she reported excellent staining with azure C; but it is still uncertain whether it gives results sufficiently different from thionin on the one hand and azure A on the other to be of decided histological value.

AZURE A

This is now recognized as asymmetrical dimethyl thionin:

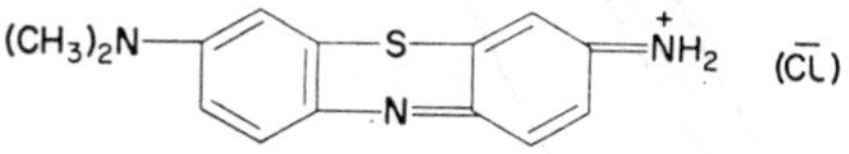

$C_{14}H_{14}N_3SCl$; mol. wt. 291.799

(A basic dye; absorption maximum 625–632)

Curve 2 in Fig. 12, p. 98, is a spectrophotometric graph of a typical sample of azure A. (Its similarity to toluidine blue is well brought out in these curves.)

It is not a textile dye; but is probably present in much of the methylene blue on the market. It must be distinguished from the isomeric symmetrical compound:

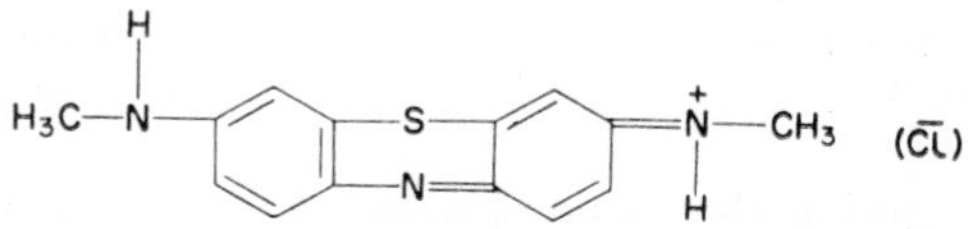

which has never been given a special name. For some time after its recognition by Kehrmann (1906) the impression was current that this latter dye has no staining value and was of a distinctly different category from the azures. It is difficult to tell how this impression arose, but possibly it may have been due to work with an impure dye. Haynes (1927) found both isomers to have almost identical staining properties.

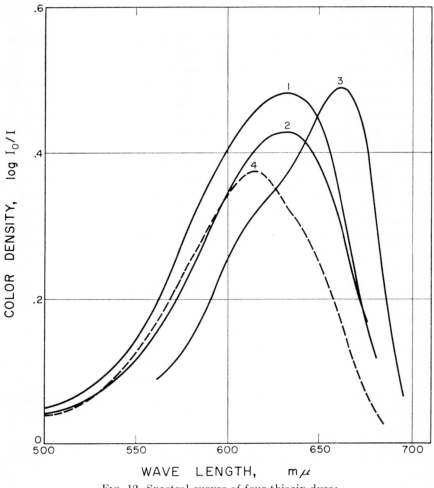

FIG. 12. Spectral curves of four thiazin dyes:
1. Toluidine blue   3. Azure B
2. Azure A   4. Azure C

There is no mistaking the value of azure A; it was in fact regarded by MacNeal (1925) as the most important nuclear staining constituent of polychrome methylene blue. It was called for in the originally proposed formulae for the tetrachrome blood stain (see p. 256). It has been certified by the Commission for some time. It was formerly recommended for all purposes for which methylene azure or azure I was specified; more recent work, however, shows that there are other constituents of the German azure I (particularly azure B) which have special value in blood stains.

Haynes (1926a) employed this dye as a nuclear stain preceding eosin; and (1926b) following phloxine in a procedure similar to the Mallory phloxine-methylene-blue technic. Douglas (1932) mixed it with methylene blue for a counterstain to acid-fast bacteria.

For use in **buffered azure-eosinate method** see *Staining Procedures*, p. 45; in Kinyoun's diphtheria stain, see p. 234.

AZURE B   C. I. NO. 52010   (1 *ed.*: 720)

Azure B is the trimethyl derivative of thionin:

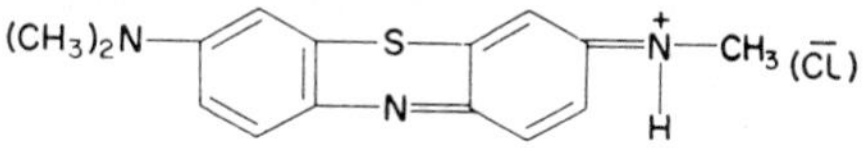

$C_{15}H_{16}N_3SCl$; mol. wt. 305.825

(*A basic dye; absorption maximum 648–653*)

Like azure A, this compound was first recognized by Kehrmann (1906) as a constituent of polychrome methylene blue. It is quite probably the dye prepared by Bernthsen as methylene azure in 1885. It can easily be prepared in impure form by oxidation of methylene blue, and is now readily available.

Curve 3 in Fig. 12, p. 98, shows its spectral characteristics. It is distinctly less red than any of the other azures.

MacNeal (1925) stated that its staining effects were much the same as could be obtained with a mixture of azure A and methylene blue, and that it therefore could be of little importance in polychrome methylene blue. His statement was generally interpreted as meaning that azure B is not a satisfactory stain. Holmes and French (1926) also stated that this dye had little staining value; but their conclusions were based upon work with an impure sample, the performance of which was so poor as not apparently to justify further purification. Haynes' later work (1927) on sections of fixed tissue, with this same sample of azure B, agreed partially with this, although she found the dye, if used in buffered solution, rather better than fairly pure methylene blue in fresh solution. Jordan and Heather (1929) definitely specify this dye in a stain for Negri bodies. Moreover, later tests by the Stain Commission of certain exceptionally good Giemsa stains indicate the presence of more azure B than in less satisfactory batches. Roe, Lillie, and Wilcox (1940), in fact, have concluded that azure B is one of the most important constituents of Giemsa stain, especially when used for staining malaria parasites in thick blood films. This work was followed up by a series of other papers by Lillie and his associates, and they distributed samples to other laboratories for testing; as a result it seems difficult to question their conclusions. Accordingly it is now recognized that azure B is one of the most important constituents of "azure I."

METHYLENE BLUE

C. I. NO. 52015 (1 *ed.:* 922)

(C. I. Basic Blue 9)

Synonym: *Swiss blue*

Various grades denoted: *Methylene blue BX, B, BG, BB*; grade preferred for biological work: *Methylene blue chloride.*

Methylene blue is theoretically tetra-methyl thionin:

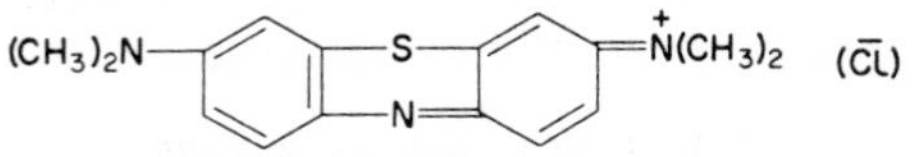

$$(CH_3)_2N \overbrace{\hspace{2cm}}^{S} \overbrace{\hspace{2cm}}^{N} = \overset{+}{N}(CH_3)_2 \quad (\overline{Cl})$$

$C_{16}H_{18}N_3SCl$; mol. wt. 319.851

(A basic dye; absorption maximum, if pure, about 664–666)
Solubility at 26°C: in water 3.55%; in alcohol 1.48%

The dye is so readily oxidized that it is practically impossible to obtain in pure form, the presence of some of the azures or of methylene violet being almost universal. Methylene blue has long been recognized as an important nuclear stain. It is notable, however, that all the staining solutions recommended for use on sections of fixed tissue call for some ripening or for the addition of alkali. Such solutions are bound to contain one or more of the azures. There are indications, in fact, that pure methylene blue is a relatively poor histological stain.

A spectrophotometric graph of a reasonably pure sample of methylene blue is given in curve 1, Fig. 11, p. 95. It is to be noticed that this curve has a distinct "hump" at about 610 mμ; this is characteristic of methylene blue and may indicate the presence of either a tautomeric form or of some product of oxidation. It is interesting to observe that 610 mμ is practically the absorption maximum of azure C.

The methylene blue of commerce is generally a double salt, the chloride of zinc and methylene blue. The zinc salt is toxic, however; so for some time the zinc-free methylene blue chloride has been prescribed for medicinal purposes, and is frequently designated methylene blue Med. U. S. P. The zinc double salt is less soluble, particularly in alcohol, so for most staining purposes is less desirable. Some samples have been found to give excellent results in controlled pH staining of nuclei; nevertheless, for all ordinary staining purposes the zinc-free compound is the form at present recommended.

Methylene blue is perhaps the stain which the pathologist and bacteriologist would have the greatest difficulty in doing without, and it is of great value to the zoologist as well. It is employed for a greater variety of purposes than any other biological stain except possibly hematoxylin; and for this reason was the first dye to be given a thorough investigation by the Commission. It is used: first, as a nuclear stain in histology, for which purpose its strongly basic character as well as the ease with which it can be applied without over-staining, make it quite valuable; second, as a bacterial stain, notably in milk work and in the diagnosis of diphtheria, where it is especially useful because it has an affinity for the bacterial protoplasm as great as that of the rosanilin dyes, but is less intense, more selective in its action and more subject to differentiation; third, in the vital staining of nervous tissue, as it is a non-toxic dye which becomes colorless when nerves are deprived of oxygen; fourth, in combination with eosin in the blood stains, thanks to the ease with which it can be partly converted into lower homologs such as the azures, and thus acquire polychrome properties; fifth, as an oxidation-reduction indicator, particularly in milk; and lastly, as an indicator in the Levine eosin-methylene-blue medium for differentiating the colon and aerogenes organisms.

It can be readily understood that an especially pure product is needed when the dye is to be used for vital staining or in blood work. For vital staining the U. S. P. zinc-free dye is always recommended, sometimes with even further purification; although the investigations carried on by the Commission indicate that the U. S. P. product is sufficiently pure. For blood work some companies have sold a "methylene blue rectified for blood stains." This grade, however, is generally less pure than the medicinal or U. S. P. grade, and there seems no reason for specifying it. The same is true of various other grades such as those denoted BX, BG, etc., which are ordinarily purer than the textile dye, but less pure than the medicinal grade.

In former years, one or both of the German stain companies sold a grade designated "methylene blue for bacilli." This was often erroneously assumed to be specially adapted for staining bacteria. As a matter of fact, it proved to be the zinc salt, quite impure, and was probably labeled under the specified designation because it was not considered good enough for any other purpose! Even for staining bacteria it did not prove especially satisfactory. (It is, among other things, almost insoluble in alcohol, and cannot be used in any formula—such as that of Loeffler—which is derived from a stock alcoholic solution of the dye.) At present the American manufacturers, at least, have wisely discontinued the sale of the zinc salt under this designation. One American concern, however, still sells a "methylene blue for bacilli," but it is entirely different from the former imported product of that name. It is apparently methylene blue chloride, less pure than the medicinal grade but entirely satisfactory for staining bacteria and for many other staining purposes. The Commission has been unable, however, to find that it has any special advantages over the medicinal product as a bacterial stain. It must be repeated that for all staining purposes, except possibly some lines of vital staining, medicinal methylene blue is an eminently satisfactory grade. When ordered for staining purposes it is best specified under the name: *methylene blue chloride*.

There is just one salt of methylene blue, other than the chloride, which is recommended by the Commission—namely *methylene blue thiocyanate*. This form of the dye, however, is not recommended as a stain but as an oxidation-reduction indicator for use in milk. Thornton and Sandin (1935) have shown that this salt has distinct advantages over the chloride in determining the rate of reduction of milk by its bacterial flora; the thiocyanate contains no water of hydration and hence can be obtained in almost 100 % dye strength—a fact which makes for more ready standardization of solutions. Accordingly tablets of methylene blue for use in the reduction test in milk, which are put on the market in America are now wholly the thiocyanate.

Procedures Recommended by the Commission in Which This Stain Is Used

Name of Procedure	Page Reference to *Staining Procedures*
Modified Wright stain (buffered azure eosin) for general tissue.	45
Tänzer-Unna orcein method for connective tissue..............	68–9
Supravital staining of nerve endings (Ehrlich).................	130
Wright stain......................................	133
Tetrachrome stain, MacNeal.........................	135
Giemsa stain......................................	136–7
Staining smears of bone marrow.....................	143
Staining sections of bone marrow...................	144
Counterstain to alizarin red S for calcium deposits...........	150
General staining of bacterial smears.................	224
Counterstain in acid-fast staining...................	229
Staining the diphtheria organism....................	232
Macchiavello's stain for Rickettsiae.................	244
Harris stain for Negri bodies.......................	247
Breed method for bacteria in milk smears....................	248
Mallory's phloxine-methylene-blue stain....................	49; 250
Lillie modification of Ziehl-Neelsen technic.................	258
Kinyoun's diphtheria stain..........................	234
Stains for Negri bodies in sections..................	259–62

Polychrome methylene blue. The oxidation of methylene blue into one or more of the compounds of lower methylation described on the preceding pages takes place in any methylene blue solution upon standing, especially rapidly if the solution be alkaline as in the Loeffler formula. All methylene blue solutions therefore, particularly if they have been standing any length of time, contain small amounts of the lower homologs, primarily azure A and azure B. These lower homologs are not only more violet in color than methylene blue itself but are more selective in their staining action. It has indeed been claimed (Scott and French, 1924b) that the dye owes much of its value as a nuclear stain to the azures that are present, and that an extremely pure methylene blue is not so satisfactory for such use. A later paper by Haynes (1927) indicated the correctness of such conclusions.

A methylene blue containing noticeably large proportions of the lower homologs is called *polychrome methylene blue*. The formation of these oxidation products may be hastened by boiling with alkali, as in Unna's formula.

Polychrome methylene blue is employed in many blood stains such as Leishmann's and Wright's; in the latter a methylene blue solution containin sodium bicarbonate is heated, and then eosin is added. Eosin enters into chemical combination with the basic dyes present, forming an insoluble compound which precipitates. This precipitate dissolved in methyl alcohol is Wright's stain. (For a more detailed discussion of the subject see Chapter XIII).

METHYLENE VIOLET (Bernthsen)

Methylene violet is formed whenever methlyene blue is heated with a fixed alkali or alkali carbonate. It is a weak base with the formula.

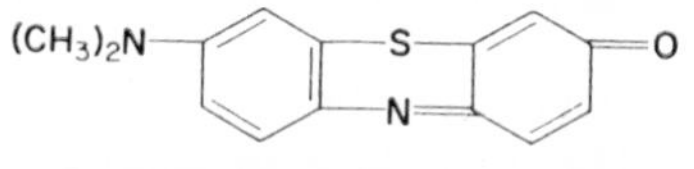

$(CH_3)_2N$ ⬡ S ⬡ $= O$ / N $=$

$C_{14}H_{12}N_2OS$; mol. wt. 256.318

(Absorption maximum 579–581)

Its preparation from methylene blue is more difficult than that of azure A. A fair yield (30 to 40 percent) may be obtained by oxidizing methylene blue in dilute ammoniacal solution with potassium chromate and then driving off the ammonia by boiling with the addition of sodium carbonate. It may also be prepared from azure A by boiling this with dilute alkali carbonate. Methylene violet precipitates out as needle crystals, insoluble in water. It may be recrystallized from dichlorethane ($CH_2Cl \cdot CH_2Cl$) in which it forms a deep carmine red solution. Although insoluble in water when pure, methylene violet is soluble when mixed with methylene blue or with the azures. It behaves much like a fat-soluble dye, and can be extracted from acid aqueous mixtures by shaking with chloroform or ether. It has a rather unusual shaped absorption curve, as shown in graph 3, Fig. 11, p. 95.

It plays an important part in the nuclear and granule staining of the polychrome methylene blue stains. A definite quantity of this dye is employed in the tetrachrome blood stain of MacNeal. It is thought to be responsible for the sky blue color assumed by the cytoplasm of lymphocytes in such blood stains.

For formula and technic of **MacNeal's Tetrachrome Stain,** see *Staining Procedures*, p. 135.

Methylene violet (Bernthsen 1885) is not a textile dye and must not be confused with methylene violet RRA or 3RA, which is C. I. No. 50205 (Basic violet 5).

METHYLENE GREEN

C. I. NO. 52020 (1 *ed.*: 924)

(C. I. Basic Green 5)

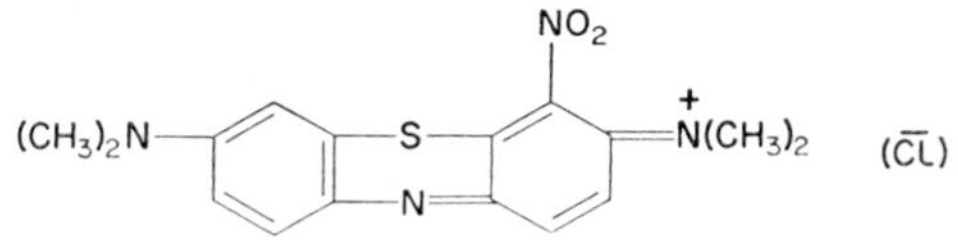

$C_{16}H_{17}N_4O_2SCl$; mol. wt. 364.851

(A basic dye; absorption maxima at about 660, 607)
Solubility at 26°C: in water 1.46%; in alcohol 0.12%

This dye is a mononitro methylene blue, obtained by the action of nitrous acid on methylene blue. The formula is probably as given above, but the exact position of the nitro group is uncertain.

It is occasionally used as a substitute for methyl green, especially by botanists in the case of wood and fixed chromatin, and gives good results in combination with eosin. It has also been employed by Lison (1938) as a vital stain for insects. Its dark green metachromasia has been utilized for staining those mast cells in the mouse or rat which fail to color by the periodic acid Schiff reaction (Lillie, 1950).

TOLUIDINE BLUE O

C. I. NO. 52040 (1 *ed.*: 925)

(C. I. Basic Blue 17)

Synonym: *Methylene blue T 50 or T extra*

This dye is closely related to thionin and to methylene blue in structure, and even more closely to azure A:

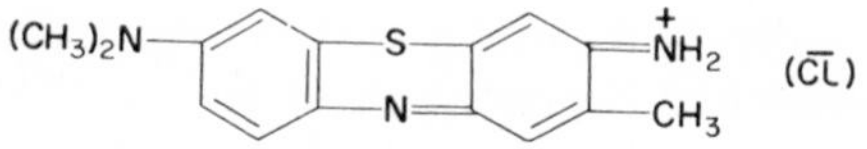

$$(CH_3)_2N \text{—} \underset{N}{\overset{S}{\diagup\diagdown}} \text{—} \overset{+}{N}H_2 \quad (\overline{Cl})$$
$$CH_3$$

C$_{15}$H$_{16}$N$_3$SCl; mol. wt. 305.825

(*A basic dye; absorption maximum 620–622*)
Solubility at 26°C: in water 3.82%; in alcohol 0.57%

In practice it proves difficult to distinguish this dye from azure A by spectrophotometric tests. This is particularly true because a shift in the absorption band of toluidine blue O sometimes occurs in storage as a result of which the two dyes may become almost identical optically. Their great similarity is well brought out by comparing curve 1 (toluidine blue) and curve 2 (azure A) in Fig. 12 on p. 98. Ball and Jackson (1953) have shown by chromatography that toluidine blue O seems to be a mixture, and suggest that this may account for much of the observed variation between samples.

Although not a common textile dye, toluidine blue is more easily prepared than thionin or azure A—a fact of considerable importance, since in many procedures it may be substituted for one or the other of these dyes. It may be employed like azure A as a nuclear stain for sections of fixed tissue, and may be substituted for thionin in staining frozen sections of fresh tissue. It is a valuable general nuclear stain, being ordinarily employed in 0.3–1 percent aqueous solutions. It is widely employed in stains for Nissl granules or chromophylic bodies and has been proposed in a great variety of special procedures. Well known among the latter is Pappenheim's panchrome stain (of which it is an important ingredient) and the Albert stain which is widely replacing methylene blue in the diagnosis of diphtheria. It has use as a chemical reagent in the standardization of heparin and as a histochemical reagent in determining deoxyribonucleic acid.

Procedures Recommended by the Commission in Which This Stain Is Used

Name of Procedure	Page Reference to *Staining Procedures*
Staining frozen sections	47 (note)
Bulk staining of Nissl granules	96
Alizarin red S method of staining bone	148
Stain for metachromatic substances	170
Albert's stain for diphtheria organism	233
Kinyoun's stain for diphtheria organism	234

NEW METHYLENE BLUE N

C. I. NO. 52030 (1 *ed.*: 927)

(C. I. Basic Blue 24)

Synonym: *Methylene blue NN*

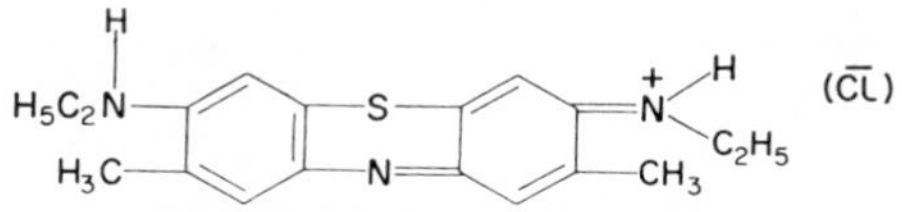

$C_{18}H_{22}N_3SCl$; mol. wt. 347.903

(A basic dye; absorption maxima about [636.4], 588)
Solubility at 26°C: in water 13.32%; in alcohol 1.65%

This dye has seldom been called for in microscopic work. An interesting fact concerning it relates to the Van Wijhe technic as applied by Louise Smith (1920) for staining the cartilage of frogs. The latter specified methylene blue, but the results could not be duplicated with any domestic or foreign methylene blue subsequently obtained. When furnished through the Commission with samples of various stains to try, she found that her earlier results could be duplicated with new methylene blue—a fact which not only implied mislabeling of her original supply of methylene blue, but suggested that new methylene blue may have some value in histological work. In fact, the dye is now highly recommended by Brecher (1949) for staining reticulocytes in human blood smears.

For use as a **reticulocyte stain,** see *Staining Procedures*, p. 140.

4. THE OXAZINS

This group is like the thiazins in chemical formula except that the sulfur atom is replaced by an oxygen atom. Only a few of the dyes find use in microscopic technic, and they are not stains having very general application.

BRILLIANT CRESYL BLUE

c. i. no. 51010 (1 *ed.*: 877)

Synonyms: *Cresyl blue 2 RN or BBS. Brilliant blue C*

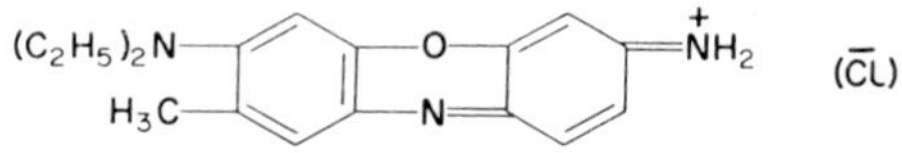

$C_{17}H_{20}N_3OCl$; mol. wt. 317.811

(A basic dye; absorption maxima about 624–628)

This dye is expensive to manufacture, and as it is not at present employed in any line of commercial dyeing, it must be prepared specially for the biologist.

The spectral curve of a typical sample of brilliant cresyl blue is given in Fig. 13, p. 107, where it is compared with curves for resazurin and Nile blue sulfate.

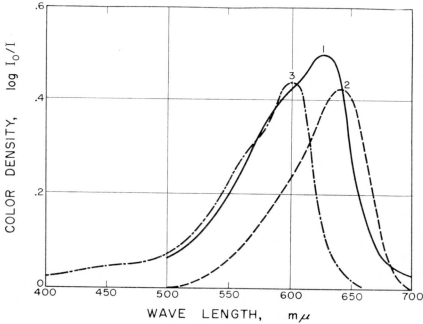

Fig. 13. Spectral curves of three oxazin dyes:
1. Brilliant cresyl blue   2. Nile blue sulfate   3. Resazurin

The dye has been employed to some extent in vital staining, Irwin (1927), for instance, having found it the most favorable dye available for investigating penetration into living cells; in vital staining it has special value because of its properties as an indicator of oxidation-reduction. It has been employed for numerous other purposes: staining protozoa, nematodes; in animal cytology; and as an amebicide. Its best known use, however, is as a blood stain to bring out reticulated cells and platelets. A well-tried procedure is that of Cunningham (1920), as modified by Isaacs (in McClung, 1937, p. 319); a somewhat different technic is that of Robertson (1917) for counting reticulated cells, and that of Buckman and Hallisey (1921) for platelets.

Some interest has been aroused by observations that certain derivatives of brilliant cresyl blue stain tumor cells selectively and retard the growth of tumors. (See Lewis, Sloviter and Goland, 1946.) The relation between ability to stain and to retard growth is a very interesting fact which may prove of practical significance.

For **methods of staining reticulated corpuscles and platelets** see *Staining Procedures*, p. 139–40.

GALLOCYANIN   C. I. NO. 51030 (1 *ed.:* 883)

(C. I. Mordant Blue 10)

Synonyms: *Alizarin blue RBN; Chrom blue GCB; Fast violet*

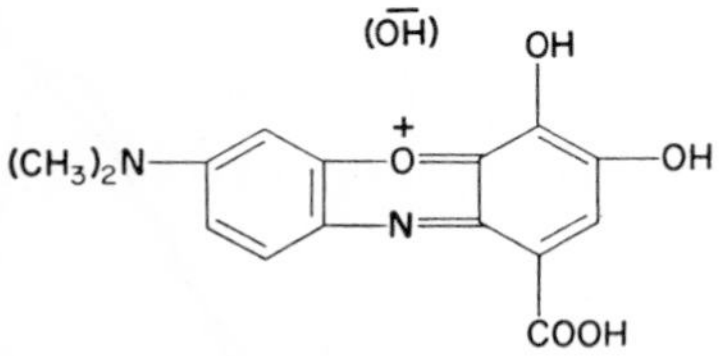

$C_{15}H_{14}N_2O_6$; mol. wt. 318.278

(*Absorption maximum about 636*)

Proescher and Arkush (1928) found the iron lake of this dye, prepared by boiling 2–3 minutes in a 5 percent aqueous solution of ferric ammonium sulfate, to be a splendid nuclear stain to be employed as a substitute for hematoxylin. Buzaglo (1934) used it, in combination with orcein and an acid alizarin blue, as a tissue stain. It has also found employment (Foley, 1943) as a counterstain in one of the protargol staining methods for nervous tissue. In common with hematoxylin and other dyes containing the catechol grouping, this dye stains keratohyaline granules; see Lillie (1956).

GALLAMIN BLUE

C. I. NO. 51045 (1 *ed.:* 894)

(C. I. Mordant Blue 45)

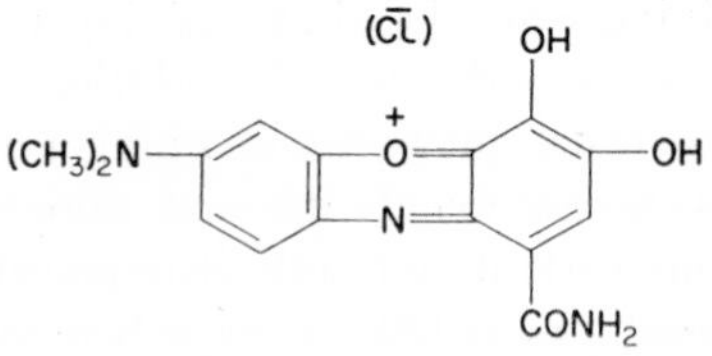

$C_{15}H_{14}N_3O_4Cl$; mol. wt. 335.743

(*Absorption maximum about 651*)

Employed in the form of its iron lake by Proescher and Arkush (1928) as a nuclear stain; the lake is prepared as described for gallocyanin above. It has been recommended by Stock (1949) for detecting calcium in tissues.

The following very similar dye has also been mentioned in biological literature, chiefly for its value as an oxidation-reduction indicator:

Prune pure; C. I. No. 51040, C. I. Mordant violet 54. *Synonyms:* Violet

PDH; Gallo blue E. Very similar to gallamin blue, but a methyl ester instead of an amide.

CELESTIN BLUE B

C. I. NO. 51050 (1 ed.: 900)

(C. I. Mordant Blue 14)

Synonym: *Coreine 2R*

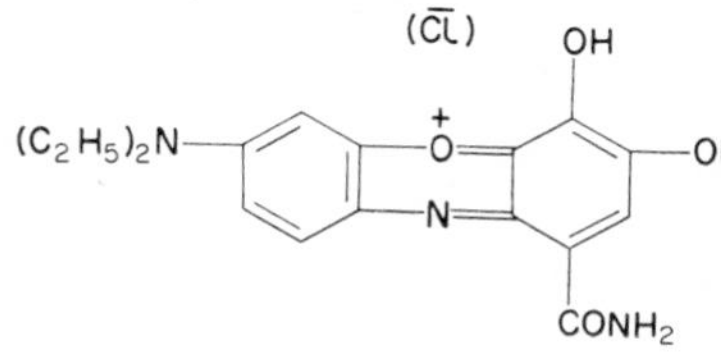

$(\overline{Cl})$ OH

$(C_2H_5)_2N$— ... —$\overset{+}{O}$— ... —OH

N

$CONH_2$

$C_{17}H_{18}N_3O_4Cl$; mol. wt. 363.795

(Absorption maxima about 654.5 [600])

Preferred by Proescher and Arkush (1928) to either gallocyanin or gallamin blue as a nuclear stain. As in the case of these two other dyes, the iron lake, prepared by boiling 2 to 3 minutes in a 5 percent aqueous solution of ferric ammonium sulfate, is employed for the staining solution. Lendrum and McFarlane (1940) recommend this dye in a modification of the Mallory connective tissue stain.

RESORCIN BLUE

C. I. NO. 51400 (1 ed.: 908)

Synonyms: *Iris blue; Fluorescent blue*

There is some confusion as to the actual chemical structure of this dye. It is recorded differently in different sources; and there is little question but that it varies according to the manufacturer from which is it obtained. At least one product of American manufacture is believed to have the following structure:

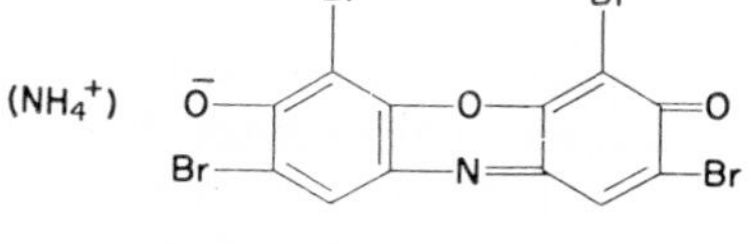

Br Br

(NH_4^+) $\overset{-}{O}$— ... —O— ... =O

Br— ... —N= ... —Br

$C_{12}H_6N_2O_3Br_4$ mol. wt. 545.848

This dye has indicator properties and was used by Tsvett (1911) as a histochemical reagent for the detection of callose.

The unbrominated homolog is known as lacmoid and has frequently been confused with resorcin blue. Nebel (1931) for instance, specified *lacomid* with Martius yellow as a stain for pollen tubes.

For use in **stain combination for phloem,** see *Staining Procedures*, p. 190.

NILE BLUE SULFATE

C. I. NO. 51180 (1 *ed.*: 913)

(C. I. Basic Blue 12)

Synonym: *Nile blue A*

There are two products sold at present under this name, one is a dimethyl aminophenol derivative, the other derived from diethyl aminophenol. The formula of the latter is:

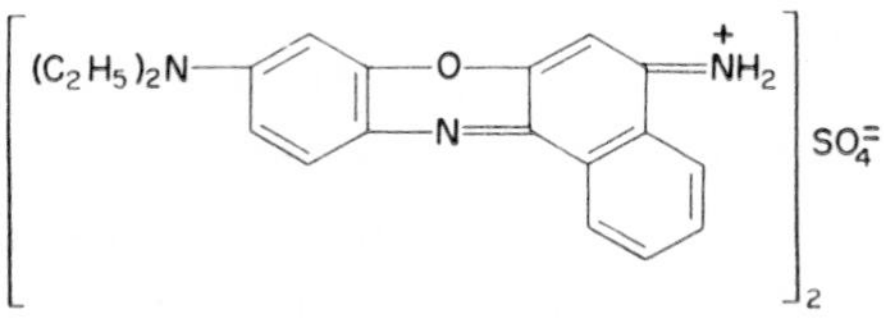

$$(C_{20}H_{20}N_3O)_2SO_4 ; \text{ mol. wt. } 732.834$$

(*A basic dye; absorption maxima 635–645*)

A spectral graph of brilliant cresyl blue, compared with resazurin and Nile blue sulfate, is given in Fig. 13, p. 107.

The use for which this dye is best known to the biologist is the Lorrain Smith fat stain (Smith and Mair, 1911). In this procedure the dye is boiled with dilute sulfuric acid, and thus hydrolyzed, with the introduction of oxygen in the place of the radical $NH_2(SO_4)_{\frac{1}{2}}$, in other words producing a new dye of the class known as oxazones. This oxazone dye is red, and is fat-soluble; the color acid is also red. Nile blue sulfate itself, on the other hand, is not fat-soluble but combines readily with fatty acids. As a result it is possible by this technic to stain fatty acids blue, but neutral fats and methylated fatty acids red. Knaysi (1941), however, calls attention to the fact that other dyes (e.g., neutral red or methylene blue) can be similarly employed.

Nile blue sulfate is used unaltered for staining living tadpoles previous to making transplants, in order to distinguish the grafts, also as a supravital stain for embryos (Detwiler, 1917) and as a vital stain for hydrae (Weimer, 1927), protozoa (Carter, 1933), yeasts (Gutstein, 1932) and amphibian eggs (Wintrebert, 1932). Ökland (1939) recommends it for staining bone sections, Tarao (1940) for histochemical studies of the Golgi apparatus. Foshay (1931) employs it for staining bacteria in tissues. The dye has been employed in culture media, containing emulsified fat, for the purpose of recognizing lipolytic bacteria; see Hammer and Collins (1934). Loosanoff (1937) finds it useful in marking starfish for identification.

For technic of **Smith and Mair's stain for fats,** see *Staining Procedures*, p. 154–155.

CRESYL VIOLET ACETATE

(Cresyl Violet; Cresyl Fast Violet)

The exact chemical nature of the imported cresyl violet is not yet known. Some samples appear to be mixtures of two dyes or possibly two different forms of the same dye. Samples from different sources frequently differ from one another but they are all closely related dyes. Spectral curves of three foreign samples are given in Fig. 14. They probably represent the type of dye with which biologists were familiar in the days before the world wars. Possibly to distinguish them from the following, the name "cresyl fast violet" should be retained for this foreign product.

Since 1954 the Matheson Company has produced a dye which closely resembles some of the imported samples in its absorption characteristics and by paper chromatographic analysis. Powers and Clark (1955) find that its staining characteristics compare favorably with the formerly available German samples. From the chemical synthesis of this material it is believed to have the formula:

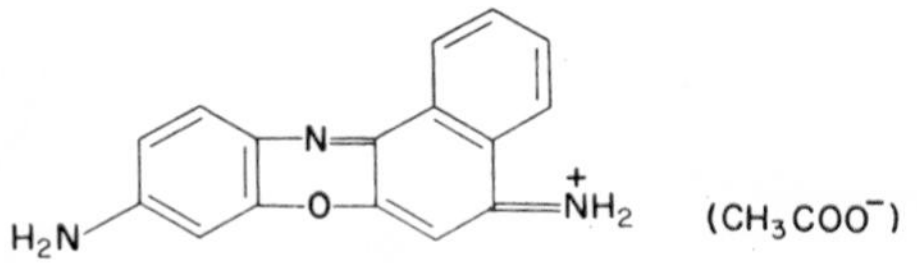

$C_{18}H_{15}N_3O_3$; mol. wt. 321.324

(A basic dye; absorption maximum 596–598)

A spectral curve for this material is included in Fig. 15, graph 2, and illustrates its similarity to the foreign product. It will be noted that acetate is the anion shown in the above formula. In producing this dye it was found that with chloride as the anion the dye not only is too insoluble for use as a stain, but also has a spectral curve quite different from the one shown in Fig. 15. For this reason the dye has been designated as cresyl violet acetate, a name which also serves to distinguish it from other products of as yet uncertain chemical structure which are marketed under the names cresyl violet and cresyl echt violet.

Like brilliant cresyl blue, this dye is not employed on a commercial scale. Its chief value in histology is on account of its metachromatic properties.

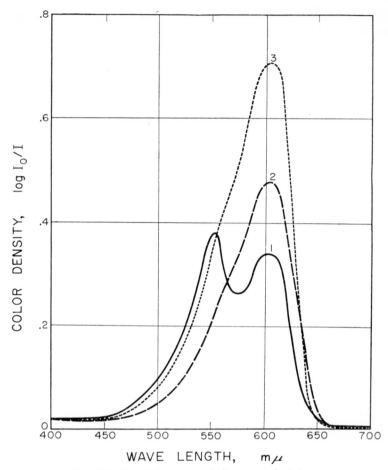

FIG. 14. Spectral curves of three cresyl violets.
1. Cresyl echt violet   2. Cresyl fast violet V   3. Cresyl echt violet R

It has been employed in making permanent preparations of nervous tissue, and is excellent for staining fresh areolar connective tissue, as it brings out various histological elements. According to Ehrlich (1910, II, p. 78) it stains nuclei violet, plasma blue, amyloid, mucin and mast cell granules red. Spiridonovitch (1924) employs it in the vital staining of white blood cells. Williams (1923) uses it for staining sections of fresh tumor tissue in biopsy work. It is also employed for making permanent preparations of fixed tumor tissue. Landau (1934) proposes it for bulk staining of nervous tissue.

For use in **staining Nissl substances,** see *Staining Procedures*, p. 93.

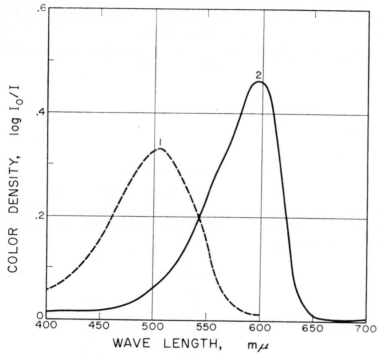

FIG. 15. Spectral curves of Darrow red and cresyl violet acetate:
1. Darrow red   2. Cresyl violet acetate

DARROW RED

$C_{18}H_{14}N_3O_2Cl$; mol. wt. 339.773

(A basic dye; absorption maximum about 500)

This dye is closely related to cresyl violet acetate, and in fact is an acetyl-ated intermediate in the production of the latter. It was first isolated by paper chromatography as a red impurity in cresyl violet acetate, and has subsequently been manufactured in its own right. Its absorption spectrum is shown in Fig. 15, graph 1. With its red color and with staining affinities similar to those of cresyl violet acetate, it has been employed by Powers *et al.* (1960) to stain the Nissl substance of nerve cells in the differential staining of cells and fibers in the nervous system.

NEW BLUE R   C. I. NO. 51175 (1 *ed.:* 909)

(C. I. Basic Blue 6)

Synonyms: *Naphthol blue R; Fast blue 3R; Phenylene blue; Meldola's blue; Indin blue 2RD*

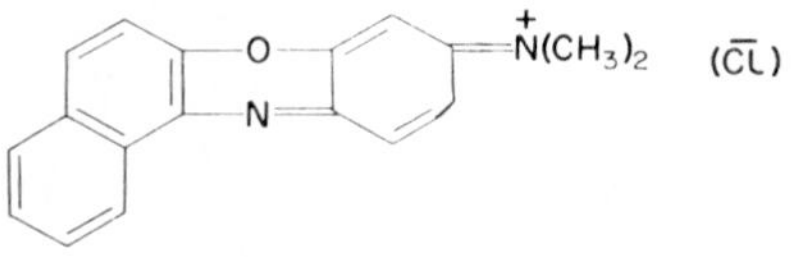

$C_{18}H_{15}N_2OCl$; mol. wt. 310.773

(*A basic dye; absorption maxima about* [622], *573,* [533])

Occasional reference has been made to this dye in the biological literature, under the name of naphthol blue R, most recently by Lewis (1938) in in staining fat drops in bacteria.

RESAZURIN

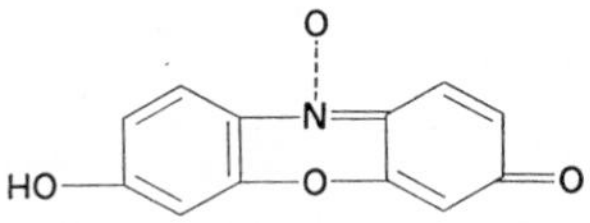

$C_{12}H_7NO_4$; mol. wt. 229.184

This is not a dye, but a colored compound that has interesting properties as an oxidation-reduction indicator. It is blue in its completely oxidized state, and upon reduction becomes pink and then colorless according to the following reaction:

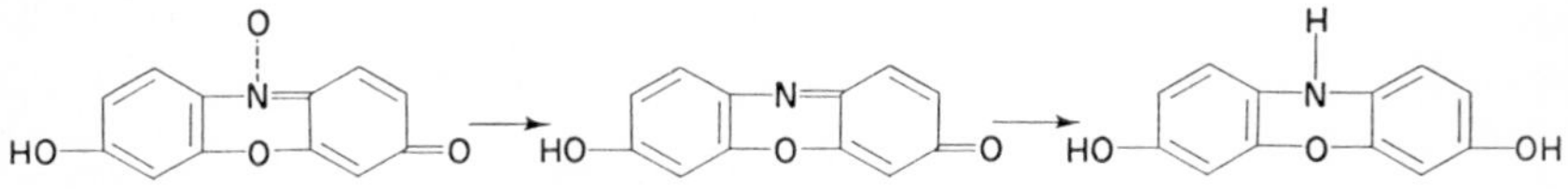

Resazurin	*Resorufin*	*Hydroresorufin*
(blue)	(pink)	(colorless)

Various shades between blue and light pink can occur.

A spectral curve of resazurin is included in Fig 13, p. 107 (graph 3).

It was first suggested by Ramsdell *et al.* (1935) that it might be more valuable than methylene blue as an indicator of reduction in milk, partly because of its greater speed in showing reduction and partly because of the value of the intermediate pink stage which does not occur with methylene blue. Its use was taken up quite promptly in Great Britain, but more slowly in the United States. It is now recognized as an alternate procedure by the Standard Methods of the American Public Health Association, and standardized tablets specially prepared for such use are on the market. For papers on the subject see Johns and Howson (1940) and Baker *et al.* (1942). Resazurin is also used as an indicator in thioglycholate media for sterility tests.

Another oxazin dye sometimes mentioned in connection with histology is: Capri Blue. C. I. No. 51015 (1 *ed.*: 876).

<h3>5. THE AZINS</h3>

The dyes of the azin group are derivatives of phenazin, $C_6H_4 \cdot N_2 \cdot C_6H_4$, a compound containing two benzene rings linked through two nitrogen atoms in such a way as to form a third ring. Two formulae are possible:

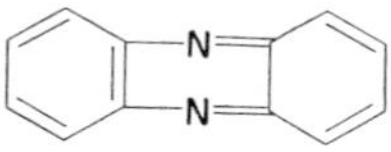

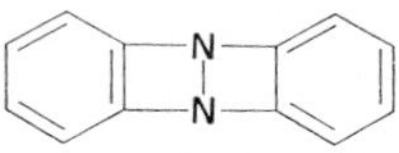

In the case of the first formula the quinoid ring is the chromophore; in the case of the second formula the azin group itself, $\begin{array}{c} -N- \\ | \\ -N- \end{array}$, (see page 21) is assumed to be the chromophore. The quinoid formula is generally preferred today.

Phenazin is weakly basic, but is not a dye as it does not contain auxochrome groups. In other words, it is a chromogen. Either an —OH group or one or more —NH_2 groups may be introduced to give it dye properties. The acids and bases are very weak if there is only one auxochrome group present, and their salts are readily decomposed. For this reason some of them are of use as indicators. Strong bases are encountered only among the safranins where basic character is derived not only from the two —NH_2 groups but also from one of the azin nitrogen atoms which becomes pentavalent and takes part in salt formation.

<h3>A. AMINO-AZINS OR EURHODINS</h3>

If one or more amino groups are introduced into a phenazin, a dye is formed of the class known as eurhodins. They are very weak bases, and therefore weak dyes; but as their salts are readily decomposed with a resulting color change, they form useful indicators. The best known of the group is toluylene red, base:

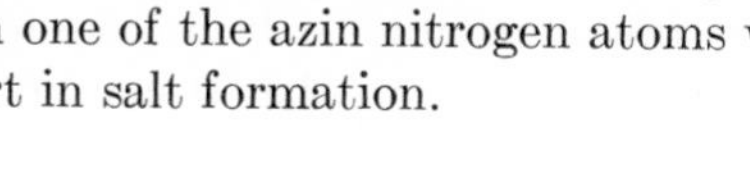

The chloride of toluylene red is the well known neutral red.

NEUTRAL RED   C. I. NO. 50040 (1 *ed.:* 825)

(C. I. Basic Red 5)

Synonym: *Toluylene red*

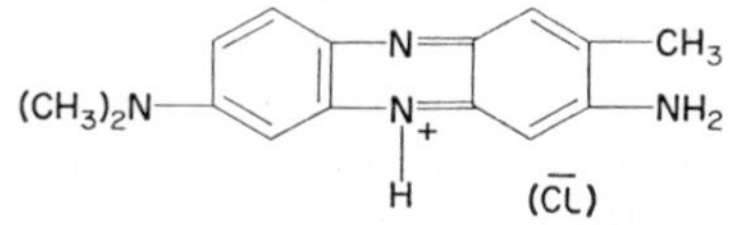

$C_{15}H_{17}N_4Cl$; mol. wt. 288.775

(A weakly basic dye; absorption maximum 540–542)
Solubility at 26°C: in water 5.64%; in alcohol 2.45%

This dye is yellow in solutions more basic than the neutral point (i.e., pH = 7.0) in reaction, and red in weak acids, even the reaction of ordinary tap water being sufficient to bring out the acid color; at a higher range of acid it turns blue. This gives it some value as an indicator. As an indicator it is also used in bacteriological media, for distinguishing the colon from the typhoid organisms, and for differentiating virulent from non-virulent strains of the tubercle organism.

A spectral curve of this dye is included in Fig. 16, p. 117, together with one of azocarmine G.

Neutral red is employed in a variety of staining methods. It is a weak nuclear stain, and has value for that purpose in certain procedures. Twort's (1924) stain for parasites in tissues is a neutral stain (see Chapter XIII) formed by combining neutral red with light green and dissolving the precipitate in alcohol. Neutral red finds use in the study of the Golgi apparatus in cells; but there is a dispute as to whether it is actually a specific strain for this structure or merely for the inclusions of the Golgi apparatus. Old ripened solutions are employed for bringing out the Nissl granules in nerve cells. It also has some use in general histological staining, particularly for embryological tissue in combination with Janus green, as recommended by Faris (1924). Knaysi (1941) points out that it can be employed in place of Nile blue A in demonstrating hydrolysis of fats.

It has special value where a weakly basic, non-toxic dye is called for, as in vital staining. It is used for staining living protozoa, and as a vital stain for nuclei in tissue; also for the "vital" staining of blood, that is of fresh blood, observed under a microscope in a moist chamber, and for staining fresh gonorrheal pus under similar conditions. It proves useful as an indicator of reaction of the contents of living plant cells. The chief draw-back to neutral red in vital staining is the toxicity of certain lots that have been on the market. This toxicity seems to be due to impurities present in the dye. Phillips and Cohen (1927) have, in fact, shown that these impurities can be eliminated more readily by preparing the dye as an iodide instead of a

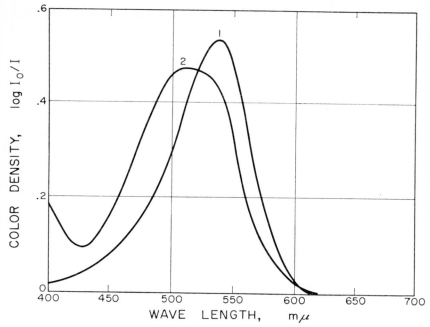

FIG. 16. Spectral curves of two azin dyes:
1. Neutral red   2. Azocarmine G

chloride. Their process, however, has not been adopted by manufacturers as yet, because of technical difficulties. Nevertheless the recent samples of neutral red chloride submitted for certification have been so well purified that they seem to be free from toxicity.

For technic of **supravital staining of blood, with Janus green,** see *Staining Procedures,* p. 141.

NEUTRAL VIOLET

C. I. NO. 50030 (1 *ed.:* 826)

$3_{22}H_{25}N_6Cl$; mol. wt. 408.925

(A weakly basic dye; absorption maximum 533)
Solubility at 26°C: in water 3.27%; in alcohol 2.22%

This dye is very similar in its properties to neutral red, except that, due to its greater molecular weight, it is more bluish, giving a violet instead of a red color. It can be used as an indicator, but has been seldom used in histology. Unna (1921) however, has used it in a dye mixture employed in the study of chromolysis.

B. SAFRANINS

Quite a long series of azin dyes are known in which one of the nitrogen atoms of the azin group is pentavalent and another benzene ring is attached to it. This pentavalent nitrogen allows the compounds to behave like ammonium bases; so with the amino groups which are always present, the basic properties of these dyes are very strong. The theoretical base of the simplest safranin would have the formula:

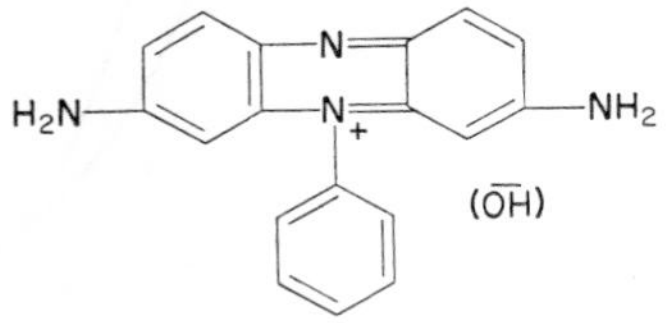

This form of ammonium base does not actually exist, as the safranin bases really occur in the form of anhydrides; but salts of these ammonium bases are the commonly known dyes. The commercial dyes are ordinarily chlorides.

There are two groups of safranins: the *benzo*safranins in which the azin group unites two benzene rings; and the *naphtho*safranins in which it unites two naphthalene groups. The simplest safranin is phenosafranin, which is the chloride of the theoretical base just given, namely:

PHENO-SAFRANIN

C. I. NO. 50200 (1 *ed.*: 840)

Synonym: *Safranin B extra*

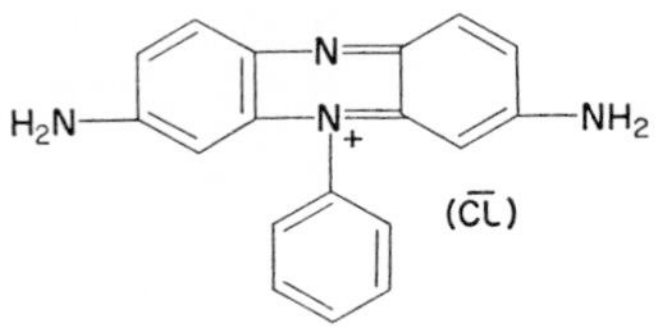

$C_{18}H_{15}N_4Cl$; mol. wt. 322.789

Moore (1933) called for phenosafranin in staining colonies of bacteria and fungi. The commercial safranins are ordinarily methyl or ethyl substitution products of this; or occasionally phenyl substitution products. The one of greatest value to the biologist is generally called safranin O.

SAFRANIN O   C. I. NO. 50240 (1 *ed.*: 841)

(C. I. Basic Red 2)

Synonyms: *Safranin Y or A; Gossypimine; Cotton red*

Slightly different shades: *Safranin AG, T, MP, and G.* (*Although all included in C. I. No. 841 they are different from the grade here described.*)

The common safranins of commerce, under various shade designations, are mixtures of dimethyl and trimethyl phenosafranin:

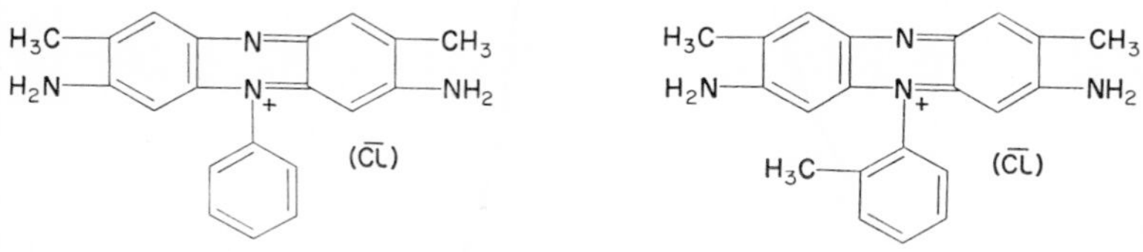

$C_{20}H_{19}N_4Cl$; mol. wt. 350.841 $C_{21}H_{21}N_4Cl$; mol. wt. 364.867

(A basic dye; absorption maximum about 530)
Solubility at 36°C; in water 5.45%; in alcohol 3.41%

The shade differs according to the proportion of these compounds present, the red being deeper according to the proportion of the trimethyl compound in the mixture. The type safranin O, which proves best for ordinary biological purposes, can be defined as having its absorption maximum at 530 mμ.

A spectral curve of safranin O is given in Fig. 17, p. 120.

Safranin has always been a problem, because of its variability, especially in cytological work where it is often employed together with another basic dye, and a delicate balance between the two stains is necessary. The reason for this variation has been a puzzle ever since the Commission has begun its investigations of this dye. The question is not yet answered. It is realized at present, however, that there are samples that stain too blue, and others that stain too yellow, although this difference does not correlate with dye content nor with any chemical properties of the dye yet investigated. Strangest to say, there is no difference between any of these types of safranin that can be recognized by the spectrophotometer. Under such circumstances, no truly scientific method of standardizing the stain has been devised. An empirical method is in effect, however, which results in the

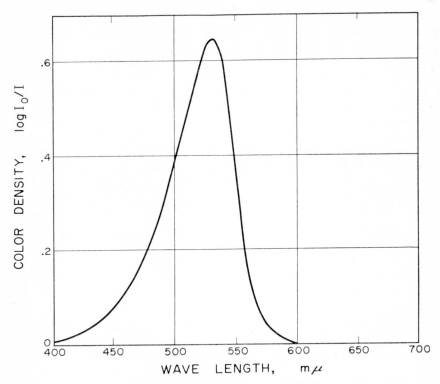

Fɪɢ. 17. Spectral curve of safranin O

present product being distinctly better than that of former years. When a stain company submits a sample showing too blue or too yellow staining, the fault is called to the manufacturer's attention, and they try to submit another sample without that fault or with the opposite fault. This often means the submission of two batches, one too blue in its staining properties, the other too yellow; then it is a fairly simple matter to determine the proper mixture of the two to give best results. This has to be determined by actual staining tests, not by means of any colorimeter or spectrophotometer.

These observations undoubtedly explain the directions given by Chamberlain* to mix equal parts of alcohol soluble safranin and water soluble safranin for use in the Flemming triple stain. There is no such thing as a safranin insoluble in either alcohol or water; and the products formerly sold by Grübler as "wasserlöslich" and "spirtlöslich" respectively have been

* In early editions of his *Methods in Plant Histology.*

found to be identical so far as chemical and optical analysis show. Probably, however, the particular batches formerly employed by Chamberlain were neither of them the correct shade in staining properties, while a mixture of the two gave good results. In other words he did about the same thing that the Commission now often recommends stain companies to do.

Grübler also sold other grades of safranin, none of which seems to have any special significance for biological purposes. One of these denoted "Safranin pur" was found on testing to be a more violet dye, apparently methylene violet (C. I. No. 50205 Basic violet 5).

Safranin O is one of the most important nuclear stains known to the histologist. Used with Fast green FCF as a counterstain, it is excellent in photomicrography. The botanist finds it especially valuable, as it brings out lignified and cutinized tissues in vascular plants, and can be employed in combination with a variety of contrast stains; it is valuable as a protein stain in plants, and can be used to stain spore coats. The cytologist makes use of it in the Benda technic to stain chromatin in combination with light green as a contrast stain; and even more widely in the Flemming triple stain, in which it is employed as a chromatin stain, together with gentian violet and orange G. The bacteriologist has some use for it, especially as a counterstain in the Gram technic.

Safranin is readily diazotized with sodium nitrite and hydrochloric acid, and has been used by Lillie *et al.* (1953) for demonstrating enterochromaffin cells. (Only the first NH_2 group is diazotized by this treatment.)

Procedures Recommended by the Commission in Which This Stain Is Used

Name of Procedure	Page Reference to Staining Procedures
Counterstain to Weigert's iron hematoxylin	34
Counterstain to AgNO₃ for calcium deposits	141
In Prussian blue method for hemosiderin	168
In azo-coupling reactions	176
With Delafield's hematoxylin	185
Counterstain to iron alum hematoxylin in plant histology	185
With light green SF yellowish in plant histology	194
With picro-aniline-blue in plant histology	194
In Flemming's triple stain	213–4
With fast green FCF in plant cytology	219
With aniline blue WS in plant histology	187
Counterstain to Foster's tannic acid and FeCl₃	187
With tannic acid and orange G for shoot apex	188
Counterstain in Gram technic, for smears	226
Schaeffer and Fulton spore stain for bacteria	231
Counterstain in Gram technic, for sections	255

AMETHYST VIOLET

C. I. NO. 50225 (1 ed.: 847)

Synonyms: *Heliotrope B; Iris violet*

This dye is tetra-ethyl pheno-safranin:

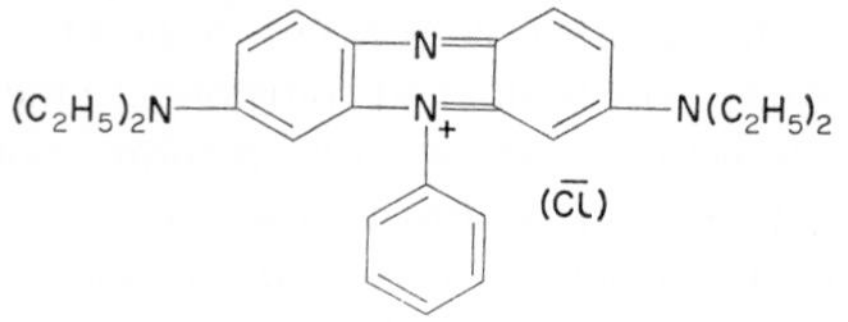

$(C_2H_5)_2N$ ———— N=, N_+= ———— $N(C_2H_5)_2$

$(\overline{CL})$

$C_{26}H_{31}N_4Cl$; mol. wt. 434.997

(A basic dye; absorption maxima about 589, [545.5])
Solubility at 26°C: in water 3.12%; in alcohol 3.66%

Amethyst violet was used by Ehrlich and Lazarus (1898) as a basic dye in certain triple staining technics.

A further dye of this group which the biologist must take into account, although probably of no significance as a stain, is methylene violet RRA or 3RA, C. I. No. 50205, C. I. Basic violet 5 (synonym: fuchsia or safranin extra bluish). This dye is a di-methyl safranin in which the methyl groups are introduced into one of the amino groups instead of directly into the benzene ring. It has no connection with the methylene violet of Bernthsen, which is one of the constituents of polychrome methylene blue; see p. 103. A sample has been found labeled "Safranin, pur," Grübler.

AZOCARMINE G

C. I. NO. 50085 (1 ed.: 828)

(C. I. Acid Red 101)

Synonyms: *Azocarmine GX; Rosazine; Rosinduline GXF*

Azocarmine G is a sodium salt of a disulfonic acid of phenylrosinduline, the formula of which is:

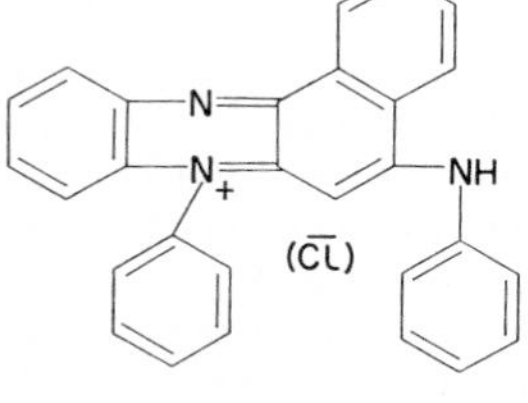

$C_{28}H_{20}N_3Cl$; mol. wt. 433.921

(An acid dye; absorption maxima about 512)

A spectral curve for this dye, together with one for neutral red, is given in Fig. 16, p. 117.

This dye is occasionally employed in tissue staining, notably after M. Heidenhain (1916) who used it as a tissue stain either alone or preceding some nuclear stain. Heidenhain gave special attention to its use in the Mallory aniline blue connective tissue stain; in which procedure he employed it in place of acid fuchsin in the Mallory technic. This azocarmine modification of the Mallory stain is very commonly followed according to the schedule given by McGregor (1929) which calls for staining in azocarmine, differentiation in aniline alcohol, then treatment in 5 percent phosphotungstic acid before application of the Mallory aniline-blue-orange-G mixture. Heidenhain used the abbreviated term "azan technic"; unfortunately McGregor calls the dye itself "azan carmine." Another modification is that of Volkmann and Strauss (1934) who used azocarmine after a resorcin gentian violet.

There is a closely related dye, azocarmine B (C. I. No. 50090, 1 ed.: 829) which is a trisulfonate instead of a disulfonate. Heidenhain employed either, finding a stronger solution necessary in the case of azocarmine B, which required more application of heat (56°C) in order to bring it into solution.

One also frequently sees the name of the dyes written as two words "azo carmine." The latter is not a serious mistake, but it is preferred here to write it as one word, so as not to imply that it is one of the azo dyes.

For technic of **Mallory-Heidenhain "azan" connective tissue stain,** see *Staining Procedures*, p. 53.

For technic of **Mollier's quadruple stain,** see Id. p. 57.

MAGDALA RED

C. I. NO. 50375 (1 ed.: 857)

(C. I. Basic Red 6)

Synonyms: *Naphthalene red; Naphthalene pink;
Naphthylamine pink; Sudan red*

This is a naphtho-safranin, and is a mixture of the monamino and diamino compounds:

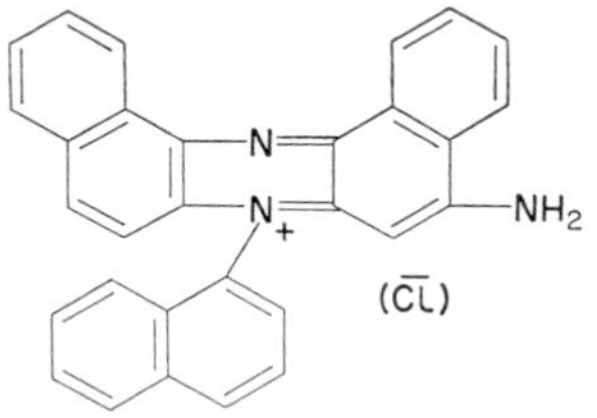

and

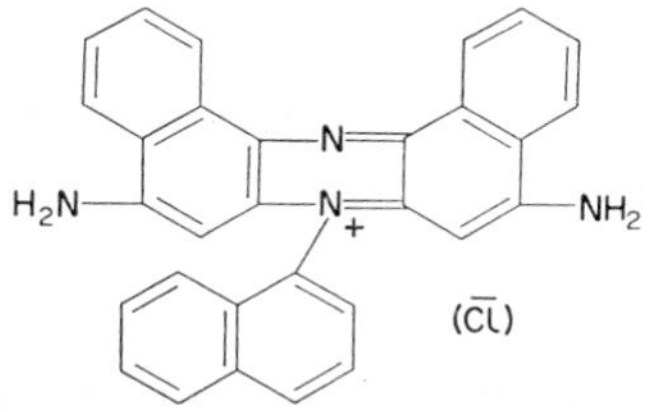

$C_{30}H_{20}N_3Cl$; mol. wt. 457.941 $C_{30}H_{21}N_4Cl$; mol. wt. 472.957

(A basic dye; absorption maximum about 524)

A true magdala red put on the market before 1914 by Grübler and Co., under the name of magdala rot *echt*, is quite expensive. This same company also sold a product "magdala rot der Handels," and a similar type has been sold by Coleman and Bell in this country. This so-called commercial magdala red is an entirely different dye, erythrosin or phloxine (see p. 182)— an acid instead of a basic dye, and one of an entirely different group. Chamberlain (1927) stated that his work with magdala red was done with the latter type, hence actually with phloxine instead of the dye he thought he was using; his results cannot be duplicated with true magdala red. This means that in the well known procedure for staining algae, using this dye in combination with aniline blue, one should actually employ phloxine, not magdala red. (See also discussion under phloxine, p. 182.) The same statement probably applies in the case of Dixon's (1920) magdala red and light green stain for mycelium in plant tissue.

A magdala red has been employed by Flemming as a nuclear stain, and by Kultschitzky for staining elastic tissue. No information is available, however, as to whether they used phloxine or true magdala red.

c. The Indulins

Indulins are similar to safranins but are more complex: being quite highly phenylated amino derivatives. Only a few concern us.

INDULIN, SPIRIT SOLUBLE

c. i. no. 50400 (1 *ed.*: 860)

(C. I. Solvent Blue 7)

Synonyms: *Indulin (with various shade designations); Spirit indulin; Spirit nigrosin R*

This consists of mixtures of the following:

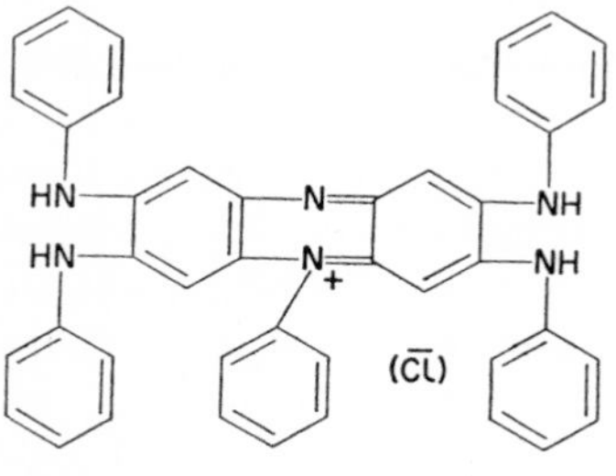

and

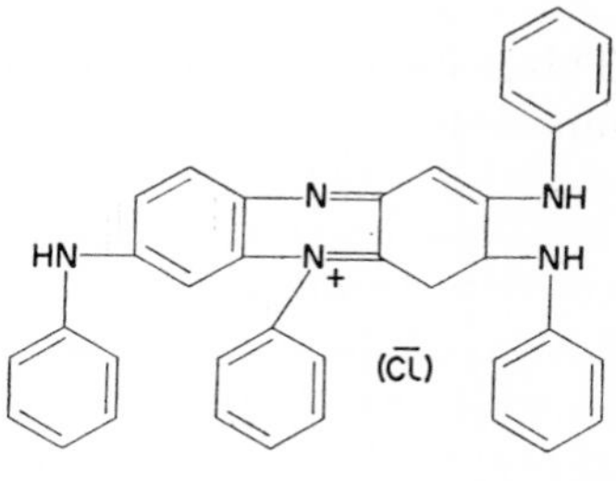

$C_{42}H_{33}N_6Cl$; mol. wt. 657.189 $C_{36}H_{28}N_5Cl$; mol. wt. 566.081

(*A basic dye; absorption maximum varies from 541.5 to 560.5*)

INDULIN, WATER SOLUBLE

C. I. NO. 50405 (1 *ed.:* 861)

(C. I. Acid Blue 20)

Synonyms: *Indulin (with various shade designations); Soluble indulin 3B; Fast blue B, OB, R, 2R, etc.*

(An acid dye)

This is the sodium salt of the sulfonation product of indulin, spirit soluble (C. I. Solvent blue 7, No. 50400 1 *ed.:* 860). Because there are various mixtures of the latter and different degrees of sulfonation are possible, this dye may vary greatly in its composition and shade.

One of the indulins (exact nature uncertain) has been used by Lynch (1930) in the counterstaining of bulk tissue; also by Cumley (1935) in the negative staining of bacteria. For the latter purpose, however, the following dye is more commonly employed.

NIGROSIN, WATER SOLUBLE

C. I. NO. 50420 (1 *ed.:* 865)

(C. I. Acid Black 2)

Synonyms: *Nigrosin W, WL, etc.; Gray R, B, BB; Silver gray; Steel gray; Indulin black*

Nigrosin is not a pure dye, but is a mixture; and apparently the composition of different lots may vary. Ordinarily it is a mixture of a blue-black or violet indulin with a yellow dye in such a proportion that the resulting blend appears black. As the proportion of these two dyes is not always the same, different samples of nigrosin may vary in the amount of blue apparent to the eye. It is assumed that the biologist wants a nigrosin which appears distinctly black; this is certainly true in those procedures where it is used for a background stain. Accordingly the samples of nigrosin submitted which have a bluish hue have been refused certification by the Stain Commission.

Nigrosin is used in place of India ink as a background stain in the study of unstained bacteria; also as a stain for the background in contrast to fuchsin in the Dorner (1926) stain for bacterial spores. It is recommended by Ehrlich for staining the tissue of the central nervous system either alone or in combination with other stains, and by Jarotsky for staining pancreatic tissue following hematoxylin. Botanists use it in studying algae and fungi. Pfitzer's (1883) picronigrosin serves as a chromatin stain. Nigrosin was also used by Unna (1921) in combination with "orange" (orange G?) in the study of the process of chromolysis. Bean (1927) employed it as a counterstain for nervous tissue.

For the use in **negative staining of bacteria,** see *Staining Procedures,* p. 225.
For technic of **Dorner spore stain for bacteria,** see Id. p. 230–231.

VII

THE PHENYL METHANE DYES

One of the most important groups of dyes, both from the standpoint of the dyer and from that of the biologist, is a group of substituted methanes, compounds with a central carbon atom. In methane, CH_4, it is possible to replace any of the hydrogen atoms with methyl, ethyl, or phenyl groups Replacement of two or three hydrogens by phenyl groups results in di- and triphenyl methanes.

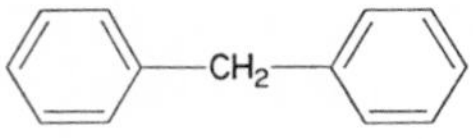

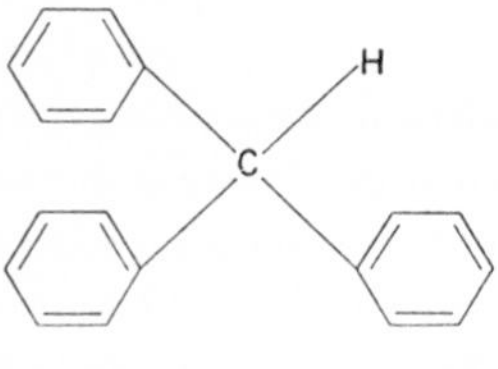

Certain substitution products of the di- and triphenyl methanes are among the most powerful dyes known.

Di- and triphenyl methane, themselves, are not dyes, nor are they chromogens. They lack both the chromophore and the auxochrome groups. The first step (theoretically) in converting them into dyes is to introduce an —OH group in the place of one of the unsubstituted H atoms of the methane nucleus. The compound thus formed, which bears the same relation to the phenyl methane as alcohol does to methane, is called a carbinol. A carbinol is methyl alcohol in which one or more of the hydrogen atoms may have been replaced with an alkyl radical or a benzene ring. Thus:

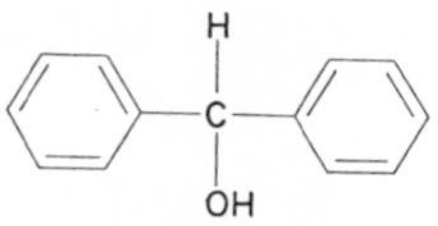

(*diphenyl carbinol*)

It is next theoretically possible to attach amino groups to the benzene rings. Thus in the case of diphenyl carbinol it is possible to obtain diamino diphenyl carbinol:

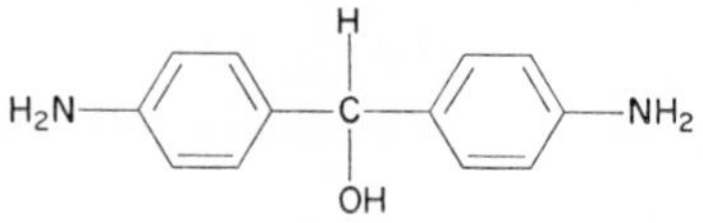

Now this latter compound contains the necessary auxochrome groups; but it is not yet a dye. No carbinol is a dye, because it lacks a chromophore group. The carbinols are important in dye chemistry, however, because upon dehydration a rearrangement of the bonds in the molecule takes place giving the quinoid benzene ring, which as we have seen is a powerful chromophore. Thus:

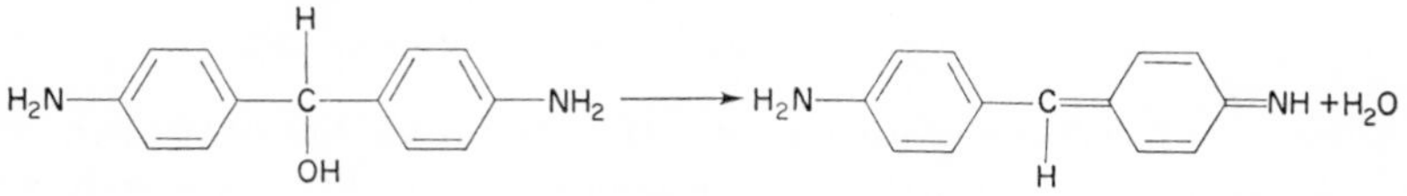

This latter compound is colored and is the anhydride of a true dye base. Upon hydration it should theoretically become:

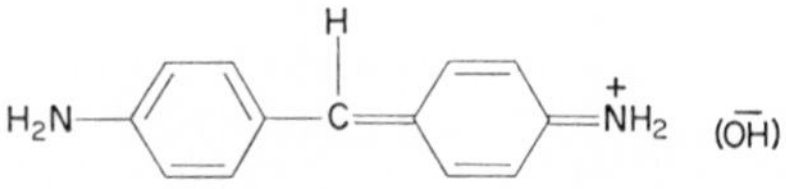

Such a compound could exist only in aqueous solution. It is known only by its salts, the true dyes, as:

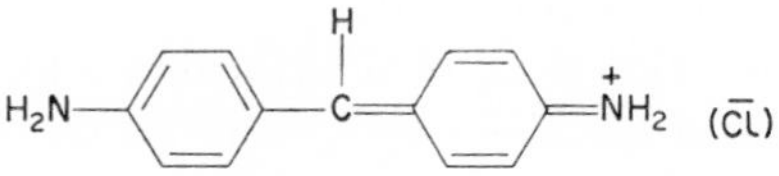

Although the theoretical compound given above is the true dye base, the carbinols are often known as carbinol bases or color bases of the phenyl methane dyes. As stated above, they lack the chromophore group, and hence are colorless.

1. DIPHENYL METHANE DERIVATIVES

The diphenyl methanes are seldom of biological significance. Only one deserves mention here.

AURAMINE O

c. i.* no. 41000 (1 *ed.*: 655)

(C. I. Basic Yellow 2)

Synonyms: *Canary yellow; Pyoktaninum aureum; Pyoktanin yellow*

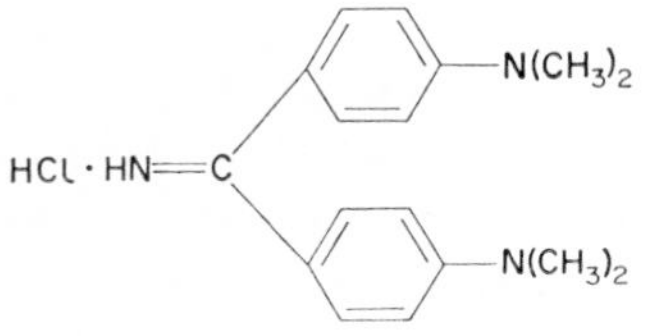

$C_{17}H_{22}N_3Cl$; mol. wt. 303.827

(*A basic dye; absorption maxima [380], 431–434*)
Solubility at 26°C: in water 0.74%; in alcohol 4.49%

Auramine O has been in use for some time as a drug, but until about 1940 was regarded as having little value in microscopic technic. A search of the literature in 1936 revealed only the following rather obscure staining procedures calling for this dye: by Vinassa (1891) for staining plant sections; by Fischel (1901) for vital staining of salamander larvae; and by Kisser (1931), with cresyl violet as a tissue stain. More recently, however, its properties as a fluorochrome have brought it into considerable prominence in fluorescence microscopy. Richards and Miller (1941) recommend it as the best, among numerous fluorochromes investigated by them, for staining the tubercle organism. Their method, because of the low magnification and large fields which it makes possible, allows such an increase in the number of positives in diagnosis that it has attracted much attention to this dye since their method appeared.

The spectrophotometric curve of a typical sample is given in Fig. 18. The most striking feature of this curve is the secondary maximum at 370.

* The abbreviation "C.I." stands for "Colour Index." The number immediately following is that of the current (2nd) edition; the one which follows is that of the first edition. The name of the dye given under the principal name is the preferred designation in the current Colour Index.

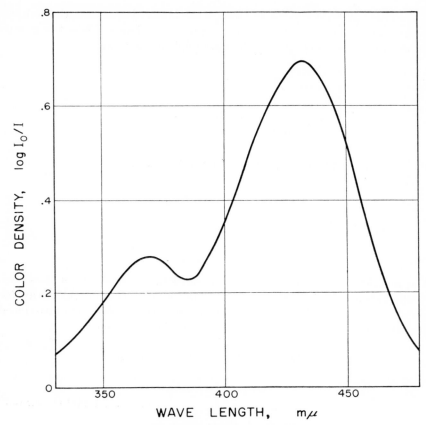

FIG. 18. Spectral curve of auramine O

For technic of **fluorescent staining of acid-fast bacteria**, see *Staining Procedures*,* p. 246.

2. TRIPHENYL METHANE DERIVATIVES

There are two groups of triphenyl methanes to concern us, the amino and the hydroxy derivatives. The former, which are much the more numerous, are very strongly basic, thanks to the amino groups, unless sulfonated like light green or acid fuchsin. The rosolic acid dyes, on the other hand, are hydroxy phenyl methanes, the amino groups being replaced by hydroxyl groups; they are therefore acid instead of basic dyes.

* Conn, Darrow, and Emmel (1960).

There are likewise two subdivisions of the amino derivatives, the diamino triphenyl methanes and the triamino triphenyl methanes. These two groups are derivatives respectively of: diamino triphenyl methane

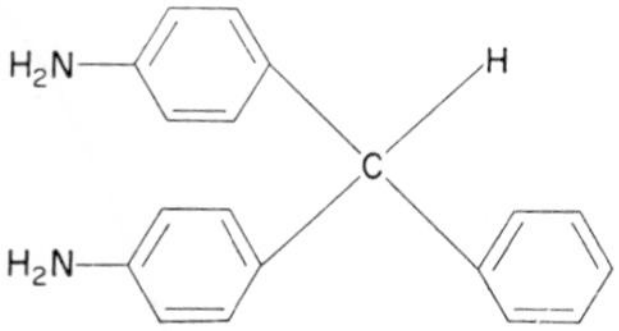

and triamino triphenyl methane, or paraleucanilin.

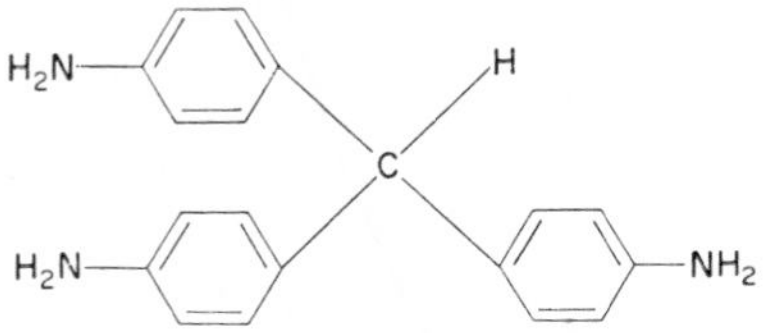

The individual dyes of this series are substitution products of these two compounds and differ from one another in the number of methyl, ethyl, or phenyl groups introduced, and according to whether they are introduced into the amino groups or directly onto the benzene rings.

A. DIAMINO TRIPHENYL METHANES

MALACHITE GREEN

C. I. NO. 42000 (1 *ed.:* 657)

(C. I. Basic Green 4)

Synonyms: *Victoria green B or WB; New Victoria green extra, O, I or II; Diamond green B, BX, or P extra; Solid green O; Light green N*

Various brands denoted: *Malachite green A, B, BX, 4B, J3E, J3ES, NB, NH, or NJ.*

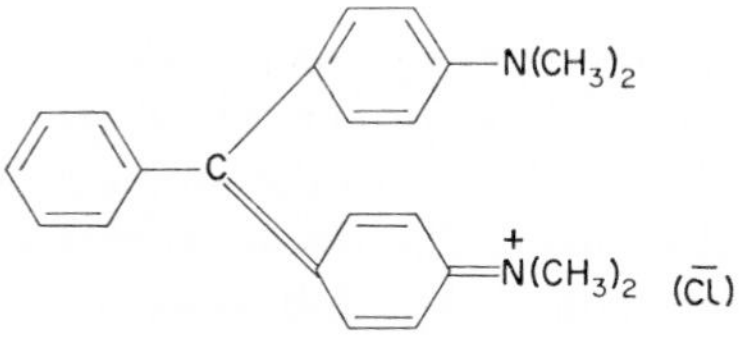

$C_{23}H_{25}N_2Cl$; mol. wt. 364.903

(*Absorption maxima: 617–619, [425]*)

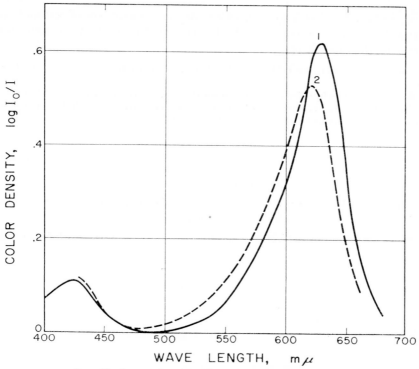

FIG. 19. Spectral curves of two phenyl methane dyes:
1. Brilliant green   2. Malachite green

See Fig. 19 for spectral curve.

Malachite green is a rather weakly basic dye that has been used in the past for various histological purposes; as by v. Beneden for staining Ascaris eggs, by Petroff for staining erythrocytes, and by Maas as a contrast stain following borax carmine; see Krause (1926–1927), p. 1353. Today it has very largely been replaced by methyl green; but it is still called for in special procedures, of which the following might be listed by way of illustration: with acid fuchsin and martius yellow in the Pianese (1896) technic which was originally applied to cancer tissue but is now much more widely used in plant pathology; in its reduced (leuco) form, by Chapman and Lieb (1937), as a reagent (although less sensitive than crystal violet) for bacterial polysaccharides; as a bacteriostatic or amebicidic agent (Verona, 1935; Tsuchiya, 1936); as a vital stain for nuclei of epidermis cells of the onion (Bank, 1938); by Schaeffer and Fulton (1933) as a bacterial spore stain; in place of methyl green in the Pappenheim stain, when combined with the Gram stain (Sandiford, 1938); also as a constituent of certain bacterial stains. It is employed in the Lowenstein-Jensen (1930) medium for culturing the tubercle organism.

For technic of **Pianese IIIB stain for fungi in plant tissue,** see *Staining Procedures,* p. 195.

For technic of **Schaeffer and Fulton method of spore staining,** see Id. p. 231.

For technic of **Laybourn modification of Albert stain for diphtheria** (which calls for this dye, mixed with toluidine blue), see Id. p. 233.

BRILLIANT GREEN

C. I. NO. 42040 (1 *ed.:* 662)

(C. I. Basic Green 1)

Synonyms: *Ethyl green; Malachite green G; Emerald green crystals;* * *Solid green JJO; Diamond green G*

This is a basic dye which is generally known in the form of the acid sulfate:

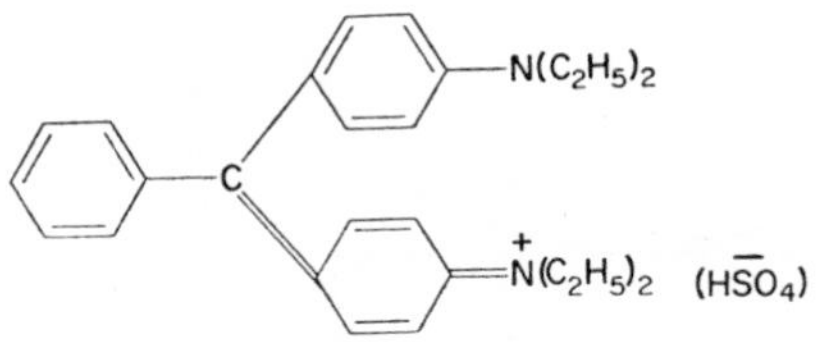

$C_{27}H_{34}N_2O_4S$; mol. wt. 482.624

(Absorption maximum: 628–631, [425])

Brilliant green is used to some extent as a stain for bacteria, spirochaetes, molds, and yeasts (see, for instance, Krajian, 1941), but finds more frequent employment as a constituent of bacteriological media. It is used, for example, as follows: (1) as a constituent of brilliant green bile media for fermentation tests to distinguish the colon organism from other lactose fermenting organisms; (2) it is employed in media used in searching for the typhoid organism in stools, where its value comes from its ability to inhibit the colon organism; (3) it is used as a constituent of enrichment media for the stimulation of the typhoid organism, in which it must prevent the growth of the normal colon types but not be toxic to the typhoid organism. It has proved much more simple to find a brilliant green satisfactory for demonstration of the colon organism in water than for the isolation and enrichment of the typhoid organism. A paper by Rakieten and Rettger (1927) has shown the difficulty encountered in this latter instance.

As the first of three purposes above mentioned is the one for which bril-

* Malachite green, also, has been exported from Germany under this name.

liant green is now most commonly used in America, all samples submitted for certification are tested for use in the brilliant green bile medium.

Spectrophotometric curves of typical samples of malachite green and brilliant green are given in Fig. 19. All green dyes have two absorption maxima, one about 430, the other about 620–630. The primary maximum for malachite green, however, is at a definitely shorter wave length than that of brilliant green or either of the two following dyes.

LIGHT GREEN SF YELLOWISH

C. I. NO. 42095 (1 *ed.*: 670)

(C. I. Acid Green 5)

Synonyms: *Light green 2G, S or 2GN; Acid green (with various shade designations); Fast acid green N*

This is a derivative of brilliant green, which is sulfonated and is therefore an acid dye.

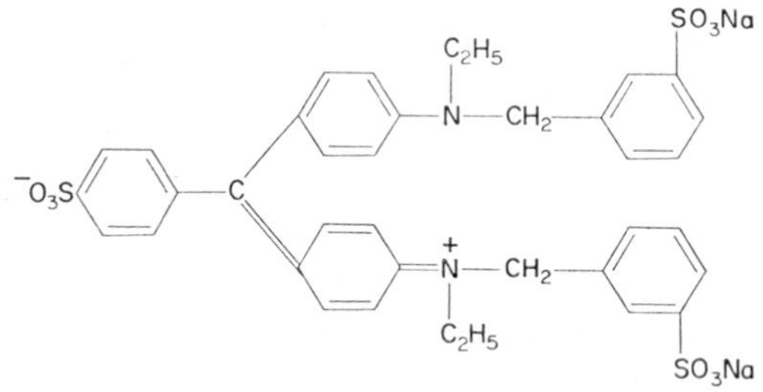

$C_{37}H_{34}N_2O_9S_3Na_2$; mol. wt. 792.850

(Absorption maximum: 629–634, [428])
Solubility at 26°C: in water 20.35%; in alcohol 0.82%

Light green is a valuable plasma stain often used for staining animal tissues in contrast to iron hematoxylin or other nuclear dyes, although it fades badly if exposed to bright light. It is a very valuable counterstain to safranin, especially after Flemming fixation, thus finding employment in cytological work. It photographs well. It is a constituent, together with neutral red, of the compound dye employed in the Twort (1924) stain for microorganisms in tissues and has been applied to the staining of bacteria, yeasts, algae, etc., under various conditions. In plant histology it is a useful cytoplasm and cellulose stain and has been employed by Buchholz (1931), mixed with acid fuchsin, for staining pollen tubes. Its greatest drawback is lack of permanence. Where greater permanency is desired fast green FCF may often be substituted for it.

Procedures Recommended by the Commission in Which This Stain is Used*

Name of Procedure	Page Reference to Staining Procedures
Crossman's modification of Mallory collagen stain.............	54
Counterstain to Heidenhain's hematoxylin for plant tissue.....	183
Counterstain to Feulgen stain for nucleoli in plant cytology.....	216

* Under this heading are given references to procedures described in detail in *Staining Procedures*, edited by Conn, Darrow, and Emmel (1960).

FAST GREEN FCF   C. I. NO. 42053

(C. I. Food Green 3)

This is a dye, very closely related to light green SF yellowish, which was originally proposed by Johnson and Staub (1927) as a food dye.

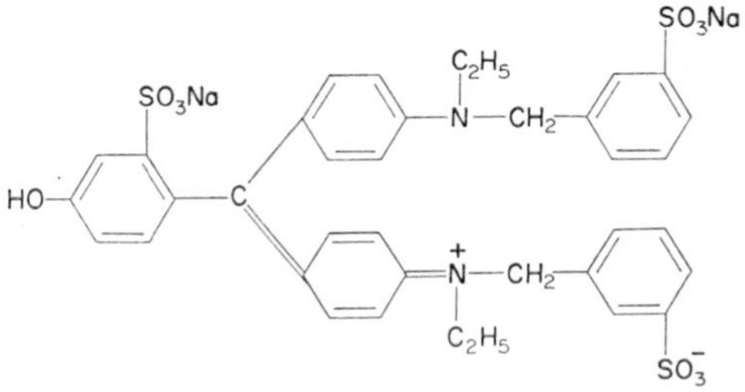

$C_{37}H_{34}N_2O_{10}S_3Na_2$; mol. wt. 808.850

(An acid dye; absorption maximum about 625, [420–430])
Solubility at 26°C: in water 16.04%; in alcohol 0.35%

This dye was first tried in the Commission laboratory as a substitute for light green SF yellowish (see Haynes 1928) and has now come into general use in plant histology and cytology. It gives staining effects very much like light green and is considerably less subject to fading. Slides have been exposed to direct sunlight for a few weeks and have still retained the green color. This dye is therefore to be recommended for such use as it has all the advantages of light green without the disadvantages. This dye is now employed in a large number of procedures, among which might be mentioned the following as illustrating two widely different types of methods: the quadruple staining technic of Johansen (1939), for plant histology, in which it is combined with safranin, methyl violet, and orange G; its use as a bacterial stain by Maneval, (1941), who recommends this and other acid dyes (e.g., acid fuchsin, aniline blue W.S., and orseilline) as preferable to the conventional basic dyes because of the better differentiation afforded and the less tendency for slime and debris to take the stain. Mention should

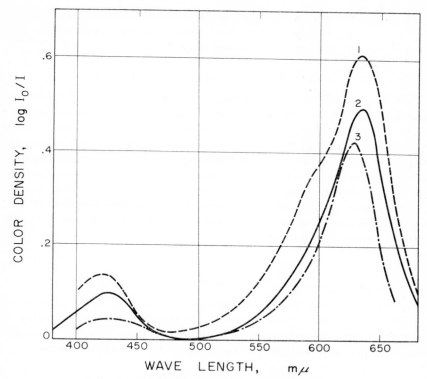

FIG. 20. Spectral curves of three phenyl methane dyes:
1. Methyl green   2. Light green SFY   3. Fast green FCF

also be made of its value as a cytoplasmic stain, for embryos stained in bulk with carmine.

Procedures Recommended by the Commission in Which This Stain is Used

Name of Procedure	Page Reference to *Staining Procedures*
Kornhauser's "Quad" stain for tissue	58
Modification of Van Gieson stain	50
Lillie modification of Masson trichrome stain	72
Safranin and fast green in plant cytology	186
De Tomasi modification of Feulgen stain in plant cytology	215
Stain for nuclear histone	219

Spectrophotometric curves of typical samples of light green and fast green are given in Fig. 20. It will be seen that they are both very much like the curve for brilliant green, although slightly different from malachite green in the location of the primary absorption maximum.

Another dye of this group which has been mentioned in biological literature is: C. I. Acid Green 3, C. I. No. 42085 (1 *ed.*: 666). Synonyms: *Acid green G, B extra, L extra, GV; Pontacyl green B.*

B. TRIAMINO TRIPHENYL METHANES (ROSANILINS)

The simplest rosanilins are the dyes sold as basic fuchsin. This term is somewhat loosely used to apply to two or three different dyes or to various mixtures of them. The dyes known as fuchsin differ from the methyl violets and other rosanilins in that the amino groups are not methylated or substituted in any other way. The fuchsins may, however, have methyl groups introduced directly onto the benzene rings instead of into the amino groups; and the different fuchsins vary from one another in the number of such methyl groups present. There are four primary compounds theoretically possible, namely with no methyl group, and with one, two, and three substituent methyl groups respectively.

BASIC FUCHSIN

Synonyms: *Fuchsin RFN; Magenta; Basic rubin; Aniline red**

The dyes ordinarily known to commerce as basic fuchsin are mixtures of pararosanilin, rosanilin and magenta II. Pararosanilin is obtainable in fairly pure form, as is also the compound with three substituent methyl groups, namely new fuchsin. The formulae of these compounds follow:

PARAROSANILIN (MAGENTA O)

c. i. no. 42500 (1 *ed.*: 676)

(C. I. Basic red 9)

Synonyms: *Basic rubin; Parafuchsin; Paramagenta*

This compound is triamino-triphenyl-methane chloride.

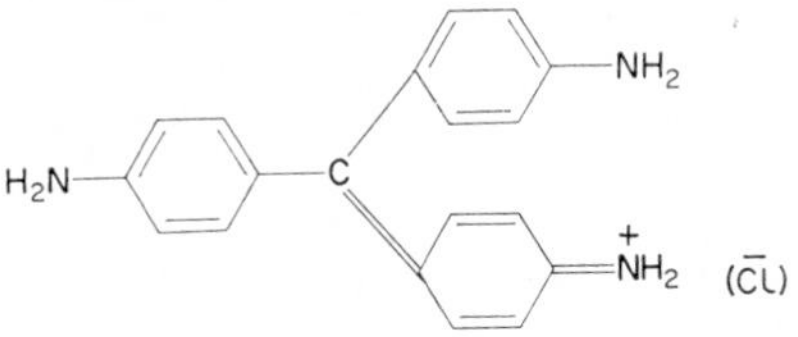

$C_{19}H_{18}N_3Cl$; mol. wt. 323.815

(A basic dye; absorption maximum about 545)
Solubility at 26°C: in water 0.26%; in alcohol 5.93%

It is the chief constituent of the majority of samples of basic fuchsin

* An impure basic fuchsin known as *cerise* has been mentioned in the biological literature.

submitted for certification as biological stains. It is sometimes furnished as
the chloride, sometimes as the acetate, generally the latter.

ROSANILIN (MAGENTA I)

c. i. no. 42510 (1 ed.: 677)

(C. I. Basic violet 14)

This compound is monomethyl fuchsin, or triamino-tolyl-diphenyl-
methane chloride.

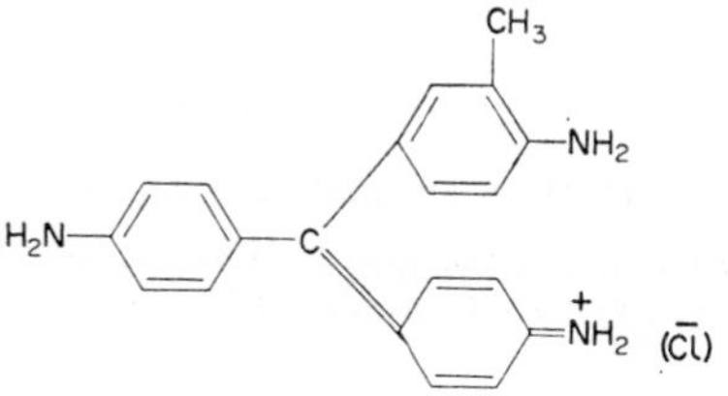

$C_{20}H_{20}N_3Cl$; mol. wt. 337.841

(A basic dye; absorption maximum about 550)
Solubility at 26°C: in water 0.39%; in alcohol 8.16%

It is not a textile dye, and is not found free from pararosanilin unless
specially prepared.

MAGENTA II

This theoretical constituent of basic fuchsin is never encountered pure
except as specially prepared in the laboratory, but probably is present in
market samples of the dye. It is dimethyl fuchsin, or triamino-ditolyl-
phenyl-methane chloride.

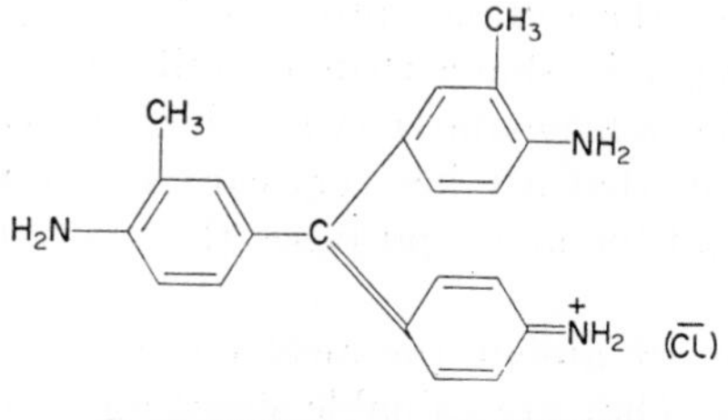

$C_{21}H_{22}N_3Cl$; mol. wt. 351.867

(A basic dye; absorption maximum about 554)

NEW FUCHSIN (MAGENTA III)

c. i. no. 42520 (1 ed.: 678)

(C. I. Basic violet 2)

Synonyms: *Isorubin; Fuchsin NB*

This compound is trimethyl fuchsin, or triamino-tritolyl-methane chloride:

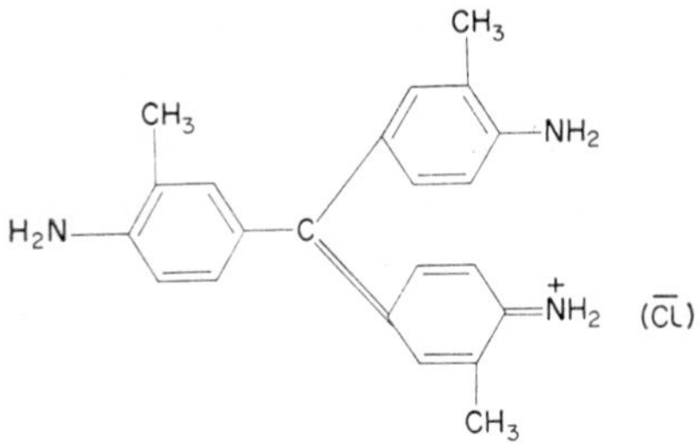

$C_{22}H_{24}N_3Cl$; mol. wt. 365.893

(A basic dye; absorption maximum about 556)
Solubility at 26°C: in water 1.13%; in alcohol 3.20%

From the general rule concerning alkyl substitution it will be understood that new fuchsin is the deepest in shade of these four dyes, pararosanilin the least so. The commercial fuchsins, therefore, which consist of mixtures of the first three vary in depth according to the proportions in which they are present.

A typical spectrophotometric curve of rosanilin (magenta I) is given in Fig. 21. Those for magentas O, II, and III are not given here, as they are so nearly the same that they can be distinguished only by careful measurement, and the differences would not show in such a graph as those here included.

It has proved from the investigations of the Stain Commission that not all basic fuchsins furnished as biological stains are mixtures of these three compounds. Many of the samples prove to be fairly pure pararosanilin; while others are deeper in shade than rosanilin and presumably contain appreciable quantities of magenta II. All of these dyes differ so very slightly from each other in hue that it takes very careful comparison to distinguish one from another, and for many purposes they may be used interchangeably.

The basic fuchsins are among the most powerful nuclear dyes, and find many biological uses. They are valuable stains for mucin, for elastic tissue, and for bringing out the so-called fuchsinophile granules. This group of dyes is almost indispensable in bacteriology, particularly in the Ziehl-Neelsen method, with its various modifications, for demonstrating acid-fast bacteria, such as the tubercle organism.

Basic fuchsin is also employed as a chemical reagent in a determination

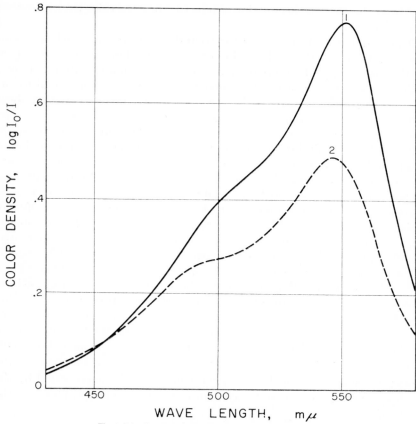

FIG. 21. Spectral curves of two rosanilins:
1. Basic fuchsin   2. Acid fuchsin

which is coming to be of considerable interest to the biologist. Basic fuchsin is the main constituent of Schiff's reagent, often employed for the detection of aldehydes, although not an absolutely specific reagent for the purpose. In preparing this reagent, basic fuchsin is reduced through the action of sulfite to a colorless form, having the type of the formula for leuco fuchsin which is given at the middle of page 23. (The formula there given for leuco fuchsin, however, is not exactly that of Schiff's reagent, as it is believed that the sulfite radical in some way enters into its composition.) In the presence of aldehyde some chemical reaction not wholly understood takes place which evidently restores the quinonoid structure of the molecule and, accordingly, the color of the compound. Apparently a slightly different dye from the basic fuchsin is thus produced, since the color is violet rather than pure red.

This reaction is of interest to the bacteriologist, as basic fuchsin is employed similarly in the Endo medium for distinguishing between members of the colon-typhoid group of bacteria. This medium contains lactose, which is not acted upon by the typhoid organism but is fermented by organisms like *Bacterium coli*. It has been known for many years that these lactose fermenting organisms of the group restore the red color of the medium, while the non-lactose-fermenters do not. The suggestion was naturally made that this Endo reaction might depend upon the production of aldehyde by the organisms, but for years no one was able to demonstrate the presence of aldehyde in such cultures. Neuberg and Nord (1919) suggested, however, that aldehyde might be produced but not ordinarily accumulate in sufficient quantity to be detected; and that the sulfite in the medium might act as a "trapping agent" so as to allow it to accumulate. This has since been verified by Margolena and Hansen (1933). Apparently, therefore, the Endo medium is a biological application of Schiff's reagent.

Feulgen and his associates (Feulgen and Rossenbeck, 1924; Feulgen and Voit, 1924) employed this compound of basic fuchsin and sulfurous acid in histological technic, regarding it as a microchemical reagent for detecting the presence of aldehyde-like substances in the nuclei. Feulgen called this the "nucleal reaction," the ending "-al" indicating the aldehyde-like nature of the substance which he considered the reaction to demonstrate. This interpretation of the Feulgen reaction is now regarded as only part of the story; the significance of the deoxyribosenucleic acid demonstrated by the method is appreciated more today than it was when Feulgen proposed the method.

As a matter of fact, the Schiff reagent, employed by some modification of the Feulgen technic, has given histochemistry its greatest impetus. Special significance has attached to the HIO_4-Schiff technic, in which the use of the Schiff reagent is preceded by oxidation with periodic acid (HIO_4), as first proposed by McManus (1946). It is considered that certain polysaccharides (and their derivatives), which contain adjacent hydroxyl groups, or a hydroxyl adjacent to an amino group, react with the periodic acid (or other oxidant) to produce aldehyde groups, and that the latter react with the Schiff reagent to bring out the red-purple color. This has enabled histochemists to determine the locations of the compounds in question within the cell. Histochemists are proving much more exacting in their requirements for a basic fuchsin than were histologists or chemists using the Schiff reagent. As a result of trying to meet their requirements, the quality of basic fuchsin on the American market has been improving in recent years.

Early editions of this book contained statements, realized at the time to be largely provisional, to indicate which types of fuchsin are most satisfactory for the various purposes. Data that have been accumulated since 1929, however, seem to show pretty definitely that the exact chemical nature of basic fuchsin itself is of comparatively little importance. Good results for practically any purpose have been obtained with pararosanilin, rosanilin, new fuchsin, and even with the seldom-encountered magenta II; and the dyes have proved equally satisfactory whether in the form of chlorides or acetates, the two most common salts of this dye. From the standpoint of ordinary staining, in fact, it was realized a long while ago that the samples furnished by the stain companies varied very little in their performance.

In their behavior in the Endo medium and in the Feulgen technic, however, the samples were found to be quite dissimilar, and it was some time before any clue could be obtained as to the cause of their differences. It has finally been concluded, however, that the variations which occur are due to foreign ingredients which are almost always present in these dyes.

The problem of the Endo medium was solved first. It was learned (Conn and Darrow, 1934) that almost any sample of basic fuchsin will give good results in the Endo medium if the formula of that medium is carefully adjusted so as to avoid either an excess or a deficiency of sulfite in proportion to the fuchsin. It is also recognized today that many basic fuchsins contain an impurity which does not completely decolorize under the action of sulfite, and which becomes evident in such a reduced solution by the yellowish, or even brownish pigment remaining. The nature of this pigment has not been learned, although Scanlan and Melin (1937) report an investigation of the subject. Following the publication of Scanlan and Melin's paper, the stain companies have begun to find ways of preparing fuchsins that are free from the undesirable impurity; and batches submitted for certification since then have ordinarily proved satisfactory for the Feulgen technic as well as for the other purposes discussed above. Not long after the above paper appeared Coleman (1938) reported a method of eliminating this impurity from a decolorized fuchsin by agitation with a decolorizing carbon; his method seems to make a sample of this dye usable in the Feulgen technic, even though previously entirely unsatisfactory. The histochemists, however, want a glass-clear Schiff reagent; and modern producers of stains in America are doing their best to supply basic fuchsins that will suit. A few samples now (1960) on the market decolorize completely; the others usually do so with treatment by charcoal. Those that do not thus decolorize are regarded as unsatisfactory and are not approved by the Commission. Lillie (1951) has contributed considerable information on the subject.

Procedures Recommended by the Commission in Which This Dye Is Used

Name of Procedure	Page Reference to Staining Procedures
HIO₄ leuco fuchsin method for glycogen......................	167
Weigert's resorcin fuchsin......................................	64
Lillie modification of Gallego elastic tissue stain..............	67
Bauer's leuco fuchsin method for glycogen....................	161
Aldehyde fuchsin for cell granules...........................	171–2
Aceto-carmine and basic fuchsin for pollen tubes in style......	197
DeTomasi modification of Feulgen stain in plant cytology.....	215
Colchicine Feulgen stain for leaf smears......................	217
Feulgen stain for nucleoli in plant cytology...................	216
General staining of pure cultures of bacteria..................	224
Ziehl-Neelsen stain for acid fast bacteria....................	229
Dorner's spore stain for bacteria.............................	230
Snyder modification..	230
Casares-Gil's method for bacterial flagella....................	236
Gray's method for bacterial flagella..........................	237
Liefson's method for bacterial flagella.......................	238
Bailey's method for bacterial flagella........................	238
Hiss' method for bacterial capsules...........................	241
Macchiavello's stain for Rickettsiae.........................	244
Counterstain in Burdon's fat stain...........................	242
Weigert's stain for fibrin and bacteria in tissues..............	256
Verhoeff's carbol fuchsin for tubercle bacilli in tissues........	257
Lillie modification of Ziehl-Neelsen technic...................	258
MacCallum's stain for influenza bacilli in tissues.............	263
Williams' stain for Negri bodies..............................	261
Goodpasture's stain for influenza bacilli in tissues............	263

One complaint concerning certain samples of basic fuchsin related to their behavior in staining tubercle bacteria by the acid-fast technic. It was claimed that with certain samples of the dye these organisms show a tendency to decolorize partially or wholly, thus resulting in poorly stained cells that tend to appear as a string of beads. This proved a difficult complaint to investigate, because consistent results are not obtained by different investigators. In fact, Yegian and Porter (1944) have shown that a normally staining culture may be converted into one which is not acid-fast or which shows beaded staining by improper methods of smearing on the slide. Nevertheless, it seems true that the "beaded" staining is most apt to occur with pararosanilin samples; rosanilin usually gives a rather uniform staining. This situation is, however, confused by the fact that some workers seem actually to prefer the "beaded" staining.

In general it can be stated, that in spite of all variations reported, the standardization of this dye seems to have been accomplished in a practical way, even if there is still much to be learned about it from a theoretical standpoint.

ACID FUCHSIN   C. I. NO. 42685 (1 *ed.*: 692)

(C. I. Acid violet 19)

Synonyms: *Fuchsin S, SN, SS, ST, or S III; Acid magenta; Acid rubin*

(An acid dye; absorption maximum: pararosanilin
540–543, rosanilin 543–546)

This dye owes its acid character to the fact that it is a sulfonated derivative of basic fuchsin. Acid fuchsins are ordinarily rather complex mixtures. As there are four primary basic fuchsins possible, according to the degree of methyl substitution, and as each may yield at least three different compounds on sulfonation, fully a dozen acid fuchsins are theoretically possible, and samples are hardly to be expected which are not mixtures of several.

The generally accepted formula of one of the homologs present in acid fuchsin, namely the disodium salt of rosanilin trisulphonic acid, is:

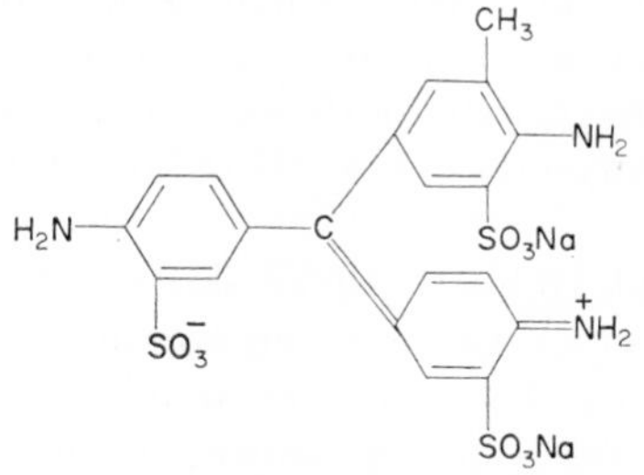

$C_{20}H_{17}N_3O_9S_3Na_2$; mol. wt. 585.52

It is to be noted that this is a case of intramolecular salt formation, and the compound acts as though it has no free acid. When the trisodium salt is formed the quinoid ring disappears and the following compound is produced:

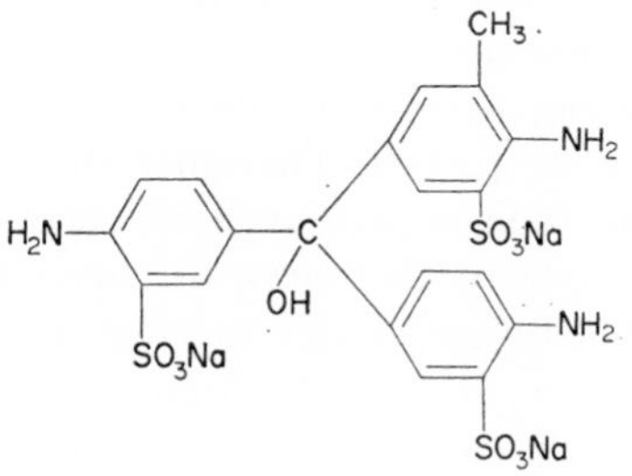

This compound, it will be seen, is a carbinol in structure, and as it lacks the quinoid ring it is colorless; but it is very readily converted into the disodium salt by the addition of acid, whereupon the color again appears. This property makes acid fuchsin of use as an indicator. The decolorized solution of acid fuchsin neutralized with sodium hydroxide is called the Andrade indicator. It was once used extensively in bacteriological work, because of the striking reaction when its color is restored by acid-forming bacteria. (See Andrade-Penny, 1895.) As an indicator to show hydrogen-ion concentration at all accurately, however, it is found to have much less value than the phthalein and sulphonphthalein dyes (see pp. 185–194).

Acid fuchsin is a widely used plasma stain, which has also been recommended for a number of special uses. Among the best known are: the Van Gieson (1889) connective tissue stain, in which it is used with picric acid after hematoxylin to differentiate smooth muscle from connective tissue; the Ehrlich-Biondi tri-acid stain for blood, which is a "neutral" combination with orange G and methyl green (see Krause, 1926–1927; pp. 457, 1707). In plant histology it is used to stain the cortex, pith and cellulose walls: while the Pianese (1896) stain (with malachite green and martius yellow), which was originally applied to cancer tissue, is now used by plant pathologists in studying infected vascular plants. It is used with methyl green, by Altmann, Bensley and Cowdry as a stain for mitochondria (see Lee, 1937, pp. 167–168). To the pathologist it is quite valuable as a constituent (with aniline blue and orange G) of the Mallory (1900) connective tissue stain.

Scanlan, French and Holmes (1927) showed that many lots of acid fuchsin are unsatisfactory because of the rapidity with which they fade in Van Gieson preparations. These writers found that this fault arises from lack of control of the process of sulfonation. Their results indicated that a satisfactory product could be obtained if this process were carefully controlled by the use of a low temperature (85°C), fuming sulfuric acid containing sufficient free SO_3 to insure complete sulfonation to the trisulfonic acid, and careful acidification to yield only the disodium salt. Since the method which they proposed in this article was called to the attention of manufacturers, the American product has improved; it not only gives permanent Van Gieson preparations, but proves more satisfactory in the Mallory connective tissue stain.

The spectrophotometric curve of a typical acid magenta I (rosanilin) is given in Fig. 21 (curve 2), p. 139. The chief difference between this and the corresponding basic fuchsin is that it has a distinct secondary maximum at about 500 mμ, where the curve for basic rosanilin shows merely an almost imperceptible bulge. A dye having its primary maximum at

500 would be orange in shade, which is approximately the color of the acid phase of the Andrade indicator.

Procedures Recommended by the Commission in Which This Stain Is Used

Name of Procedure	Page Reference to *Staining Procedures*
Van Gieson stain with iron hematoxylin......................	50
Mallory's aniline blue collagen stain........................	52
Crossman's modification.......................................	54
Acid alizarin blue modification............................	55
Masson's trichrome stain.....................................	70
Altmann's aniline acid fuchsin................................	165
Pianese IIIB stain for fungi in plant tissue...................	195

HOFMANN'S VIOLET

C. I. NO. 42530 (1 *ed.:* 679)

Synonyms: *Dahlia; Iodine violet; Red violet; Violet R,*
RR or 4RN; Primula R water soluble

These various names are applied in a somewhat indiscriminate way to dyes intermediate in shade between basic fuchsin and methyl violet. Theoretically they are mixtures of methylated and ethylated pararosanilins and rosanilins, having fewer than five ethyl or methyl groups. Of these compounds, the formula for triethyl rosanilin is:

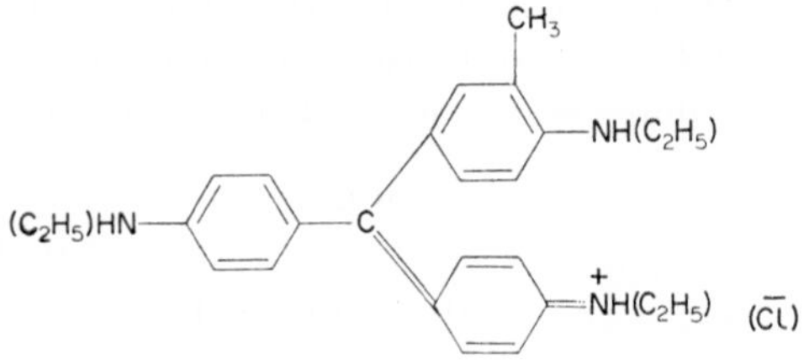

$C_{26}H_{32}N_3Cl$; mol. wt. 421.997
(*A basic dye*)

In actual practice, however, the names applied to this group of dyes are very loosely employed, and one is often furnished under such a label as dahlia or Hofmann's violet a mixture of basic fuchsin and methyl violet, having a shade about the same as one of the compounds just mentioned. Two samples of "dahlia" have been called to the attention of the Commission which actually differed very greatly, one being nearly as red as fuchsin, the other nearly as blue as methyl violet. There was every reason to believe that one was a fuchsin with a small addition of methyl violet, the other a methyl violet with a little fuchsin added. The latter dyes are much more cheaply prepared than the true Hofmann violets, and the substitution is natural considering that the shade obtained can be the same.

Hofmann's violet has been called for by Ehrlich and by Unna for staining mast cells; by Juergens for staining amyloid, which it colors red, while the cytoplasm is colored blue. (See Krause, 1926–1927, p. 1123). Now it is possible that for one of these procedures or for some other similar one, a true Hofmann's violet is necessary; on the other hand the shade obtained may be the important matter, in which case as satisfactory results should be obtainable with a mixture of fuchsin and methyl violet. This is a matter that should be further investigated; for if the cheaper fuchsins and methyl violets can be substituted for the Hofmann violets, the substitution can be made by the biologist himself. It is interesting to remark that one supply house not long ago sent out a bottle of crystal violet, unintentionally mislabeled dahlia, to a biologist ordering the latter dye. This biologist shortly wrote to the company that he would like more of it, as it was the best lot of dahlia he had ever used; in looking the matter up to duplicate the former order, the company discovered its mistake.

It is extremely difficult to determine just what dye in this group is referred to by any given name. Thus a rosanilin violet has been mentioned as having been employed in a stain for Negri bodies; and it is uncertain whether it is a dye of the above group or of the group following. Any biologist employing one of the violet rosanilins should be especially careful in publishing his work to give all the information furnished on the label as to manufacturer and the nature of the dye; and should preferably verify all such work, before publication, by using a dye of known composition.

METHYL VIOLET 2 B

C. I. NO. 42535 (1 *ed.:* 680)

(C. I. Basic Violet 1)

Synonyms: *Dahlia B; Paris violet; Pyoktaninum coeruleum; Gentian violet*
Various shades denoted: *Methyl violet 2R, R, B, 2B, 3B, BBN, BO, V3*

The various dyes denoted methyl violet are mixtures of tetra-, penta-, and hexamethyl pararosanilin:

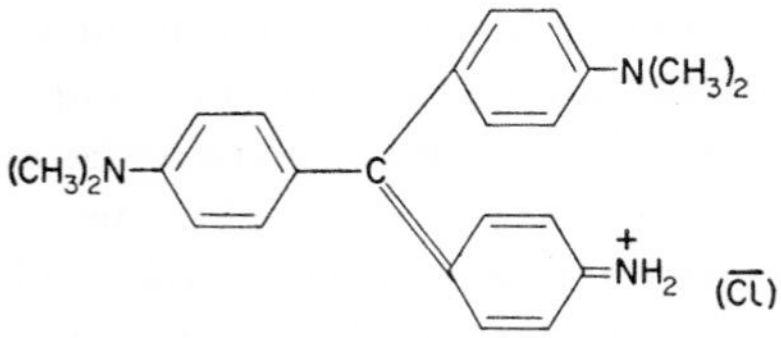

(*tetramethyl pararosanilin*)

$C_{23}H_{26}N_3Cl$; mol. wt. 379.919

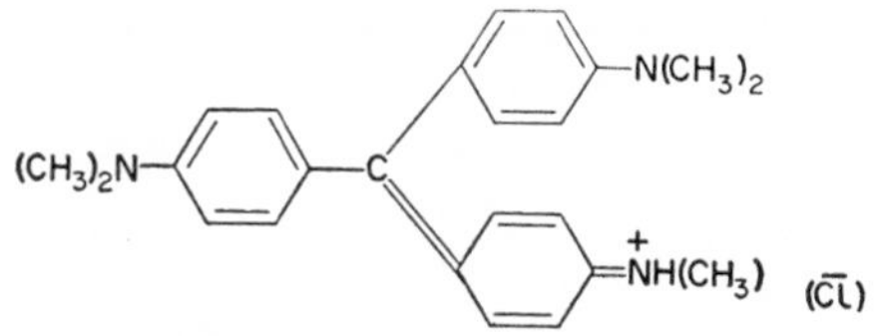

(*pentamethyl pararosanilin*)

$C_{24}H_{28}N_3Cl$; mol. wt. 393.945

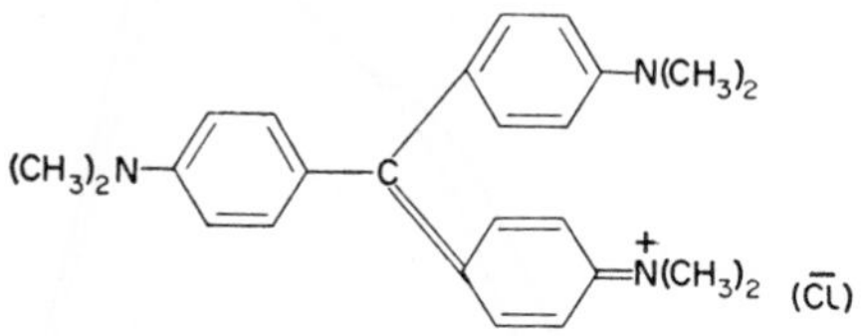

(*hexamethyl pararosanilin*)
(crystal violet)

$C_{25}H_{30}N_3Cl$; mol. wt. 407.971

(*Basic dyes; absorption maximum: 583–587 in 90% alcohol*)
Solubility at 26°C: in water 2.93%; in alcohol 15.21%

In the case of these compounds, as in the case of other series of homologs differing in extent of methylation, the shade is deepened by the introduction of each methyl group. Hence the various mixtures known to the trade as methyl violet vary from reddish to bluish violets according to the relative amounts of the more and the less completely methylated compounds present in the mixture. This is the significance of the various shade designations listed above, R's indicating the reddish shades, and B's the bluish shades. Of these various shades the bluer ones seem to be best for biological purposes, methyl violet 2B having been found satisfactory for practically all purposes for which methyl or gentian violet is ordinarily called for. This indicates that the biologist requires the higher homologs in this group. Now the most completely methylated methyl violet is the hexamethyl compound, which is easily obtained pure and is known to the trade as crystal violet. This dye, in fact, is coming to be the one member of this group in most common use in biology.

Spectrophotometric curves of typical samples of crystal violet and methyl violet 2B are given in Fig. 22. Their great similarity is apparent, but the two products can be distinguished by accurate measurement of the absorption maximum.

Gentian Violet. A poorly defined mixture of violet rosanilins is well known to biologists under the name gentian violet. The name is not used at present in the dye or textile industries. It apparently applied originally to a certain mixture containing about half dextrin and half dye, the dye being

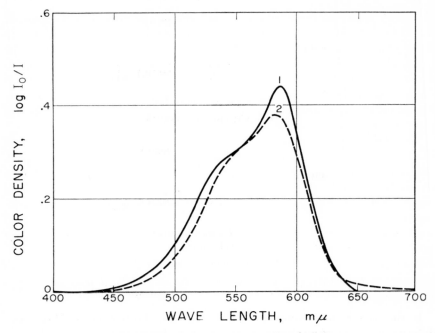

Fig. 22. Spectral curves of two violet rosanilins:
1. Crystal violet   2. Methyl violet 2B

a methyl violet, that is a mixture of crystal violet with lower homologs of the same series. The statement was formerly common in biological literature that gentian violet is a mixture of crystal and methyl violet; but the looseness of the statement is evident when it is realized that crystal violet is a component of all the deeper shades of methyl violet. It is possible that before 1914 gentian violet did represent a fairly constant mixture, but there seems to be some doubt even on this point. It is certain that immediately following the first World War each company used its own judgment as to what to furnish when gentian violet was ordered. As a result there were placed on the market under this name various methyl violets, with or without dextrin, and also crystal violet; of course the purchaser had no knowledge as to what he was obtaining in any given instance.

Under the circumstances the Commission faced a difficult problem in trying to standardize gentian violet. The question was whether to recognize the name at all, or to approve some particular dye or mixture of dyes of this group as gentian violet. The former course was almost impossible because of the wide demand among biologists for a stain labeled gentian violet; it was plain that the stain companies would meet this demand in some way. The second course (unless considerable latitude were recognized) would be entirely arbitrary, inasmuch as no information was available to show which members of this group of dyes were especially needed in histology or bacteriology. Accordingly in the first edition of this book gentian violet was defined as either pentamethyl or hexamethyl pararosanilin, or else a mixture of methylated pararosanilins composed primarily of the two compounds just named and having a shade at least as deep as that recognized in the trade as methyl violet 2B.

This definition was quite broad and did not exclude anything sold at that time as gentian violet. As a result there were for several years various different products sold under this name. At present (1960) the name is no longer recognized as suitable for a certified stain. Certified stains are now listed either as crystal violet or methyl violet 2B, as indicated by spectrophotometric analysis. Users should specify crystal violet, for bacteriological work and for histological purposes where a deep blue-violet is required; but should order methyl violet 2B in histological procedures where a reddish shade is called for. With this knowledge at hand, gentian violet, as such, is not necessary.

CRYSTAL VIOLET

C. I. NO. 42555 (1 ed.: 681)

(C. I. Basic Violet 3)

Synonyms: *Violet C, G, or 7B; Hexamethyl violet;*
Methyl violet 10B; Gentian violet

$C_{25}H_{30}N_3Cl$; mol. wt. 407.971

(A basic dye: absorption maximum 589–593)
Solubility at 26°C: in water 1.68%; in alcohol 13.87%

This dye is a hexamethyl-pararosanilin, whose formula is given above as one of the components of methyl violet. The Commission has made as careful an investigation of this dye as of any other and recommends it highly.

Methyl or gentian violet is of chief value to the biologist as a nuclear or chromatin stain, having many histological and cytological applications, the one for which it is most commonly used at present being the Flemming (1891) triple stain in which it is employed with orange G and safranin—a technic which gives a very high degree of cytological differentiation. It is also used for staining amyloid in frozen sections of fresh and fixed tissue, and for staining the platelets in blood while it is much used by the Weigert (1887) technic for staining fibrin and neuroglia. The bacteriologist also finds it a useful stain and probably purchases more at the present time than all other biologists together; the chief bacteriological use is in the Gram technic for distinguishing between different kinds of bacteria. It is also called for in media for fungi and in various bacteriological media, on account of its selective bacteriostatic action. An important example is Petroff's (1915) gentian violet egg medium for isolation and cultivation of the tubercle organism. For most of these purposes, crystal violet is in general use. As a result of its bacteriostatic properties it has come into use as a medicinal agent for the control of staphylococcic infection. It has not yet been definitely established, however, whether crystal violet alone or some mixture thereof with the lower homologs should be used for this purpose.

The Flemming and Gram stains have seemed the most delicate procedures for which it is used; so they have been given the most careful study. In the case of the Gram stain it was discovered that there are a score or more different procedures all referred to by the name "Gram" stain, and a study was made of all the methods that were found (see Hucker and Conn, 1923). The result of the investigation was to conclude without reservation that crystal violet may be substituted for gentian violet in both the Gram and Flemming technics, and probably for gentian or methyl violet in any of the bacteriological or histological methods for which either stain is designated. The advantage of crystal violet is obvious; for it is a definite chemical compound, while methyl and gentian violet are both variable mixtures.

It is of interest to note that in the literature of microscopic technic crys-

Procedures Recommended by the Commission in Which This Stain Is Used

Name of Procedure	Page Reference to Staining Procedures
Crystal violet stain for amyloid...............................	37
Jackson's crystal violet stain for woody tissue................	191
Newcomer's method for pollen tubes..........................	199
Newton's crystal violet iodine technic for plant cytology......	207
Randolph's crystal violet iodine technic for plant cytology.....	208
Permanent smear preparations of sporocytes..................	209
Flemming triple stain in plant cytology.....................	213
Same, with iodine...	214
General staining of pure cultures of bacteria..................	224
Gram stain: Hucker modification.............................	226
Burke and Kopeloff-Beerman modifications........	227
Ljubinski stain for diphtheria organism.......................	234
Anthony's method for bacterial capsules......................	241
Hiss' method for bacterial capsules..........................	241
Tyler's wethod for bacterial capsules.........................	242
Gram-Weigert method for bacteria in tissues..................	254
Gram stain for tissues.......................................	255
Weigert's stain for fibrin and bacteria in tissues..............	256
MacCallum's stain for influenza bacilli in tissues.............	263

tal violet has been specified instead of gentian violet for some special procedures. Especially important is Benda's crystal-violet-alizarin method for staining mitochondria, and its modifications by Meves and Duesberg (1908); and also its use in combination with erythrosin by Jackson (1926) for staining lightly lignified walls, in which technic it proves more uniform than gentian violet.

A loose compound of crystal violet and bismuth, formed by treating an aqueous solution of the dye with an aqueous solution of bismuth ammonium citrate, has been prepared by Wilkinson and Barksdale (1928) and called bismuth violet. It is claimed to have much greater bacteriostatic action on Gram-positive bacteria than crystal violet itself.

ETHYL VIOLET   C. I. NO. 42600 (1 *ed.:* 682)

(C. I. Basic Violet 4)

Synonym: *Ethyl purple 6B*

Ethyl violet is hexa-ethyl pararosanilin having the following formula:

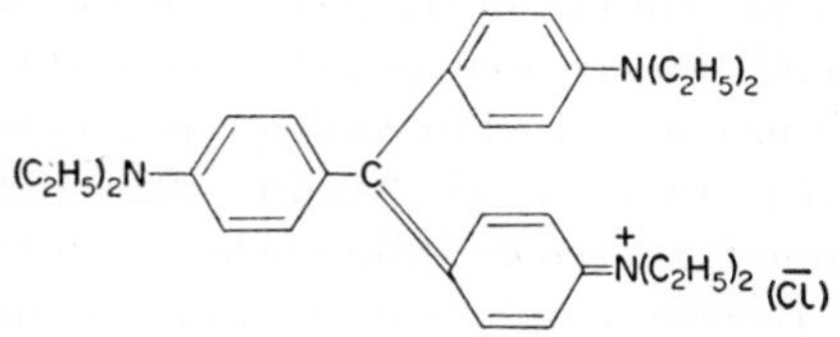

$C_{31}H_{42}N_3Cl$; mol. wt. 492.127

(*A basic dye; absorption maximum about 596*)

It has been called for by Bowie (1924) in a neutral stain combination with Biebrich scarlet to stain the islets of Langerhans. Kernohan (1931) and Proescher (1934) have each employed it in staining nervous tissue; while Ono (1934) used it for staining spirochaetes in blood.

METHYL GREEN

C. I. NO. 42585 (1 *ed.:* 684)

(C. I. Basic Blue 20)

Synonyms: *Double green SF; Light green*

Methyl green is crystal violet into which a seventh methyl group has been introduced by the action of methyl chloride or methyl iodide upon it, forming the compound:*

* This ordinarily occurs in trade as a zinc chloride double salt.

$$(CH_3)_3 \overset{+}{N} - \underset{(\bar{Cl})}{\text{—}} \text{—} C \begin{cases} \text{—} N(CH_3)_2 \\ = \overset{+}{N}(CH_3)_2 \quad (\bar{Cl}) \end{cases}$$

$C_{26}H_{33}N_3Cl_2$; mol. wt. 458.462

(A basic dye; absorption maximum 630–634, [420])

As the seventh methyl group is very loosely attached, there is always some methyl or crystal violet present, either because it is not all converted into the higher homolog or because it has broken down again. It has been stated that to obtain free methyl green the commercial dye should be shaken in a separatory funnel with amyl alcohol or chloroform, which dissolves the methyl violet. As a matter of fact, however, pure methyl green may not always be desired by the biologist, as the dye owes part of the polychromatic or dichromatic properties for which it is prized to the presence of small amounts of the violet compounds.

Methyl green is at present one of the most valuable nuclear stains known to the histologist, and is widely used as a chromatin stain by the cytologist. On the other hand it has been used by Galeotti as a cytoplasm stain following acid fuchsin and picric acid; see Krause, 1926–1927, p. 1417). In the Ehrlich-Biondi technic it is used to stain nuclei in contrast to acid fuchsin; (Id. p. 457); while Bensley employs it to stain chromatin in contrast to acid fuchsin which stains the mitochondria; (see Lee, 1937, p. 166). It is an ingredient of the Ehrlich triacid mixture (with orange G and acid fuchsin) for staining blood smears. Botanists find it a valuable stain, combined with acid fuchsin, for lignified xylem. One of its most valuable uses today is in the Pappenheim (1899) stain, in which it is combined with pyronin and used for staining the gonococcus and mast cells as well as by Unna in studying chromolysis; more recent applications of these same two dyes in animal cytology and histology are those of Kurnick (1952) and Taft (1951). It is also a useful chromatin stain for protozoa, and is employed in weak acetic acid solution for staining fresh material beneath the cover glass.

When the foreign supply of dyes was shut off by the first World War, this stain proved one of the most difficult to obtain in satisfactory quality, largely due to the looseness with which the seventh methyl group is attached and the resulting instability of the compound. At first certain green dyes of an entirely different nature were furnished, but as soon as an investigation of the dye was begun manufacturers proved perfectly able to produce methyl green; the difficulty came in obtaining the right degree of purity. Samples were finally furnished so pure that they lacked completely the necessary metachromatic staining quality; and it proved necessary to add a certain small percentage of the violet dye to obtain the proper results. This problem seems to have been solved at present and satisfactory methyl green is available. The chief problem now is to standardize it. With other stains this can ordinarily be done on the batch basis, approving some batch large enough to meet the demand for a period of years. With methyl green this cannot safely be done, on account of its instability. Hence large batches are impractical; and the stain ought to be sold with the caution that the dye does not keep indefinitely without change.

This instability complicates standardization by spectrophotometer tests. Fig. 20, p. 135, shows a spectrophotometric curve of this dye in comparison with those of light green SFY and fast green FCF. The three are much alike with two maxima at about 430 and 630. All the green dyes show disagreement between dye content determinations by means of $TiCl_3$ titration and comparisons of the density at the peak of the chief maximum. Methyl green has an additional source of inconsistency in its assay: the ratio between two points of the curve equal distances each side of the maximum fluctuates, due apparently to the fact that solutions change on standing.

There seems, since 1930, to have been a change in the nature of the methyl green samples supplied as biological stains. One of the companies admits that its methyl green is not C. I. No. 42585, but the following:

ETHYL GREEN

C. I. NO. 42590 (1 *ed.:* 685)

Synonym: *Methyl green**

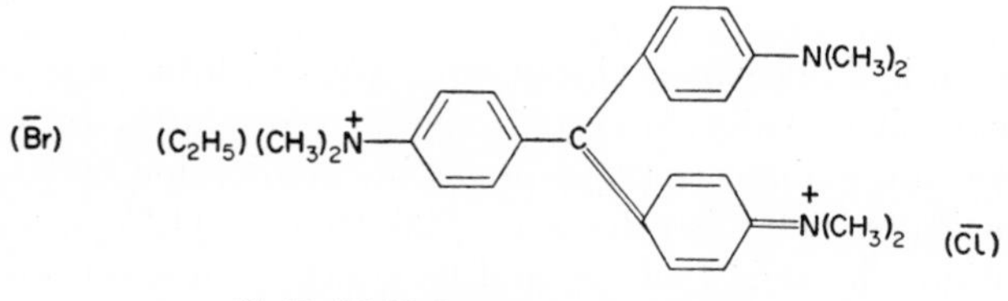

$C_{27}H_{35}N_3Cl$ Br; mol. wt. 516.947

(*A basic dye*)

This dye differs from the preceding only in that it is prepared from crystal violet by the action of an ethyl instead of a methyl halide. It is almost, if not entirely, indistinguishable from C. I. 42585 by spectrophotometric tests, and apparently acts very similarly for biological purposes. It is entirely possible that it is even better than the other for use in staining; certainly the present methyl greens are more satisfactory than those on the market between 1920 and 1930.

* This ordinarily occurs in trade as a zinc chloride double salt.

Procedures Recommended by the Commission in Which Either
Methyl Green or Ethyl Green is Used

Name of Procedure	Page Reference to *Staining Procedures*
Bismarck brown with methyl green in animal histology.......	33
With Altmann's aniline acid fuchsin.........................	165
With pyronin in animal cytology and histochemistry..........	166
Methyl green in glycerin jelly for pollen grains...............	197
Albert's stain for the diphtheria organism	233
Pappenheim-Saathof stain for gonorrheal pus.................	245
Saathof stain for bacteria in tissue.........................	251

IODINE GREEN   C. I. NO. 42556 (1 *ed.*: 686)

This dye is closely related to methyl green, the generally accepted formula being:

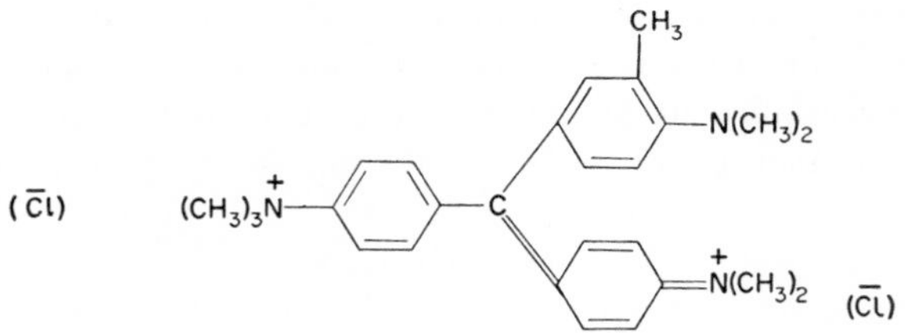

$C_{27}H_{35}N_3Cl_2$; mol. wt. 472.488

(*A basic dye*)

Iodine green is a nuclear or chromatin stain which has selective properties that make it of value in certain special procedures. It was used by Ciaccio (1906) for staining nervous tissue, in combination with acid fuchsin and picric acid; by Lefas (see Krause, 1926–1927, p. 1122) as a blood stain in combination with acid fuchsin; and by others as a stain for mucin and amyloid which it colors red instead of green. It was employed by Zimmermann (1893) with basic fuchsin for staining chromatin in plant tissue; while together with acid fuchsin it has been proposed by other botanists for staining lignified xylem. Torrey and Buckell (1922) have recommended a differential medium for the isolation of the gonococcus which includes this dye.

ACID VIOLET

There are various dyes on the market known as acid violet with some shade designation. These dyes vary extremely in composition and they are listed under various Colour Index numbers. They are in general sulfonated violet dyes of the rosanilin group, some of them simple methylated para-rosanilins, others benzylated compounds.

Some acid violet—its exact identity uncertain—was employed by Bailey (1921) in cytological studies on the human pituitary gland; also by Maurer and Lewis (1922) for staining similar tissue from the pig; by Ono (1934) for staining spirochaetes in blood, and by Weiss for staining both spiro-chaetes (1929) and bacterial flagella (1928). It is very unfortunate that any biologist should have been furnished a stain labeled merely acid violet; the term is too indefinite for identification.

BENZYL VIOLET

There is a group of dyes known as benzyl violets, which are pararosanilins with benzyl substitution in one or more of the amino groups. Some of them are acid and some basic dyes. There is occasional reference in the biological literature to the use of a benzyl violet, but without any indication as to which of the dyes in question is intended.

SPIRIT BLUE   C. I. NO. 42775 (1 ed.: 689)

(C. I. Solvent Blue 3)

Synonyms: *Gentiana blue 6B; Aniline blue, alcohol soluble; Light blue; Lyon blue; Paris blue*

This is a mixture of diphenyl rosanilin chloride:

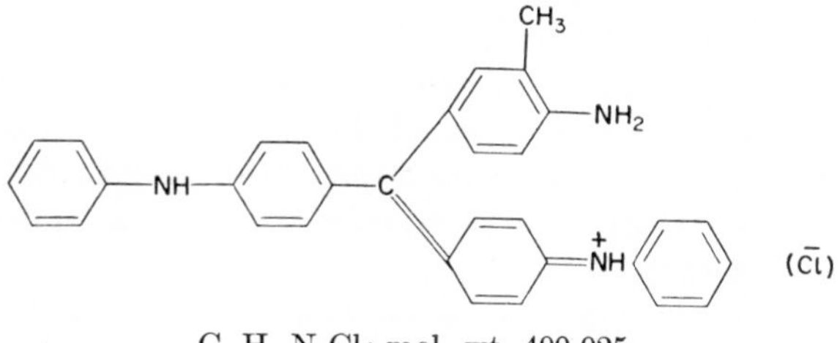

$C_{32}H_{28}N_3Cl$; mol. wt. 490.025.

and triphenyl pararosanilin chloride:

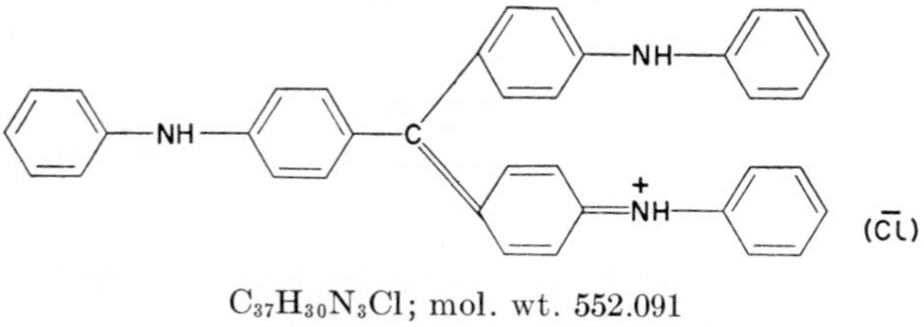

$C_{37}H_{30}N_3Cl$; mol. wt. 552.091

(*Basic dyes; absorption maximum of spirit blue 2R about 581 in alcohol*)
Solubility at 26°C: in water nil; in alcohol 1.10%

Lynch (1930) mentioned Lyons blue (undoubtedly this dye) as a satisfactory counterstain to carmine in bulk staining of protozoa and other small animals and embryos. It has, moreover, been reported by others as a good contrast stain for carmine, bringing out nerve fibers well in embryonic tissue; for this purpose it is used in strong alcoholic solution. Knaysi (1942) has mentioned this dye as one whose color base can be used in determining hydrolysis of fats.

VICTORIA BLUE 4R   C. I. NO. 42563 (1 *ed.:* 690)

(C. I. Basic Blue 8)

Synonym: *Fat blue 4R*

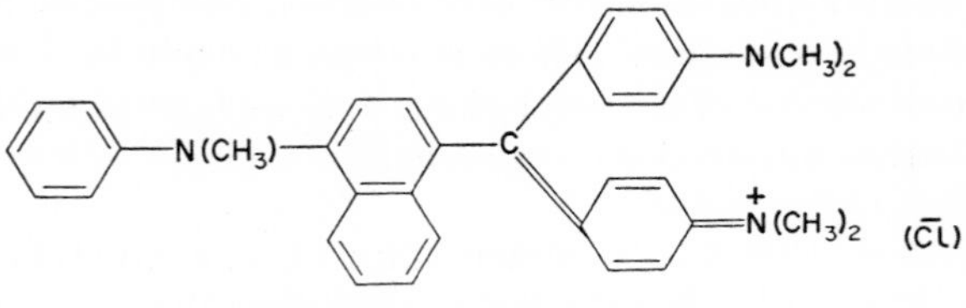

$C_{34}H_{34}N_3Cl$; mol. wt. 520.093

(A basic dye; absorption maximum 593.5 [538.5])
Solubility at 26°C: in water 3.23%; in alcohol 20.49%

Herzberg (1934) suggested this dye for staining minute granules in the case of certain virus diseases, claiming these granules to be the filterable virus itself. Others (e.g., Gutstein, 1937) followed the same technic, staining the "elementary bodies," but without committing themselves to Herzberg's theory. Isada (1938) mentioned this dye as one of several that may be used in staining bacterial flagella. Lipp (1940) proposed it, either alone, or mixed with methyl green and pyronin, for staining spirochaetes, particularly *Treponema pallidum*.

The various Victoria blues are often confused; see also Victoria blue R and B, a few pages below.

ANILINE BLUE, W. S. (I.E., WATER SOLUBLE)

C. I. NO. 42755 (1 *ed.:* 707)

(C. I. Acid Blue 22)

Synonyms: *China blue; Soluble blue 3M or 2R; Marine blue V; Cotton blue; Water blue*

This is a mixture of the trisulfonates* of triphenyl pararosanilin (C. I. 42780) and of diphenyl rosanilin. The latter is:

* The location of the sulfonic groups is uncertain.

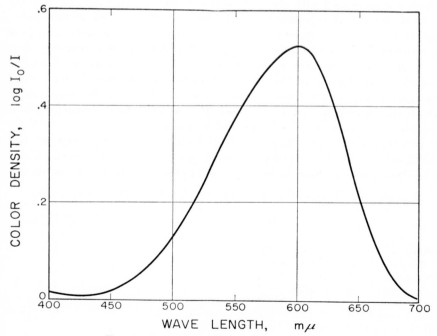

$C_{32}H_{25}N_3O_9S_3Na_2$; mol. wt. 737.736

*(An acid dye; absorption maximum of samples submitted for
certification 595–610 in alcohol)*

Aniline blue W. S. should be regarded as a group of dyes rather than as a simple dye. The composition of the various commercial products sold under this name is uncertain, and no method seems to be known for controlling the process of manufacture so as to yield a constant product.

The spectrophotometric curve of a sample typical of those sold as biological stains is given in Fig. 23.

Certain dyes of this group (apparently only the rosanilin derivatives, because they are most likely to be free from undesirable colored impurities),

FIG. 23. Spectral curve of aniline blue W.S.

have indicator properties, decolorizing almost completely on addition of alkali, and slowly becoming blue again if the reaction becomes acid. It is not a specially valuable indicator, however, partly because of the slowness with which it responds to change in reaction, and partly because it is quite subject to protein and other errors. In spite of these drawbacks it has sometimes been used in bacteriological media, when accuracy is not important and the slow response to acid production is of no significance.

Hendrickson, Baldwin, and Riker (1934) employed it in bacteriological media for a different purpose, the isolation of the crown gall organism; in their medium it holds fungi in check while the desired organism absorbs the blue color and is thus easy to recognize. For some reason not yet explained, those samples (apparently pararosanilin derivatives) which do not decolorize properly in alkaline solution, fail to work in this medium.

By far the best known use of aniline blue, W.S., is as a counterstain in histology. Among its histological applications are: by Stroebe and Huber (see Krause, 1926–1927, p. 63) as a cytoplasm stain preceding safranin; by Galli for axis cylinders; frequently by botanists as a contrast for safranin in vascular plant tissue, or for erythrosin or phloxine in algae; and very widely by pathologists in the Mallory (1900) connective tissue stain, in which it is combined with orange G and acid fuchsin; by Unna in contrast to orcein for staining epithelial sections (see Lee, 1937, p. 438) and in studying the process of chromolysis; by Koneff (1936) in combination with iron hematoxylin as a polychrome staining method for routine laboratory use.

On account of the lack of constancy in this group, anyone publishing a technic calling for one of these dyes should be very careful to give all the information obtainable from the label and should specify the source from which the sample used was obtained. If a Commission certified stain is employed, its certification number should of course be given.

Although some uncertainty exists concerning the composition of the "aniline blue" used by Mallory in developing his connective tissue stain, it has been presumed to have corresponded to the mixture of dyes marketed

Procedures Recommended by the Commission in Which This Stain Is Used

Name of Procedure	Page Reference to Staining Procedures
Mallory's aniline blue collagen stain	52
Heidenhain's "azan" modification	53
Crossman's modification	54
Acid alizarin blue modification	55
Biebrich scarlet and picro-aniline blue in animal histology	62
Lillie modification of Gallego elastic tissue stain	67
Masson's trichrome stain	70
Lillie modification	74
Safranin and picro-aniline-blue in plant histology	194

as C.I. 42755 (1 *ed.*: 707). However, methyl blue, C. I. 42780 (1 *ed.*: 706) serves equally well in this procedure and its many variants. Since commercially available samples of the latter dye may be more nearly homogeneous, further study may show the latter to be preferred to the traditionally recommended aniline blue (see Lillie, 1954).

METHYL BLUE   C. I. NO. 42780 (1 *ed.*: 706)

(C. I. Acid Blue 93)

Synonyms: *Cotton blue; Helvetia blue*

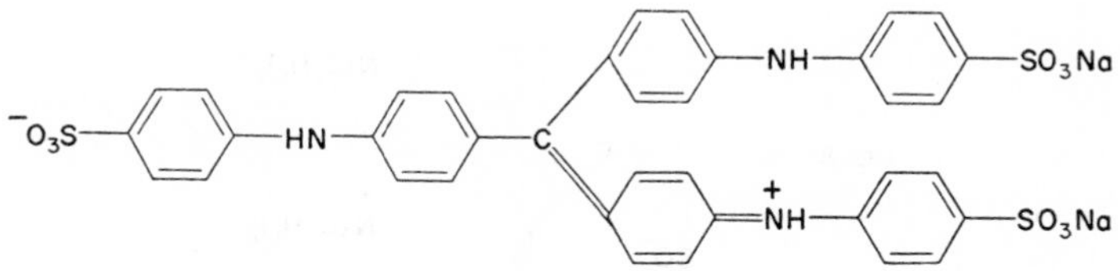

$C_{37}H_{27}N_3O_9S_3Na_2$; *mol. wt.* 799.802

(An acid dye; absorption maximum about 607)

On account of the sulfonic groups, this dye is strongly acidic and makes a good counterstain. It is sometimes sold under the label "aniline blue W.S." (instead of C.I. 42755) and seems to give equally good results in the Mallory connective tissue stain. Such uses of this dye are too numerous to list, but one might mention that of Dubreuil (see Krause, 1926–1927, p. 1382) who employed it, combined with picric acid, in contrast to a red nuclear stain such as carmine or safranin; a similar picric acid mixture is still in use. One of its oldest and best known uses is that of Mann (1894) who mixed it with eosin and showed the value of the mixture in staining nerve cells. Later workers have suggested it for other purposes: Clauser and Strani (1930) for staining unfixed tissue; Cumley (1935) for the negative staining of bacteria; Monné (1935) in the vital staining of protozoa.

For use in **rhodocyan technic** see *Staining Procedures*, p 48.
For use in **technic with Biebrich scarlet** see *Staining Procedures*, p. 63.

ISAMINE BLUE   C. I. NO. 42700

(C. I. Direct Blue 41)

Occasional reference is made, especially in the European literature, to a dye called isamine blue. Its exact chemical nature is not at present known, although it is probably the dye referred to under the above name and C.I. number. It is not yet manufactured in America but was available from German sources before the second World War. It is known to be an acid dye, a sulfonated naphthyl-rosanilin or naphthyl-pararosanilin.

Isamine blue is employed to some extent in Europe as a vital dye by intravenous injection, followed by lead salts or radiation. Exact references to such uses, however, are not now available. Dean (1937) employs it for determining the proportion of antigen to antibody in immune sera.

PATENT BLUE V   C. I. NO. 42045 (1 *ed.:* 672)

(C. I. Acid Blue 3)

Synonyms: *Alphazurine 2G; Patent blue VF; Pontacyl brilliant blue V*

Usually the calcium salt of the following:

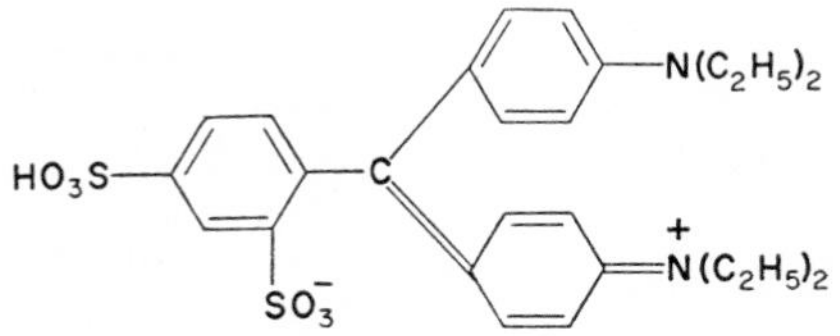

$(C_{27}H_{31}N_2O_7S_2)_2$ Ca; mol. wt. 1159.412

(An acid dye)

This dye has rarely been mentioned in biological literature; but was included by Ono (1934) among those employed for staining spirochaetes; it was mentioned by McMaster and Parsons (1938) as a vital stain, and by Yoe and Boyd (1939) as an acid-base and oxidation-reduction indicator. It has been used by Dunn (1946) as an indicator of hemoglobin oxidase activity.

XYLENE CYANOL FF

C.I. NO. 43535 (1 *ed.:* 715)

Synonym: *Cyanol FF*

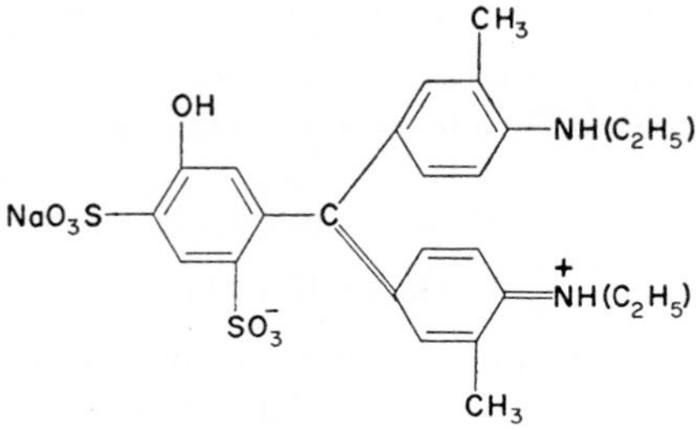

$C_{25}H_{27}N_2O_7S_2Na$; mol. wt. 554.611

(An acid dye)

Chambers (1935) included this among several dyes which he studied in connection with the uptake of dyes by cells in tissue culture. A cyanol, probably this one, has been used by Fautrez (1936) in histochemistry, as an intracellular indicator; and by Ivanov and Braun (1938) in the study of permeability of tissue membranes.

c. Hydroxy Triphenyl Methanes (Rosolic Acids)

The rosolic acid dyes, as stated above, are triphenyl methane derivatives in which the amino groups of the rosanilins are replaced with hydroxyl groups, thus giving them acidic instead of basic character. The compounds of this group are not very important as dyes and are scarcely used as stains. The greatest interest of the biologist in them is due to their use as indicators. In acid solution rosolic acid is yellow but it is converted by alkali to the disodium salt which is red, thus:

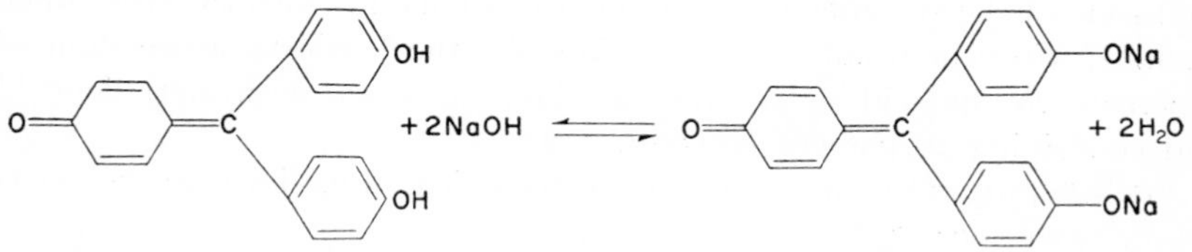

(*pararosolic acid*)   (*disodium pararosolate*)

There is considerable confusion in the nomenclature of these dyes, as the names employed may be used in a strict chemical sense or in a looser sense in practice. Chemically there are two rosolic acids, which are related just as are rosanilin and pararosanilin. Pararosolic acid differs from pararosanilin, only in having hydroxyl groups in place of the amino groups:

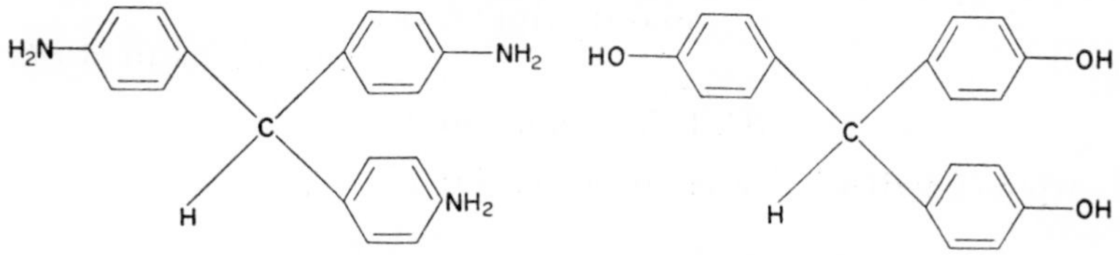

(*leuco pararosanilin*)   (*leuco pararosolic acid*)

Rosolic acid, on the other hand, is a mono-methyl derivative, and bears the same relation to rosanilin:

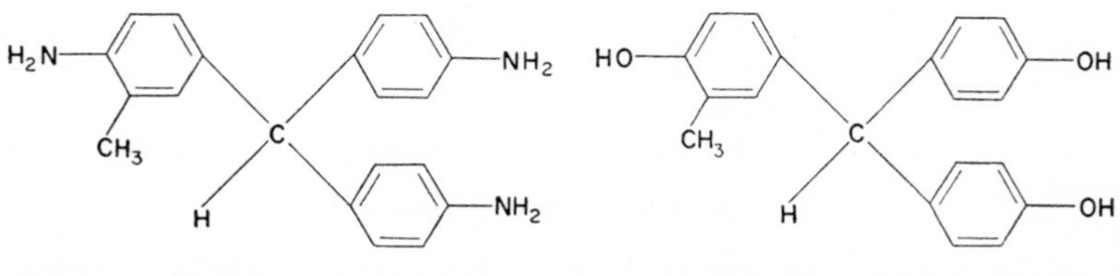

(*leuco rosanilin*)   (*leuco rosolic acid*)

Now the dye to which the name rosolic acid or aurin is generally given in practice is a mixture consisting of both rosolic acid and pararosolic acid together with other closely related compounds. This dye is:

AURIN OR ROSOLIC ACID

C. I. NO. 43800 (1 *ed.:* 724)

The above names apply to the free acid. *Yellow corallin* is the sodium salt.

A mixture of rosolic acid and pararosolic acid, with oxidized and methylated derivatives of the latter. This product is of considerable use as an indicator.

This dye was employed by Pappenheim (1898) in a decolorizing solution following carbol fuchsin. The method was intended to safeguard against confusion of the smegma and other acid-fast bacteria with the true tubercle bacillus. After the usual carbol fuchsin stain, the decolorizing was done with 1 percent rosolic acid in absolute alcohol, saturated with methylene blue and containing 20 percent glycerol.

No other dyes of this group have biological use. Two others perhaps deserve mention:

RED CORALLIN   C. I. (1 *ed.*) NO. 726

Synonym: *Aurin R*

Probably a pararosolic acid salt of pararosanilin, forming an intermediate stage in the c onversion of pararosolic acid into pararosanilin.

CHROME VIOLET CG

C. I. NO. 43810 (1 *ed.:* 727)

(C. I. Mordant Violet 39)

A carboxyl derivative of pararosolic acid:

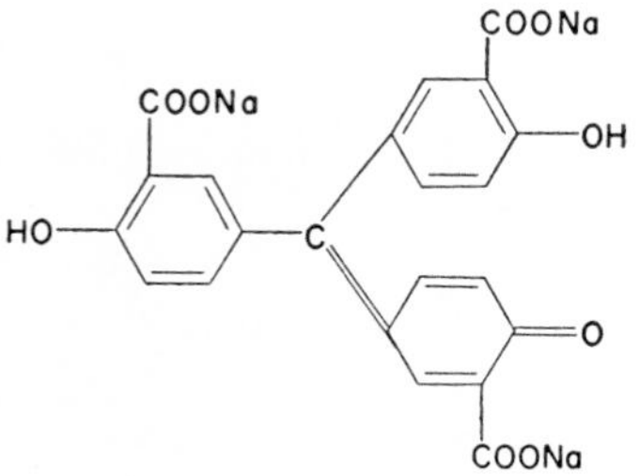

$C_{22}H_{11}O_9Na_3$; mol. wt. 488.299

(*An acid dye*)

3. DIPHENYL-NAPHTHYL METHANE DERIVATIVES

VICTORIA BLUE R

C. I. NO. 44040 (1 *ed.:* 728)

(C. I. Basic Blue 11)

Synonyms: *New Victoria blue B or R; Corn blue B*

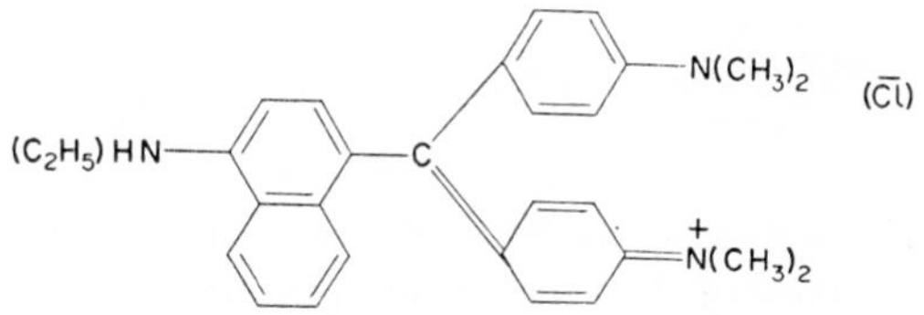

$C_{29}H_{32}N_3Cl$; mol. wt. 458.027

(A basic dye; absorption maximum 614.7 [558])
Solubility at 26°C: in water 0.54%; in alcohol 3.98%

Some Victoria blue, possibly this or the following or possibly C. I. No. 42563 (1 *ed.:* 690), has been employed by Gutstein (1932) as a vital stain for yeast, by Hausdorff (1927) for staining spermatozoa in the testicle, and by Ono (1934) for staining spirochaetes in blood. The various Victoria blues are frequently confused in the literature.

VICTORIA BLUE B

C. I. NO. 44045 (1 *ed.:* 729)

(C. I. Basic Blue 26)

Synonyms: *Fat blue B; Corn blue BN*

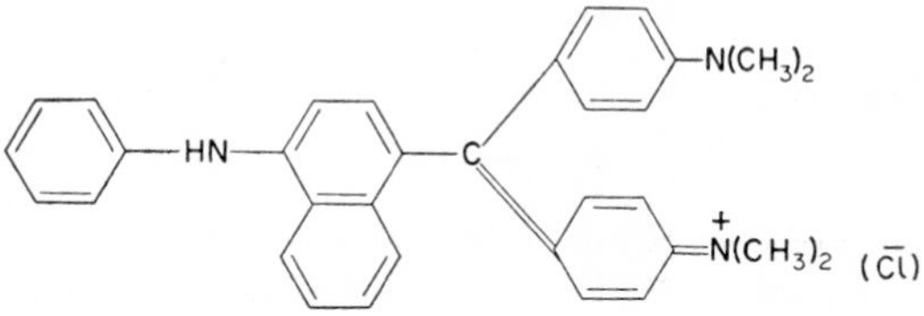

$C_{33}H_{32}N_3Cl$; mol. wt. 506.067

(A basic dye; absorption maximum 619.2 [567])

This dye was employed by Proescher (1934) for staining neuroglia, and its eosinate by Geschickter (1930a) for fresh frozen tissue.

NIGHT BLUE   C. I. NO. 44085 (1 *ed.:* 731)

(C. I. Basic Blue 15)

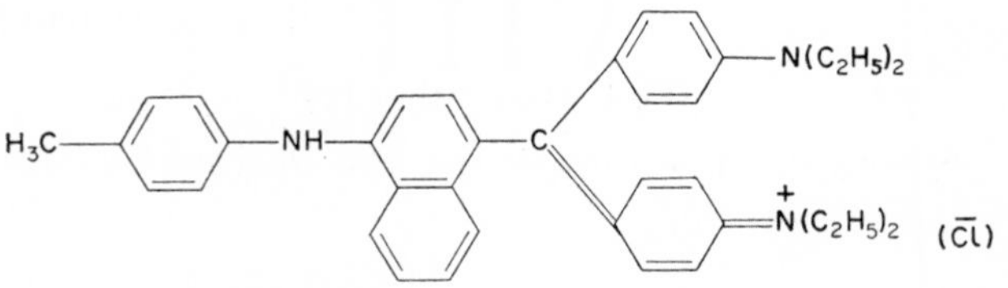

$C_{38}H_{42}N_3Cl$; mol. wt. 576.197

(*A basic dye*)

Hallberg (1946) recommended this dye in place of carbol fucshin as a stain for acid fast bacteria, with phenolic pyronin as a counterstain. The procedure has been followed to some extent in Europe, but is not much used in America. The dye has recently become hard to obtain commercially.

WOOL GREEN S   C. I. NO. 44090 (1 *ed.:* 737)

(C. I. Acid Green 50)

Synonyms: *Wool green BS, BSNA or C; Lissamine green B, BS; Pontacyl green S; Calcoid green S extra; Acid green S; Cyanol green B; Fast light green*

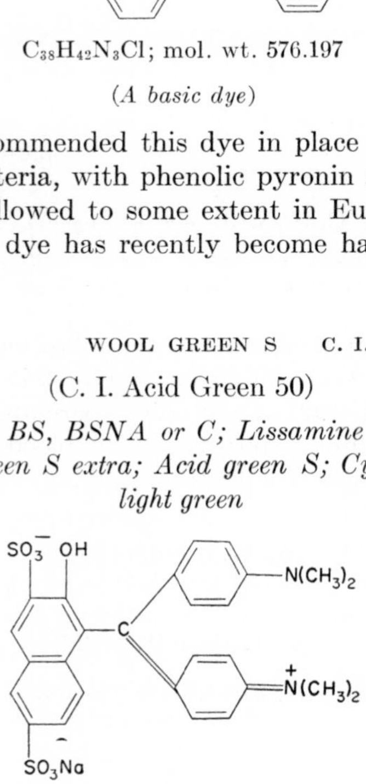

$C_{27}H_{25}N_2O_7S_2Na$; mol. wt. 576.625

(*An acid dye; absorption maximum 634*)

This dye has been mentioned by Lillie (1940, 1945c) as a satisfactory substitute for fast green FCF in his modification of the Masson trichrome stain.

For use in **Lillie Modification of Masson trichrome stain,** see *Staining Procedures,* p. 72.

VIII

THE XANTHENE DYES

The group of compounds known as xanthene dyes comprises a number of basic and acid dyes and quite a series of indicators. In fact, the most valuable indicators known to the chemist fall in this group. They are derivatives of the compound xanthene:

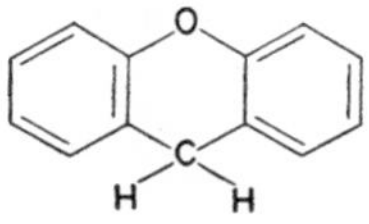

1. THE PYRONINS

The pyronins are methylated di-amino derivatives of xanthene. They are closely related to the diphenyl methanes and are sometimes classed with them, as they have a carbon atom attached to two benzene rings, and show the same tendency toward quinone structure. Their formula, on the other hand, is like that of the oxazins except that the nitrogen of the central ring is replaced by a methenyl (CH) radical. Like the oxazins, the atomic grouping may be assumed to be in either the paraquinoid or the orthoquinoid form, thus:

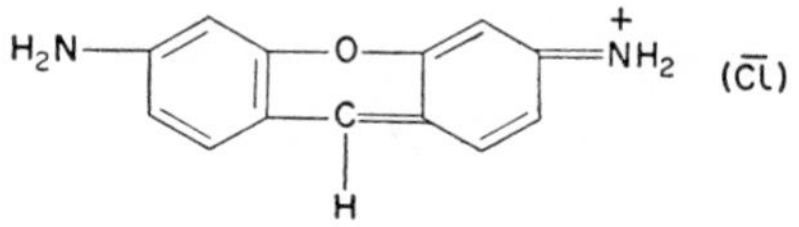

or

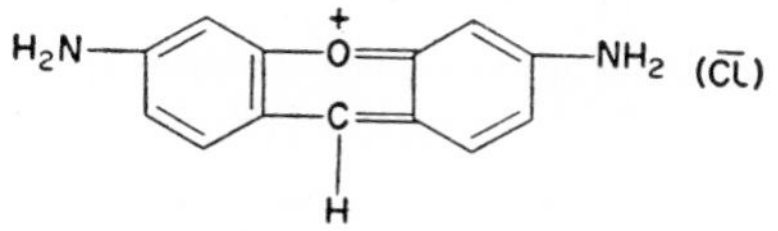

Another arrangement of the atoms is possible in which no quinoid ring exists, namely:

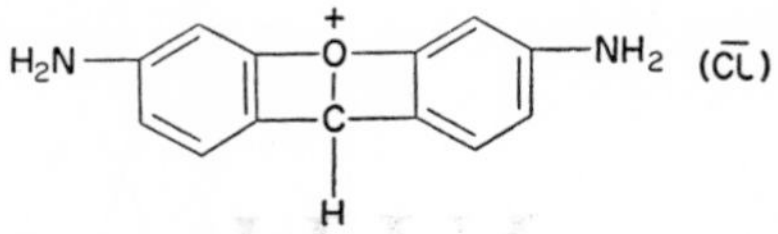

This latter form might also be assumed for the oxazins and thiazins as well, and this type of formula is frequently used for the azins; but the xanthene dyes are more often represented in this form. If this formula is adopted the quinoid ring cannot be accepted as their chromophore. For this reason one of the quinoid formulae seems preferable; and for the sake of uniformity the paraquinoid form will be given in the following pages. It must be remembered, however, that the other formulae are equally admissible; and it is possible that the compounds occur in two or even all three of the different forms.

ACRIDINE RED 3B

C. I. NO. 45000 (1 ed.: 740)

This dye, in spite of its name, is not an acridine derivative, but a pyronin, a lower homolog of pyronin G or Y:

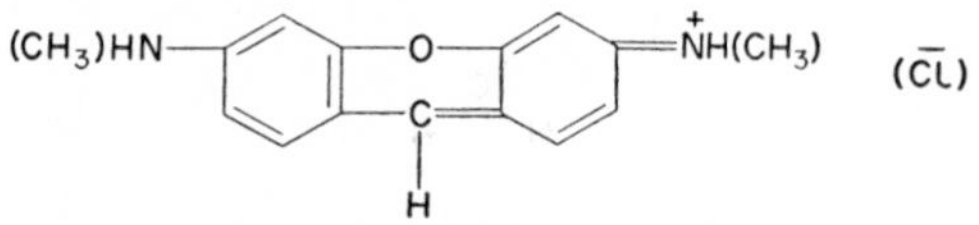

$C_{15}H_{15}N_2OCl$; mol. wt. 274.743

(A basic dye; absorption maximum: [508] 547.5)

It is rarely called for in biological work, but has been used by Gomori (1943), mixed with methyl green, in a procedure for staining tissue to demonstrate deposits of calcium salts and sites of phosphatase activity.

PYRONIN Y   C. I.* NO. 45005 (1 ed.: 739)

Synonym: *Pyronin G*

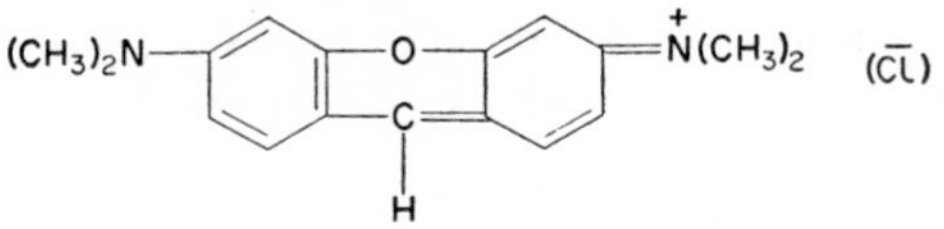

$C_{17}H_{19}N_2OCl$; mol. wt. 302.795

(A basic dye; absorption maximum about 552)
Solubility at 26°C: in water 8.96%; in alcohol 0.60%

---

* The abbreviation "C. I." stands for "Colour Index." The number immediately following is that of the current (2nd) edition; the one which follows is that of the first edition. The name of the dye given under the principal name is the preferred designation in the current Colour Index.

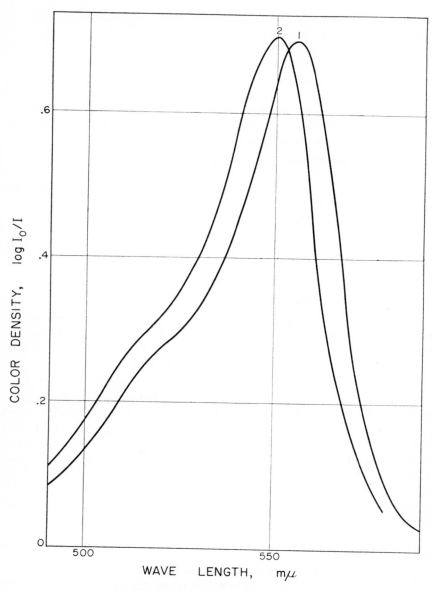

FIG. 24. Spectral curves of two pyronins:
1. Pyronin B   2. Pyronin Y

This dye, finding occasional application as a biological stain in pre-war days, was not manufactured in America until 1931. For most purposes pyronin B may be substituted for it; but Scudder (1931) found it necessary in her combined Gram-Pappenheim stain. In conjunction with methyl green, this dye is a useful histochemical reagent; see Kurnick (1955).

A typical spectral curve of this dye is given in Fig. 24, in which it is compared with pyronin B. This graph, together with the others in this chapter, is from Stotz *et al.* (1950) in which the spectrophotometric characteristics of the xanthene dyes are discussed.

For use **with methyl green in cytology** see *Staining Procedures*, p. 166.

PYRONIN B   C. I. NO. 45010 (1 *ed.*: 741)

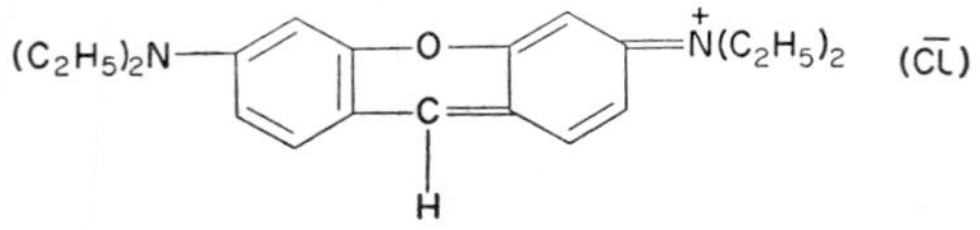

$C_{21}H_{27}N_2OCl$; mol. wt. 358.899

(*A basic dye; absorption maximum about 555*)

This dye differs from pyronin Y only in that it is an ethyl instead of a methyl derivative. As a result it is very slightly deeper in shade but has almost identically the same staining behavior. The two dyes have very similar spectral curves, as shown by the graphs in Fig. 24.

The pyronins find their principal use in the Pappenheim (1899) combination, where a pyronin is employed with methyl green for staining basophile elements, especially the mast cells, and for staining the gonococcus in smears of pus. The same two dyes have been used by Taft (1951) and Kurnick (1952) in animal cytology. It is also used sometimes as a counterstain in the Gram technic for bacteria (see p. 150); and by Ehrlich and Lazarus (1898) as a component of certain "neutral" stains. Monné (1938) has employed a pyronin for staining mitochondria; while Huddleson (1931) makes use of its bacteriostatic properties in distinguishing between species of the bacterial genus, *Brucella*.

For technic of **Pappenheim-Saathof stain for gonorrhoeal pus,** see *Staining Procedures,** p. 245.

For technic of **Saathof stain for bacteria in tissues,** see Id. p. 251.

For use, **with methyl green, in animal histology and cytology,** see Id. p. 166.

2. THE RHODAMINES

The rhodamines are similar to the pyronins except that there is a third benzene ring attached to the central carbon atom and attached to this ring

* Conn, Darrow and Emmel (1960).

is a carboxyl group in the ortho position. This latter group, although of acid tendency, does not counteract the basic action of the amino groups, so the dyes are basic in character.

RHODAMINE B   C. I. NO. 45170 (1 *ed.:* 749)

(C. I. Basic Violet 10)

Synonyms: *Rhodamine O; Brilliant pink B*

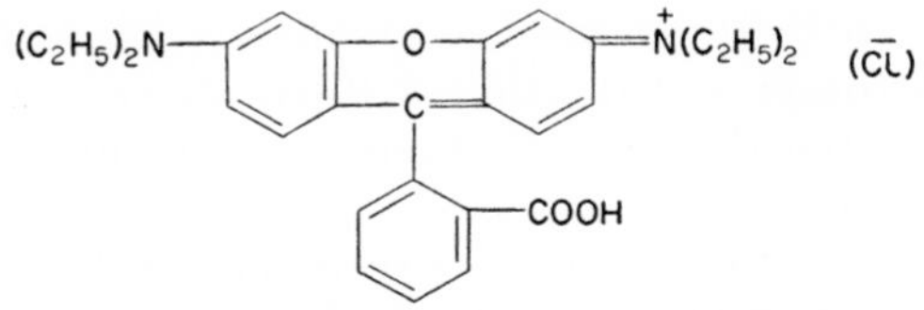

$C_{28}H_{31}N_2O_3Cl$; mol. wt. 479.001

(A basic dye; absorption maximum about 556.5, [517])
Solubility at 26°C: in water 0.78%; in alcohol 1.47%

A rhodamine, probably the above dye, was used by Griesbach with osmic acid to fix and stain blood simultaneously; by Ehrlich as a component of "neutral" stain mixtures; also for histological work in contrast to methylene blue; and by others in contrast to methyl green. (See Krause, 1926–1927, p. 2023.) Although these early users were not always careful to specify which rhodamine had been employed in their work, rhodamine B has been definitely specified by later workers, e.g., by Houcke (1928) as a stain for glandular tissue, when mixed with methylene blue; by Strugger (1938) as a vital stain for *Allium* epidermis, calling attention to its fluorescence under ultraviolet light; by Monné (1939) in studies on the Golgi apparatus; by Levaditi *et al.* (1940), as a fluorochome of value in virus studies; by Metcalf and Patton (1944), as a fluorochrome for use in insect histology; and by Frederick (1941), as a microchemical reagent for the estimation of antimony. It seems to be coming into more common use at present, thanks in good part to its fluorescent properties in ultraviolet light.

As a rhodamine is not infrequently specified without a shade designation, it is sometimes not possible to be sure that the above dye is intended. If not, the following is the dye most probably indicated.

RHODAMINE 6G   C. I. NO. 45160 (1 *ed.:* 752)

(C. I. Basic Red 1)

Synonyms: *Rhodamine 6GX and 6GDN extra; Calcozine red 6G extra*

By esterification of a compound closely related to rhodamine B, the following is obtained:

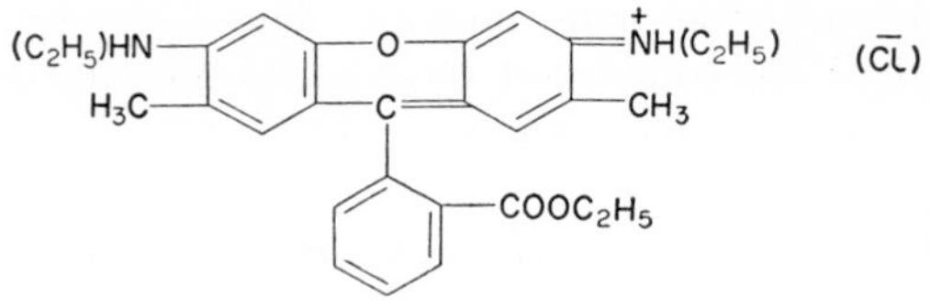

$C_{28}H_{31}N_2O_3Cl$; mol. wt. 479.001

(A basic dye; absorption maximum [492] 526)

This dye has not been specified as frequently as rhodamine B, but is mentioned by Strugger and by Monné (cited above), each of whom employed both dyes. Whether this ethyl ester has any advantage over rhodamine B is not stated.

A somewhat different dye, known as rhodamine S (C. I. No. 45050, C. I. Basic Red 11) has been mentioned in the same connection and may have been used for some of the above-mentioned purposes. It is not a true rhodamine, however, but belongs to a closely related group of compounds, the succineins; for it does not have the three benzene rings, the radical $C_6H_4 \cdot COOH$ being replaced by $C_2H_4 \cdot COOH$.

VIOLAMINE R   C. I. NO. 45190 (1 *ed.:* 758)

(C. I. Acid Violet 9)

Synonyms: *Acid violet 4R; Fast acid violet 3RL, A2R and R*

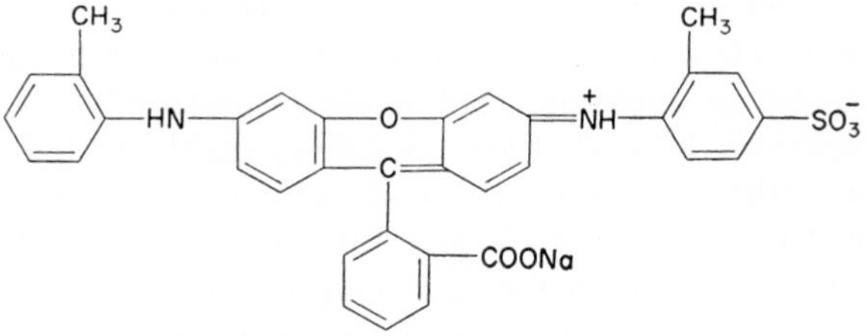

$C_{34}H_{25}O_6N_2SNa$; mol. wt. 612.619

(An acid dye)

Lillie (1945c) has mentioned this dye, among others, as a stain for collagen in tissue sections.

FAST ACID BLUE R

C. I. NO. 45205 (1 *ed.:* 760)

(C. I. Acid blue 19)

Almost the same as: *Violamine 3B*

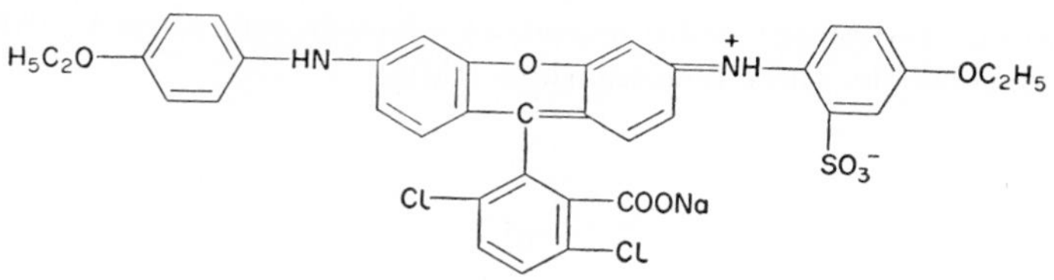

$$C_{36}H_{27}N_2O_8SNaCl_2 \; ; \; mol. \; wt. \; 741.569$$

(An acid dye; absorption maximum 534)

In the first edition of the Colour Index violamine 3B is listed as almost synonymous with this. Violamine 3B, however, is a mixture containing a small amount of some red dye. Some samples of fast acid blue R, made for textile application, are also mixtures, although pure samples have been obtained. It is hoped that pure dye of this type may become regularly available for use as a biological stain.

This dye has been recommended by Romell for use in phenolic solution for staining bacteria in soil. In the case of soils (mucks, forest soils, etc.) containing much brownish or reddish matter, this blue dye gives greater visibility of the microorganisms than dyes of the eosin series.

In practice the rhodamines are prepared not from xanthene but by the condensation of two molecules of dialkyl meta-amino phenols,

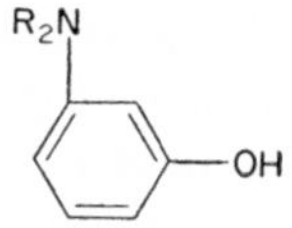

with one of phthalic anhydride:

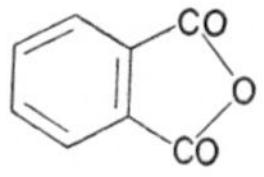

This shows their close relation to the next group of dyes, namely the fluoran derivatives, which as will be seen are also prepared from phthalic anhydride. In fact these two groups of dyes, acid and basic respectively, are related in exactly the same way as the rosolic acids and the rosanilins, the one group having hydroxyl radicals where the other has amino groups.

3. FLUORAN DERIVATIVES

Fluoran is not a dye, but is a very important compound in dye chemistry. It is a derivative of phthalic anhydride, and contains a xanthene ring (five C atoms and one O atom) as well as a lactone ring (four C atoms and one O atom) besides three benzene rings; thus:

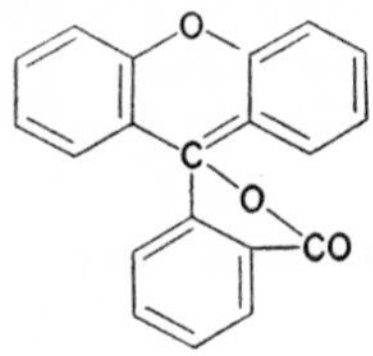

The fluoran dyes are derivatives of this by the introduction of hydroxyl groups into two of the benzene rings at the para position to the central carbon atom and the further introduction of halogen atoms at various positions in all three benzene rings.

It proves convenient here to class these compounds with the xanthene dyes. They may, however, be equally well considered triphenyl-methane dyes, as can be seen by a glance at the formula of any of them; in fact they are generally so considered by the chemists. To the biologist they stand in a distinctly different class from the triphenyl-methanes; and for that reason are treated here instead of in the preceding chapter. The dyes of this group are also, and equally correctly, spoken of as the fluorescein derivatives, fluorescein being, as will be seen on p. 174, a salt of dihydroxy-fluoran. Sometimes, moreover, the fluorescein dyes are referred to as the eosins. This term to cover the whole group is hardly justified, as it is better to call eosins only the dyes definitely so named below.

The fluorescein dyes are all similar in their action, but with certain decided differences. In order for the reader to obtain a real understanding of these stains and their behavior, a general discussion of the whole group is necessary.

The dyes in this group most important to the biologist are: eosin Y (C. I. acid red 87, No. 45380—also called eosin yellowish or eosin water soluble); ethyl eosin (C. I. solvent red 45, No. 45386—also called eosin alcohol soluble); eosin B (C. I. acid red 91, No. 45400—also called eosin bluish); erythrosin B (C. I. acid red 51, No. 45430); phloxine (C. I. acid red 98, No. 45405); rose bengal (C. I. acid red 94, No. 45440). It is not yet absolutely certain which of these dyes is most suitable for any particular purpose; but some information is available on the subject. The difference in behavior of the different dyes of this group seems to depend upon two factors: difference in color and difference in acidity. The relation between these two factors and chemical structure was discussed by Conn and Holmes (1926); by reference to which paper it will be seen that in color the dyes above listed increase in depth in the following order: eosin Y, ethyl eosin, eosin B, erythrosin B, phloxine, rose bengal. In the case of each of these, the color is lighter or deeper according to the number of halogen atoms present. Eosin B is the strongest acid in the group, and eosin Y the next strongest; erythrosin is weaker, phloxine weaker than eosin and possibly weaker than erythrosin, and rose bengal is the weakest of all.

To interpret this information into terms of actual use, it is necessary to remember that there are two main types of histological procedures in which eosin is used: first as a general counterstain (usually in alcoholic solution) following a basic dye; secondly, as a cytoplasm stain (always in aqueous solution) preceding a basic dye. In the first of these types of procedure it is important that the dye be one with diffuse staining properties and with a color showing good contrast to the basic dye employed (generally methylene blue or hematoxylin). The more acid and lighter colored dyes in the series (eosin Y, ethyl eosin, and eosin B) seem to possess these properties to the greatest extent and accordingly to be best adapted to such procedures. The particular dye to choose depends undoubtedly on the exact shade desired.

The second type of procedure (i.e., preceding a basic dye) is represented by the Mallory phloxine-methylene-blue stain and the Held erythrosin-methylene-blue technic. In such procedures as these, both dyes are used in aqueous solution; and there is therefore much more opportunity for chemical interaction between the acid dye already in the tissue and the basic dye subsequently added than when the acid dye is used in alcoholic solution. (It is well known that acid and basic dyes in alcoholic solution do not form insoluble reaction products.) In procedures like the Mallory technic, there seems to be a tendency (possibly on account of this interaction) for the acid dye to stain the cytoplasm too weakly when followed by a basic dye, in case the very acid eosin Y is used. Thus Held employs erythrosin, and Mallory who formerly specified eosin discovered later that his original eosin was not a true eosin Y, phloxine giving better results in his technic than one of the true eosins. Now phloxine and erythrosin are not only deeper in color than eosin Y, but are also less strongly acidic; and it is possible that their chemical nature rather than their color may be the decisive factor in determining their superiority for such procedures as this. Rose bengal is even deeper in color, and is still less strongly acidic; in fact, it seems to be too purple to contrast well with methylene blue and of such a weakly acid character that it tends to remain in the nuclei when used by the technic in question. It might prove valuable preceding some basic dye; but it has been found to give poor results preceding methylene blue in the Mallory technic.

In the procedure for staining bacteria in soil, as developed by Conn (1918) and by Winogradsky (1924), the matter is still further complicated by the fact that the dye must be of such a color and such a strong acid as to stain the bacteria, but not the dead organic matter present.

Another factor of much importance in the staining action of these dyes is the amount of mineral salt present. It has, in fact, been shown by Conn and Holmes (1928) that the intensity with which a dye of this group can stain bacteria may be greatly increased by adding a minute amount (0.001 to 0.1 percent) of some mineral salt such as $CaCl_2$. This matter is discussed in Chapter II.

There was in the past much mislabeling of the dyes of this group. Thus it is evident that the eosin used by Mallory when he first worked out his eosin-methylene-blue technic must have been a phloxine or some closely related dye rather than a true eosin. There is evidence that erythrosin B and phloxine have been put on the market labeled eosin bluish; so has a blend of eosin Y shaded with some one of the higher members of the group. Phloxine has been sold as magdala red and is even now sometimes marketed under that name both by American and foreign concerns. All this has caused much confusion; but dealers in stains are using greater caution in the matter at present.

FLUORESCEIN   C. I. NO. 45350 (1 *ed.:* 766)

(C. I. Acid Yellow 73)

This is the simplest of the fluoran dyes, and is the mother substance of the eosins. Its sodium salt is known as *uranin.*

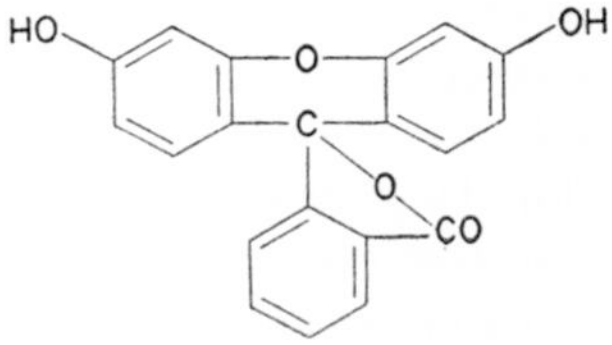

$C_{20}H_{12}O_5$; mol. wt. 332.296 $C_{20}H_{10}O_5Na_2$; mol. wt. 376.274
fluorescein   *uranin*

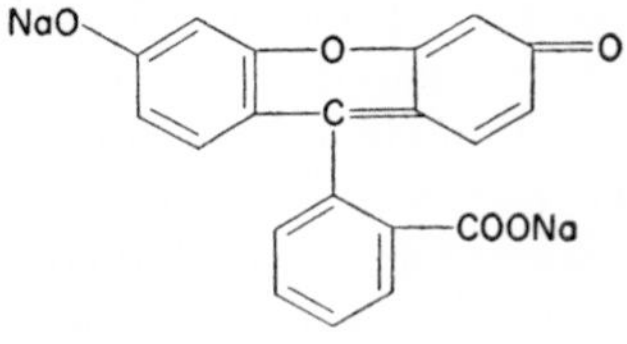

(An acid dye; absorption maximum about 490)
Solubility at 26°C:
  Of fluorescein: in water, 0.03%; in alcohol, 2.21%.
  Of uranin: in water, 50.02%; in alcohol, 7.19%.

Fluorescein is a yellow dye of very low tinctorial power, and hence of no value for ordinary staining purposes. It is on the other hand extremely fluorescent, the greenish yellow fluorescence being detectable in high dilution. On account of this latter property the dye is used to determine the possibility of contamination from some suspected source getting into a neigbhoring water supply.

This fluorescence is even more pronounced in ultraviolet light, a fact which makes the dye useful in fluorescence microscopy. Thus Hercik (1939) employs it as a fluorochrome in the study of epidermis cells of *Allium*; Levaditi *et al.* (1940) in virus studies; Metcalf and Patton (1944) in insect entomology. Of these uses, the demonstration and localization of antibodies in viral (and other) diseases has become specially important; see Coons and Kaplan (1950).

It has been included by Williams and Green (1935) in a series of dyes that prove useful in media in which fungi are growing, the absorption of the dye by the fungi giving characteristic colors to the colonies.

EOSIN Y (I.E., YELLOWISH)

C. I. NO. 45380 (1 *ed.:* 768)

(C. I. Acid Red 87)

Synonyms: *Eosin, water soluble; Bromo acid, J, TS, XL or XX; Bromofluorescein; Bronze bromo ES*

Various shades denoted: *Eosin B extra, BP, BS, DH, G, GGF, J extra, 3J, 4J, JJF, KS, S extra, Y extra and YS*

This dye is typically tetrabromo fluorescein:

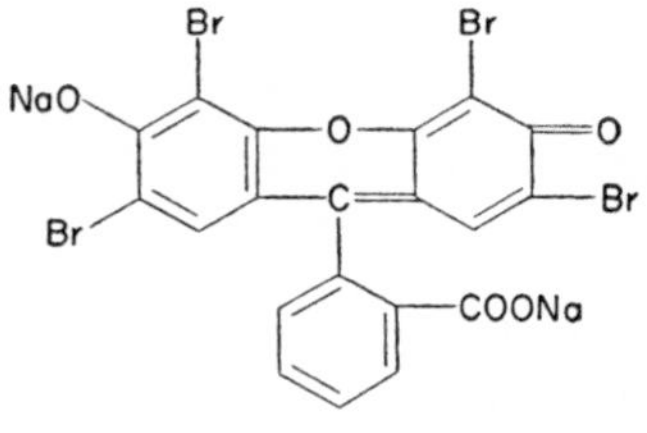

$C_{20}H_6O_5Br_4Na_2$; mol. wt. 691.906

(An acid dye; absorption maximum 515–518)
Solubility at 26°C: in water 44.20%; in alcohol 2.18%

but the mono- and dibromo derivatives are also known and frequently occur in eosin. This affects the shade, as the more bromine present the redder the dye. It is plain that various mixtures of these compounds are on the market; but it has not yet been determined which are more suitable for biological purposes. Considerably more work on eosin is needed than has been done at the present time. From the name "water soluble eosin" it is often assumed that this dye is not soluble in alcohol. This is not true, however.

A typical absorption curve of eosin Y is given in graph 2, Fig. 25, in which it is compared with the similar spectral data for eosin B and ethyl eosin.

Like fluorescein, eosin Y shows greenish yellow fluorescence, especially in alcoholic solution. This fluorescence is visible in ordinary light, but although quite strong, is not so pronounced nor visible in such great dilution

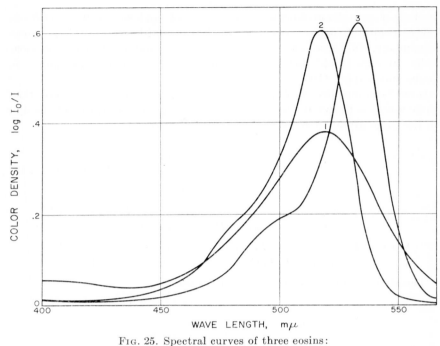

FIG. 25. Spectral curves of three eosins:
1. Eosin B   2. Eosin Y   3. Ethyl eosin

as in the case of fluorescein. It is interesting that in this series of fluoran derivatives, tictorial power increases but fluorescence decreases with the ascending members of the series; thus the erythrosins are less fluorescent than eosin, while phloxine and rose bengal show scarcely any fluorescence in ordinary light. In spite of the marked fluorescence of eosin Y, it does not seem to have been suggested as a fluorochrome.

Yellowish eosin is one of the most valuable plasma stains known. It is used in various technics for staining the oxyphil granules of cells (i.e., the granules having special affinity for acid dyes); these cell elements, in fact, being often called eosinophil granules because their presence was first recognized through the use of this dye. It is often employed as a counterstain for hematoxylin and the green or blue basic dyes; as for example by List with methyl green. Its uses, however, are really too numerous to list. At the present time one of the uses for which it is in greatest demand is as a blood stain in the technic of Romanovsky, with its various modifications, in which it is combined with methylene blue to form a "neutral" stain.

A dye mixture sold under the name of "Triosin," was described by Galigher (1934), and sold by him without stating its composition. The mixture proves valuable as a counterstain in some procedures where eosin Y alone gives less satisfactory results. Recently Emery and Stotz (1952) used this product as an unknown in a test of filter paper chromatography for dye analysis. In the course of this investigation the composition of the mixture became evident, and was stated by these authors as being apparently 62 percent eosin Y, 28 percent orange G, and 10 percent erythrosin Y. A spectral curve of the mixture, however, does not reveal the presence of either of the two latter dyes, but seems practically identical with that of eosin Y alone.

Procedures Recommended by the Commission in Which This Stain is Used*

Name of Procedure	Page Reference to *Staining Procedures*
Delafield's hematoxylin with eosin Y	39
Ehrlich's hematoxylin with eosin Y	40
Mayer's acid hemalum with eosin Y, Lillie modification	43
Buffered thiazin eosinates in tissue staining	45
Wright stain for blood films	133-5
MacNeal's tetrachrome stain for blood films	135
Giemsa stain for blood films	136-7
Wright, Giemsa, or May-Gruenwald stain for bone marrow	143
Counterstain in Gram-Weigert technic for bacteria in tissues	254

* Under this heading are given references to procedures described in detail in *Staining Procedures*, edited by Conn, Darrow, and Emmel (1960).

METHYL EOSIN

C. I. NO. 45385 (1 *ed.:* 769)

(C. I. Solvent Red 44)

Synonym: *Eosin, alcohol soluble*

This is the methyl ester of yellowish eosin, the sodium salt of which is:

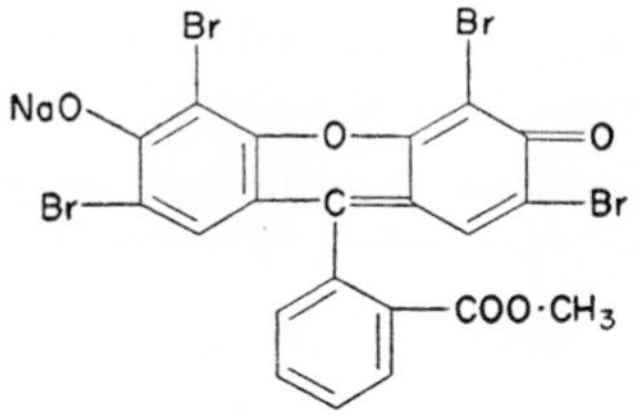

$C_{21}H_9O_5Br_4Na$; mol. wt. 683.943

(An acid dye; absorption maximum about 520, [485.5])

There is no evidence that this dye has been furnished to biologists as a stain. The alcohol soluble eosin known in the biological laboratory is apparently the following.

ETHYL EOSIN   C. I. NO. 45386 (1 *ed.*: 770)
(C. I. Solvent Red 45)

Synonyms: *Eosin, alcohol soluble; Eosin S*

This is similar to methyl eosin, but is the ethyl ester:

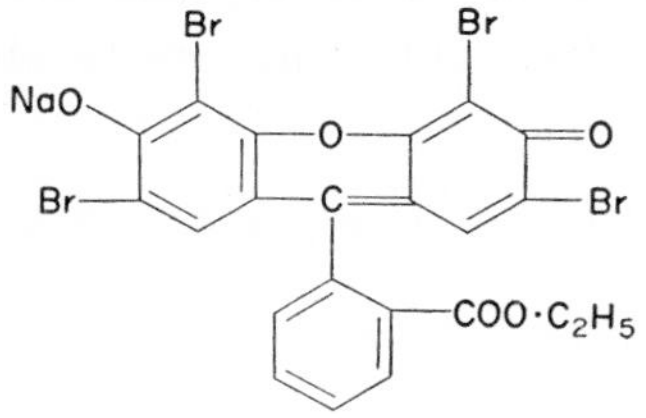

C$_{22}$H$_{11}$O$_5$Br$_4$Na; mol. wt. 697.969

(An acid dye; absorption maximum 524–527)
Solubility at 26°C: in water 0.03%; in alcohol 1.13%

A spectral curve of this dye is given in graph 3, Fig. 25.

Ethyl eosin is apparently the alcohol soluble eosin ordinarily sold by biological supply houses. For some time after the first World War it was difficult to secure this dye in America, and one stain company for a few years furnished the color acid of eosin Y when alcohol soluble eosin was ordered. (The color acids of all these dyes are alcohol soluble but almost insoluble in either hot or cold water; methyl and ethyl eosin, on the other hand, are slightly soluble in cold water but strongly soluble in hot water and alcohol.) This error has now been corrected, and true ethyl eosin as obtainable from American manufacturers, is on the Commission certification basis, and can be ordered from any biological supply house. It should be ordered as ethyl eosin rather than alcohol soluble eosin, as the latter name is less definite.

Ethyl eosin is a valuable counterstain after Delafield's hematoxylin. Preceding methylene blue, it is employed in demonstrating Negri bodies in the central nervous system of rabid animals.

For technic of **Harris stain for Negri bodies,** see *Staining Procedures*, p. 247.
For technic of **staining Negri bodies in sections,** see Id. p. 259–61.

EOSIN B (I.E. BLUISH)
C. I. NO. 45400 (1 *ed.*: 771)
(C. I. Acid Red 91)

Synonyms: *Eosin BN, BA, BS, BW, or DHV; Saffrosin; Eosin scarlet; Eosin scarlet B; Scarlet J, JJ, V; Nopalin G; Imperial red*

This is a dibrom derivative of dinitro fluorescein:

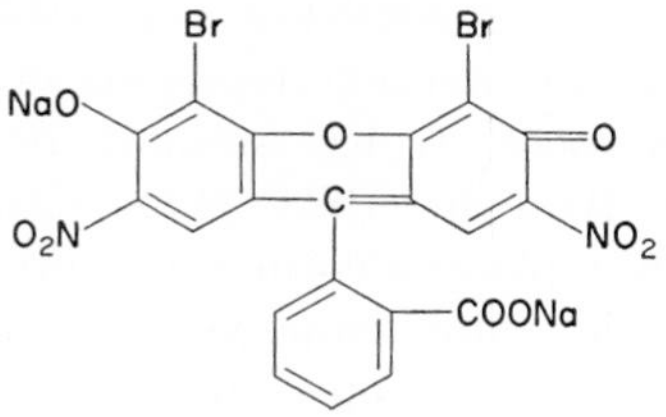

$C_{20}H_6N_2O_9Br_2Na_2$; mol. wt. 624.090

(An acid dye; absorption maximum 516–519)
Solubility at 26°C: in water 39.11%; in alcohol 0.75%

This dye has a distinctly bluer shade than eosin Y; although its absorption maximum is not very different, it has a distinctly different spectral curve, as shown by Fig. 25, p. 176.

It has occasionally been called for as a counterstain in some histological procedure as, for example, in aqueous solution following Mayer's hemalum (Kornhauser, 1930), but is not in general very valuable. Lillie (1944c) finds it useful, for tissues, with azure A or toluidine blue, especially when freshly mixed with the basic dye; eosin B is too weakly acid to perform satisfactorily in a Romanowski type "neutral" stain.

Ordinarily, if a shade deeper than eosin Y is desired, better results can be obtained with erythrosin, phloxine or rose bengal than with eosin B. Coleman and Bell, in fact, put on the market a product labeled "eosin, bluish blend," which is a mixture of eosin Y with some one of the dyes just named; it is very satisfactory for certain staining procedures, but must not be confused with true eosin B.

For technic of **Mayer's hemalum with eosin B,** see *Staining Procedures,* p. 64.
For technic of **buffered azure eosinate method,** see Id. p. 45.
For use in **rhodocyan technic,** see Id. p. 48.

MERCUROCHROME 220

This is a proprietary name applied to a fluorescein derivative closely related to eosin: dibromo-hydroxy-mercuri-fluorescein.

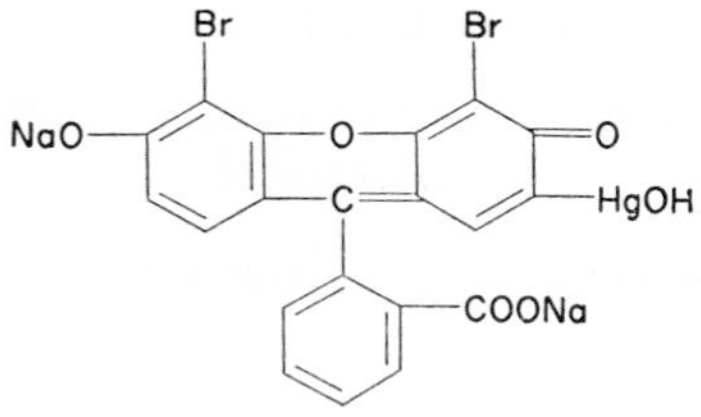

$C_{20}H_8O_6HgBr_2Na_2$; mol. wt. 750.700

The dye has been widely advertised as a disinfectant especially for the skin; and there has been considerable discussion in the literature as to its actual value for the purpose. It has staining properties not unlike an erythrosin, or phloxine. Baldwin (1928) states that it may be used in 2 percent aqueous solution in place of eosin, especially for blood work and for tissues after Zenker fixation; thus employed it is more intense than eosin and has a stronger affinity for cytoplasmic structures. Detwiler and Mc-Kennon (1929) employed it in concentration of from 1:500,000 to 1: 1,000,000 as a fungicidal agent for the treatment of amphibian embryos. Conklin (1934) recommended it as a counterstain to malachite green in the Wirtz spore stain for bacteria.

ERYTHROSIN, YELLOWISH

C. I. NO. 45425 (1 *ed.:* 772)

(C. I. Acid Red 95)

Synonyms: *Erythrosin R or G; Pyrosin J; Dianthine G; Iodeosin G*

This is a fluorescein in which there are two substituent iodine atoms instead of four bromine atoms as in yellowish eosin.

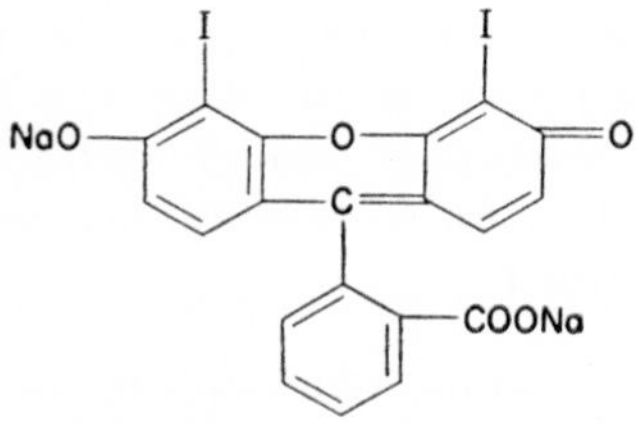

$C_{20}H_8O_4I_2Na_2$; mol. wt. 628.098

(An acid dye; absorption maximum about 510.5)

ERYTHROSIN, BLUISH

C. I. NO. 45430 (1 *ed.:* 773)

(C. I. Acid Red 51)

Synonyms: *Erythrosin B, N, or JN; Pyrosin B; Eosin J; Iodeosin B; Dianthine B*

This is the tetraiodo compound corresponding to the tetrabrom compound of typical eosin.

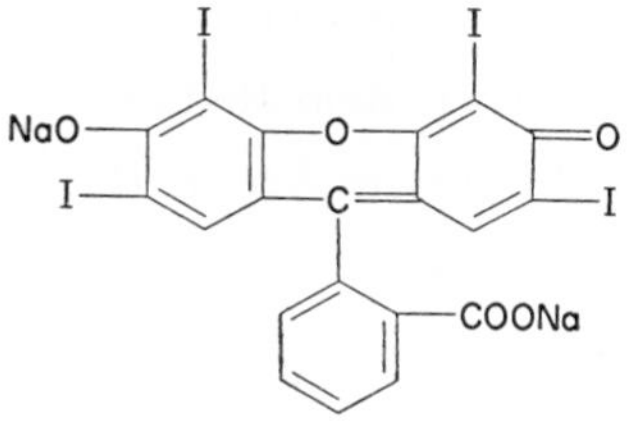

$C_{20}H_6O_5I_4Na_2$; mol. wt. 879.922

(An acid dye; absorption maximum 524–527)
Solubility at 26°C: in water 11.10%; in alcohol 1.87%

There is some uncertainty as to which of these two very similar dyes is preferable in any given technic. At present, the latter, erythrosin B, is ordinarily furnished by supply houses when "erythrosin" is ordered. Its spectral curve is given in Fig. 26, p. 183.

Erythrosin has some use as an indicator. It is also employed as a contrast stain for hematoxylin and certain blue and violet nuclear stains. Thus, for example, Held (1895) used it, preceding methylene blue, as a plasma stain for nerve cells. Similarly the technic of Jackson (1926) called for it as a counterstain to crystal violet in plant histology. It was employed by Winogradsky (1924) for staining bacteria in soil. Gellhorn (1931) applied it to the vital staining of sea urchin eggs. These procedures are mentioned merely by way of illustration; the uses of erythrosin are quite numerous, and the list could be extended almost indefinitely. For these purposes probably the tetra-iodo compound (i.e., erythrosin bluish) is desired; but the literature is vague on the subject.

A sample of erythrosin of pre-war origin that was labeled magdala red has been examined by the Commission. This mislabeling undoubtedly explains Chamberlain's results already mentioned (page 124) in staining algae. Chamberlain, it will be recalled, was able to obtain good results with a low-priced produce called magdala red but not with the high-priced stain called magdala red *echt*.

For technic of **Jackson stain for woody tissue,** see *Staining Procedures,* p. 191.

If in the manufacture of fluorescein, dichloro or tetrachloro phthalic acid is used for condensation with resorcin, a series of halogenated derivatives may be obtained differing from those just named by having halogen atoms in the phthalic acid residue of the molecule as well as in the resorcin residue. These compounds are slightly deeper in shade than the corresponding derivatives of simple phthalic acid; and they are generally regarded as being of more pleasing shade than the ordinary fluorescein dyes. The phloxines and rose bengals are the best known of these dyes.

PHLOXINE   C. I. NO. 45405 (1 ed.: 774)

(C. I. Acid Red 98)

Synonyms: *Erythrosin BB, or B extra; New pink*

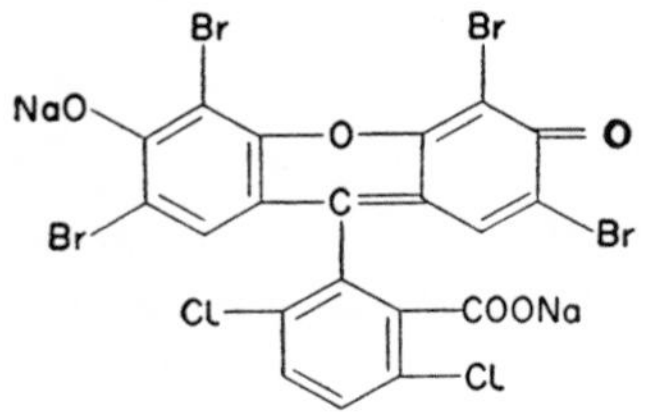

$C_{20}H_4O_5Br_4Cl_2Na_2$; mol. wt. 760.804

(An acid dye; absorption maximum about 535.7, [497.1])
Solubility at 26°C: in water 50.9%; in alcohol 9.02%

This dye and the following are often denoted interchangeably phloxine or phloxine B, and there is some question as to whether biologists have always been furnished the same type. The phloxines of American manufacture at present on the market are the following type.

PHLOXINE B   C. I. NO. 45410 (1 ed.: 778)

(C. I. Acid Red 92)

Synonyms: *Phloxine TA, N, BP super, RB, TB, or BB;*
Cyanosine; Eosin 10B

$C_{20}H_2O_5Br_4Cl_4Na_2$; mol. wt. 829.702

(An acid dye; absorption maximum 546-548)

This dye differs from C. I. No. 45405 in having four instead of two chlorine atoms in the phthalic acid residue of the molecule. Samples of phloxine recently submitted to the Commission for certification seem to vary in degree of bromination or chlorination, but correspond to this C. I. number rather than to the preceding. Although some of the procedures given below may have been worked out originally with the other type of phloxine, this type has been found to give satisfactory results.

A spectral curve of this dye, in comparison with erythrosin B and rose bengal, is given in Fig. 26.

Unna (1921) used phloxine in combination with several other acid dyes in studying the process of chromolysis. The dye was seldom specified for biological work until about 1925, but has recently been applied to staining bacteria, Negri bodies, and to various histological procedures. It has, moreover, frequently been used under other names.

Chamberlain (1932, p. 69; 1927), mentioned having used it successfully

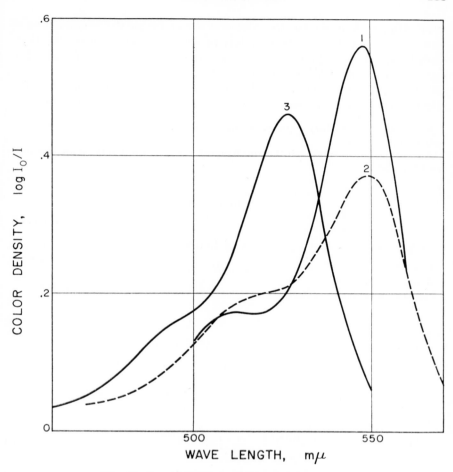

Fig. 26. Spectral curves of three xanthene dyes:
1. Phloxine B   2. Rose bengal   3. Erythrosin B

in place of magdala red in staining algae. His original technic called for magdala red; but true magdala red does not serve his purposes. Inasmuch as erythrosin (see above) was evidently sold in the past as magdala red and Chamberlain could duplicate his original results with phloxine, the chances are that some of the magdala red formerly available was either phloxine or else that phloxine and erythrosin give similar results by Dr. Chamberlain's technic.

About 1920 Dr. F. B. Mallory, like many others, found it difficult to obtain an eosin of either domestic or foreign origin which would give consistently reliable results by his eosin-methylene blue method described in

1904. After testing out, on the advice of a member of the Commission, a series of eosins and closely related dyes he wrote that phloxine is "the best *eosin* I have yet found for use in the eosin-methylene blue stain for paraffin sections of tissues fixed in Zenker's fluid."* Here again is a case where phloxine apparently was obtained before the war under an incorrect name and the incorrect name used in the publication of a well known technic.

For technic of **Mallory's phloxine-methylene-blue stain,** see *Staining Procedures*, pp. 49, 250.

For use as **counterstain in Gram-Weigert technic for bacteria in tissues,** see Id. p. 254.

ROSE BENGAL G

c. i. no. 45435 (1 *ed.:* 777)

(C. I. Acid Red 93)

Synonym: *Rose SA*

Various shades denoted: *Rose bengal N, AT, NT, NTO, and B*

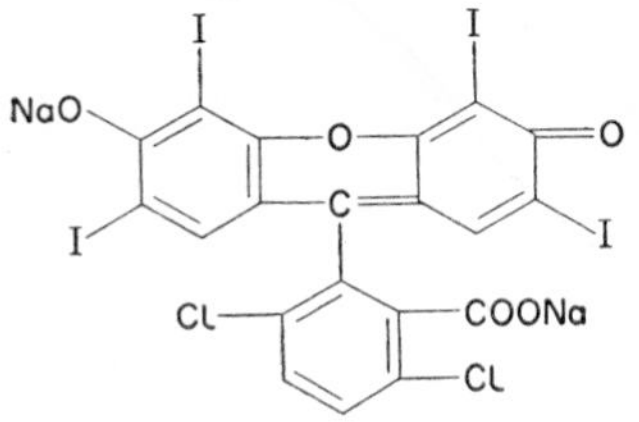

$C_{20}H_4O_5I_4Cl_2Na_2$; mol. wt. 948.820

(*An acid dye*)

This particular rose bengal apparently has not been employed by biologists. The dye of that name sold by stain companies at present is the following.

ROSE BENGAL   c. i. no. 45440 (1 *ed.:* 779)

(C. I. Acid Red 94)

Various shades denoted: *Rose bengal extra, 3B conc., N extra, DY, B and 2B*

* Quoted from personal letter.

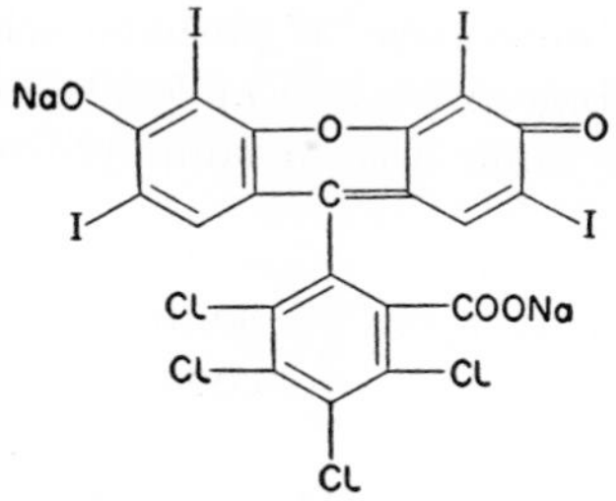

$C_{20}H_2O_5I_4Cl_4Na_2$; mol. wt. 1017.718

(An acid dye; absorption maximum 544–548)
Solubility at 26°C: in water 36.25%; in alcohol 7.53%

The dye has a pleasing deep pink color; and although an acid dye it proves to have considerable affinity for bacterial protoplasm, and to have good selective properties when used as a bacterial stain. It has been recommended (Conn 1918, 1921) for staining bacteria, especially in soil suspensions. It has also been used as a cytoplasm stain following hematoxylin or preceding toluidine blue. Maneval (1934) employed it in the negative staining of bacteria and Ono (1934) for spirochaetes in blood. It also finds use in Delprat and Stowe's test (1931) for liver function. Popper (see Metcalf and Patton, 1944) mentions it as a useful fluorochrome in the study of fats under ultraviolet illumination. Smith and Dawson (1944) employed this dye as a bacteriostatic agent in media designed to permit the growth of soil fungi while repressing the bacteria; this is the only instance yet noted of one of the fluoran derivatives being thus used.

From Fig. 26, in which the spectral curve of this dye and phloxine B are compared, it will be seen that they differ more in shape than in the position of the absorption maximum.

For technic of **general staining of pure cultures of bacteria,** see *Staining Procedures,* p. 224.

For technic of **Conn's stain for bacteria in soil,** see Id. p. 248.

4. PHENOLPHTHALEIN AND THE SULFONPHTHALEINS

A phthalein is a compound of phthalic acid:

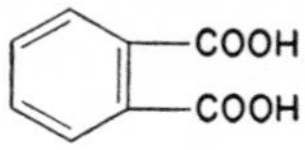

or rather of phthalic anhydride:

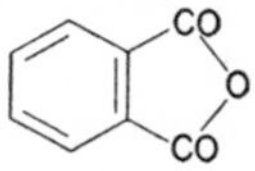

with phenol or a phenol derivative. If phthalic acid is heated with phenol and sulfuric acid it combines with two molecules of the phenol and forms phenolphthalein. In the same way, a sulfonphthalein is a compound of ortho-sulfo-benzoic acid:

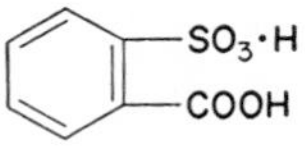

and phenol or a phenol derivative. These compounds, although sometimes behaving as dyes, are not used as dyes or stains, but as indicators. For this purpose the members of the group are very valuable.

Phenolphthalein, although not used as a dye, is colored and is apparently capable of salt formation. In acid solutions it is colorless, and is assumed to have the formula:

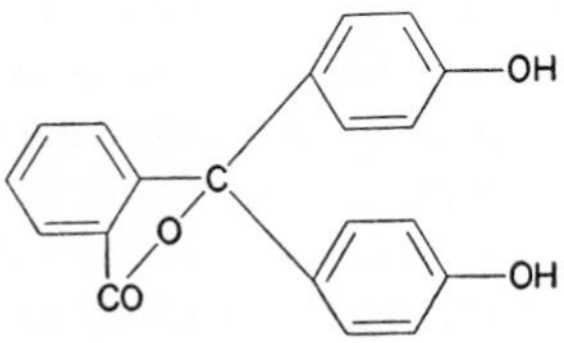

Upon neutralization the alkali is believed to attach itself to the CO-group, which breaks the five-sided ring (the lactone ring) and causes one of the benzene rings to take on quinoid form, thus:

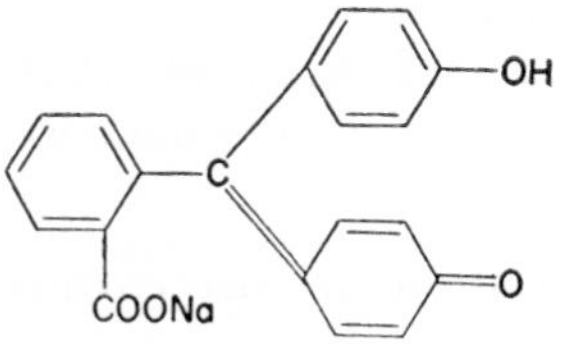

With this change, the red color of the compound appears, but disappears again if the solution is made acid so as to destroy the quinoid structure. This makes the compound a very valuable indicator.

The dyes of this group have no value in practical dyeing, although they are all weakly acid dyes. Similarly they are of little use as biological stains, except occasionally in vital staining. Their real value is as acid-base indicators. Even when they are employed as vital stains, they serve primarily to study the reaction of tissues or body fluids. They are also valuable indicators in micro-injection of cells.

Hydrogen-ion Indicators. The sulphonphthaleins, together with phenolphthalein, are among the most useful indicators known to the chemist. Quite a long series of them has been prepared, which in general show their deepest color in alkaline solutions and turn yellow on the addition of acid. Some of them, such as thymol-sulfonphthalein (thymol blue), show two colors besides yellow, one in strong acid solutions and the other in strong basic solutions, while in solutions near the neutral point they are yellow. That these color changes are due to alterations in the structure of the molecule, such as the disappearance and reappearance of the quinoid ring, is generally assumed; but in the case of these compounds the relation of structure to color is complicated and has not yet been worked out to general satisfaction.

The colorimetric measurement of H-ion concentration depends upon these color changes. The color change of an indicator takes place within a short range on each side of that point in the H-ion scale at which the dye is 50 percent dissociated, i.e., occurs half in the form of the undissociated dye and half in the form of free ions. This point on the pH-scale (at which an indicator is 50 percent dissociated) is important, and corresponds to the logarithm of the reciprocal of its dissociation constant. The dissociation constant of an indicator, in other words, is a quantity the logarithm of whose reciprocal is the pH-value of the point at which the indicator is half dissociated. The approximate pH-value of the apparent dissociation constant is denoted by chemists by the symbol pK; the value of this quantity is given in the case of each of the indicators listed below.

For a short distance on each side of the dissociation constant, every shade of the indicator corresponds to a definite pH-value; this zone is known as the sensitive range of the indicator. Roughly speaking, the sensitive range of any indicator extends for about 0.8 pH to each side of its pK-value. Throughout its sensitive range, an indicator can be used to determine the H-ion concentration of a solution by comparing its shade with that produced in standards of known reaction. The various indicators of this group differ in their strengths as acids (i.e., the extent to which they dissociate); and the greater their strength the lower the pH-value of the point at which they are 50 percent dissociated. It is plain, therefore that different indicators may be selected according to their dissociation constants to cover successive portions of the pH scale. Fortunately nearly all of them have different dissociation constants; so that by employing a series of them one can determine the H-ion concentration of solutions of any reaction ordinarily encountered.

There are two general types of indicators, those which show only one color in the useful range, and those which change from one color to another. The phthaleins, such as phenolphthalein, change from colorless substances in their acid ranges to colored compounds in their alkaline ranges. The sulfonphthaleins, on the other hand, change from yellow to some deeper

TABLE 3
Color Changes of the Indicators of Clark and Lubs and of Cohen

Indicator	Molecular Weight	Concentration Recommended*	Full Acid Color	Full Alkaline Color	Sensitive Range pH	pK†
Meta cresol purple (acid range)......	382.414	0.04	Red	Yellow	1.2–2.8	1.5
Thymol blue (acid range)............	466.570	0.04	Red	Yellow	1.2–2.8	1.5
Brom phenol blue....	669.994	0.04	Yellow	Blue	3.0–4.6	4.1
Brom chlor phenol-blue..............	581.076	0.04	Yellow	Blue	3.0–4.6	4.0
Brom cresol green...	698.046	0.04	Yellow	Blue	3.8–5.4	4.7
Chlor cresol green...	520.210	0.04	Yellow	Blue	4.0–5.6	4.8
Methyl red.........	269.294	0.02	Red	Yellow	4.4–6.0	5.1
Chlor phenol red....	423.260	0.04	Yellow	Red	4.8–6.4	6.0
Brom phenol red.....	512.178	0.04	Yellow	Red	5.2–6.8	6.2
Brom cresol purple..	540.230	0.04	Yellow	Purple	5.2–6.8	6.3
Brom thymol blue...	624.386	0.04	Yellow	Blue	6.0–7.6	7.0
Phenol red.........	354.362	0.02	Yellow	Red	6.8–8.4	7.9
Cresol red..........	382.414	0.02	Yellow	Red	7.2–8.8	8.3
Meta cresol purple (alkaline range)...	382.414	0.04	Yellow	Purple	7.4–9.0	8.3
Thymol blue (alkaline range)........	466.570	0.04	Yellow	Blue	8.0–9.6	8.9
Cresolphthalein.....	346.364	0.04	Colorless	Red	8.2–9.8	9.4
Phenolphthalein.....	318.312	0.04	Colorless	Red	8.3–10.0	9.7

* In 95 per cent ethyl alcohol.

† Approximate invert logarithm of apparent dissociation constant.

color. With the first type of indicator the H-ion concentration may be determined by the alteration in intensity of color, with the second type by alteration in hue. The two-color indicators, such as the sulfonphthaleins, are more satisfactory because one can measure changes in hue more accurately than changes in color intensity, especially when one must depend on rather crude methods of colorimetry as is usually the case when indicators are employed.

The sulfonphthalein indicators are especially valuable as indicators for still other reasons. Unlike the azo compounds, such as methyl red, they are very stable chemically, while they are less affected by the presence of neutral salts and proteins than are many other indicators.

The first list of sulfonphthalein indicators was published by Clark and Lubs (1917), who to make their series complete had to include methyl red, an azo dye, less satisfactory because its solutions are subject to reduction on standing. Later Cohen (1923, 1926) added six new sulfonphthalein indicators, among them two (brom cresol green and chlor cresol green) which have sensitive ranges so close to methyl red as to make the latter unnecessary.

These indicators, unlike the usual dyes, are ordinarily furnished in the form of color acids, which are practically insoluble in water. They must accordingly be employed in alcoholic solution or must be converted into the disodium salt with the proper amount of NaOH, the quantity of the latter to use being figured by the following formula:

$$\text{Weight NaOH} = \frac{\text{Weight indicator} \times 40}{\text{Molecular weight indicator}}.$$

The alcoholic solutions are simpler to prepare and for ordinary indicator purposes are equally satisfactory; they cannot, of course, be employed, in vital staining.

Table 3, above, quoted from the *Manual of Microbiological Methods** shows the color changes and sensitive ranges of the indicators described below. (This table also includes methyl red, which is an azo dye, and is described in Chapter V of this book.)

In the following list the compounds are arranged in the order of their dissociation constants and hence in that of their sensitive ranges in the pH-scale.

META-CRESOL PURPLE

pK = 1.5, 8.3

This indicator is *m*-cresol sulfonphthalein.

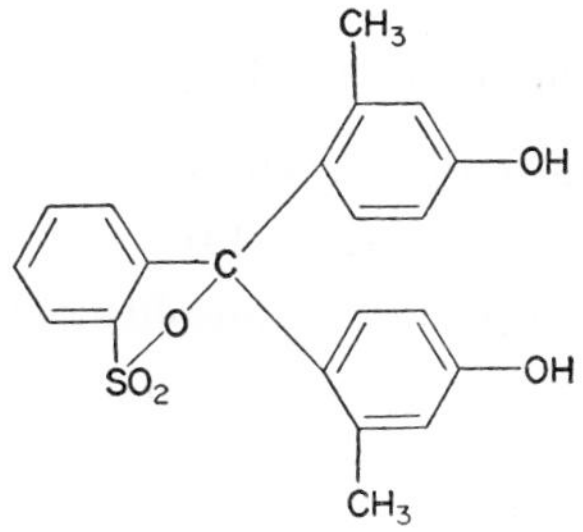

An indicator changing from red to yellow in its acid range and from yellow to purple in its alkaline range.

THYMOL BLUE

pK = 1.5, 8.9

This is thymol sulfonphthalein:

* Society of American Bacteriologists (1957).

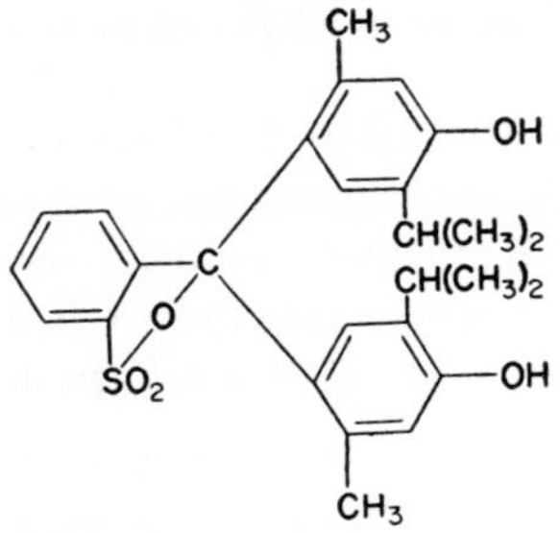

Thymol blue is now a well known indicator, used both in its acid range (red to yellow) and in its alkaline range (yellow to blue). In the latter range it may well be replaced with meta-cresol purple.

BROM PHENOL BLUE

$$pK = 4.0$$

This is tetrabromo-phenol sulfonphthalein.

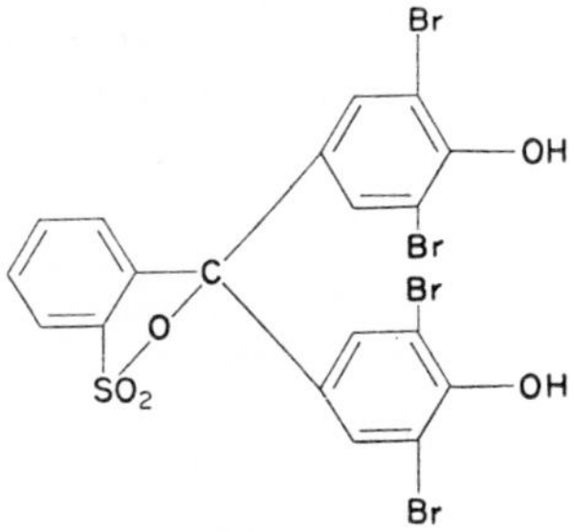

An indicator changing from yellow to blue.

BROM CHLOR PHENOL BLUE

$$pK = 4.0$$

This is dibromo-dichloro-phenol sulfonphthalein.

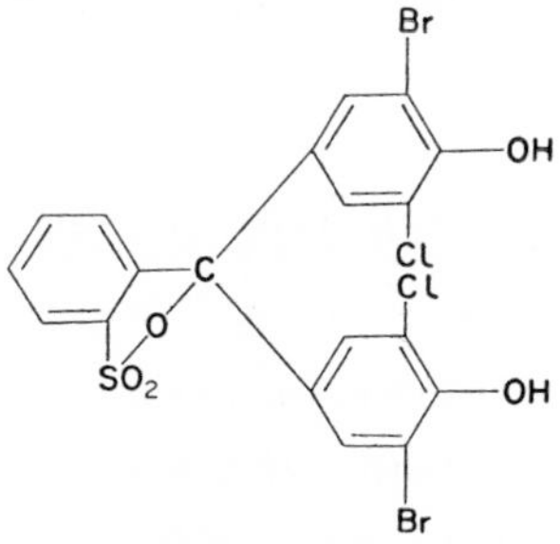

An indicator almost identical with the last in range, and showing the same change in color.

$$pK = 4.7$$

This is tetrabromo-metacresol sulfonphthalein:

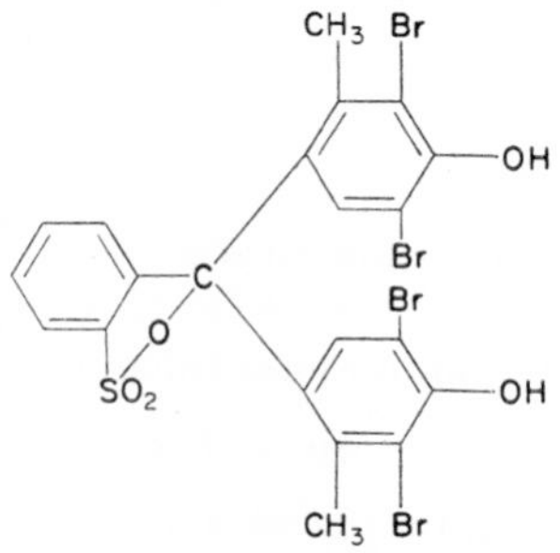

An indicator changing from yellow to blue.

CHLOR CRESOL GREEN

$$pK = 4.8$$

This is tetrachloro-metacresol sulfonphthalein.

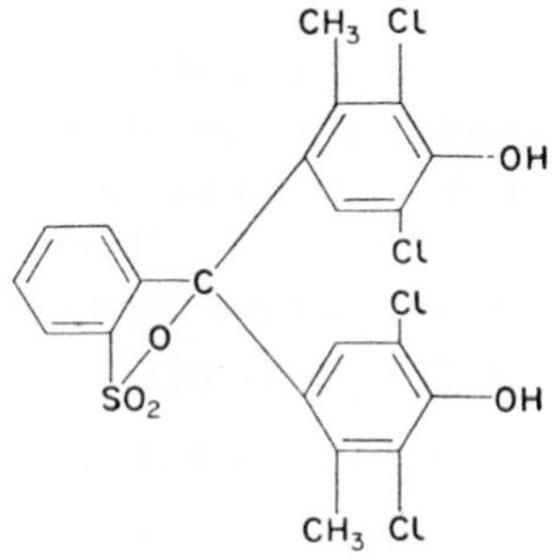

An indicator changing from yellow to blue through a range only a little more acid than that of methyl red.

CHLOR PHENOL RED

$$pK = 6.0$$

This is dichloro-phenol sulfonphthalein.

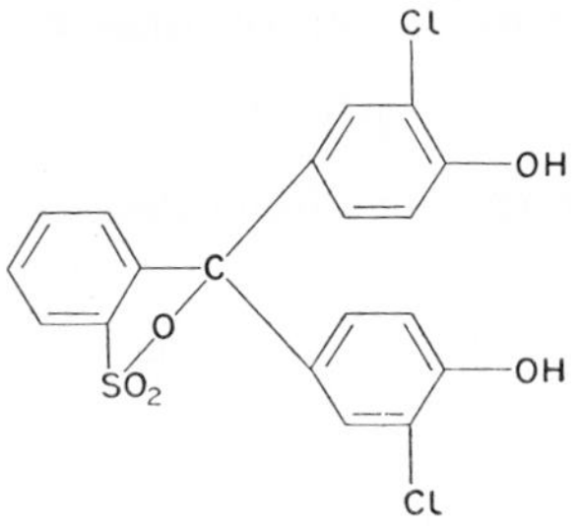

An indicator changing from yellow to red.

BROM PHENOL RED

pK = 6.2

This is dibromo-phenol sulfonphthalein.

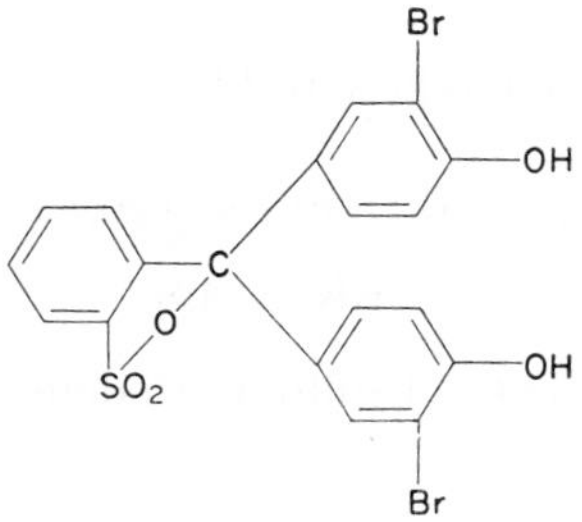

An indicator changing from yellow to red through a range almost identical with that of the better known brom cresol purple. It is recommended in place of the latter because it is free from troublesome dichromatism.

BROM CRESOL PURPLE

pK = 6.3

This is dibromo-orthocresol sulfonphthalein:

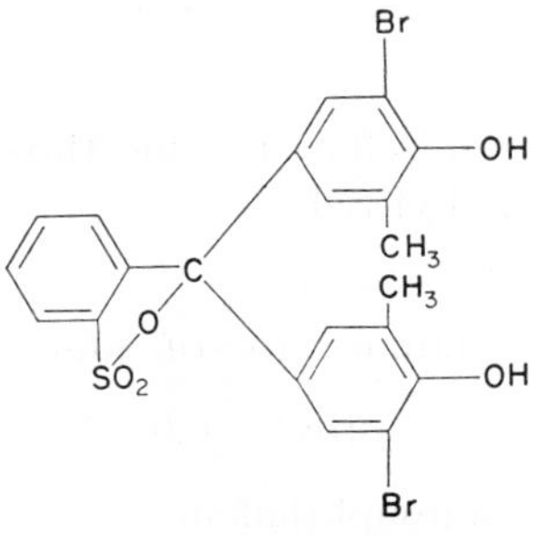

A well known indicator changing from yellow to purple. It has been used by McMaster and Parsons (1938) as a vital stain, and has frequent employment as an indicator in culture media.

BROM THYMOL BLUE

$$pK = 7.0$$

This is dibromo-thymol sulfonphthalein:

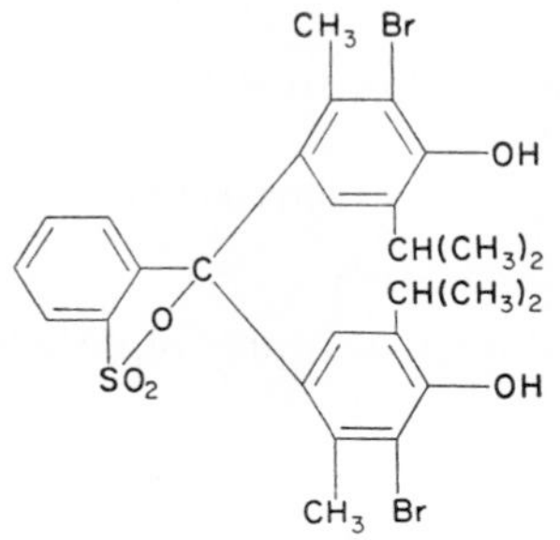

It is a very valuable indicator because of its dissociation constant at close to true neutrality. It is yellow in acid, green in neutral, and blue in alkaline solutions. It has also been employed as a vital dye by McMaster and Parsons (1938), and as a stain for fungi in roots by Garrett (1937), and as an indicator in culture media.

PHENOL RED

$$pK = 7.9$$

This is phenol-sulfonphthalein:

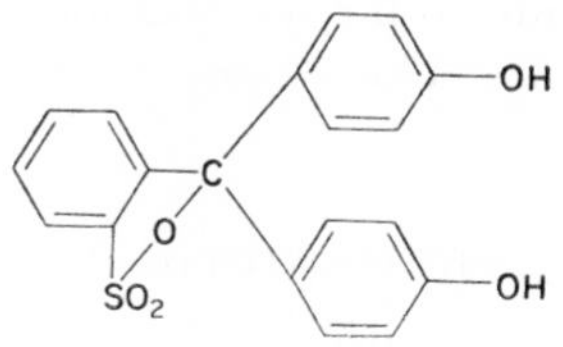

An indicator changing from yellow to red, employed for some time in physiological work, and well known before the paper by Clark and Lubs above mentioned. The range of this indicator (approx. pH 6.8–8.4) makes it quite valuable in much biological work (e.g., in culture media); it is quite commonly used in the study of kidney function.

CRESOL RED

$$pK = 8.3$$

This is orthocresol-sulfonphthalein:

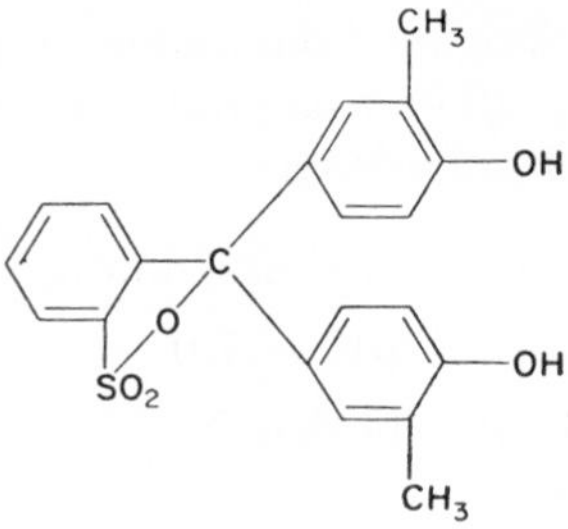

An indicator changing from yellow to red.

CRESOLPHTHALEIN

pK = 9.4

This indicator is closely related to phenolphthalein, having the constitution:

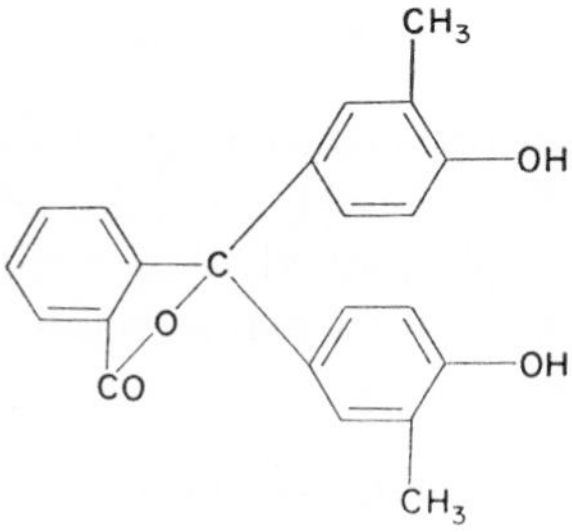

It is a newer indicator than phenolphthalein, and is generally regarded as preferable when used in conjunction with the sulfonphthaleins, because its range does not overlap quite so far the alkaline range of thymol blue. It is a one-color indicator and its color change is the same as that of phenolphthalein.

PHENOLPHTHALEIN

pK = 9.7

This indicator, of which the formula is given on p. 186, is one of the longest known of acid-base indicators. It is quite useful in the alkaline range centering around pH 9.7, with a color change from red in alkaline solutions to colorless in acid ones. It has the disadvantage of a one-color indicator discussed on p. 188.

5. ACRIDINE DYES

There is a small group of dyes derived from the compound acridine which is closely related to xanthene. They are not xanthene dyes, but are included in this chapter for convenience. There are a few of interest to the biologist.

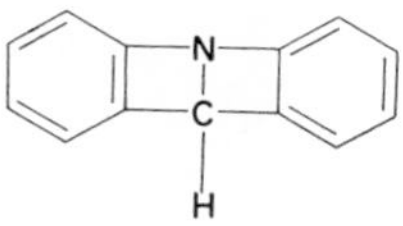

ACRIDINE YELLOW

C. I. NO. 46025 (1 ed.: 785)

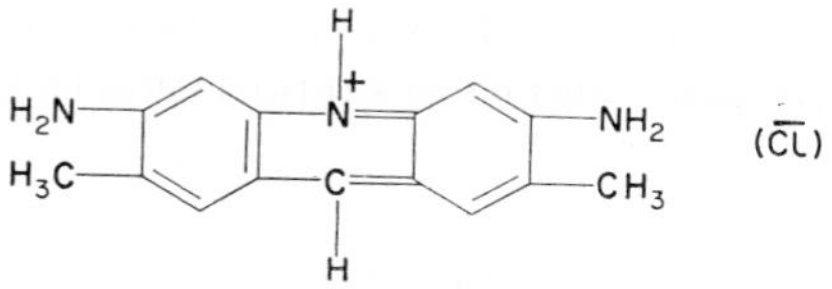

$C_{15}H_{16}N_3Cl$; mol. wt. 273.759

(A basic dye; absorption maximum about 455 [Formánek])

This dye is rarely called for in microtechnic, but has been referred to by Metcalf and Patton (1944) as a fluorochrome useful in insect histology.

CORIPHOSPHINE O

C. I. NO. 46020 (1 ed.: 787)

(C. I. Basic Yellow 7)

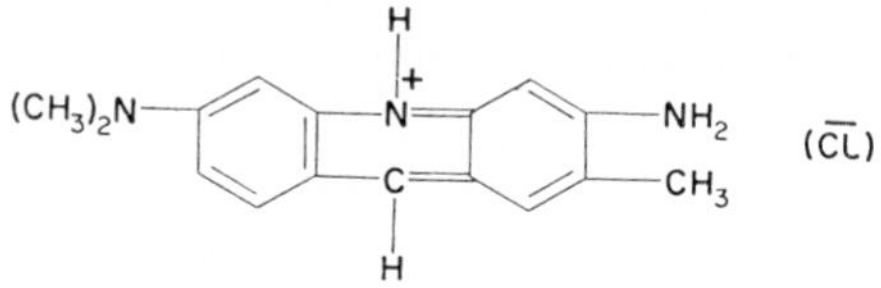

$C_{16}H_{18}N_3Cl$; mol. wt. 287.785

(A basic dye; absorption maxima about 643, 482 [Formánek])

ACRIDINE ORANGE NO

C. I. NO. 46005 (1 ed.: 788)

(C. I. Basic Orange 14)

Synonyms: Basic orange 3RN; Euchrysine 3RXA

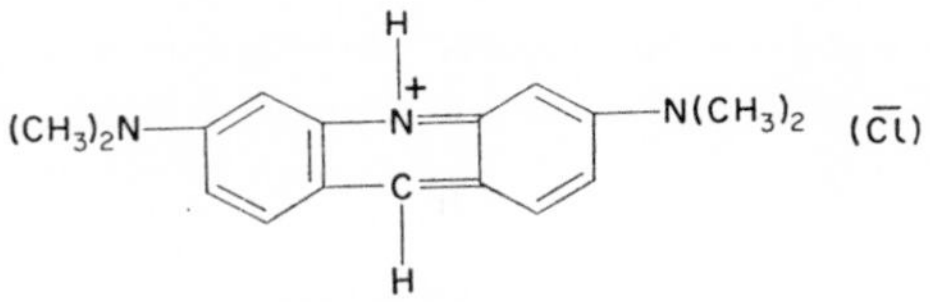

$$(CH_3)_2N—\overset{\overset{H}{\overset{|}{\overset{+}{N}}}}{\underset{\underset{H}{\overset{|}{C}}}{}}—N(CH_3)_2 \quad (\overline{Cl})$$

$C_{17}H_{20}N_3Cl$; mol. wt. 301.811

(A basic dye, ordinarily obtained as the zinc chloride double salt;
absorption maxima about [467] 497 [Formánek])

Both of these dyes are among those employed as fluorochromes by Metcalf and Patton (1944). Strugger (1948) has used acridine orange for demonstrating bacteria in soil suspensions, by means of ultraviolet light; bacteria are green, humus particles red. Their chief use, in fact, is as fluorochromes; but acridine orange has attracted some attention because it stains tumor cells selectively, *intra vitam*, and causes retardation of tumor growth (Lewis and Goland, 1948).

RIVANOL

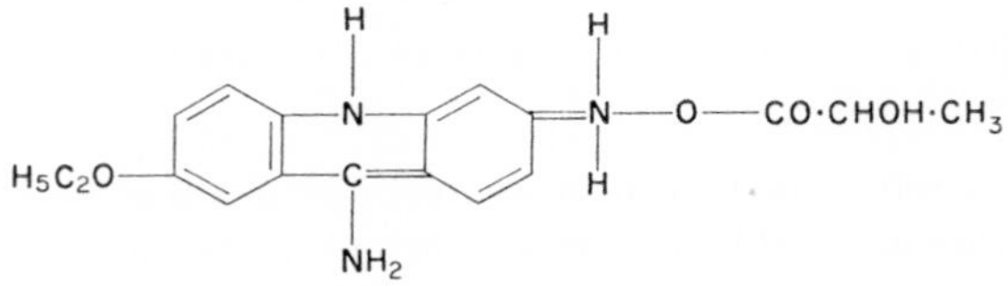

$$H_5C_2O—\overset{\overset{H}{\overset{|}{N}}}{\underset{\underset{NH_2}{\overset{|}{C}}}{}}\overset{\overset{H}{|}}{=N}—O—CO·CHOH·CH_3$$

$C_{18}H_{21}N_3O_4$; mol. wt. 343.372

This has also been called for by the two authors above mentioned, as a fluorochrome.

ACRIFLAVINE   C. I. NO. 46000 (1 *ed.:* 790

Synonym: *Trypaflavine; Flavine*

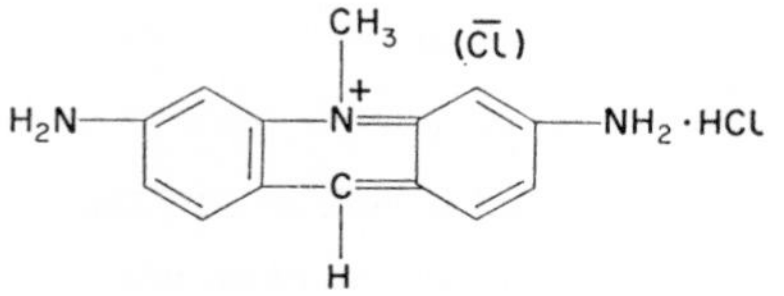

$$H_2N—\overset{\overset{CH_3 \quad (\overline{Cl})}{\overset{|}{\overset{+}{N}}}}{\underset{\underset{H}{\overset{|}{C}}}{}}=NH_2·HCl$$

$C_{14}H_{15}N_3Cl_2$; mol. wt. 296.198

(A basic dye)

This yellow dye is one of those developed by Ehrlich for its therapeutic value. It is marketed at present as a disinfectant. It was employed as a bacteriostatic agent by Churchman (1927) mixed with methyl and crystal violets under the name of "acriviolet." Acriflavine has little use as an ordinary stain, but is coming to be employed to some extent as a fluorochrome; see Levaditti *et al.* (1940), Metcalf and Patton (1944).

NEUTRAL ACRIFLAVINE

C. I. NO. 46000 (1 *ed.:* 790)

Synonyms: *Neutral trypaflavine; Euflavine; Neutroflavine; Gonacrin*

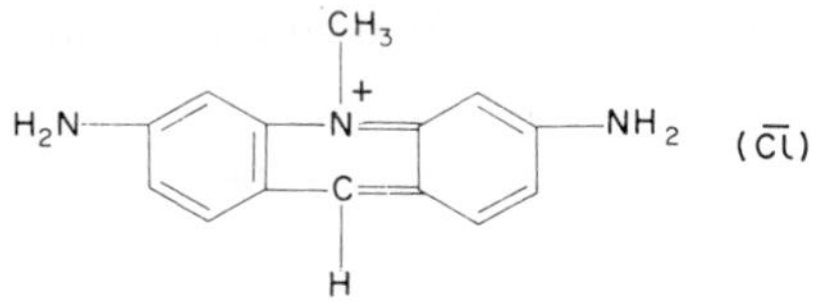

$$\text{H}_2\text{N} \underbrace{}_{} \overset{\overset{\displaystyle\text{CH}_3}{|}}{\underset{\underset{|}{\text{C}}}{\overset{+}{\text{N}}}} \underbrace{}_{} \text{NH}_2 \quad (\bar{\text{C}}\text{l})$$

$$\text{H}$$

$$\text{C}_{14}\text{H}_{14}\text{N}_3\text{Cl}; \text{ mol. wt. } 259.733$$

This dye finds use as a disinfectant. It is said to be less irritating than acriflavine, because it is neutral.

PROFLAVINE C. I. (1 *ed.*) NO. 790

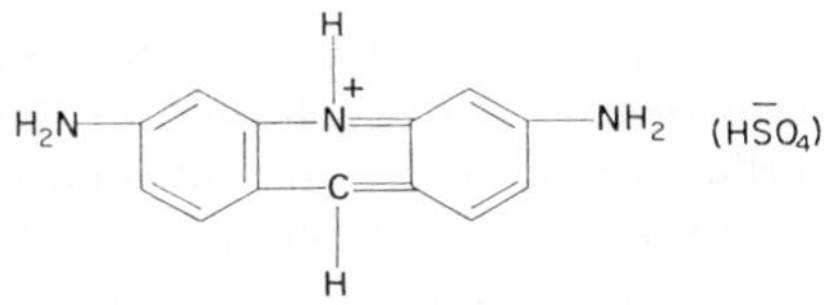

$$\text{H}_2\text{N} \underbrace{}_{} \overset{\overset{\displaystyle\text{H}}{|}}{\underset{\underset{|}{\text{C}}}{\overset{+}{\text{N}}}} \underbrace{}_{} \text{NH}_2 \quad (\text{H}\bar{\text{S}}\text{O}_4)$$

$$\text{H}$$

$$\text{C}_{13}\text{H}_{12}\text{N}_3\text{SO}_4 \text{ ; mol. wt. } 306.316$$

(A basic dye ordinarily supplied as the sulfate)

Like the very similar acriflavine, this is used primarily as a disinfectant. It has been called for by Rogers (1940) as an agent for inhibiting sulfate-reducing bacteria.

ATABRINE

Synonym: Atebrine (in Germany)

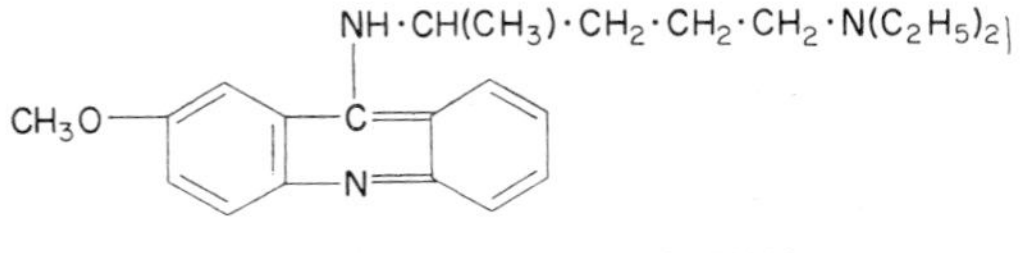

$$\text{CH}_3\text{O} \underbrace{}_{} \overset{\overset{\displaystyle \text{NH}\cdot\text{CH(CH}_3)\cdot\text{CH}_2\cdot\text{CH}_2\cdot\text{CH}_2\cdot\text{N(C}_2\text{H}_5)_2}{|}}{\underset{\underset{}{\text{N}}}{\text{C}}} \underbrace{}_{}$$

$$\text{C}_{23}\text{H}_{31}\text{N}_3\text{O}; \text{ mol. wt. } 365.502$$

This is a yellow compound used primarily for its medicinal value (as an antimalarial agent). It shows fluorescence in ultraviolet light, and was called for by Metcalf and Patton (1944) as a fluorochrome in insect histology.

Atebrine and a few other acridine antimalarials are among the dyes which Lewis and Goland (1948) found to stain and to retard tumors in mice.

PHOSPHINE   C. I. NO. 46045 (1 *ed.*: 793)

(C. I. Basic Orange 15)

Synonyms: *Leather yellow; Xanthin*

A mixture of nitrates of chrysanilin, and probably some of its higher homologs, chrysanilin having the following formula:

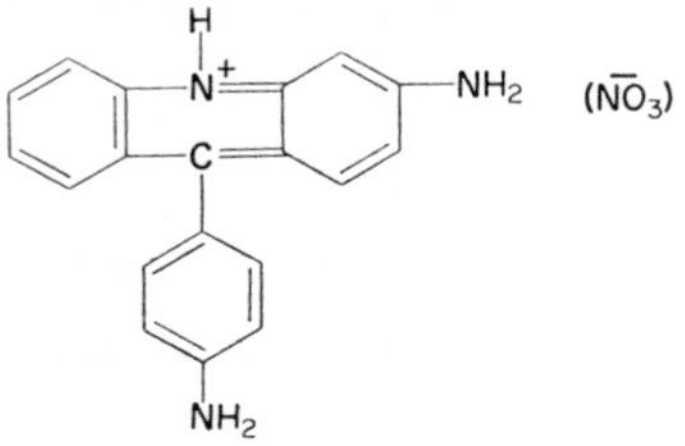

$C_{19}H_{16}N_4O_3$; mol. wt. 348.350

(*A basic dye; principal absorption in the neighborhood of 480–490*)

This dye was used (in 1 percent solution) by Schumacher (1922) following methylene blue (1 percent phenolic solution) to stain bacterial nucleins and nucleoproteins yellow while the free or unbound nucleic acid is green. Metcalf and Patton (1944) employed phosphine 3R, one of the redder shades of this dye, as a fluorochrome in the study of insect histology by fluorescence microscopy.

RHEONINE A   C. I. NO. 46075 (1 *ed.*: 795)

(C. I. Basic Orange 23)

Synonyms: *Rheonine AL, G or N; Fast phosphine NAL*

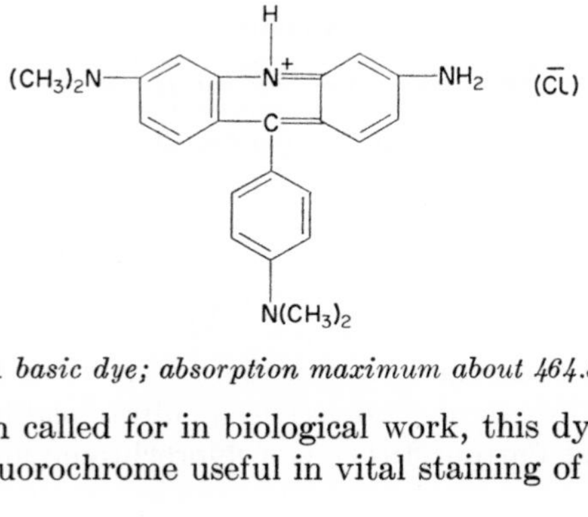

(*A basic dye; absorption maximum about 464.5*)

Although seldom called for in biological work, this dye is mentioned by Pick (1935) as a fluorochrome useful in vital staining of the frog.

IX

MISCELLANEOUS DYES AND PIGMENTS

1. THE ANTHRAQUINONE GROUP

The anthraquinone dyes include derivatives of anthracene,

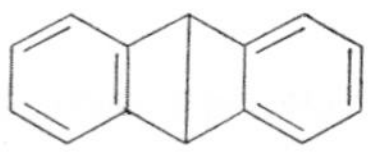

through its oxidation product anthraquinone:

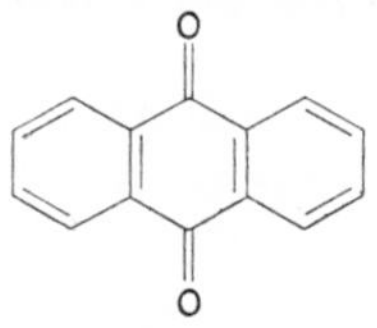

The chromogen anthraquinone is converted into a dye by the addition of hydroxyl groups, its best known derivatives among the dyes being: 1,2-dihydroxy-anthraquinone (alizarin) and 1,2,4-trihydroxy-anthraquinone (purpurin). Both of these compounds occur in nature in the root of madder, being the colored principles of madder extract. They have the property of combining with metallic oxides to form so-called "lakes," insoluble compounds of different color from the dye entering into them. This makes them valuable dyes to use after mordanting with aluminum, iron or chromium compounds.

ALIZARIN   c. i.* no. 58000 (1 *ed.:* 1027)

Various grades denoted as: *Alizarin P, VI, Ie.*

(C. I. Mordant Red 11)

* The abbreviation "C.I." stands for "Colour Index." The number immediately following is that of the current (2nd) edition; the one which follows is that of the first

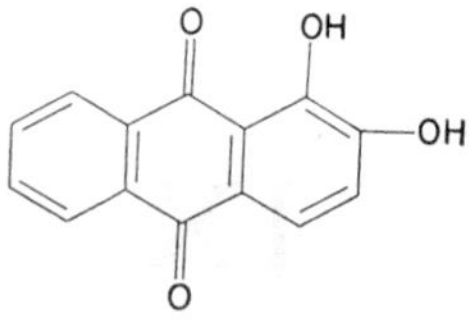

$C_{14}H_8O_4$; mol. wt. 240.204

(An acid dye; absorption maximum about [601.8], 566.5, [527.6] in alkaline solution)
Solubility at 26°C, in water nil; in alcohol 0.125%

Alizarin stains tissues a feeble yellowish red if used on them directly. In the presence of aluminum compounds intense red colors are formed; bluish violet in the presence of iron; and brownish violet in the presence of chromium. It has been used as a stain for nervous tissue and for the vital staining of protozoa. Geyer (1932) employs it to distinguish cows' from goats' milk. The chief present use of alizarin, however, is as an indicator.

ALIZARIN RED S

c. i. no. 58005 (1 *ed.:* 1034)

(C. I. Mordant Red 3)

Synonyms: *Alizarin red, water soluble; Alizarin carmine*

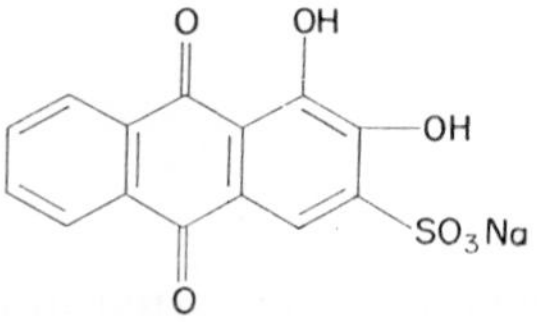

$C_{14}H_7O_7SNa$; mol. wt. 342.259

(An acid dye)

(Absorption maxima in alkaline solution about 557 [594–9])
Solubility at 26°C, in water 7.69%; in alcohol 0.15%

A spectral curve of this dye is given in Fig. 27.

This dye, sodium alizarin sulfonate, was used by Benda for staining chromatin in combination with crystal violet, the chromatin staining brown, while the mitochondria stain violet. It has also been used as a vital stain for nervous tissue in small invertebrates, and by Schrötter (See Lee, p. 465) for sections of nerve tissue. An important application is for the gross

edition. The name of the dye given under the principal name is the preferred designation in the current Colour Index.

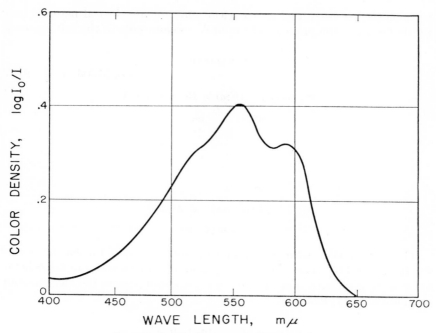

FIG. 27. Spectral curve of alizarin red S

staining of skeletons especially in fetuses (Dawson, 1926, Lipman, 1935, Hollister, 1934); in fact, its most frequent modern use is as a stain for bone. Backman (1935) employs it as a chromosome stain in plant cytology.

For various methods calling for this dye in **staining bone,** see *Staining Procedures,* pp. 146–150.

PURPURIN   C. I. NO. 58205 (1 *ed.:* 1037)

Synonyms: *Alizarin No. 6; Alizarin purpurin*

$C_{14}H_8O_5$; mol. wt. 256.204

(An acid dye; absorption maximum about [521.1], 485.5, [455.5] in alcohol.)

Purpurin is very similar to alizarin, but forms scarlet red lakes with alumina. It has been used as a nuclear stain for histological material, and for determining the presence of insoluble calcium salts in the cell contents.

QUINALIZARIN

C. I. NO. 58500 (1 *ed.:* 1045)

Synonym: *Alizarin Bordeaux BA*

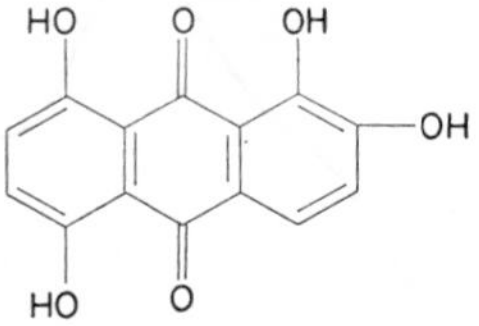

$C_{14}H_8O_6$; mol. wt. 272.204

(*An acid dye*)

This compound is seldom called for in biological work but has been used by Broda (1939), mixed with azo blue and Titan yellow, as an histochemical reagent for magnesium. It is also used in a spot test for the identification of indium (Feigl, 1958).

CARYCINEL RED

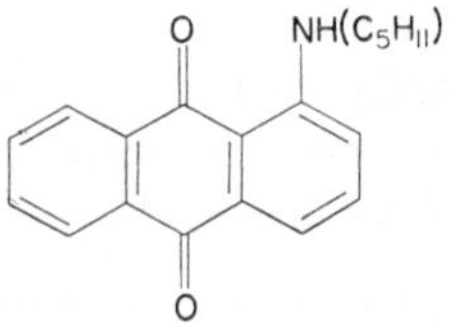

$C_{19}H_{19}NO_2$; mol. wt. 294.350

COCCINEL RED

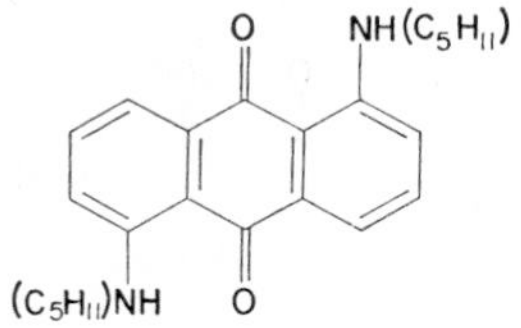

$C_{24}H_{30}N_2O_2$; mol. wt. 378.496

These are two oil-soluble dyes first described and named by Lillie (1945b). He regarded them, together with the following dye (oil blue NA) as good fat stains when employed in the supersaturated isopropanol technic (Lillie, 1945a). Coccinel red stains fat scarlet, carycinel red a deep crimson.

OIL BLUE NA

Probably of the following chemical formula:

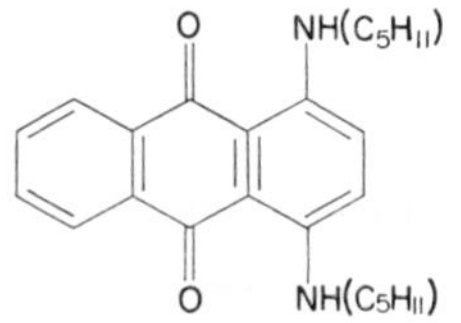

$C_{24}H_{30}N_2O_2$; mol. wt. 378.496

(*Absorption maxima about* [*595*], *640*)

This dye has come into prominence since 1940, as a stain for rubber in plant sections. Whittenberger (1944) thus employs it without a counterstain, while Addicott (1944) suggests either safranin or Congo red for counterstaining. According to Lillie (1945a) it may also be used for staining fat in animal tissue.

ACID ALIZARIN BLUE GR

C. I. NO. 63015 (1 *ed.:* 1048)

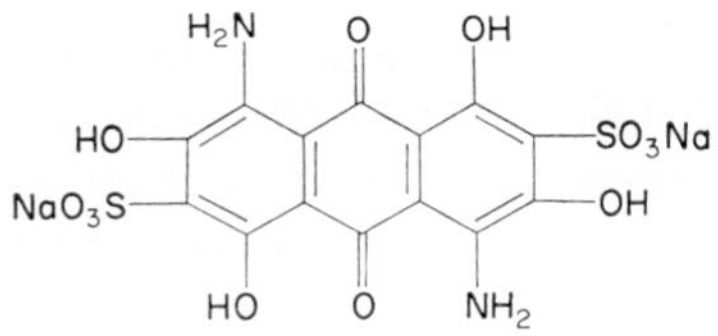

$C_{14}H_8N_2O_{12}S_2Na_2$; mol. wt. 506.346

(*An acid dye*)

Some acid alizarin blue, probably either this or the following, has been employed by Buzaglo (1934) in combination with orcein and gallocyanin as a tissue stain. Peterson (1924) has recommended acid alizarin blue in a modification of the Mallory connective tissue stain; the procedure seems to be well worth recommending, but there proves to be some difficulty in standardizing this dye for the purpose.

For the **acid alizarin blue modification of the Mallory technic,** see *Staining Procedures,* p. 55.

ACID ALIZARIN BLUE BB

C. I. NO. 58610 (1 *ed.:* 1063)

(C. I. Mordant Blue 23)

Synonyms: *Anthracene blue SWX, SWX extra*

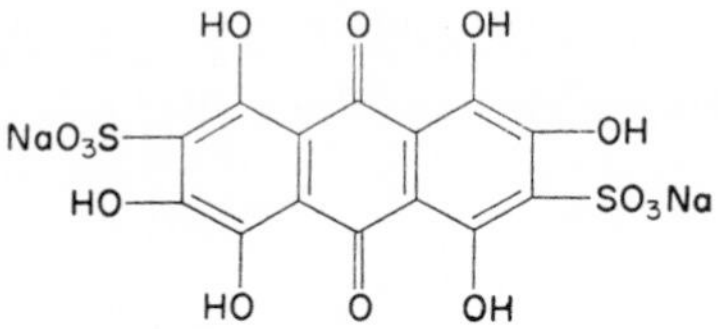

$C_{14}O_6H_{14}Na_2$; mol. wt. 508.314

(An acid dye)

This dye has come into use in connection with fluorescence microscopy, because of the color which it imparts to various tissue elements under ultraviolet illumination. It is an important nuclear stain, and is an ingredient of the Kornhauser "Quad" stain (1943). Some anthracene blue has been called for occasionally in aqueous solution with aluminium sulfate. There are, however, two or three other anthracene blues besides this dye; so it is not certain whether this is the one called for in the technic in question.

For use in **Kornhauser's "Quad" stain,** see *Staining Procedures,* p. 58.

ALKANET   c. i. (1 *ed.*) no. 1240

A natural dye of the anthraquinone group, closely related to alizarin. See C. I. Nos. 75320, 75420, 75520, 75530 (Natural reds 6, 8, 9, 10, 11, 12, 14, 20). It has rarely been specified for biological use, but Artschwager (1943) has employed it as a stain for rubber in plant sections.

2. THIAZOLE DYES

A small group of dyes of rather complex formula contain the thiazole ring:

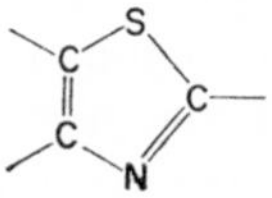

in which the indamine group is the chromophore. References to these dyes in biological literature are rare, but the following have been mentioned; two of them, it will be noticed are also azo dyes and thus possess two chromophores.

GERANINE G

c. i. no. 14930 (1 *ed.:* 127)

(C. I. Direct Red 48)

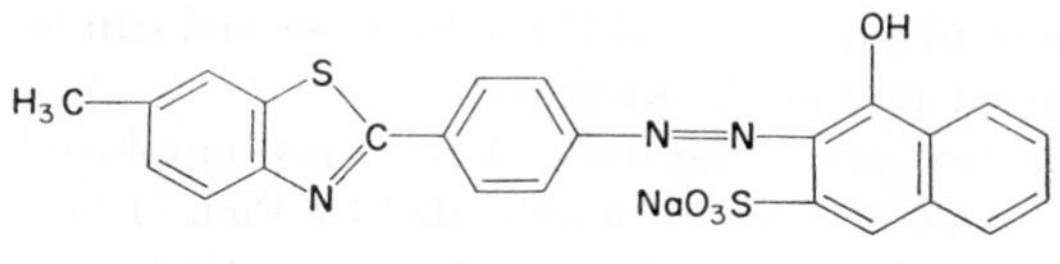

$C_{24}H_{16}N_3O_4S_2Na$; mol. wt. 497.521

(An acid dye)

This is a useful dye in fluorescence microscopy; see Pick (1935) and Jenkins (1937).

PRIMULIN   C. I. NO. 49000 (1 *ed.:* 812)

(C. I. Direct Yellow 59)

Synonym: *Primuline yellow*

A mixture, consisting mainly of the following:

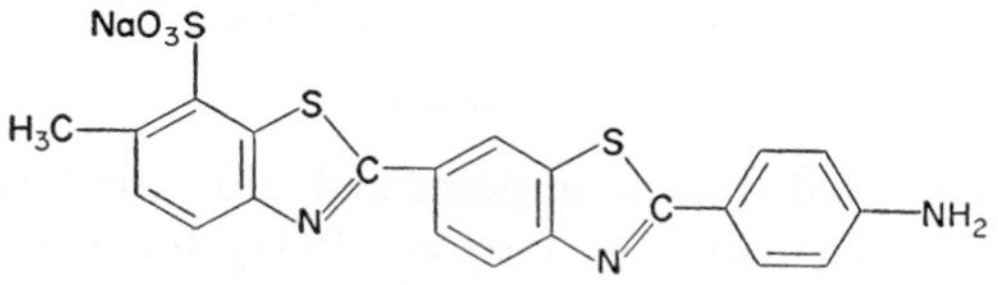

$C_{21}H_{14}N_3O_3S_3Na$; mol. wt. 475.541

(An acid dye)

Among various other thiazole dyes, Pick (1935) employed primulin as a vital stain, for which it is useful because of its fluorescence under ultraviolet illumination. It has since become quite widely used for the purpose.

TITAN YELLOW G   C. I. NO. 19540 (1 *ed.:* 813)

(C. I. Direct Yellow 9)

Synonym: *Thiazol yellow*

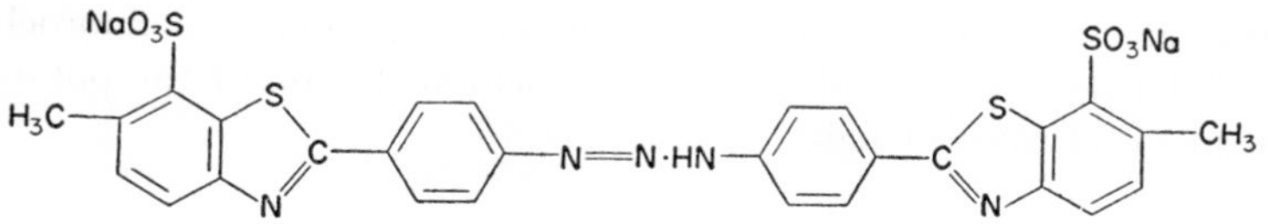

$C_{28}H_{19}N_5O_6S_4Na_2$; mol. wt. 695.730

(An acid dye)

This dye has been recommended as an indicator for determining magnesium in body fluids. After removing the organic matter and calcium from such solutions the dye is added; under alkaline conditions it becomes red in the presence of magnesium and the color observed can be compared with that of a standard previously prepared.

Also, like the two preceding dyes, it has been employed in fluorescence microscopy; it is one of those recommended by Pick (1935) and by Jenkins (1937) as a vital stain under ultraviolet illumination.

THIOFLAVINE T   C. I. NO. 49005 (1 *ed.:* 815)

(C. I. Basic Yellow 1)

Synonym: *Thioflavine T G*

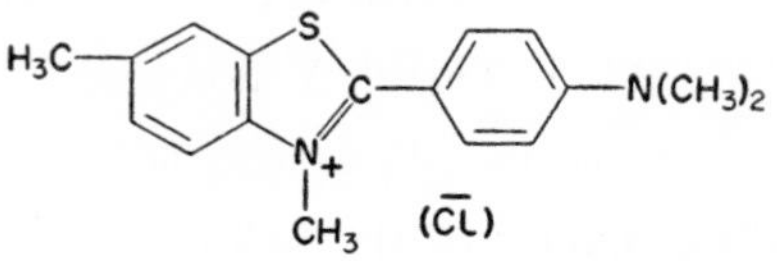

$C_{17}H_{19}N_2SCl$; mol. wt. 318.861

(*A basic dye*)

Like the other related dyes here described, this one has properties as a fluorochrome; thus Metcalf and Patton (1944) have employed it, with ultraviolet light, in insect histology.

THIOFLAVINE S   C. I. NO. 49010 (1 *ed.:* 816)

(C. I. Direct Yellow 7)

(*An acid dye; a methylated and sulfonated derivative of primulin*)

This is among the dyes that has recently come into use in connection with fluorescence microscopy. Pick (1935) employed a thioflavine as a vital stain, depending on its fluorescence under ultraviolet light; probably he referred to this although there is also a thioflavine T. Subsequent authors (Jenkins, 1937, Levaditti *et al.*, 1940) definitely refer to thioflavine S, and the dye has now come to have a distinct recognition as a fluorochrome. Thus Richards (1943) employs it in the demonstration of the potato scab organism by ultraviolet light.

3. QUINOLINE DYES

Of the quinoline dyes only the following is of interest to biologists:

PINACYANOL   C. I. (1 *ed.*) NO. 808

Synonym: *Sensitol red*

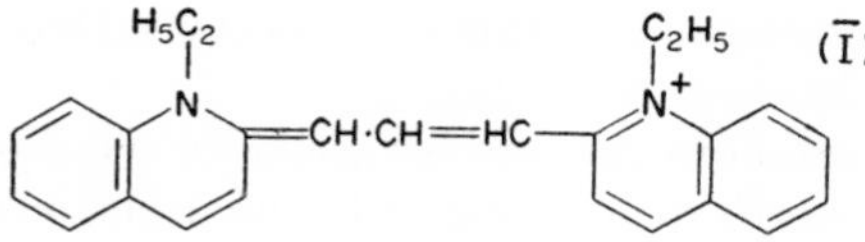

$C_{25}H_{25}N_2I$; mol. wt. 480.386

(A basic dye; absorption maxima [526, 563] 608 in alcohol)

This dye is used primarily for color sensitization in photography, but has been employed by Proescher (1933) for staining frozen sections, and by Hetherington (1936) and Schwind (1950) as a supra-vital stain for mitochondria in blood. It has been employed in combatting streptococci. S. E. Bensley (1952) has prepared a neutral stain from it (an erythrosinate) and uses it for staining mast cells.

Another quinoline dye mentioned in biological literature is: Quinoline yellow; C. I. (1 *ed.*) No. 801.

4. PHTHALOCYANINE DYES

The phthalocyanine dyes are complex chemical compounds, similar in structure to chlorophyll, with $C_6H_4 \cdot C_2N_2$ radicals surrounding a central metal atom (usually copper). Only one member of the group seems to have attained significance as a biological stain.

ALCIAN BLUE 8GX   C. I. NO. 74240

(C. I. Ingrain Blue 1)

The exact chemical structure of this dye is uncertain. In fact, there is reason to believe that the original manufacturer has changed the nature of the product since it was first used by biologists. Several samples have been obtained by the Stain Commission which do not seem to be all the same dye.

Steedman (1950) introduced this dye, and his work was followed up by Lison (1954; see also Mowry, 1956). It has been proposed as a differential stain for acidic polysaccharides; some of the samples investigated seem to be effective for that purpose, but others do not. The dye requires standardization.

5. MINERAL PIGMENTS

There are a considerable number of pigments of non-organic nature, which are much better known to the manufacturer of paints than to the biologist. They are in no sense dyes; but a few of them are occasionally used in microscopic work or for some other biological purpose. They were not listed in the first editions of this book because they were regarded as lying outside the field covered.

The following three, however, are occasionally mentioned by the biologist; and they seem worth mentioning, if for no other reason, to keep them from being confused with the dyes. Of these three, the first one is generally known for what it is; but the other two are more apt to be ordered as though they were dyes instead of mineral salts.

PRUSSIAN BLUE

c. i. no. 77510 (1 *ed.*: 1288)

Synonyms: *Berlin blue; Chinese blue; Paris blue; Milori blue; Steel blue*

The well known colored salt, ferric ferrocyanide, $Fe_4(FeC_6N_6)_3$, finds its greatest use in the manufacture of paints, but it has occasional biological employment, chiefly for coloring anatomical specimens, for demonstration of the circulatory system by means of injection, and for coloring injection masses for blood vessels and lymphatics. It is mentioned in connection with the Gomori (1936) technic in which $K_4Fe(CN)_6$ is used as a microchemical reagent for iron in tissues; by this procedure Prussian blue is formed *in situ* in the tissues.

For **Prussian blue method for hemosiderin,** see *Staining Procedures,* p. 168.

For **ferric ferricyanide method for reducing groups,** see *Staining Procedures,* p. 169.

SKY BLUE   c. i. no. 77368 (1 *ed.*: 1286)

Synonyms: *Coelestin blue; Coeline; Coeruleum*

This pigment is essentially cobaltous stannate, $CoOSnO_2$. It is called for primarily as a constituent of artists' oil or water colors, but has been given occasional mention in biological literature.

RUTHENIUM RED

An ammoniated ruthenium oxychloride prepared by making an ammoniacal solution of ruthenic chloride, $RuCl_3$. It has been employed, with or without the addition of acetic acid, in microscopic work, primarily as a test for pectin. It is thought by some to be specific for this purpose.

It should also be mentioned that the name emerald green, listed on p. 132 as a synonym of brilliant green, should more correctly be applied to a hydrated chromium oxide; while Victoria green is a mixture of this compound with two other mineral pigments—although mentioned elsewhere in this book (p. 130) as a synonym of malachite green. These two pigments seem to have no biological use, but are mentioned here to avoid possible confusion with the two dyes to which the same names have been given.

6. SILVER PROTIENATES

Mention should be made here of a class of compounds which are used in certain staining procedures but are neither dyes nor mineral pigments. They are reaction products of a salt of silver (usually nitrate) and protein that has been partially hydrolyzed. No exact chemical formula for such a compound can be given. Under the name of Protargol such a compound has been well known in the drug trade for some time as a local antiseptic.

The use of Protargol for neurological staining was introduced by Bodian (1937), and the method has often been followed by later workers. Difficulty has been experienced, however, because Bodian used a German-made product that is no longer available, and many compounds now on the market, although named the same, are quite different. A product satisfactory as an antiseptic is not necessarily usable as a staining agent. During the 1950's, however, an American product became available, called Protargol S, to distinguish it from the pharmaceutical variety, which does prove satisfactory for neurological staining. It has been put on the certification basis by the Biological Stain Commission.

X

DIAZONIUM AND TETRAZONIUM SALTS*

R. D. LILLIE

Medical School, Louisiana State University, New Orleans, Louisiana

Histochemistry has brought into microscopic use certain compounds which are not dyes. Some of the histochemical reagents, like basic fuchsin, are dyes used in decolorized state, and are discussed elsewhere in this book; others, like the oxidizing agents periodic acid and tetra-acetic acid, are simple chemicals hardly calling for special consideration. There are, however, certain important histochemical reagents which are so closely related to dyestuffs that they can hardly be omitted from these pages. They are especially the diazonium, tetrazonium and tetrazolium salts.

The diazonium and tetrazonium salts have the same basic structure, and are considered in this section. They are salts of a theoretical base $R{-}\overset{+}{N}{\equiv}N$ (or $R{-}N{=}NOH$). These bases are usually quite unstable, and in many instances their simple halides are also, though some reasonably stable chlorides and acid sulfates exist. Combinations as double salts of zinc chloride, boron trifluoride, sodium bisulfate and naphthalene-1,5-di-sulfonic acid are the usual commercially available salts, and many keep quite well even with (dry) room temperature storage. Solution stability, especially in the alkaline range, is generally brief.

In the formulae given below, both the undiazotized amine and one or more of the stabilized salts are presented. Diazonium salts, in the strict sense, contain only one $R{-}\overset{+}{N}{\equiv}N$ grouping, tetrazonium salts contain two and hexazonium pararosaniline (Davis and Ornstein, 1959) is said to contain three; the term diazonium salts is often applied to cover all of these.

---

* Abbreviations of manufacturers in this section are, as in the Colour Index (2 ed.), as follows: duP, DuPont & Nemours; ICI, Imperial Chemical Industry; FH, Farbewerke Höchst; NAC, National Aniline Division of Allied Dye and Chemical Corporation.

Many of these salts are colorless, but when the chromophore azo group —N=N— is formed by coupling with tissue phenols and aryl amines, or with enzymatically released naphthols and naphthylamines, color results. Some diazotizable amines are already dyestuffs, such as safranin, pararosaniline, fast garnet GBC base, fast black K base and others. In these instances this new azo color is usually of a much deeper shade than the original, and should be stable to acid washing, in contrast to simple basic dye staining. This stable color production is the basis of their use as histochemical reagents.

Azo coupling of tissue phenols was apparently first used by Cordier and Lison (1930) for the demonstration of enterochromaffin. At first only freshly diazotized amines were used; sulfanilic acid, benzidine and α-naphthylamine. Lison (1931) added naphthionic acid, m-phenylene diamine, o-dianisidine and its disulfonic acid and benzidine disulfonic acid. Clara and Canal (1932) introduced p-nitroaniline, both as freshly diazotized base, and as the first stable diazonium salts to be used histochemically. Nitrosamine red and nitrazol CF (Hollborn) were somewhat different preparations of this salt, which is now widely designated as fast red GG. Clara (1934) also introduced as a stable diazonium salt Echtrotsalz B (fast red B, C. I. 37125, o-methoxy-p-nitroaniline).

A further, and much more extensive use for stable diazonium salts has appeared in the esterase and phosphatase technics, in which various naphthols are enzymatically liberated from their acetate, other alicarboxylate and phosphate esters and demonstrated by azo coupling with concurrently present or subsequently applied diazonium salts.

In addition the azo coupling reaction has been used to enhance the visibility of phenols and phenylamines previously reacted with tissues by various end group reactions, such as those with hydroxynaphthoic acid hydrazide or m-aminophenol for carbonyl groups, p-dimethylaminobenzaldehyde for indoles and pyrroles and the post-coupled tetrazonium reaction apparently first applied by Clara (1935), who tried both primary tetrazotization and a sequence two step method, and preferred the latter.

The use of fresh diazotates has recently been confined largely to very special histochemical studies, and additions to Lison and Clara's original lists are few. Safranin O (see Lillie et al., 1953) gave blue black with enterochromaffin, dark reds at sites of high tyrosine, (histidine and tryptophan?) concentration.

On a number of occasions fresh and stable diazotates of the same amine have been compared and the fresh diazos have usually given somewhat better results on enterochromaffin. However, their use in the enzyme technics is inconvenient, and many of the stable diazonium salts are very good for all purposes.

In the ensuing specific description the structural formulae of the amines are taken from the Colour Index, citing also the Colour Index numbers and the "azoic diazo" numbers. The formulae for the stabilized diazonium salts are from Lubs (1955) but it is not to be inferred that the formulae cited are the only formulae used commercially for the individual stable diazo salts.

An attempt to cite some of the major histochemical uses has been made, and to give some of the pertinent references.

Solubilities are those given in the ICI handbook (1951) for Brentamine diazonium salts. (See footnote on p. 210.)

Coupling Rate: Given first are the ratings as given in the ICI handbook (1951) which grades in 5 arbitrary grades: very rapid, rapid, fairly rapid, slow and very slow. These are followed by the "half reaction times" in seconds for reaction with α-naphthol-8-sulfonic acid, β-naphthol-6-sulfonic acid and β-naphthylamine-6-sulfonic acid, taken from Table I in Nachlas *et al.* (1959).

Solution stability data from the ICI handbook (1951) is supplemented on occasion from Pearse, Burstone and Gössner.

FAST SCARLET CG   C. I. 37010

(C. I. Azoic Diazo No. 3)

Synonyms: *Scarlet GG, Scarlet 2G, Scarlet A, Scarlet I (Ciba Inga);
Michrome scarlet salt 615; Fast scarlet GGS or GGN or 2J or DS*

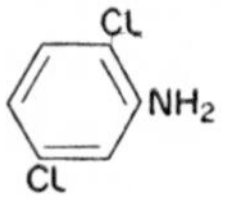

The amine; mol. wt. 162.028

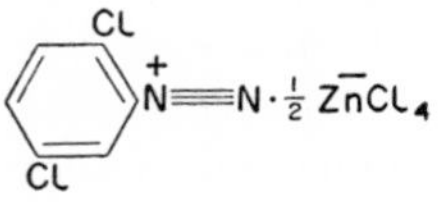

The zinc chloride double salt; ½ mol. wt. 277.624

Color: With naphthol: AS, bright yellowish red

       With enterochromaffin: orange to orange red (Lillie *et al.*)

Content of primary amine: Possible amine content of $ZnCl_2$ double salt 58.4%

Solubility: 200 gm per liter (ICI)

Coupling rate: Very rapid (ICI) 0.8, 0.4, 2 (Nachlas *et al.*, 1959)

Solution stability: Very good

References: E. Gurr, 1960, mentions; Lillie *et al.*, 1960

FAST BROWN RR   C. I. NO. 37020

Synonym: *Brown RR*

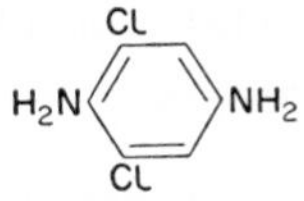

The amine; mol. wt. 177.044

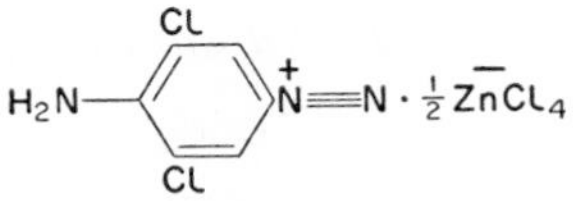

The $ZnCl_2$ double salt; mol. wt. 292.640

Color: With naphthol: AS, brown

Content of primary amine: Possible content for $ZnCl_2$ double salt 60.5 %

Coupling rate: Rapid (Burstone, 1958c)

References: Burstone (1958c) finds it a rapid coupler for alkaline phosphatase with AS phosphates.

FAST RED RC   C. I. NO. 37120

(C. I. Azoic Diazo No. 10)

Synonyms: *Diazo red RC; red RC; brown salt III, C; red salt I; fast red 4CA, RS; red RCS*

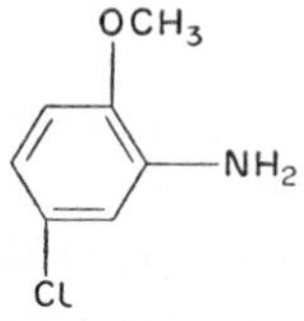

The amine; mol. wt. 157.606

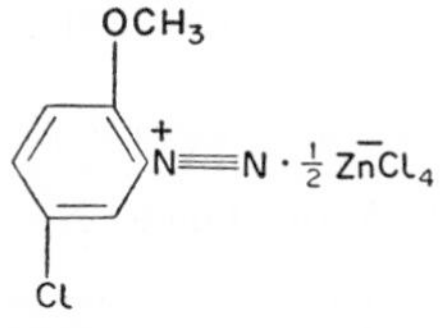

The $ZnCl_2$ double salt; mol. wt. 273.202

Color: With naphthols: α, red brown; AS, red

Content of primary amine: 16.3 % (FH) with Al and Na sulfates, 20 % (ICI); possible content for $ZnCl_2$ double salt 57.7 %

Solubility (ICI): 160 gm per liter

Coupling rate: Rapid (Sensitive to acetic acid)

Solution stability: Very good

References: Gomori (1952), Gössner (1958), Pearse (1953), Burstone (1957, 1958a). Pearse found phosphatase inhibition slight; presumably ICI used. Burstone cites as "useful" in phosphatase methods. Gössner thought it not especially good.

FAST RED B   C. I. NO. 37125

(C. I. Azoic Diazo No. 5)

Synonyms: *Fast red salt B; red B; red salt base V; fast red 5 NA, BN, E*

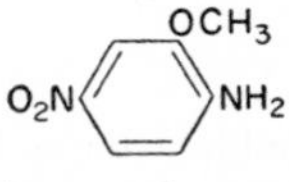

The amine; mol. wt. 168.157

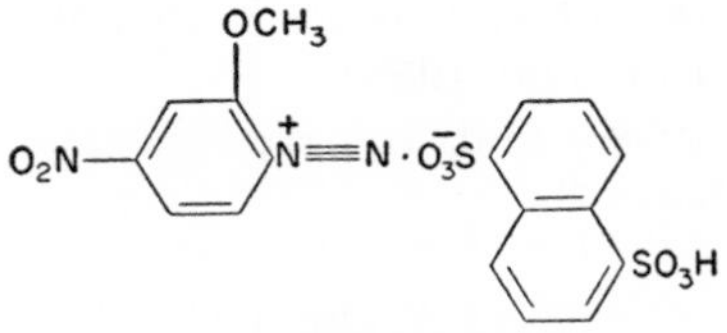

The acid 1,5-naphthalene disulfonate; mol. wt. 467.447

Color: With naphthol AS, B: deep red

With enterochromaffin: deep red, background pale yellow

Content of primary amine: 20% (ICI). Possible for 1,5-naphthalene disulfonate 36.9%

Solubility: 200 gm per liter (ICI)

Coupling rate: Very rapid (ICI, 1951); 1″–7″ (Nachlas *et al.*, 1959)

Solution stability: Very good

References: Clara (1934, 1935), Gomori (1952, 1954), Pearse (1953), Gössner (1958), Burstone (1958a). Has been widely used for enterochromaffin, (see Lillie *et al.*, 1960) for which it is one of the best, but not especially good in esterase and phosphatase methods.

FAST SCARLET R   C. I. NO. 37130

(C. I. Azoic Diazo No. 13)

Synonyms: *Scarlet R; diazo scarlet R; brown salt IV, D; fast scarlet 4NA, RC, RN; scarlet RS, RC, NSR, III; michrome scarlet 329*

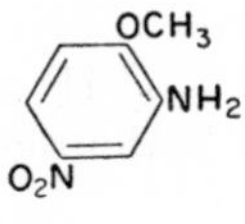

The amine; mol. wt. 168.157

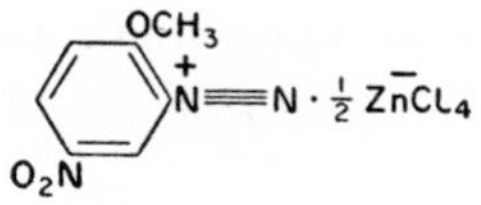

The double ZnCl₂ salt; mol. wt. 283.753

Color: With naphthols: α, red brown; AS, red
Content of primary amine: 20% (NAC) (ZnCl₂) salt. Possible content for ZnCl₂ double salt 59.3%
Solubility (ICI): 200 gm per liter
Coupling rate: Very rapid (ICI, 1951); 0.4, 0.3 7″ (Nachlas *et al.*, 1959)
Solution stability: Fair
References: Gomori (1954), Lillie (1954), Pearse (1953). Pearse recorded considerable phosphatase inhibition.

FAST BORDEAUX GP   C. I. NO. 37135

(C. I. Azoic Diazo No. 1)

Synonyms: Bordeaux GP, fast Bordeaux GDN, 3 NA, NGP, GPS, GPN; Bordeaux IV, with and without the words "salt" and "base"

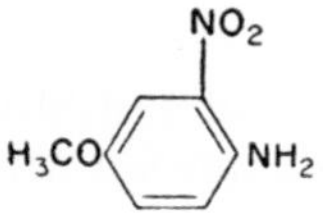

The amine; mol. wt. 168.157

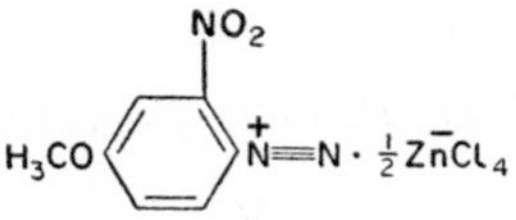

The ZnCl₂ double salt; ½ mol. wt. 283.753

Color: With naphthols: α, purple; AS, purple red
    With enterochromaffin: brown to orange (Gomori, 1952, orange to
        orange red (Lillie *et al.* 1960)
Content of primary amine: 20% NAC, ICI; possible for ZnCl₂ double salt 59.3%
Solubility (ICI): 250 gm per liter
Coupling rate: Rapid (ICI); 1, 1, 12″ (Nachlas *et al.*, 1959)
Solution stability: Fair
References: Gomori (1952)

FAST RED VIOLET LB

Synonym: *Red violet LB*

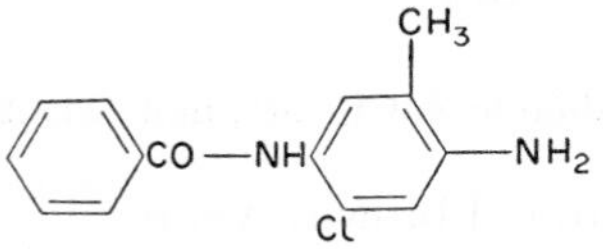

The amine; mol. wt. 260.731

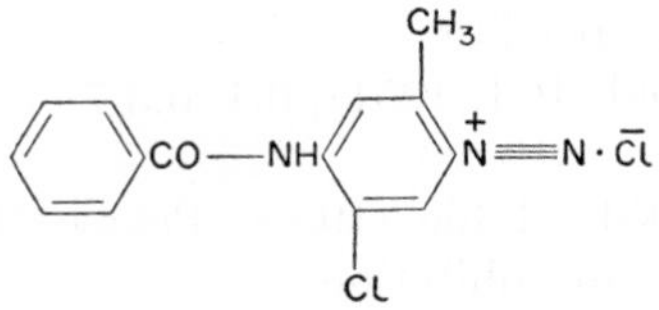

The diazonium chloride; mol. wt. 308.180

Color: With naphthols: AS-BI, -TR, -MX, -BS, red to purple red

Content of primary amine: Not stated. Marketed by Verona Chemical Co. and is said to be the diazonium chloride with possible content for the diazonium chloride 84.6%

Coupling rate: Rapid (Burstone, 1957b)

Solution stability: Stable (Id.)

References: Burstone used for acid (1958b), and alkaline (1957, 1958a) phosphatases with the above naphthol AS phosphates. It gives excellent results.

FAST ORANGE GR   C. I. NO. 37025

(C. I. Azoic Diazo No. 6)

Synonyms: *Orange GRS, II, B; Fast orange O, JR, fast orange salt GR*

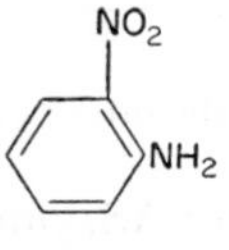

The amine; mol. wt. 138.130

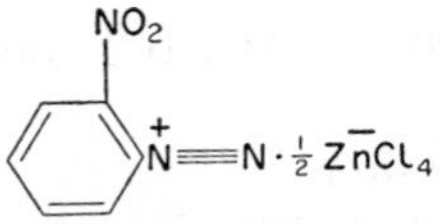

The ZnCl₂ double salt; ½ mol. wt. 253.726

Color: With naphthol AS, red orange

    With enterochromaffin: pink to orange-red (Lillie *et al.*, 1961)

Content of primary amine: 20% (ICI); Possible content as $ZnCl_2$ double salt 54.4%

Solubility: (ICI) 260 gm per liter

Coupling rate: Very rapid (ICI, 1951); 0.2, 0.4, 8″ Nachlas *et al.*, 1959

Solution stability: Very good

Reference: Gössner (1958) found it not especially useful in esterase and phosphatase methods.

FAST RED GG   C. I. NO. 37035

(C. I. Azoic Diazo No. 37)

Synonyms: *Nitrazol CF, nitrosamine red, paranitraniline red, para red, red GG, 2GS, fast red 2G, 2J, michrome red salt 610*

O_2N⟨benzene⟩NH_2

The amine; mol. wt. 138.130

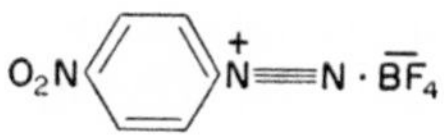

O_2N⟨benzene⟩$\overset{+}{N}\!\!\equiv\!\!N \cdot \overline{\overline{B}}F_4$

The borofluoride diazonium salt; mol. wt. 236.942

    The *p*-chlorobenzene sulfonate is also used (mol. wt. 341.743), also the bisulfate.

Color: With naphthols: red

    With enterochromaffin: deep red; background staining of tissue apt to be rather deep yellow and some fading in sections (Clara and Canal, 1932; Lillie *et al.*, 1961)

Content of primary amine: Possible for borofluoride 58.3%, for chlorobenzene sulfonate 40.4%

Solubility (ICI): 100 gm per liter

Coupling rapidity: Very rapid (ICI, 1951); 0.3, 0.5, 6″ Nachlas *et al.*, 1959

Solution Stability: Good

    Nitrazol CF was a borofluoride complex; para red was a Na-2-naphthol-1-sulfonate; see Gomori (1952)

Reference: Clara and Canal (1932). Has been widely used for enterochromaffin cells, for which it was the first stable diazo employed.

FAST RED 3GL   C. I. NO. 37040

(C. I. Azoic Diazo No. 9)

Synonyms: *Red 3G, diazo red 3G, fast red salt 3G, red salt VI, diazo fast red 3GL, red 3GK, F, fast red 2NC, 3JL, NBGL*

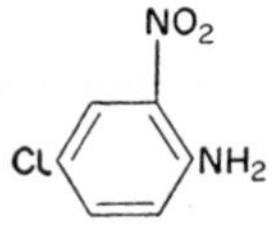

The amine; mol. wt. 172.579

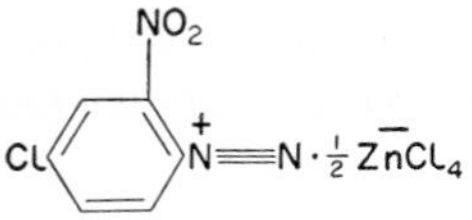

The ZnCl$_2$ double salt; ½ mol. wt. 288.175

Color: With naphthol AS, red to orange-red
    With enterochromaffin: brown (Lillie, 1954)
Content of primary amine: 20% (NAC), 40% (ICI), possible for ZnCl$_2$ double salt 60%
Solubility (ICI): 160 gm per liter
Coupling rate: Rapid (ICI, 1951); 0.9, 1, 6″ Nachlas *et al.*, 1959.
Solution Stability: Fair
References: Lillie (1954), Gössner (1958), Pearse (1953); Pearse noted strong inhibition of phosphatase.

FAST RED TR   C. I. NO. 37085

(C. I. Azoic Diazo No. 11)

Synonyms: *Red TR, fast red 5CT, TRN, fast red salt TR, red TA, TRS, IX*

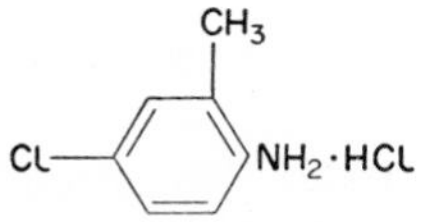

The amine; mol. wt. 178.071

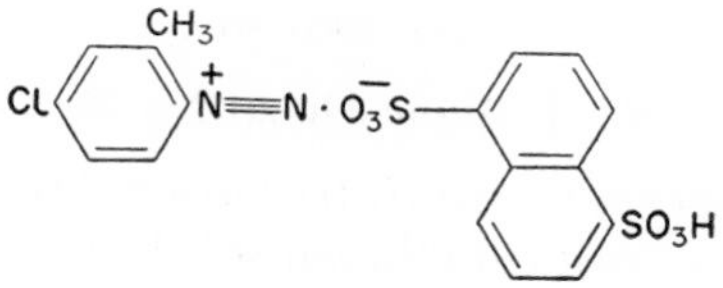

The acid naphthalene-1,5-disulfonate; mol. wt. 477.361

Color: With naphthols: AS, deep red; α, brown

Content of primary amine: 14.7% as $ZnCl_2$ double salt with Al and Na sulfates (FH); 21.4% as naphthalene di- and trisulfonate (FH); 21.45% as an organic Na sulfonate (FH); 20% (ICI); possible content for acid naphthalene disulfonate, 32.0%

Solubility (ICI): 200 gm per liter

Coupling rate: Rapid (sensitive to acetic acid) (ICI, 1951)

Solution stability: Very good

References: Burstone (1958a), Gössner, Lewis (1958). Burstone found it useful in phosphatase methods specially recommended by Gössner for alkaline phosphatase and esterase.

FAST RED RL   C. I. NO. 37100

(C. I. Azoic Diazo No. 34)

Synonyms: *Red RL, fast red NRL, red base X; fast red salt RL*

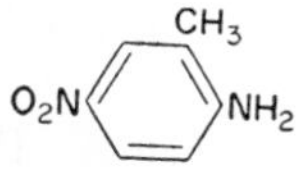

The amine; mol. wt. 152.157

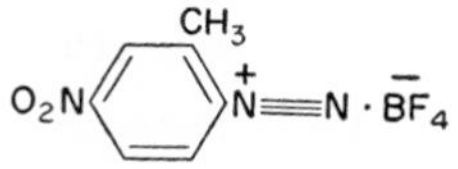

The borofluoride diazonium salt; mol. wt. 250.969

Color: With naphthol AS, purplish red

With enterochromaffin: red to deep red (Lillie *et al.*, 1961)

Content of primary amine: 20.5% with Na_2SO_4 and borax (FH), 20% (ICI); possible content as BF_3 double salt 60.4%

Solubility (ICI): 65 gm per liter

Coupling rate: Very rapid (ICI, 1951)

Solution stability: Good

References: Burstone and Folk (1956) noted as satisfactory in naphthol phosphatase methods; Gössner (1958) did not note it as especially adapted to esterase and phosphatase technics; Lillie *et al.*, 1960, for enterochromaffin cells.

FAST RED GL — C. I. NO. 37110

(C. I. Azoic Diazo No. 8)

Synonyms: *Diazo red G; red G, GL; fast red G, JL, 3NT; diazo fast red GL; red salt VII*

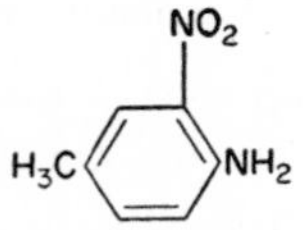

The amine; mol. wt. 152.157

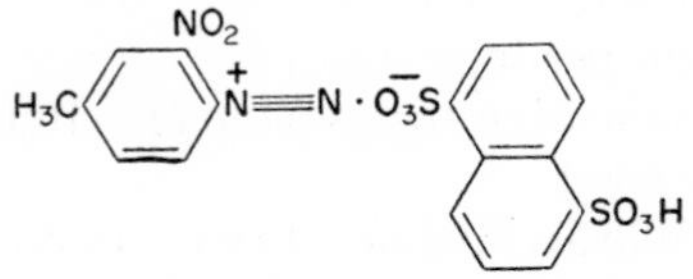

The acid naphthalene-1,5-disulfonate; mol. wt. 451.447

Color: With naphthol AS, deep red
With enterochromaffin: purplish red to pink (Lillie *et al.* 1961)
Content of primary amine: 20% (ICI) possible for naphthalene disulfonate 33.5%
Solubility (ICI): 90 gm per liter
Coupling rate: Rapid (ICI, 1951); 0.5, 7, 6″ (Nachlas *et al.*, 1959)
Solution stability: Fair
References: Gomori (1952), Pearse (1953). Pearse noted a strong inhibitory effect on phosphatase.

FAST RED ITR — C. I. NO. 37150

(C. I. Azoic Diazo No. 42)

Synonyms: *Brentamine fast red LTR; fast red ITRN; fast red salt ITR; michrome red salt 614; red ITR*

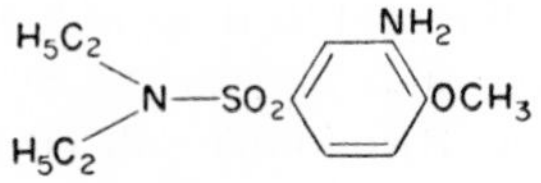

The amine; mol. wt. 258.347

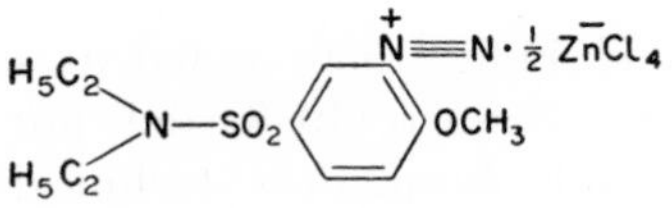

The $ZnCl_2$ double salt; ½ mol. wt. 373.943

Color: With naphthol AS, red

Content of primary amine: $ZnCl_2$ salt with Na and Al sulfates 35.8 % (FH), 40 % (ICI). Possible content for $ZnCl_2$ double salt 69.1 %

Solubility (ICI): 60 gm per liter

Coupling rate: Fairly rapid (ICI, 1951)

Solution stability: Good

Reference: Gössner (1958), recommends it in acid phosphatase technics, noting good stability and no non-specific staining.

FAST BLUE RR   C. I. NO. 37155

(C. I. Azoic Diazo No. 24)

Synonyms: *Diazo blue RR; fast blue salt RR; blue RR, NRR; diazo fast blue RR*

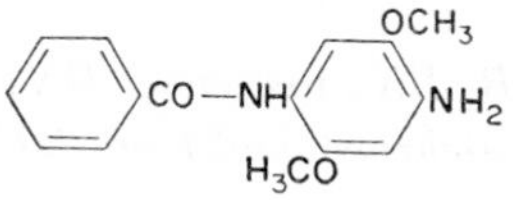

The amine; mol. wt. 272.309

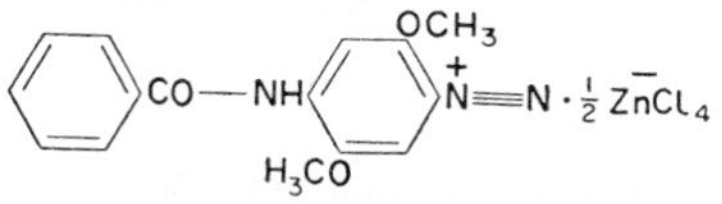

The $ZnCl_2$ double salt; mol. wt. 387.905

Color: With naphthols: α, black; β, purple red; AS, deep violet blue
        With enterochromaffin: pink (Lillie *et al.*, 1961)

Content of primary amine: 36 % with $ZnSO_4$ and Na_2SO_4 (FH). Possible content for the $ZnCl_2$ double salt, 70.2 %

References: Pearse (1953), Gössner (1958), Gomori (1952), Burstone (1958a). Used by Gomori for acid phosphatase and esterase methods, by Pearse for phosphatases, by Gössner for esterases, by Burstone for phosphatases.

FAST CORINTH LB   C. I. NO. 37160

(C. I. Azoic Diazo No. 43)

Synonyms: *Corinth LB; diazo fast corinth LB; fast corinth salt LB*

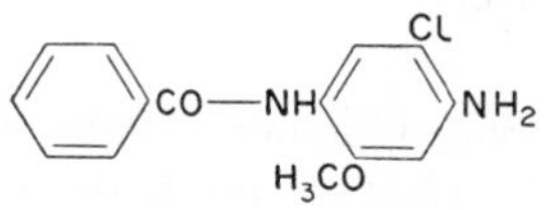

The amine; mol. wt. 276.731

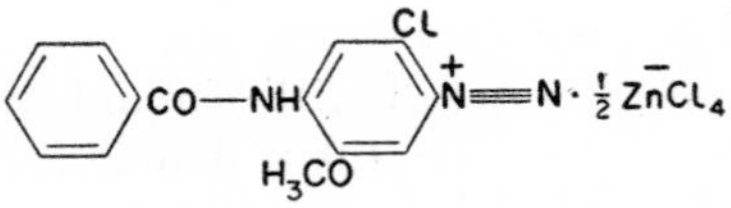

The ZnCl₂ double salt; mol. wt. 392.327

Color: With naphthol: AS, purple red
Content of primary amine: Possible content for ZnCl₂ double salt, 70.5%
References: Burstone (1957a) finds this a satisfactory salt in esterase technics. Gössner (1958) did not think it especially adapted for esterase and phosphatase methods.

FAST VIOLET B C. I. NO. 37165

(C. I. Azoic Diazo No. 41)

Synonyms: *Violet B, BN; fast violet BN; diazo fast violet B; michrome violet salt 294*

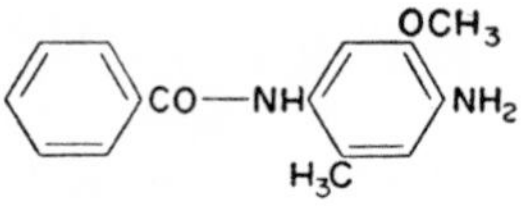

The amine; mol. wt. 256.315

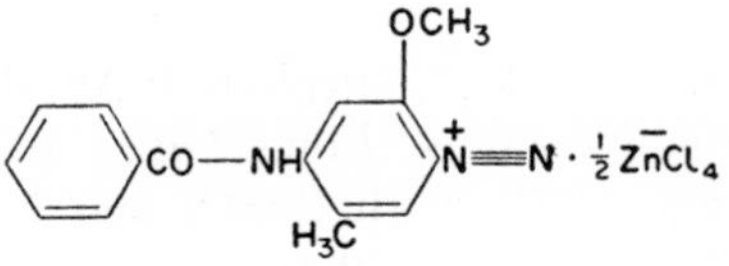

The ZnCl₂ double salt; mol. wt. 371.905

Color: With naphthol AS, blue violet
  With enterochromaffin: orange brown (Gomori, 1954; Lillie *et al.*, 1961)
Content of primary amine: 20% (ZnCl₂ salt, NAC); 20% (ICI). Possible content for ZnCl₂ double salt 69%
Solubility (ICI): 100 gm per liter
Coupling rate: Slow (ICI, 1951)
Solution stability: Good
References: Burstone (1958a), Gössner (1958), Gomori (1954). Burstone noted it as useful in phosphatase methods; not in Gössner's preferred list for esterases and phosphatases.

FAST BLUE BB   C. I. NO. 37175

(C. I. Azoic Diazo No. 20)

Synonyms: *Blue BB, 2BS, NBB; Fast blue salt BB; fast blue 2B, EB, BBN; Diazo fast blue BB*

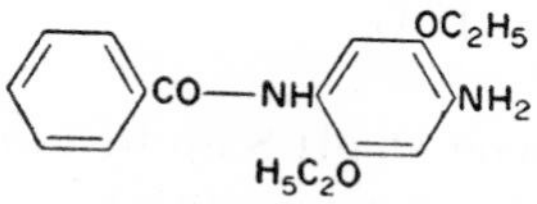

The amine; mol. wt. 300.363

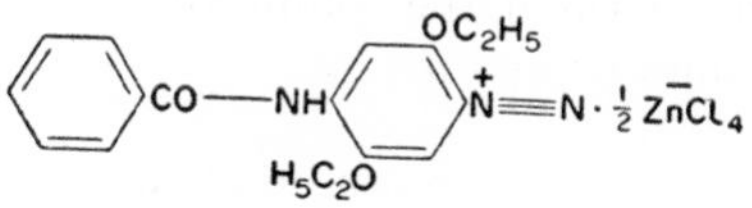

The ZnCl$_2$ double salt; mol. wt. 415.959

Color: With naphthols: AS, deep violet blue, α, black

     With enterochromaffin: orange brown (Gomori, 1954), to orange red (Lillie, 1961)

Content of primary amine: 40% (ICI). Possible content for ZnCl$_2$ double salt, 72%

Solubility (ICI): 40 gm per liter

Coupling rate: Slow, sensitive to acetic acid (ICI, 1951)

Solution stability: Good (ICI, 1951); some unstability in alkaline media (Burstone, 1958a)

References: Burstone (1957b, 1958a), Gössner (1958), Gomori (1954). Burstone used it for phosphatases. Gössner notes unspecific staining and decomposition but uses it for esterases and alkaline phosphatase.

FAST BLACK K   C. I. NO. 37190

(C. I. Azoic Diazo No. 38)

Synonyms: *Black NK, Michrome black salt 601*

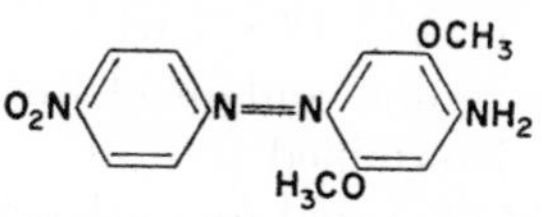

The amine; mol. wt. 302.298

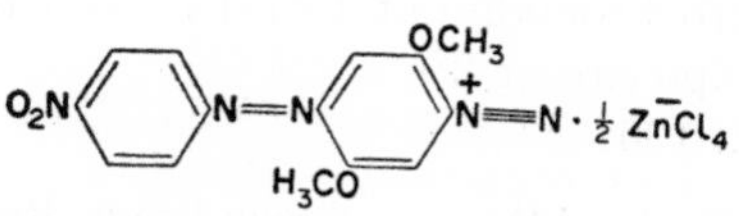

The ZnCl$_2$ double salt ½ mol. wt. 417.894

Color: With naphthol: AS, blue black

With enterochromaffin: black or blue black with pink to red background (Lillie *et al.*, 1961)

Content of primary amine: Possible amine content of $ZnCl_2$ double salt, 72.2%

Solubility: 40 gm per liter (ICI)

Coupling rate: Slow ICI

Solution stability: Poor; good at pH 8 up to 3 hr. (Lillie, laboratory notes)

References: Lillie *et al.*, 1960; Burstone 1958b.

This appears to be a very useful salt for the direct study of tissue protein azo coupling reactions, without the complexities and complications of the post-coupled tetrazonium procedure.

FAST DARK BLUE R   C. I. NO. 37195

(C. I. Azoic Diazo No. 51)

Synonym: *Navy Blue RN (base, salt)*

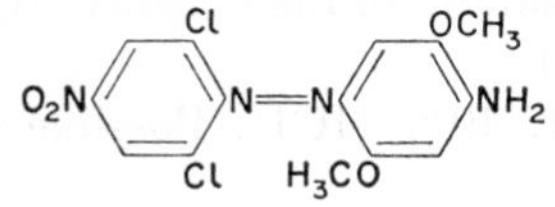

The amine; mol. wt. 371.196

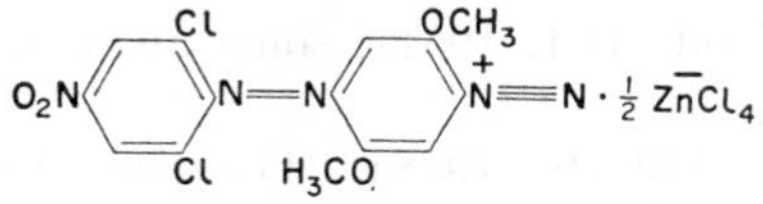

The $ZnCl_2$ double salt ½ mol. wt. 486.792

Color: With naphthol AS; reddish navy blue

With enterochromaffin: black with light orange to red tissue background (Lillie *et al.*, 1961)

Available from Farbwerke Hoechst, Verona Chemical Co., National Aniline Division Allied Chemical Corp.

Content of primary amine: (NAC) 18.8% with Zn and Al

Content of amine: Possible amine content of $ZnCl_2$ double salt, 76.3%

Solubility: Adequate, not determined

Coupling rate: I slow (NAC)*; rapid for enterochromaffin

Solution stability: Good or average (NAC)

Very good for enterochromaffin at 1 mM concentration in pH 8.5 M/10 Veronal HCl, 1'–5' exposure at 3°C

Reference: Lillie *et al.*, 1961.

* Canad. Text. J., 1958, April 18, p. 57: Group I slow. Ratings are I to IV in order of decreasing rapidity with further subdivision into rapid, medium and slow.

FAST BROWN V   C. I. NO. 37200

(C. I. Azoic Diazo No. 21)

Synonym: *Fast brown VA; fast brown salt V*

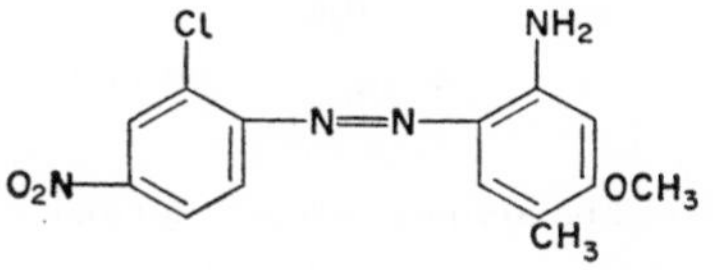

The amine; mol. wt. 320.747

FH only, nature of complex not public

Color: with naphthol AS, red brown

References: Gössner (1958). This is not in Gössner's "recommended" list. Burstone found it unsuccessful in phosphatase and esterase methods.

FAST GARNET GBC   C. I. NO. 37210

(C. I. Azoic Diazo No. 4)

Synonyms: *Garnet GB, GBC, G, Bordeaux Salt II*

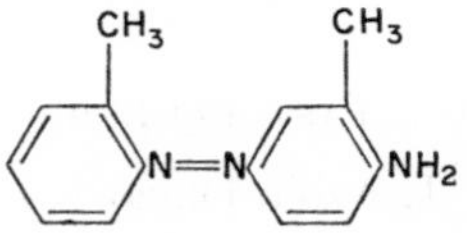

The amine; mol. wt. 225.298

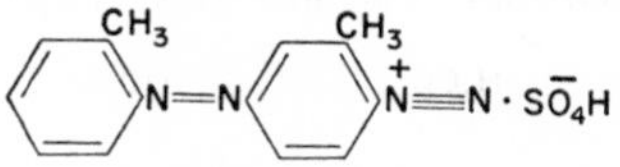

The acid sulfate mol. wt. 334.364

Color: With naphthols: α, red brown; β, red; AS, deep red

With enterochromaffin: red and orange red (Gomori, 1954), background light yellowish

Content of primary amine: 18% NAC; 15.8% FH, 20% (ICI); the (FH) contains Al, Mg and Na sulfates; possible concentration for acid sulfate, 67.4%

Solubility: 50 gm per liter (ICI)

Coupling rate: Very rapid (ICI, 1951) 8, 8, 29″(Nachlas *et al.*, 1959)

Solution stability: Fair

References: Gössner (1958), Gomori (1952, 1954), Pearse (1953). Gössner used it for acid phosphatase and esterase methods. Burstone recommended it for esterase (1957) and aminopeptidase (1956, 1958a), but not phosphatase (1958a).

FAST GARNET GC   C. I. NO. 37215

(C. I. Azoic Diazo No. 27)

Synonyms: (*Diazo or Fast*) *Garnet GC, GCD, AC*

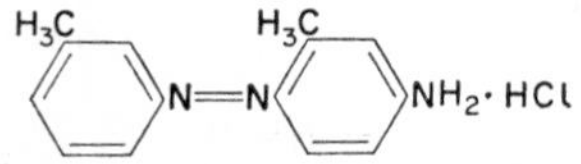

The amine; mol. wt. 261.763

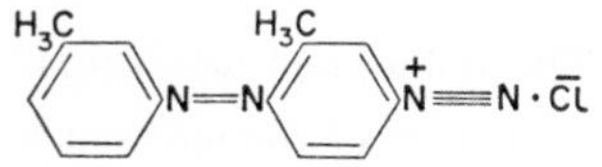

The diazonium chloride; mol. wt. 272.747

Color: With naphthol AS, (Bordeaux) dull brownish red

Content of primary amine: Verona Chemical Co., said to be the diazonium chloride; possible content for the diazonium chloride, 96 % of the amine hydrochloride or 82.7 % of the free base

Coupling rate: Rapid (Burstone and Folk, 1956)

References: Burstone and Folk (1956) found it excellent in aminopeptidase technics.

FAST BLUE B   C. I. NO. 37235

(C. I. Azoic Diazo No. 48)

Synonyms: *Diazo blue B; Blue BNS salt; Dianisidine blue; Fast blue salt BN; Michrome blue salt 250; Naphthanil blue B*

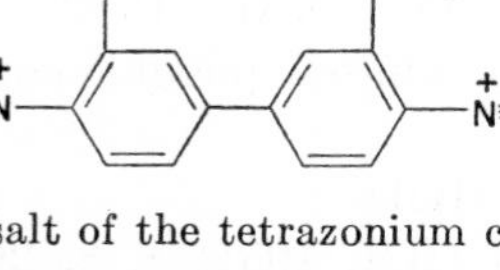

The amine; mol. wt. 244.298

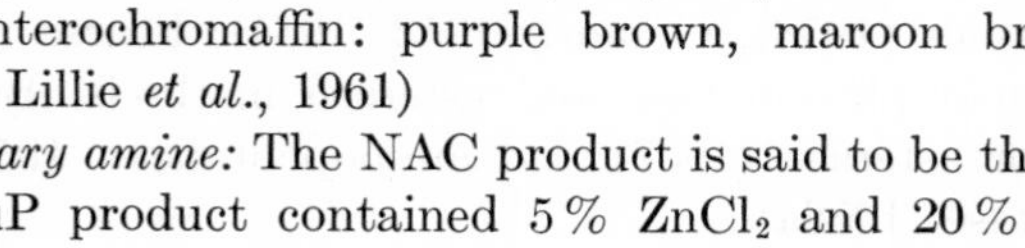

The zinc chloride double salt of the tetrazonium chloride; mol. wt. 475.490

Color: With naphthols: α, brown black; AS, deep blue

      With enterochromaffin: purple brown, maroon brown (Gomori, 1954; Lillie *et al.*, 1961)

Content of primary amine: The NAC product is said to be the $ZnCl_2$ double salt. The duP product contained 5 % $ZnCl_2$ and 20 % $Al_2(SO_4)_3$, its amine content not stated. ICI, 20%; FH, 20.5% with $ZnCl_2$ and Na_2SO_4, 20.2% with Na and Al sulfates.

Possible content for $ZnCl_2$ double salt 50.9%

Solubility (ICI): 100 gm per liter

Coupling Rate: Very slow (ICI, 1951); 0.9″, 2″, 8″ (Nachlas *et al.*, 1959)

Solution stability: Good

This preparation has been widely used in the "coupled tetrazonium" methods for identification of aromatic residues in proteins according to the technics of Danielli, largely as presented by Pearse (1953). It is also used for intensification of the 2-hydroxy-3-naphthoic acid hydrazide reaction for carbonyls.

References: Nachlas and Seligman (1949), Gomori (1952, 1954), Lillie (1953, 1954), Gössner (1958).

FAST BLACK B   C. I. NO. 37245

Synonyms: *Black BS salt; Michrome Black salt 296*

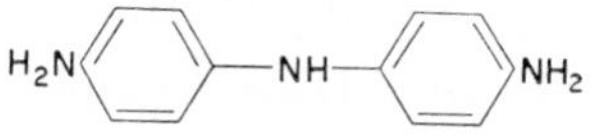

The amine; mol. wt. 199.260

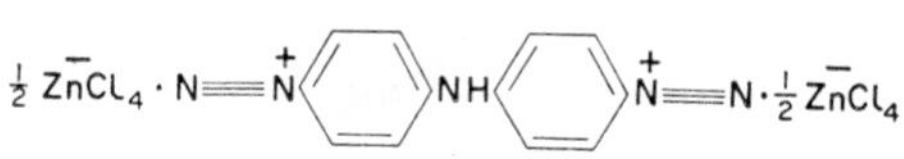

The $ZnCl_2$ double salt (tetrazo); ½ mol. wt. 430.452

Color: With enterochromaffin: red brown (Gomori, 1952; Lillie, 1954) to black (Lillie *et al.*, 1961)

Content of primary amine: 16% (the $ZnCl_2$ double salt, NAC); possible content for $ZnCl_2$ double salt, 46.3%

References: Gomori (1952), Lillie (1954) and Gössner (1958) do not recommend for esterase and phosphatase methods.

VARIAMINE BLUE B   C. I. NO. 37255

(C. I. Azoic Diazo No. 35)

Synonyms: *Fast blue VB, MB, BL; Blue V, B, VB, NS, NSV;*
Variamine blue BA, BD, BN; Michrome blue salt 602

Fast blue VB is the "preferred common name" for the Journal of Histochemistry and Cytochemistry.

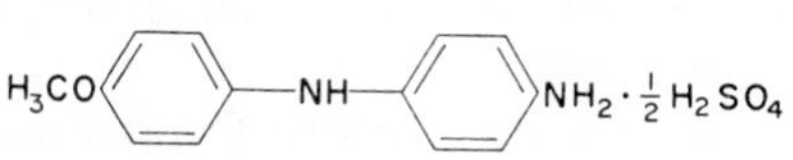

The amine; mol. wt. 263.307

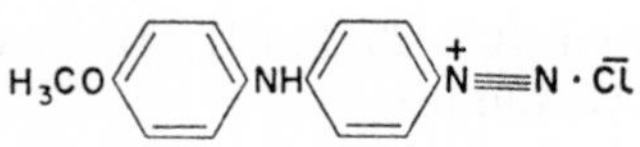

$$H_3CO \diagbig NH \diagbig \overset{+}{N}\!\!=\!\!N \cdot \overline{Cl}$$

The diazonium chloride; mol. wt. 261.720

Color: With naphthol: AS, deep violet blue
   With enterochromaffin: Orange to orange brown (Gomori, 1952; Lillie, 1961)
Content of primary amine: 99.8 % (No diluent; see Gössner, 1958) (FH); possible content for diazonium chloride on basis of the half sulfate, 100.4 %
Solubility (ICI): 90 gm per liter
Coupling rate: Very slow (Burstone, 1958c; Lillie *et al.*, 1953)
Solution stability: Good
References: Gössner (1958), Gomori (1952, 1954). Gössner recommended it especially for alkaline phosphatase naphthol AS methods.

α-NAPHTHYLAMINE   C. I. NO. 37265

(C. I. Azoic Diazo Component)

Synonym: *1-Aminonaphthalene*

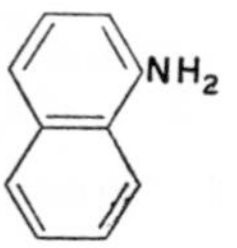

$$\diagbig NH_2$$

The amine; mol. wt. 143.190

$$\overset{+}{N}\!\!=\!\!N \cdot \overline{O_3}S \diagbig SO_3H$$

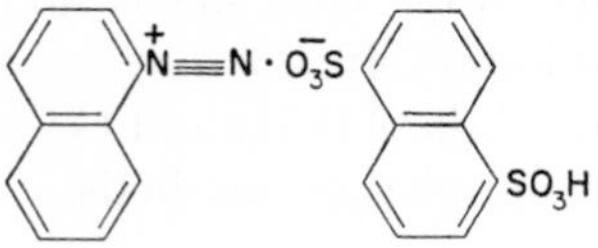

The acid naphthalene-1,5-disulfonate; mol. wt. 442.480

Color: With naphthols: Reds
   With enterochromaffin: Red (see Cordier and Lison, 1930)
Content of primary amine: Possible content for acid naphthalene disulfonate, 32.4 %

Said to be available from Dajac. This salt has more often been used as a freshly diazotized amine; see Clara and Canal (1932), Lison (1951), Gomori (1954), Cordier and Lison (1930).

References: Nachlas and Seligman (1949); Cordier and Lison (1930). (The fresh diazo.)

(C. I. Azoic Diazo No. 36)

Synonyms: *Naphthanil diazo red AL; Fast red salt (Ciba); Red AL, ALS; Michrome red salt 330*

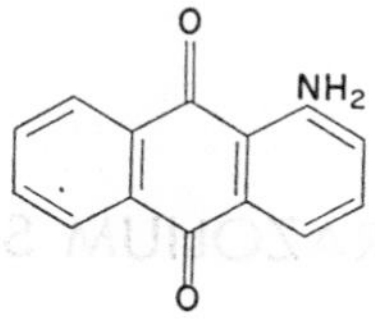

The amine; mol. wt. 223.234

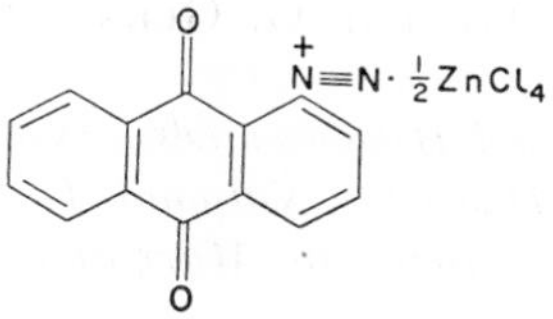

The ZnCl₂ double salt; ½ mol. wt. 338.830

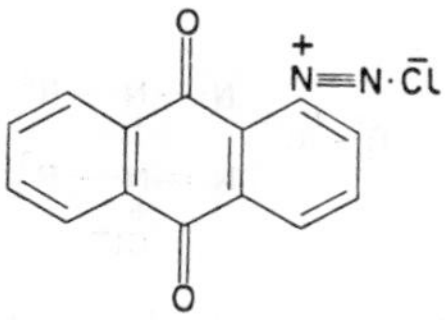

The dizonium chloride; mol. wt. 270.683

Color: With naphthol: AS, pink, bright red
    With enterochromaffin: brown (Lillie, laboratory notes)
Content of primary amine: As ZnCl₂ double salt, 20 % (NAC); with 5 % ZnCl₂ and 12 % Al₂(SO₄)₃ (duP); diazonium chloride available from Dajac; amine content of last 2 not stated; not much used today; possible content for diazonium chloride, 82.5 %; for ZnCl₂ double salt, 65.9 %.
Solubility (ICI): 60 gm per liter
Coupling rate: Rapid (ICI, 1951); 1, 1, 7″ (Nachlas et al., 1959)
Solution stability: Good
References: Seligman and Mannheimer (1949) for acid phosphatase with α-naphthyl phosphate. See also Lillie (1954).

Also used by Burstone (1958b) without outstanding results have been fast orange GR, C. I. 37025; fast scarlet VD, C. I. 37055; fast brown V, C. I. 37200; fast red KB, C. I. 37090; fast Corinth LB, C. I. 37160; fast black G, C. I. 37260; 3-aminocarbazole.

XI

TETRAZOLIUM SALTS

GEORGE G. GLENNER

Laboratory of Pathology and Histochemistry, National Institute of Arthritis and Metabolic Diseases, National Institutes of Health, Bethesda, Maryland

The group of compounds known as tetrazolium salts or tetrazoles, having the same basic structure

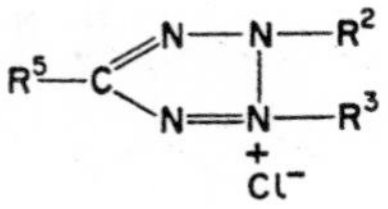

have found increasing applicability in histochemistry, particularly in the localization of oxidative enzyme systems. The water soluble tetrazolium salts are not dyes in themselves, but on reduction form deeply colored, water insoluble pigments known as formazans.

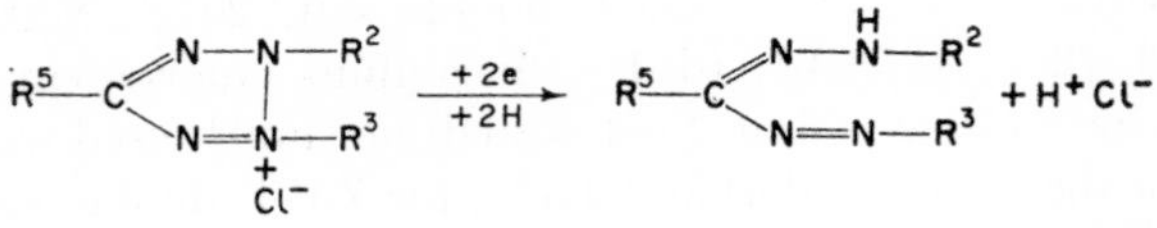

The characteristics of the more frequently used tetrazolium salts vary with regard to the following characteristics: light sensitivity, formazan crystal size, fat solubility and speed of reduction. The ditetrazolium salts

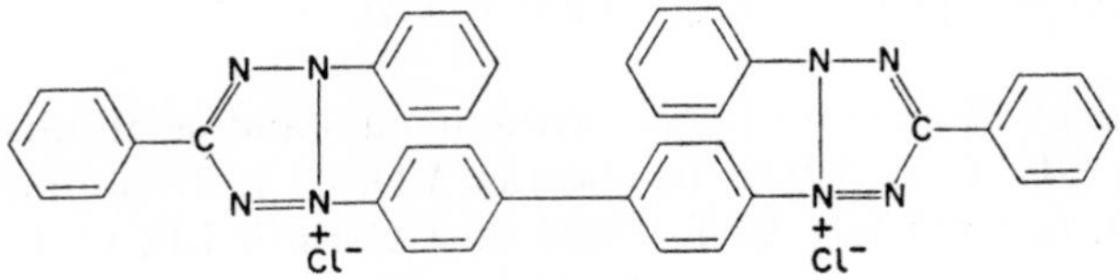

230

have generally been found to satisfy to a great degree the characteristics most desirable for histochemical work. The ditetrazolium salts are invariably contaminated to a differing extent with a monotetrazolium salt

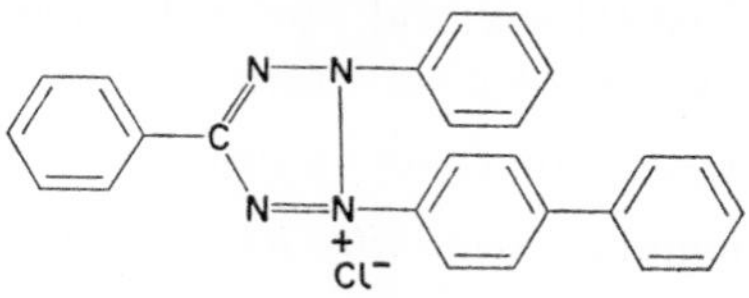

(having solubility and electronic characteristics similar to the ditetrazole) formed during the synthetic procedure. No commercially available ditetrazole has been found free of this monotetrazole contaminant; some in fact contain as much as 91% contaminating material (Burtner et al., 1957). For a detailed description of the chemistry of the formazans and tetrazolium salts the reader is referred to Nineham (1955).

The tetrazoles were first used to demonstrate the viability of seeds by Lakon (1942) using the red stain of the formazan produced in viable tissues to indicate active enzymatic processes. Straus et al. (1948) and Pratt et al., (1948), used the tetrazoles on histological sections of animal tissues. At pH values above 9.0 the tetrazolium salts are reduced by sulfhydryl compounds and this feature has been used for the localization of cystene containing proteins in histological sections (Pearse, 1953). Jerchel and Mohle (1944) showed that the apparent oxidation-reduction potential of the more typical tetrazolium salts was about -0.08 v, and that these salts were, therefore, capable of acting as electron acceptors for many pyridine nucleotide linked enzyme systems. Use of the tetrazolium salts for the histochemical demonstration of oxidative enzymes such as cysteine desulfurase and succinic dehydrogenase (Seligman and Rutenburg, 1951) cytochrome oxidase (Oda et al., 1958), monoamine oxidase (Glenner et al., 1957) as well as DPN and TPN diaphorase systems (Nachlas et al., 1958) has been established. In the latter case the classic work of Farber et al., (1956a) has shown that reduction of tetrazolium salts occurs, not as the result of direct reduction by a specific dehydrogenase, but via electron transport from the linked DPN or TPN diaphorase.

MONOTETRAZOLIUM SALTS

2,3,5 TRIPHENYL TETRAZOLIUM CHLORIDE

Synonyms: *Triphenyl tetrazolium chloride; TTC*

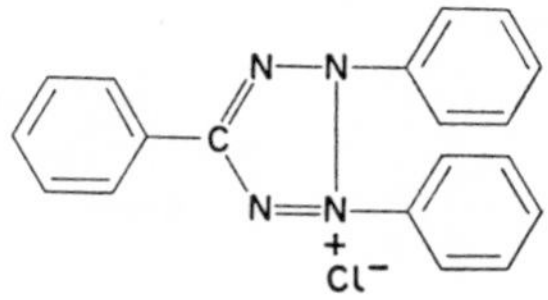

This compound was one of the first tetrazolium synthesized (von Pech-man and Runge, 1894) and was used in most of the early experimental botanical research. The formazan is extremely fat soluble and light sensi-tive, and has a large crystal size and slow reduction speed. Therefore, it is unsuitable for definitive histological work.

2(p-IODOPHENOL)-3-(p-NITROPHENOL)-5-PHENYL TETRAZOLIUM CHLORIDE

Synonyms: *Iodo-nitro tetrazolium; INT*

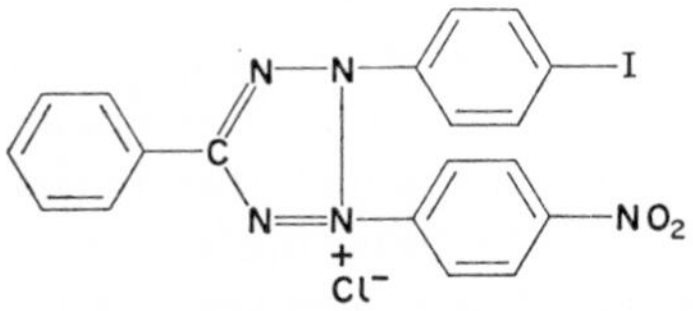

This compound has been used extensively in histochemical research (Atkinson *et al.*, 1950) since it is rapidly reduced by most enzyme systems and the formazan produced is only moderately light sensitive. However, the formazan is rather fat soluble, thereby diffusing into neighboring tissues, and has a moderately large crystal size. The formazan produced has both a dark red and orange component, the result perhaps of a contaminating byproduct formed by *iodo* ejection during the synthetic procedure.

2,5-DIPHENYL-3-α-NAPHTHYL TETRAZOLIUM CHLORIDE

Synonym: *Tetrazolium violet*

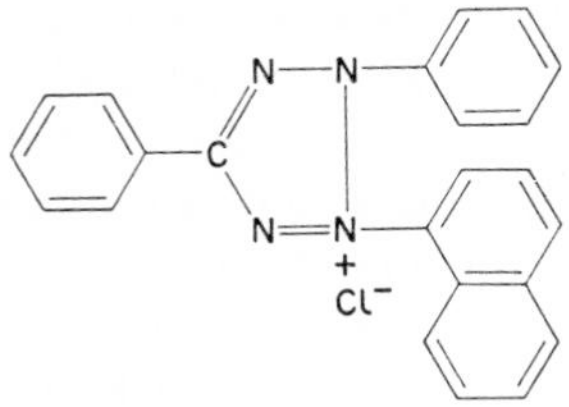

This compound has been used to a minor extent in histochemical work (Shelton and Schneider, 1952) but its characteristics, particularly large formazan crystal size and slow speed of reduction have not popularized it.

3-(4,5-DIMETHYL THIAZOLYL-2)-2,5-DIPHENYL TETRAZOLIUM BROMIDE

Synonyms: *MTT Co; Chelating tetrazole MTT*

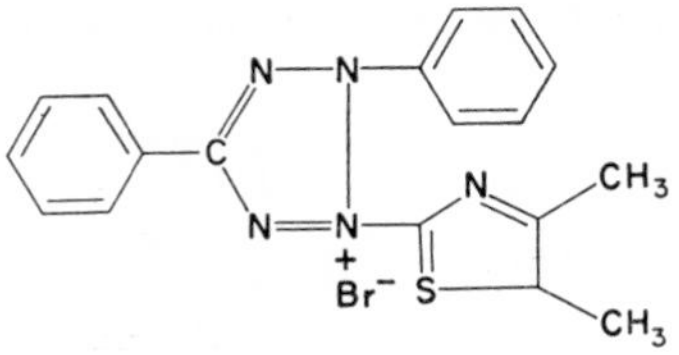

This monotetrazole has been introduced by Pearse (1957) for the demonstration of oxidative systems by the formation of an insoluble cobalt-formazan chelate on tetrazole reduction. The formazan will chelate other cations, *i.e.* nickel and copper salts and the color and size of the formazan precipitate varies with the metal chelate, *e.g.* cobalt produces a small black crystal and nickel a larger greenish blue crystal. Mitochondrial localization of enzyme systems in many tissue sites has been claimed, but this has been denied by Novikoff *et al.* (1961). The tetrazole is rapidly reduced and the initial formazan crystal size is small with a definite fat solubility. TPN-linked enzyme systems cannot be demonstrated with this tetrazole due to binding of the cation by the cyanide trap used (Pearse, 1958).

DITETRAZOLIUM SALTS

3,3'(4,4'-DIPHENYLENE)-BIS(2,5-DIPHENYL) DITETRAZOLIUM CHLORIDE

Synonyms: *Neotetrazolium; Ditetrazolium chloride*

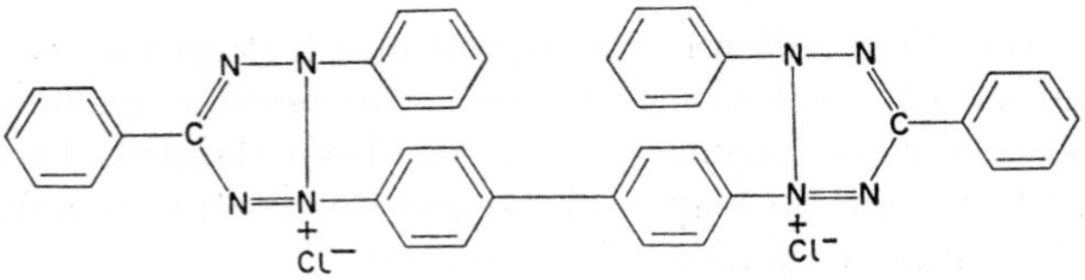

This was the first dietetrazole used histochemically (Antopol *et al.*, 1948) and until recently the most widely used of all the tetrazolium salts. The diformazan is a dark purple and the contaminating monoformazan a deep red. Preferential staining of different histological areas (particularly in kidney) by the respective mono- and diformazans is a constant and still unexplained phenomenon, perhaps predictated on the quantitative difference in electron transfer at various tissue sites and the difference in the oxidation-reduction potential of the respective tetrazoles. The formazan produced from the ditetrazole is slightly fat soluble, but otherwise has excellent histochemical characteristics and has been used for the demonstration of all currently described oxidative enzyme systems. Commercially available samples vary greatly in the extent of their monotetrazole contamination.

3,3'(4,4'-DI-*o*-ANISIDENE)-BIS(2,5-DIPHENYL) DITETRAZOLIUM CHLORIDE

Synonyms: *Blue tetrazolium; Dimethoxy neotetrazolium*

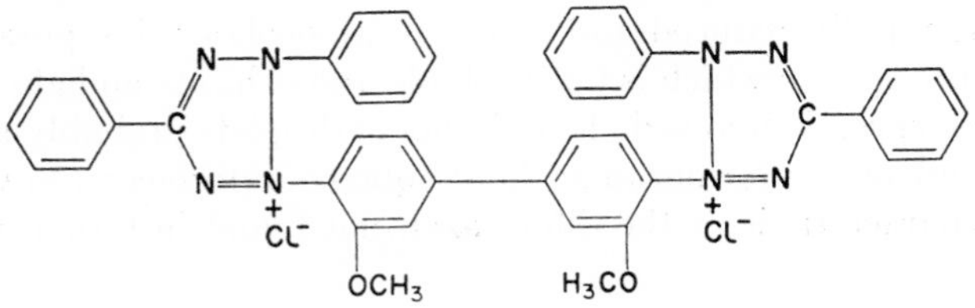

This compound has been used to demonstrate succinic dehydrogenase (Rutenburg *et al.*, 1950) and DPN linked enzyme systems (Farber *et al.*, 1956) but its use has been limited by the slow speed of reduction of the tetrazole. The diformazan is deep blue and the fat soluble monoformazan contaminant, a violet-red.

5,5'-DI(*m*-NITROPHENYL)-3,3'(*p*-BIPHENYLENE)-BIS(2-PHENYL)
DITETRAZOLIUM CHLORIDE

Synonym: *Nitroneotetrazolium*

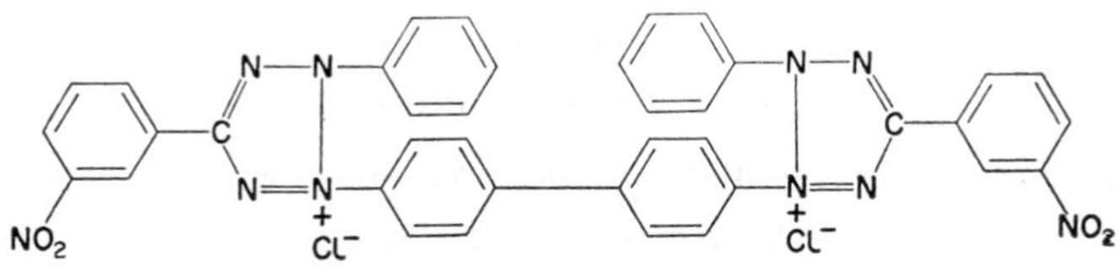

This ditetrazolium salt was introduced into histochemistry by Pearson (1957) who used it to demonstrate numerous enzyme systems. Excellent localization of various enzyme systems has been claimed. The blue-black diformazan has a fine to coarse crystal and the ditetrazole reduces slowly. The monoformazan contaminant is a dark red.

3,3'(4,4'-DI-*o*-ANISIDENE)-2,2'-DI(*p*-NITROPHENYL)-BIS(5-PHENYL)

DITETRAZOLIUM CHLORIDE

Synonyms: *Nitro blue tetrazolium; Nitro BT; NBT*

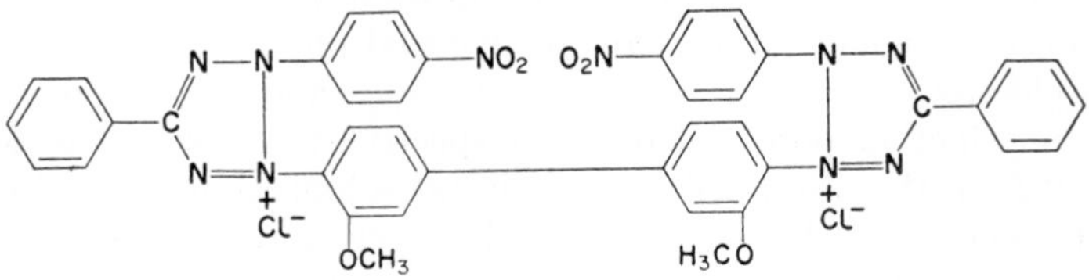

This ditetrazolium was introduced by Nachlas *et al.*, (1957) and has since become the most widely used of the tetrazolium salts. It has been found applicable for use with all histochemically demonstrable oxidative enzyme systems (Nachlas *et al.*, 1958). Using this compound many investigators have described mitochondrial localization of these enzyme systems. The tetrazole is rapidly reduced and forms an amorphous fine pure blue black formazan precipitate which is fat insoluble and exhibits no light sensitivity. Diformazan crystal clumps do form in lipoid droplets probably as the result of movement of the formazan to lipid-aqueous interfaces (Novikoff *et al.*, 1961). A characteristic of the diformazan not found in formazans of other available tetrazolium salts is an intense degree of substantivity, permitting dehydration and mounting of tissue sections in nonaqueous media. The monoformazan contaminant is a dark violet, is highly fat soluble and shows no evidence of the substantive properties apparent in the diformazan. False localization resulting from the monoformazan contaminant can be eliminated from the section by solution in acetone (Glenner *et al.*, 1957).

XII

NATURAL DYES

As stated in Chapter II the group of natural dyes is shrinking, as more and more of them are being produced by artificial means. Alizarin, for example, in the form of madder, used to be extracted from the roots of *Rubia tinctorum,* but the artificial manufacture of this dye is now much more economical. The group of natural dyes, as ordinarily recognized, contains only those which are not yet produced by artificial means. Indigo, however, is listed in this chapter, because in its chemistry it does not fall in well with any groups of artificial dyes. It is still obtained in part, moreover, from the indigo plant, although under present-day conditions its artificial manufacture is ordinarily the more economical. Similarly, orcein can now be synthetically prepared, but is still included in this chapter because of its relationship to other dyes that are secured from natural sources only.

The chemistry of the natural dyes is less definitely known than that of the artificial dyes. This is easily understood; for it will be recalled that there are two ways of obtaining information as to the chemistry of unknown compounds of known composition: the first by decomposing them into simpler compounds of known composition: and the second by manufacturing them from known compounds. In the case of dyes not yet prepared artificially the second of these two lines of procedure is out of the question; hence there is special difficulty in learning their exact chemical structure.

The most important natural dyes for the biologist are hematoxylin, indigo, cochineal (and its derivatives), orcein, and litmus.

SAFFRON   C. I.* NO. 7510

(C. I. Natural Yellow 6)

Saffron is a natural pigment of uncertain composition extracted from the stigmas of *Crocus sativus.* It has been employed by Masson (see Foot,

* The abbreviation "C. I." stands for "Colour Index." The number immediately following is that of the current (2nd) edition; the one which follows is that of the first edition. The name of the dye given under the principal name is the preferred designation in the current Colour Index.

1933) in a connective tissue stain. A special application of this procedure has been made by Block and Godin (1936) for staining yellow fever lesions in the liver. A later application by Van Hoecke and Sebruyns (1952) calls for this dye, after Bismarck brown, aniline blue W.S. and hematein, as a differential stain for glandular cells of the stomach.

THE INDIGO GROUP

INDIGO   C. I. NO. 73000 (1 *ed.*, 1177)

(C. I. Vat Blue 1)

Synonym: *Indigo blue*

The plants from which indigo was formerly exclusively manufactured are largely species of the genus known as *Indigofera*, although some indigo-bearing plants are recognized by botanists as belonging to different genera. In these plants is a glucoside, indican, which is converted by fermentation into the dye indigo. Various formulae have been given for indigo; the one favored at present is based upon its method of artificial manufacture:

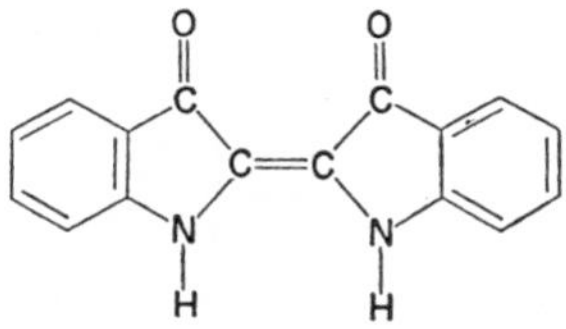

$C_{16}H_{10}N_2O_2$; mol. wt. 262.256

In this formula the exact chromophore group is uncertain; but the ketone group (CO) in a closed ring occurs so often in dyes that it is regarded as probably having chromophoric properties; the same is true of the C = C linkage.

INDIGO-CARMINE

C. I. NO. 73015 (1 *ed.:* 1180)

(C. I. Acid Blue 74)

Synonym: *Indigotine Ia*

This is the sodium salt of indigo disulfonic acid:

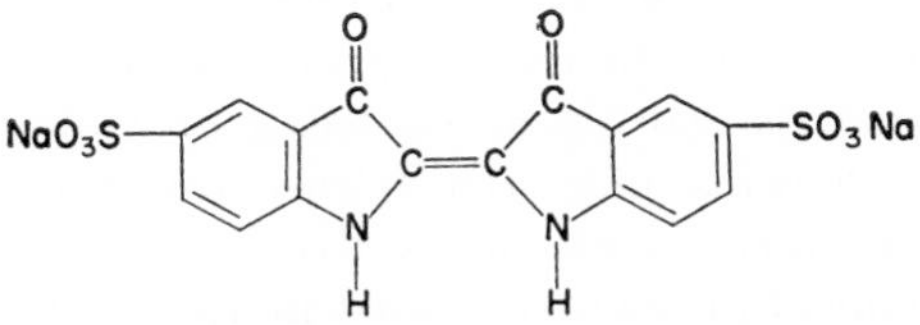

$C_{16}H_8N_2O_8S_2Na_2$; mol. wt. 466.366

Indigo carmine is a blue dye of acid properties, which is sometimes used as a plasma stain in contrast to some red dye such as carmine or basic fuchsin (see Shumway, 1926), sometimes hematoxylin. A few special applications of the stain can be mentioned: by Petragnani (1928), mixed with acid fuchsin, as a stain for Negri bodies; by Cuyler (1932), mixed with eosin Y, as a counterstain to hematoxylin for staining vaginal smears; by Brozek (see Hruby, 1933) in plant cytology where it is used in picric acid solution in contrast to basic fuchsin; by Kempton, Bott and Richards (1937) for uretral injection in studies of glomerular excretion.

For use in Fraenkel's method for elastic tissue, see *Staining Procedures*, p. 69–70.

BERBERINE

c. i. no. 75160 (1 *ed.:* 1237)

(C. I. Natural Yellow 18)

Berberine was originally obtained from barberry and is sometimes called barberry extract. It is found in other plants, however, and can also be prepared synthetically. It has the following formula:

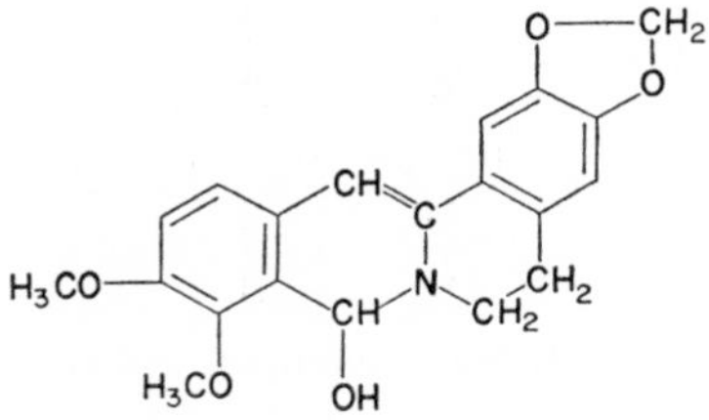

$C_{20}H_{19}NO_5$; mol. wt. 353.360

This compound acts as a basic dye. It has rarely been specified in biological work; but Metcalf and Patton (1944) mentioned it as a fluorochrome in connection with insect histology.

COCHINEAL PRODUCTS

c. i. no. 75470 (1 *ed.:* 1239)

(C. I. Natural Red 4)

Cochineal is a dye that has long been well known. It is obtained from a tropical insect generally known as the cochineal insect. By grinding and extracting the dried bodies of the female of this species a deep red dye is obtained, which is known as cochineal. On treatment with alum this solution yields a product somewhat more free from extraneous matter, known as carmine. This is the form in which the dye is generally obtained by the microscopist. Cochineal products are used in various ways in microscopic technic, generally as nuclear dyes. They are extremely valuable in cases where it is desirable to stain in bulk before sectioning.

Cochineal, itself, has been used for various purposes in microscopic technic, even though less used today than carmine. Alone it has little value, to be sure, for it has no direct affinity for tissues unless they contain iron, aluminium or some other metal. It is most commonly employed either with or following a salt of one of these metals as a mordant. A tincture of cochineal, that is an alcoholic solution containing calcium and aluminium chlorides, has been used by Mayer (see Lee, 1937, p. 149) both on sections and for staining in bulk; but its most common method of use is with alum in watery solution. An alum-cochineal of this sort was first used independently by Mayer (1878, 1892) and Czokor (1880); it can be used for sections, and is specially recommended for staining in bulk, by which technic it stains nuclei violet red, and blood and muscle cells orange, while the cytoplasm is but weakly colored. A chrom-alum-cochineal was used by Hansen (1905) for staining sections. Spuler (1901) recommended an iron-alum-cochineal for staining in bulk when the sections are to be photographed, the technic bringing out nuclei, the blood in the tissues, and the muscle striations; sections may also be stained by the same method. By this technic the iron alum is applied first to the tissues as a mordant, and then followed by the stain. In Hansen's ferri-cochineal, on the other hand, the iron alum is mixed with the dye, and the mixture used for staining sections of tissue (see Lee, 1937, p. 145). Reynolds (1936) has proposed a mixture of alum cochineal with hematoxylin in staining trematodes and nematodes, *in toto*.

Carmine. Carmine is of considerable historic interest. It was used as early as 1770 by Hill and in 1838 by Ehrenberg, although as stated elsewhere not exactly for histological purposes. It was also employed in 1849 by Göppert and Cohn, by Corti in 1851, and by Hartig in 1854–1858, these being the first uses of dyes in histology. It is still a valuable stain today, in spite of the enormous variety of synthetic dyes now available. It is much used for staining in bulk, particularly in embryological work. A well-known formula is Schneider's aceto-carmine (see Lee, 1937, p. 142), which is a valuable chromatin stain for fresh material in smear preparations; in fact, the value of aceto-carmine in cytology (especially for counting chromosomes) is appreciated today, if anything, more than it was in earlier days. Belling's (1921) iron aceto-carmine is valuable for staining chromosomes in smear preparations from anthers. Alum carmine was used by Grenacher (1879) for similar purposes. Carmine is only slightly soluble in water at a neutral reaction; so solutions must be either acid (like the three above) or alkaline. Three alkaline formulae are of considerable use: ammonia carmine, which has been used both for injection and for staining sections; soda carmine, used primarily for injection; and Mayer's (1892, 1896) magnesia carmine, useful either for sections or for staining in bulk. Orth (1883) proposed a lithium carmine (*i.e.*, dissolved in a solution of Li_2CO_3) as a nuclear stain for tissues; and the formula for this stain, as given by Krause (1926, I, p. 265), is still frequently employed. Alcoholic solutions are also used: Grenacher's borax carmine (or as modified by Mayer, 1892, 1896) being a splendid nuclear stain for sections; and the hydrochloric carmine of Mayer serving both for sections and for staining in bulk. A special formula containing aluminum chloride (known as muci-carmine) was proposed by Mayer (1892, 1896) for staining mucin. In double staining it is sometimes used with indigo carmine; but most often with picric acid or spirit blue. Picro-carmine is a very well-known combination used for double staining effects in sections, particularly for nervous tissue; it stains nuclei red and cytoplasm yellow.

One of the important uses of carmine is in Best's (1906) carmine stain for glycogen. The method is simple and the result beautiful, the red glycogen standing out in sharp contrast to the blue of the nuclei after staining in alum hematoxylin. The stain is permanent; the method is of much importance both to the pathologist and to the histologist. Mayer's alcoholic HCl carmine, with fast green as a counterstain is equally valuable.

Carminic acid. The dye principle of carmine and cochineal is carminic acid. This product is obtained by extracting the insect bodies with boiling water, treating the extract with lead acetate or barium hydrate, and then decomposing the lead or barium carminate with sulfuric acid. The exact composition of carminic acid is still somewhat uncertain; it is probably:

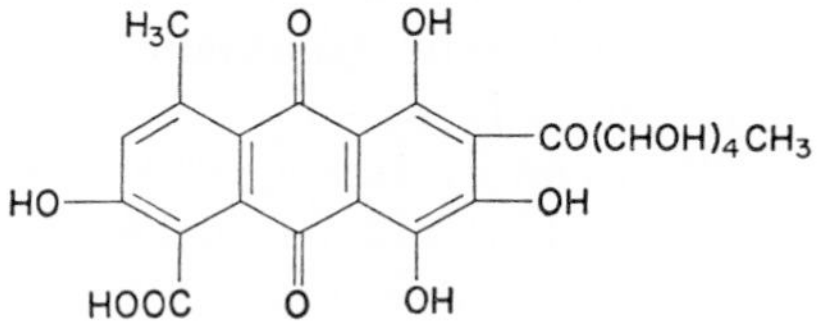

It is a fairly strong dibasic acid and forms readily soluble salts with the alkali metals, and insoluble salts with the heavy metals. Aluminum carminate (obtained by precipitation from aluminum acetate and carminic acid or ammonium carminate) is soluble in aqueous or weak alcoholic solutions of acids.

A slightly different aluminum compound, formed by mixing alum and carminic acid is used in histology. This combination was called carmalum by Mayer (1892, 1899), and was used by Grenacher (1879) and Rawitz (1899); it is a useful nuclear stain for sections; and is often employed with light green or indigo carmine as a contrast stain. A so-called muci-carmine, an acid solution containing aluminum chloride, was employed by Rawitz to stain mucin; while Mayer's para-carmine, containing aluminum and calcium chlorides, is used both for sections and for staining in bulk. By others a combination of iron with carminic acid has been used for similar purposes.

Carmein. Carmine, kept in ammoniacal solution, changes in its properties, due to oxidation. The oxidized carmine, often known as carmein, can be obtained by treating a carmine solution with hydrogen peroxide and precipitating with alcohol. It is a dark colored mass which can be ground into a black powder.

Procedures Recommended by the Commission in Which Cochineal Derivatives Are Used*

Name of Procedure	Page Reference to *Staining Procedures*
Orth's lithium carmine..	41
Mayer's mucicarmine stain....................................	35–6
Mucicarmine with hematoxylin and metanil yellow............	36
As nuclear stain with Weigert's resorcin fuchsin for elastin....	65
Best's method for glycogen....................................	160
Aceto-carmine and basic fuchsin for pollen tubes in style......	197
Swanson's method for pollen tubes...........................	200
Aceto-carmine in plant cytology..............................	203
Belling's iron-aceto-carmine for plant cytology...............	202
Aceto-carmine with chlorazol black E in plant cytology........	206

* Under this heading are given references to procedures described in detail in Staining Procedures, edited by Conn, Darrow and Emmel (1960).

ORCEIN AND LITMUS c. i. (1 *ed.:* no. 1242)

(C. I. Natural Red 28)

Both orcein and litmus are obtained from certain lichens, *Lecanora tinctoria* and *Rocella tinctoria*. These lichens are colorless, but when treated with ammonia and exposed to the air, blue or violet colors develop. The colors are due to certain phenolic compounds, one of which is orcinol:

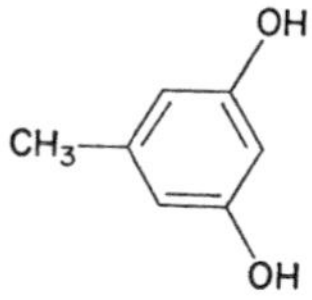

Orcinol, acted upon by air and ammonia, becomes orcein.

ORCEIN

The exact formula of orcein is unknown. It is a weak acid, soluble in alkalies, with a violet color. It is possible to synthesize this dye from orcinol by the above-indicated process. As a matter of fact very good synthetic products, for some purposes better than the natural product, are now on the market. The synthetic orceins from different manufacturers, however, are prepared by different methods and are not the same in their behavior. The reason for these differences are still unknown. The method of manufacture has never yielded exact information as to its structural formula; but it is believed to contain in its molecule the residues of four orcinol molecules. It has some indicator properties both for pH and oxidation-reduction; but is not as useful in that respect as its closely related litmus. It is a weak acid, violet in alkaline solution; in acid solutions it is orange-red.

Unna (see Lee, 1937, p. 451) used orcein in acid alcoholic solution for staining elastin tissue; he employed it for connective tissue, following polychrome methylene blue; and for plasma fibrils in the epithelium, following aniline blue; also with aniline blue or acid fuchsin in studying the process known by him as chromolysis. It has found less frequent use among other histologists; but has been employed in acetic acid solution for staining sections or dissolved in weak hydrochloric acid, for staining sections of embryos; also in combination with various other dyes for bulk staining or as a connective tissue stain. Mollier (1938) called for it in a quadruple tissue stain, with iron-hematoxylin, naphthol green B and azo-carmine G. Kornhauser (1943) used it in a somewhat different quadruple tissue stain with acid alizarin blue, orange G, and fast green FCF. Aceto-orcein is valuable for counting chromosomes in squash or smear preparations. LaCour (1941) employed it in a stain-fixative for cytological work, either for plants or animals. For this last mentioned purpose the synthetic orcein has not worked as well as that derived from natural sources; but as an elastin stain, and in the Mollier and Kornhauser quadruple stains, the synthetic orcein seems to be preferable.

Procedures Recommended by the Commission in Which Orcein Is Used

Name of Procedure	Page Reference to *Staining Procedures* 2nd. ed.
Mollier quadruple stain	57
Kornhauser quadruple stain	58
Tänzer-Unna orcein stain	68–69
Fränkel's method for elastic tissue	69
In animal cytology	164
In plant cytology	204

LITMUS

The exact composition of litmus is likewise unknown. It is obtained from the same lichens as orcein, treating them with lime and potash or soda, in addition to air and ammonia. Its primary colored principle is known as azolitmin; but there must be other colored compounds in litmus, because the color reactions of azolitmin are not exactly the same as those of litmus. Azolitmin may or may not be a single chemical compound; and in any case, its chemical formula is unknown. It can be synthesized from orcinol by methods very similar to those used in preparing orcein, and the synthetic product is very much like the azolitmin obtained from the lichens, if not identical with it. The color reactions of either litmus or of azolitmin are very similar to those of the indophenols (see p. 92); but it is difficult to figure how an indophenol could be derived from orcinol by the process employed.

Litmus is a feeble dye and is never used as a histological stain. Its classic use is for indicator purposes; at one time it was the best acid-base indicator known. Since the importance of learning actual pH of solutions came to be realized, however, litmus has proved too inaccurate an indicator, and has largely been replaced for chemical use by synthetic dyes (notably the sulfonphthaleins) which change color through a pH-range near the neutral point and which are not subject to loss of color on reduction.

This loss of color by reduction, which is an inconvenience to the chemist who wishes to use litmus as a pH indicator, happens to be of advantage to the bacteriologist. Litmus has been employed for over 50 years as an indicator in bacteriological media; and in some of these media (especially milk) it serves to indicate changes in pH and in oxidation-reduction potential simultaneously. Although chemically speaking, it is a decidedly inaccurate indicator for either purpose, it has served the bacteriologist to bring out differences between species in a way that no other indicator alone has proved able to do. Azolitmin, either the synthetic product or that derived from the lichens, does not serve the purpose, chiefly because it does not have exactly the same sensitive range in relation to the pH-scale as does litmus.

BRAZILIN AND HEMATOXYLIN

The two natural dyes, hematoxylin and brazilin, are closely related chemically and upon decomposition yield the two compounds, pyrocatechol

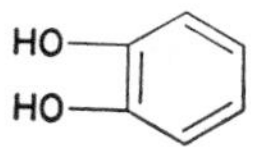

and pyrogallol

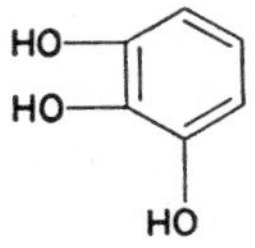

Both dyes are obtained by extraction of the bark of certain trees, hematoxylin from logwood and brazilin from brazil wood (red wood). Both trees are legumes and belong to the family Cesalpiniaceae; they are found only in the tropics. Hematoxylin comes from a single species; while brazil wood is a term applied to various different species all yielding brazilin.

BRAZILIN   C. I. NO. 75280 (1 *ed.:* 1243)

(C. I. Natural Red 24)

The composition of this substance is supposed to be:

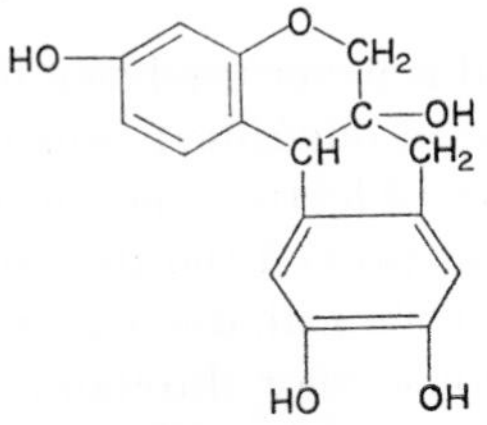

Its solution is colorless, but it becomes red on exposure to the air, as it is then oxidized into the dye brazilein, which probably has the formula:

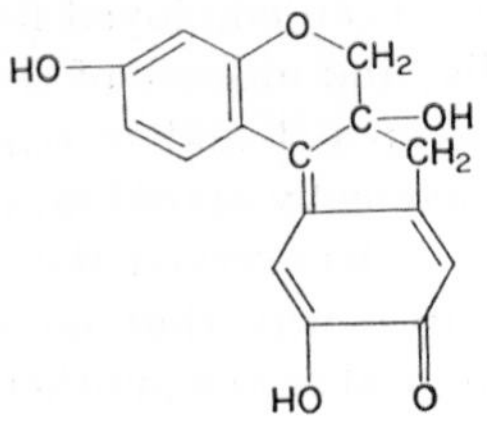

With alum it was employed as a nuclear stain (known as brazalum) by Mayer (see Lee and Mayer, 1907, p. 218). It was also used by Hickson (1901) for similar purposes following treatment with iron alum as a mordant. Belling (1928) employed it in place of carmine for staining plant chromosomes in fixed or fresh material, and Shaffer (1933) for distinguishing paper fibers bleached with sulfite from those bleached with sulfate.

HEMATOXYLIN

C. I. NO. 75290 (1 *ed.:* 1246)

(C. I. Natural Black 1 and 2?)

Hematoxylin, as is well known, is a constituent of logwood, a product of South America. It was first obtained about 1840 by extracting logwood chips with ether, evaporating, digesting with alcohol and standing with water after distilling off the alcohol; hematoxylin was found to separate out in crystals. A little later a similar method was employed, but instead of using logwood chips, the starting point of the process was with commercial logwood extract, which is the dried aqueous extract of the wood. In one modern method of manufacture the dried commercial (aqueous) extract is treated with ether in a continuous extraction apparatus, the ether extract evaporated to dryness, dissolved in water, filtered and crystallized out of the solution. All of these steps, particularly the ether extraction, are slow and difficult to handle on a factory scale, requiring special expensive apparatus.

The American manufacture of hematoxylin started during the first World War, just as in the case of the synthetic dyes. The problems presented by its manufacture, however, were quite different from those presented by the synthetics. They were discussed at about that period by McClung (1923) and Conn (1927). Briefly it can be explained here that the first American hematoxylins, marketed during that war, were very crude and proved quite unsatisfactory; but that during the decade following the war, frequent improvement in the supply was made by the manufacturers. The first American product was dark in color; and there was so much demand for a light colored hematoxylin that the manufacturers introduced the process of bleaching with sulfur dioxide. It was subsequently found that this bleaching injured the staining qualities, and the manufacturers changed their method and began turning out a darker colored but more satisfactory stain. About 1926 another change in process of manufacture was made and the staining properties seemed thereby to be improved. For some years there was only one American manufacturer of hematoxylin whose product could qualify as a biological stain; but the great demand caused by the second World War resulted in other companies entering the field and developing cheaper processes of manufacture. These cheaper methods of production yield a darker colored and presumably less pure product; it is not, however, to be compared with the crude materials put on the American market during the first World War, as it is a satisfactory stain in spite of impurities that may be present.

Hematoxylin is similar to brazilin, but has one more hydroxyl group, the generally accepted formula being:

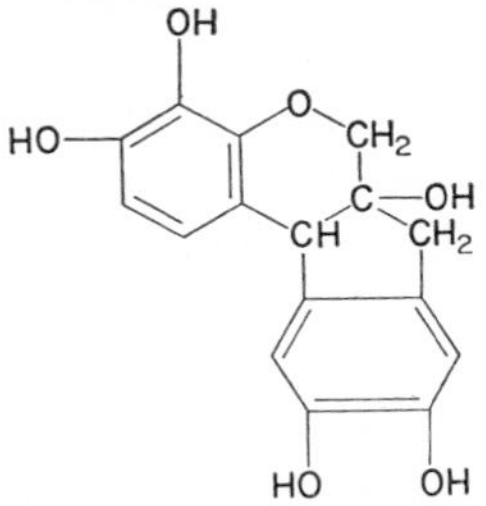

Like brazilin, it is not a dye, but its color develops in solution upon standing, due to the oxidation into hematein, which is homologous to brazilein and probably has the formula:

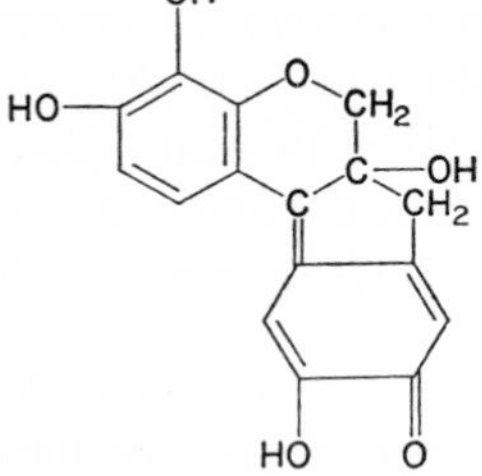

Hematein is available commercially in dry form. Less attention has been given to its production than to that of hematoxylin. Hence it frequently results that a hematein sold by some company is more crude than their hematoxylin, although theoretically hematein is a derivative of hematoxylin.

Hematoxylin is without question one of the most important biological stains. It is as valuable to the cytologist and histologist as methylene blue is to the bacteriologist; and probably is second only to methylene blue in the number of different purposes for which it is used. It is valuable not only because it is a powerful nuclear stain and a chromatin stain *par excellence*, but also because it has striking polychrome properties. With the proper differentiation it is possible to get several shades intermediate between blue and red to show in the same preparation. It does not, however, differentiate between ribonucleic acid and deoxyribonucleic acid, hence is less used today in cytology than formerly.

Hematoxylin is seldom used alone, as it has little affinity for the tissues in itself, even after "ripening" when it is largely converted into hematein. Some form of mordanting is ordinarily required; and most of the hematoxylin formulae either call for some metallic salt or specify previous treatment of the sections with one. In plant histology, however, there is some use for hematoxylin alone. Its greater affinity for plant than for animal tissue implies the presence of aluminum, copper, or iron in the former. In fact hematoxylin can be used as a very delicate reagent for iron or copper. Furthermore, in animal microtechnic, used alone in highly dilute solution, it is a slowly acting demonstration agent for keratohyalin, elastic fibrils and certain leucocyte granules. The mechanism is not understood, but is shared by other dyes with the catechol grouping.

Perhaps the best known formulae for staining with hematoxylin are the combinations with aluminum, generally in the form of alum. Böhmer's alum hematoxylin (1865), although no longer employed, is of historic interest as it was the first stain of this type to be used. The best known at present is Delafield's alum hematoxylin (see Prudden, 1885), which is a very useful tissue stain with great affinity for chromatin and nuclei, and has much value in staining cellulose walls in vascular plants. Another alum hematoxylin used for similar purposes is that of Ehrlich (see Krause, 1926–1927, p. 972), in which rapid ripening is brought about by the addition of sodium iodate. Another ripening agent is HgO, which is called for in the frequently employed Harris formula.

Mayer's hemalum (1891, 1899) is another well known alum combination. In this stain hematein is first prepared and then combined with alum. The name hemalum, proposed by Mayer, is now generally accepted for this combination, and various other hemalum formulae have since been proposed. They are useful chromatin stains and are called for in various special procedures.

Mayer (1891, 1899) also combined hematein with aluminum chloride, his hemacalcium calling for this salt and calcium chloride, while his muci-hematein contains aluminum chloride and glycerol. The latter is used for staining mucin.

The iron combinations are perhaps equally valuable. The original iron hematoxylin was that of Benda (1886); but the best known at present is M. Heidenhain's (1892, 1896), which is one of the most useful histological and cytological stains, both in botany and zoology. It is a powerful stain for chromosomes and centrosomes, and is of use for bringing out the middle lamellae in wood. Various other modifications of iron hematoxylin have been used, but they are all similar in principle. Ordinarily the iron salt is not mixed with the stain, but is used for a preliminary mordanting of the tissue. Groat (1949), however, devised a very useful formula in which iron alum is added to the staining solution itself.

Hematoxylin has been combined with chromium, one of the early staining methods being that of R. Heidenhain (1886), which called for potassium bichromate as a mordant. Various modifications are in use today, such as that of Apathy (1888), for staining general tissue. Weigert (1884) used a chrome combination for staining nervous tissue.

Benda (1893) employed hematoxylin following treatment with a copper salt for studying spermatogenesis; and Bensley (see Guyer, 1936, p. 164) a similar technic for chromosomes and mitochondria. A formula containing logwood extract, with alum and copper sulfate was suggested by Cook (1879).

Mallory (1938, p. 156) proposed a formula for hematoxylin containing phosphomolybdic acid and also one containing phosphotungstic acid. The latter method is especially valuable for staining cells in the process of mitosis, and for distinguishing fibroglia, myoglia and neuroglia fibrils from collagen and elastin fibrils, especially in tumors, but also in normal tissues. It brings out sharply the striations in skeletal and cardiac muscle fibers.

Hematoxylin is used in combination with other stains, especially eosin, but not so frequently as in the case of the common anilin dyes. The Van Gieson technic calls for hematoxylin followed by picric acid and acid fuchsin. A few other methods call for picric acid or ammonium picrate after hematoxylin: and it is sometimes used with eosin or after orange G or acid fuchsin. Most of these combinations, however, are called for only in the case of special procedures.

Procedures Recommended by the Commission in Which
Hematoxylin and Hematein Are Used

Name of Procedure	Page Reference to *Staining Procedures*
Mayer's mucihematein	36
Delafield's hematoxylin in animal histology	39
Ehrlich's hematoxylin in animal histology	40
Heidenhain's hematoxylin in animal histology	41
Mayer's hemalum and eosin bluish	64
Mayer's hemalum with Congo red	42
Mayer's acid hemalum, Lillie modification	43
Mallory's phosphotungstic acid hematoxylin	44
Weigert's iron hematoxylin	36
Hematoxylin with Van Gieson stain	50
Crossman modification of Mallory's connective tissue stain	54
Hematoxylin with Biebrich scarlet and picro aniline blue	62
Mucicarmine with hematoxylin and metanil yellow	36
Verhoeff's elastic tissue stain	66
Modified Gallego elastic tissue stain	67
For nuclei in Tänzer-Unna orcein method	68
Masson's trichrome stain	70–2
Bielschowsky's connective tissue stain, Foot's modification	73
Same; Wilder's modification	76
Pal-Weigert method for myelin sheaths	118
Hematoxylin with Herxheimer's Sudan IV fat stain	153
Smith-Dietrich method for lipoids	155
Baker's acid hematein test for phospholipids	156
Proescher's oil-red-pyridine for lipoids	158
Best's method for glycogen	160
Bauer's leucofuchsin method for glycogen	161
With aldehyde fuchsin in plant histology	171
Heidenhain's hematoxylin for plant histology	182
Delafield's hematoxylin for plant histology	183
Hematoxylin and safranin for plant histology	185
For permanent smear preparations of sporocytes	209
Heidenhain's hematoxylin in plant cytology	210
Regaud's iron alum hematoxylin in plant cytology	213
Gram-Weigert technic for bacteria in tissues	254
Weigert's stain for fibrin and bacteria in tissues	256
With Verhoeff's carbol fuchsin for tubercle bacilli in tissue	257

Isohematein. If hematein is treated with HCl in sealed tubes at 100° C and then treated with silver hydroxide to remove the chlorine, a solution is obtained of a compound known as isohematein, which can be secured as an amorphous mass by evaporation. At the request of the Stain Commission, an American manufacturer of logwood products actually prepared an experimental batch of isohematein by this method, and Cole (1931) reported on its use as a biological stain. The result of this study was to indicate that it could hardly replace hematoxylin as a routine stain, but that on account of its higher tinctorial power it may have value for some special purposes such as the selective staining of nerve cell bodies of fibrillae and cross striations in muscle cells. It has never been made available commercially, and at present there does not seem to be sufficient demand for it to justify its production.

XIII

NEUTRAL STAINS

There are two ways in which dyes may be compounded. In the first place it is possible to mix mechanically any two dyes, and if they are of different colors with different selective powers, double staining effects may be procured. In the second place, it is often possible for a chemical union to take place between two dyes, yielding an entirely new compound which may have quite striking staining properties. It is such compounds as these, rather than simple mechanical mixtures, that are ordinarily referred to as compound dyes.

The simple aniline dyes, it will be recalled (see Chapter II), owe their properties as dyes or as biological stains to the basic or acidic character of the dye molecule. Those parts of the protoplasm which are acid in nature (e.g., chromatin) tend to react with the basic dyes and to be colored by them; while those which are basic (e.g., cytoplasm) react similarly with the acid dyes. (This, to be sure, is not the whole theory of staining, as the process is quite complex and probably involves physical factors as well; but it serves to illustrate the difference between the two kinds of stains.) Now, as already explained, the dyes are not used as free acids or free bases; but rather as sodium or potassium salts of the acid dyes, and as chlorides (or salts of some other colorless acid) of the basic dyes.

It is well known that when two salts, such as sodium chloride and ammonium nitrate, are mixed in solution, there is an interchange of ions (metathesis), and the resulting solution, when it reaches equilibrium, contains not only the original salts but also the four free ions and the two alternate compounds as well, in this case sodium nitrate and ammonium chloride. Now if one of these two new compounds happens to be insoluble, as silver chloride for example, which would have been formed if silver nitrate had been substituted for ammonium nitrate, it is thrown out of solution, and equilibrium is not reached until the solution is free (or at least practically free) from the two ions which are insoluble in combination. In the same way, when a sodium salt of an acid dye and a chloride of a basic dye are mixed in solution, there is a similar tendency for the ions to interchange. Ordinarily the dyes are weaker acids and bases than the chlorine and sodium ions respectively; and if the compound dye formed were soluble in water there would be little chance for much of it to be produced. It is, however, generally insoluble and is therefore precipitated; hence the compound dye can be formed in considerable quantity.

Considering that salts of color acids are called acid dyes, and salts of color bases are known as basic dyes, a theoretically satisfactory name for the compound dyes in which a color acid is combined with a color base would be "neutral dyes." The term is not ordinarily used this way, however, because the dye chemist uses the same term in an entirely different sense. The chemist has not, however, pre-empted the term "neutral stain"; and considering that this class of compound dyes is employed for biological staining rather than general dyeing purposes, the name is quite appropriate. The Stain Commission, therefore, has adopted the use of the term *neutral stain* for this purpose and defines it as a compound of an acid dye and a basic dye in which both the anion and the cation contain chromophore groups.

Ehrlich (1898) introduced a different term, "tri-acid dyes," which he intended, apparently, to apply to the whole class of neutral stains. He seems to have introduced this term on the basis of two assumptions; first, that most of the basic dyes are triamino compounds (and therefore potentially tribasic); second, that in the ordinary mineral acid salts of these dyes only one of the affinities for acid is satisfied, but when compounded with an acid dye the other two affinities also become satisfied. The latter assumption, at least, seems to be entirely incorrect. As just explained, the reaction between an acid dye and a basic dye seems to be purely one of metathesis, and there is no reason for assuming that the dye anion attaches itself to any other place in the basic dye molecule than that previously occupied by the displaced mineral anion. Ehrlich's term, however, has persisted for the particular "tri-acid stain" which he specially recommended (see below); and since this particular neutral stain is no more a tri-acid product than any other, some explanation of the term seems necessary.

It is possible to obtain an endless variety of such dyes; but in practice only a certain number of them have proved useful. Among the basic dyes the most suitable for this purpose are the thiazins and the rosanilins (which act as strong ammonium bases); among the acid dyes, the eosins and the sulfonic acids (e.g., orange G and acid fuchsin).

Although the neutral stains are insoluble in water, they are soluble to a greater or less extent in excess of either the acid or the basic dye. Thus if an aqueous solution of acid fuchsin is neutralized by adding drop by drop an aqueous solution of methyl green, there is at first no precipitation, because the methyl green salt of acid fuchsin is kept in solution by the excess of acid fuchsin. After the proper amount of methyl green has been added, however, and the mixture has stood long enough for the reaction to take place, the neutral stain is precipitated and the solution becomes nearly colorless. Then if more methyl green is added the neutral stain is slowly dissolved again; but as a rule neutral stains are less soluble in excess of basic dye than in excess of acid dye.

As simple aqueous solutions of these compound dyes are impossible and as alcoholic solutions of dyes do not stain well, various methods are employed to secure their action on the tissues. In some instances they are kept dissolved by the presence of an excess of acid or base (particularly the former); in others a certain quantity of acetone is used to hold the neutral stain in solution; sometimes (as in the original Romanovsky stain) the compound dye is used immediately after mixing, before the reaction is complete or precipitation has taken place; or again (as in the Wright stain) methyl or ethyl alcohol may be used as a solvent, and then after applying the alcoholic solution to the slide it may be diluted with water. This latter method is particularly efficacious, possibly because a temporary state of supersaturation occurs on addition of the water, and there are other known instances where such a state enhances staining power. It should be stated that when water is mixed with such an alcoholic solution, dissociation must take place and an unstable equilibrium must exist until the compounds insoluble in the mixture of water and methanol have been precipitated; under such circumstances the staining reactions may be rather complicated.

It is assumed that these compound dyes act on the protoplasm somewhat as follows: certain parts of the cell have an affinity for the neutral stain and take it up as such; others, having an affinity for the basic dye, break up the neutral stain so as to obtain the basic portion of it, or if dissociation has taken place, take up the basic ion directly; while other parts of the cell with an affinity for acid dyes similarly combine with the acid portion of the stain. These three types of cell structures are known as neutrophil, basophil and oxyphil elements, respectively. The differentiation thus produced gives the neutral dyes their great value.

EHRLICH'S "TRI-ACID STAIN"

The first neutral stain proposed for microscopic work was the "tri-acid stain" of Ehrlich (1910, II, 313). In forming this compound dye, acid fuchsin and orange G are mixed in solution and to the mixture is then added such a quantity of methyl green that there is still an excess of the acid dye. This excess of the acid dye allows the neutral stain to stay in solution. The dye thus formed is a useful blood stain, and brings out finely the different structures in the leukocytes. It is of incidental interest that Ehrlich, as early as 1888, tested this dye combination by dropping onto filter paper or blotting paper, thus possibly originating the technic of paper chromatographic analysis!

The explanation of the name of this stain (which was based on a mistaken chemical theory) is explained on a preceding page.

Slight modifications of the stain have been used for tissues. The best known is that of Biondi and Heidenhain. (See Krause, 1926–1927, p. 457, or Lee, 1937, p. 166).

THIAZIN EOSINATES*

The first worker to combine eosin and methylene blue was Romanovsky (1891). He realized that a mixture of these two dyes had great selective properties as a stain, and showed it to be excellent for blood, particularly in bringing out the malarial parasite. He also appreciated that it was more than a mere mixture of the two dyes and that some new dye having the property of giving the nuclei a red color was present. It was some time later before the nature of this new dye was known, although it was subsequently named azure I or methylene azure; its true chemistry has scarcely been understood until recently (see p. 96). Methylene violet, and "methylene azure," which probably was also present, had already been described by Bernthsen (1885). How these new dyes were formed in the Romanovsky stain was not known then; although Romanovsky stated that different lots of methylene blue solution varied in their ability to give a good blood stain, and that old solutions on which a scum had formed were best.

One interesting point in connection with this early work is that Bernthsen made the statement that the absorption maximum of Azure I is at 650 mμ. This statement indicates, as can readily be verified by consulting the absorption data of the azures given in Chapter VI, that his azure I must have been primarily azure B. This early statement of Bernthsen's seems to have been overlooked in some of the later work on the chemistry of azure I.

Present day blood stains are often spoken of as modified Romanovsky stains; although the modifications are so great as to make them of a very different nature. The first modification was made by Nocht (1898) who concluded that the differential staining was due to the formation of other dyes by the decomposition of methylene blue. Unna (1891) had already described what he called polychrome methylene blue, made by heating a solution of methylene blue on a water bath with potassium carbonate. Nocht decided to use this in the Romanovsky stain instead of untreated methylene blue. He found that it gave very good results if properly neutralized before mixing with eosin; and then learned that better results could be

---

* An account of the history of these blood stains is given by MacNeal (1906), and by Conn *et al.* (1933, 1948).

obtained by the use of a smaller amount of alkali and a longer period of polychroming, without subsequent neutralization.

The next step in preparing blood stains was made by Jenner (1899) who collected the precipitate formed when methylene blue and eosin are mixed, and redissolved it in methyl alcohol. He did not use polychrome methylene blue, and his stain lacked the nuclear staining principle of Romanovsky's and Nocht's stains unless allowed to stand for some time before using; but it was an important step in that he showed the possibility of collecting the precipitated compound stain and of dissolving it in some solvent other than water. Jenner's stain is still called for occasionally. Although it is markedly inferior to the modern type of blood stains when used fresh, it does polychrome on standing and this fact undoubtedly explains its continued use.

Combining Jenner's procedure with the Nocht stain was the next logical step and was taken independently by Reuter (1901) and by Leishman (1901). The method thus introduced was briefly to follow Nocht's technic of combining eosin with polychrome methylene blue, but then to filter off the precipitate and to redissolve it in methyl alcohol, not adding further water until the moment of applying the stain to the blood films.

Modern blood stains are in general modifications of Leishman's, differing only in detail. Wright's modification (1902), the one most used in America, (see Mallory and Wright, 1924, p. 170) differs from Leishman's only in that he prepared polychrome methylene blue by heating for only an hour in flowing steam, whereas the Leishman technic calls for 12 hours at 65°C, with subsequent standing for 10 days.

Early editions of this book contained directions for preparing Wright stain. It is, in fact, perfectly possible for a laboratory worker to prepare a blood stain of this type that gives excellent results; and the technic of doing so is not specially difficult to one who has the necessary experience. Nevertheless, it has proved that the directions given have not yielded uniformly dependable results. It is desirable to have exactly the right amounts of acid and basic dye present to combine without much excess of either; and the relative amounts called for on theoretical grounds do not always yield best results in practice. Moreover, spectrophotometric control during polychroming seems to be necessary to attain a uniform product, and the average laboratory worker does not have the necessary facilities. Furthermore, this stain, either in powdered form or dissolved in methyl alcohol, may be purchased from stain companies at present, usually more uniform in quality than can be made up by the user. Accordingly, directions for its manufacture seem hardly called for here.

Balch's modification calls for a polychrome methylene blue prepared by standing 10 days with precipitated Ag_2O. Hastings modification (1905) differs from that of Wright or Leishman in that the polychrome methylene blue is neutralized with acetic acid, and an unpolychromed solution of methylene blue is mixed with it before eosinating. It is interesting, as a matter of fact, to note that the method of preparing Wright stain followed by some stain manufacturers is more like that of Hastings than like Wright's. In general, American manufacturers sell the same product as "Wright stain" and as "Hastings stain"; perhaps it should all be known by the latter name. Lillie (1944a) has suggested the use of a methylene blue polychromed by heating with a definite proportion of $K_2Cr_2O_7$ in acid solution, a process which he finds to yield a more uniform product.

Giemsa's and MacNeal's modifications are somewhat different. In order to start with a more definite compound than polychrome methylene blue, Giemsa (1902) used more carefully controlled methods of oxidation and obtained a product which he considered to be the same as Bernthsen's azure I. This he combined with eosin Y, to obtain a more definite compound than in the case of stains of the Leishman type. Subsequently he added methylene blue to the azure before combining with the eosin, and in that way secured better differentiation. He did not state his method of preparing azure I, but apparently gave it secretly to Dr. Grübler's Laboratory, which subsequently became K. Hollborn and Sons; and the latter company made much of this "trade secret" in claiming their Giemsa stain to be the only authentic product of that name. Besides azure I, this company put on the market an azure II which was a mixture of azure I and methylene blue in equal parts. The eosinate of this mixture, known as azure-II-eosin, was the chief ingredient of Giemsa stain. There probably is no real secret involved in the composition of these azures. Giemsa stated that he used Bernthsen's methylene azure, and Bernthsen described this as having an absorption maximum at 650 mμ; as this is approximately that of present day azure B, we can assume that Giemsa either had the latter or a mixture of higher and lower homologs having optical properties similar to azure B. There was, however, considerable confusion on this subject for some years; and in part this grew out of certain erroneous inferences derived from MacNeal's excellent work (discussed below) on these stains.

The formulae recommended by Giemsa for preparing solutions of this stain are:

	For blood	For tissue
Azure-II-eosin....................	3.0 gm	3.0 gm
Azure II..........................	0.8 gm	0.8 gm
Glycerol, c.p......................	250 gm or 200 ml	125 gm or 100 ml
Methyl alcohol, neutral, acetone free..	250 gm or 312 ml	375 gm or 457 ml

There is apparently a reason for the quantity of glycerol called for in the first of these formulae (50 percent by weight or about 40 percent by volume); work in one of the Stain Commission laboratories indicates at least 40 percent by volume to be necessary to give a reasonably stable solution.

Substituting American dyes for those in the old Giemsa formula, and following the recommendations of Lillie, the following seems advisable:

Azure A eosinate...	0.5 gm
Azure B eosinate...	2.5 gm
Methylene blue eosinate....................................	2.0 gm
Methylene blue chloride....................................	1.0 gm
Glycerol..	375.0 ml
Methyl alcohol, reagent....................................	375.0 ml

Mixed powdered dyes of approximately this formula are available from some of the American manufacturers.

MacNeal (1922) proposed a stain, intended to give similar results, although prepared on different principles. He showed that by mixing Bernthsen's methylene violet and azure I with methylene blue and eosin Y in definite proportions, dissolving in methyl alcohol, and employing like a Leishman or Wright stain, one could obtain results almost identical with those secured by these other blood stains without the uncertainties introduced by their methods of manufacture. Soon after publishing this paper he realized that methylene azure could be a mixture and certainly was by the methods he had used in preparing it (MacNeal, 1925). He showed it to contain both azure A and azure B, whose chemistry is discussed in Chapter VI of this book. He regarded the former as the more important ingredient, and stated that the staining effects of azure B are little different from those of a mixture of azure A and methylene blue. This statment of his gave rise to the impression that azure B was not a satisfactory stain; and it was some time before this impression was corrected in the minds of users of these stains. MacNeal's tetrachrome stain is ordinarily made up according to the following formula:

Methylene blue chloride (dye content about 90%)...............	1.0 gm
Azure A..	0.6 gm
Methylene violet, Bernthsen, free base........................	0.2 gm
Eosin Y (dye content 80–85%).................................	1.0 gm

It will readily be seen that the dry tetrachrome stain is a mixture rather than a chemical compound like the Leishman stain and its modifications. The four dyes mixed together combine but very slowly even after dissolving in the alcohol; and the first pronounced chemical reaction occurs only after diluting with water in actual application. There is evidence, however, that certain chemical reactions (and of an undesirable nature) take place in the alcoholic solution, and thus interfere with the keeping qualities of the solution. Manufacturers of tetrachrome stain realize this and give directions for allowing the alcoholic solution to stand 48 hours at 50°C and then filtering; this practice seems to remove whatever harmful compound may have formed, and the solution thus obtained is reasonably permanent. Undoubtedly, moreover, methyl alcohol alone is an undesirable solvent for this mixture of dyes, just as it is in the case of Giemsa stain. There can be little question but that the addition of 40 percent glycerol, by volume, as recommended by Giemsa, would make the solvent for the tetrachrome stain more satisfactory and would improve the keeping qualities of the solution.

It can readily be inferred that thiazin eosinates, made by any of the above mentioned procedures, must be very complex mixtures. Theoretically each of the azures or other oxidation products of methylene blue present in the polychromed solution may combine individually with the eosin, thus yielding several different eosinates in the precipitate. Unless the precipitate is washed with two or three changes of water it usually contains a considerable excess of one or the other of the uncombined dyes, and this may further increase the complexity of the mixture. If properly washed, the precipitate should be free, or almost free, of uncombined basic or acid dye, because of their great solubility, and possibly such is also the case in the methanolic solution of the precipitate; but it is certain that when water is added in the process of staining, dissociation must occur with the formation of the acid and basic dyes from which the compound was derived. This is another contribution to the complexity of the solution with which the staining is accomplished. Complex as the mixture is, Lillie (1942) has shown that it can be quite effectively analyzed spectrophotometrically; and that from the position and width of the absorption bands, one can get some idea as to the composition of the polychrome methylene blue from which the eosinate was prepared. By comparing such spectrophotometric results with the behavior in staining, one can obtain practical information as to the value of the different azures in a stain of this type.

In addition to the chemistry of the constituent dyes, another important factor in a blood stain of this type is the nature of the solvent. Methyl alcohol, as explained above, is the usual solvent employed; but there are many grades of this reagent available, and not all are equally suitable for the purpose—a fact which at one time was not fully appreciated. Apparently absolute purity of the methanol is not needed; but one point is very important—the solvent must be neutral in reaction. Methanol, as formerly prepared by the destructive distillation of wood, often contained considerable amounts of the other two major products of that decomposition, acetone and acetic acid. The presence of acetone seems to be unimportant (in spite of previous recommendations that methanol for blood stains should be acetone-free); acetic acid, however, is quite deleterious because it lowers the pH of the solution and tends to precipitate eosin as its color acid, when the methanolic solution is diluted with water. Special methyl alcohol for blood stains is on the market, but the modern synthetic methanol of reagent grade proves quite satisfactory; its further purification with Ag₂O, as sometimes recommended to free it from aldehydes and ketones, seems to be quite unnecessary. (See Lillie, 1944b, 1954).

The two blood stains for which there is now most demand in America are Wright stain and Giemsa stain, while the tetrachrome stain is used less frequently. Wright stain and the tetrachrome stain both give almost identical results and are handled very similarly. If one is to prepare the stain himself, there are reasons for preferring the tetrachrome stain as it can be made up with more certainty of obtaining a satisfactory product. Ordinarily today, however, one purchases his blood stains already prepared by some manufacturer; and the Wright stain on the market seems to be as reliable as the tetrachrome stain.

Giemsa stain, although originally intended to be more definite in composition than other blood stains, is possibly the most complicated of them all. As a simple stain for blood in thin smears, some find it to have no distinct advantage over stains of the Leishman-Wright type, although others claim it to show greater purity of color and sharpness of definition, with deeper staining of chromatin; such advantages as it has for this purpose are offset by the longer staining time and larger volume of solutions required. As a stain for malarial blood, however, designed to show the malaria plasmodium, Giemsa stain is definitely preferred. In searching for the malaria organism the present approved technic calls for the use of thick smears of blood in which laking of the red corpuscles is brought about by distilled water (either as a diluent of the stain or placed on the smears before staining); accordingly a stain for the red cells is not required, but one is necessary that brings out the leucocytes and the plasmodia. For this, a properly prepared Giemsa stain has decided advantages over Wright stain. Good results were quite consistently obtained with the German Giemsa stain, when it was available; and there is good reason to believe that it has been quite constant in composition. As remarked above, its manufacturers used to lay considerable stress on the "secret" character of azure I and to claim that since they alone know that secret, no other Giemsa stain except theirs could be reliable. As mentioned above, however, no real secret seems to have been involved; and recent investigations have shown that a Giemsa stain, with one of its absorption maxima at about 655 mμ, as recommended by Lillie (whether prepared in the laboratory or put on the market as a commercial product) is an excellent malarial stain, as judged by technicians familiar with the technic in question.

During the two decades from 1920 to 1940 much Giemsa stain was on the market in America which did not conform to the requirements now specified by Lillie. This was largely due to the stress laid by MacNeal on azure A as the important ingredient of azure I, and to the fact that Holmes and French later (1926) said quite definitely that azure B has no staining value. It took some time to counteract the effect of such statements, and meanwhile American manufacturers of Giemsa stain, with the endorsement of the Stain Commission, used azure A, without any appreciable azure B, in its preparation. Since Lillie has called attention to the importance of azure B, however, the practice of the stain companies has changed; and now there is an American Giemsa stain available which gives results very much like the imported product.

Other Uses of Thiazin Eosinates. Although thiazin eosinates are specially known for their use as blood stains, they are coming more and more to be employed for other purposes. Tolstoouhov (1928), for instance, recommended a Romanovsky mixture as a tissue stain, his solution proving stable because of the excess of methylene blue present; he showed that such a mixture can produce a variety of staining effects according to the reaction given to the solution by adding varying quantities of N/100 NaOH or HCl. The same author (1929) later proposed a similar mixture for differentiating one kind of bacteria from another. Churchman (1933) employed Wright stain for demonstrating bacterial capsules, and Dutton (1928) to stain bacterial spores. Giemsa stain has been used similarly, and also as a tissue stain. Lillie and Pasternack (1932, 1936), in fact, showed that various thiazin eosinates can be used very effectively as a tissue stain; Lillie (1941) has given in detail a technic for staining tissue with a specially modified Wright stain following hematoxylin. His latest recommendations (1954) call for azure A salts of eosin B which are stated to give deeper red staining of hemoglobin and granules.

*Procedures Recommended by the Commission in Which
Thiazin Eosinates Are Used**

Name of Procedure	Page Reference to *Staining Procedures*
Buffered azure eosinates for tissue.............................	45
Wright stain for blood smears..................................	133–135
MacNeal's tetrachrome stain for blood smears................	135
Giemsa stain for thin films.....................................	136
Giemsa stain for thick films.....................................	137
Giemsa or Wright stain for bone marrow smears..............	143

* Under this heading are given references to procedures described in detail in *Staining Procedures*, edited by Conn, Darrow, and Emmel (1960).

OTHER COMPOUND STAINS

Various other compounds of acid and basic dyes have been used for special purposes. The basic dyes employed in these compounds most commonly are perhaps methyl green and methylene blue; but sometimes basic fuchsin, pyronin or rhodamine or even a weak base like neutral red is used. Most common among the acid dyes in these compounds are eosin, orange G and acid fuchsin; but certain others are occasionally employed. Picric acid forms a few useful compound dyes, rosanilin picrate (i.e., the compound of basic fuchsin and picric acid) being especially well known as a tissue stain.

The Pappenheim panoptic triacid stain is a modification of Ehrlich's triacid compound. (It is to be distinguished from his May-Grünwald, Giemsa sequence, which he also calls "panoptic.") In this combination methylene blue or methylene azure is substituted for methyl green. It is a tissue stain of use in certain special technics. Another well-known neutral stain is the Twort (1924a and b) formula in which neutral red and light green are combined. The Twort stain is valuable for staining animal parasites and other animal organisms in tissues. Maurer and Lewis (1922) (see page 155) have combined safranin in a neutral stain with some acid violet and have employed the compound dye in staining glandular tissue.

Ehrlich proposed various other neutral stains, the best known being a compound of acid fuchsin and methylene blue used for staining blood; and a compound of narcein, an acid dye, with two basic dyes pyronin and methyl green or methylene blue. A combination of orange G with a gentian violet has been proposed by Bensley (1911) as a stain for the A and B cells in the islands of Langerhans.

APPENDIX I

TABLES RELATING TO STAINS

Dye Nomenclature and Index Numbers. It has been the practice in the dye industry for many years to publish indexes of dyes, in which the products are denoted by number. The original publication of this kind (Schultz Index) was German; but since the first World War this has been largely superceded by the Colour Index, of which the first edition was published by the Society of Dyers and Colourists in England. In previous editions of this book stains were identified by the C. I. Nos. as published in that edition. There is now a new edition of the Colour Index in the preparation of which the American Association of Textile Chemists and Colourists has cooperated. The C. I. Nos. in this later edition consist, each, of five figures, and bear no relation to those in the first edition.

Accordingly Table 1 in this appendix, in which the most frequently used stains are listed, together with their common synonyms, includes the old C. I. Nos. in the first column and the new ones in the second. This table, therefore, is convenient to use if one wishes to identify a dye when only the old C. I. No. is known. Since the serial order of these numbers differs in the two editions, Table 2 is added in which the two sets of numbers are listed, and are arranged in the order of those in the new edition.

Learning the Solubility of a Stain. In making solutions of stains it is often desirable to know their solubility in either water or 95 percent alcohol. Figures indicating these solubilities of recrystallized dyes are given in Table 4, which includes all the most commonly used stains, and numerous others; the arrangement in this table is alphabetical. The solubilities of commercial dyes, however, vary widely from these figures for the purified products; the former are ordinarily less soluble, though occasionally the opposite. A limited amount of information is available, thanks to the cooperation of the American Pharmaceutical Association, as to the solubilities of commercial samples of about 25 of the commonly used stains; this is given in Table 5, and in some cases may prove more useful in making up a staining fluid than that given in Table 4.

TABLE 1

Nomenclature and Synonymy of Stains. (*Arranged in Order of Their 1st Ed. Colour Index Numbers*)

(a) Synthetic Dyes

Colour Index No.		Preferred Designation	Synonyms, and Slightly Varying Shades	Page Reference
1 Ed.	2 Ed.			
2	10005	Naphthol green Y	Fast printing green; Gambine	53
5	10020	Naphthol green B	Naphthol green; Green PL Acid green O	53
7	10305	Picric acid		54
9	10315	Martius yellow	Naphthol yellow; Manchester yellow	55
12	10360	Aurantia	Imperial yellow	56
16	13015	Fast yellow	Acid yellow; Fast yellow FY, G, S, BG, etc.	57
19	11020	Oil yellow II	Butter yellow; Oil yellow D; Fast oil yellow B	58
20	11270	Chrysoidin Y	Brown salt R; Dark brown salt R	58
—	11350	Benzene-azo-α-naphthyl-amine		59
27	16230	**Orange G***	Wool orange 2G, Crystal orange GG; (Slightly differing grade: Orange GG, GMP)	59
29	16570	Chromotrope 2R	Chromotrope N2R; Chromotrope blue 2R; XL Carmoisine 6R; Fast fuchsin G; Acid phloxine GR	60
31	18050	Azophloxine GA	Fast crimson GR; Amido-naphthol red G	61
54	14895	Sorbine red	Azofuchsin 3B; Kiton red S; Eriorubine G; Azo acid red L; Azo rhodine 3G	62
59	16545	Azo acid blue B		62
—	14890	Nitrazine	Nitrazine yellow; Delta dye indicator	63
73	12140	Sudan II	Oil scarlet; Fast oil orange II; Red B; Fat ponceau; Orange RR	63
79	16150	Ponceau 2R	Ponceau R, RG, G, 4R, 2RE, NR, J, FR, GR; Scarlet R; Xylidine ponceau 3RS; Lake ponceau; Brilliant ponceau G; New ponceau 4R	64
81	12020	Oil brown D	Sudan brown; Sudan brown AN; Fast oil brown S; Brilliant fat brown B; Fat brown III	65
88	16180	Bordeaux red	Fast red B, BN or P; Cerasin R; Archelline 2B; Azo-Bordeaux; Acid Bordeaux	65
113	12150	Sudan R	Brilliant fat scarlet B; Oil vermillion	65

127	14930	Gerinine G	Diazin green S; Union green B	204
(133)†	11050	Janus green B	Diazine black	66
(134)†	11825	Janus black	Diazine black	67
138	13065	Metanil yellow	Orange MNO or MN; Acid yellow R; Soluble yellow OL; Yellow M; Tropaeolin G	68
142	13025	Methyl orange	Orange III; Helianthin; Gold orange MP; Tropaeolin D	68
—	...	Prontosil		69
143	13080	Orange IV	Orange N; Acid yellow D; Tropaeolin OO	69
144	13085	Brilliant yellow S	Curcumine; Yellow WR	70
150	14600	Orange I	Naphthol orange; Tropaeolin G, 000 No. 1	70
151	15510	Orange II	Gold orange; Orange A, P, R; Acid orange II, Y or A; Orange extra; Mandarin G; Tropaeolin OOO No. 2	70
152	15511	Narcein		71
184	16185	Amaranth	Naphthol red S, C or O; Fast red; Bordeaux; Bordeaux SF; Victoria rubin O; Azo rubin; Wool red	72
211	13020	Methyl red	Chlorazol pink Y; Rosophenine 10B	72
225	14780	Thiazine red R	Pontacyl blue-black SX, Buffalo black NBR	73
264	20470	Naphthol blue black		73
248	26100	**Sudan III**	Sudan G; Tony red; Scarlet B, fat soluble; Fat ponceau G; Oil red AS, O, B or 3B; Cerasin red	73
252	27290	Brilliant croceine	Croceine scarlet 3B, MOO	73
258	26105	**Sudan IV**	Scarlet red; Fat ponceau; Fat ponceau R or LB; Cerotine ponceau 3B; Oil red IV	75
—	26050	Sudan red 7B	Solvent red 1A	76
—	26125	Oil red O		76
—	...	Oil red 4B		77
280	26905	Biebrich scarlet, water soluble	Croceine scarlet 5R; Ponceau B; Double scarlet BSF; Scarlet B, or EC	77
282	27195	Ponceau S.	Fast ponceau 2B	78
284	26670	Orseillin BB		78

* The dyes printed in bold face type are the most commonly used stains.

TABLE 1—*Continued*

Colour Index No. (1 Ed.)	Colour Index No. (2 Ed.)	Preferred Designation	Synonyms, and Slightly Varying Shades	Page Reference
331	21000	Bismarck brown Y	Vesuvin; Phenylene brown; Manchester brown; Excelsior brown; Leather brown; Basic brown G, GX or GXP; (Slightly different shade: Bismarck brown G)	79
332	21010	Bismarck brown R	Bismarck brown GOOO; Brown R, AT, C or N; Manchester brown EE; Vesuvin NR, B, R; Basic brown BR or BXN	80
370	22120	Congo red	Congo; Cotton red B or C; Direct red C, R or Y	81
375	22145	Erie garnet B	Congo corinth G or GW; Corinth brown G; Cotton corinth G; Amanil garnet H; Direct garnet R; Buffalo garnet R; Direct violet C; Diamine Bordeaux CGN	81
438	22850	Trypan red	Cotton red 4B; Dianil red 4B; Diamin red 4B; Sultan 4B; Direct red 4B	82
448	23500	Benzopurpurin 4B		82
454	23510	Brilliant purpurin R	Brilliant Congo R; Brilliant Congo red R; Brilliant vital red; Acid Congo R; Azidine scarlet R	83
456	23570	Vital red		83
463	23680	Azo blue	Benzoin blue R; Direct violet B	84
465	23690	Dianil blue 2R	Direct steel blue BB; Benzo new blue 2B; Naphthamine brilliant blue 2R	84
477	23850	Trypan blue	Chlorazol blue 3B; Benzo blue 3B; Dianil blue H3G; Congo blue 3B; Naphthamine blue 3BX; Benzamin blue 3B; Azidin blue 3B; Niagara blue 3B	84
—	—	Evans blue		85
—	—	Vital new red		85
520	24400	Niagara blue 4B	Pontamine sky blue 5BX; Direct sky blue; Benzo sky blue	86
—	—	Marshall red		86
—	—	Hickson purple		86
581	30235	Chlorazol black E	Pontamine black E, EX or EXX; Erie black GXOO, B, or BF; Direct black MS, RL, E, GX; Direct deep black EW extra, E, EA, EAD extra; Renol black G	87
—	—	Sudan black B		87
—	—	Victoria green G		88

655	41000	Auramine O	Pyoktaninum aureum; Pyoktanin yellow; Canary yellow	128
657	42000	Malachite green	Victoria green; New Victoria green extra, O, I or II; Diamond green B, BX, or P extra; Solid green O; Light green N	130
662	42040	Brilliant green	Ethyl green; Malachite green G; Emerald green crystals; Solid green JJO; Diamond green G	132
670	42095	Light green SF yellowish	Light green 6G, S, 6GN; Acid green (with various shade designations); Fast acid green N	133
—	42053	Fast green FCF		134
676	42500	**Pararosanilin***	Basic rubin; Parafuchsin; Paramagenta; Aniline red; Magenta O	136
677	42510	Rosanilin	Magenta I	137
—		Mixture of rosanilin and pararosanilin } **Basic fuchsin†**	Magenta	
		Magenta II		
678	42520	New fuchsin	Isorubin; Fuchsin NB; Magenta III	147
679	42530	Hofmann's violet	Dahlia; Iodine violet; Primula R; Red violet; Violet R, RR, 4RN	145
680	42535	**Methyl violet**	Dahlia B; Paris violet; Pyoktaninum coeraleum; (Various shades denoted: Methyl violet 2R, R, B, 2B, 3B, BBN, BO, and V3)	146
681	42555	**Crystal violet** } **Gentian violet‡**	Violet C, G or 7B; Hexamethyl violet; Methyl violet 10B; Gentian violet	149
682	42600	Ethyl violet	Ethyl purple 6B	151
684	42585	**Methyl green**	Double green SF; Light green	15
685	42590	Ethyl green	Methyl green	153
686	42556	Iodine green		154
689	42775	Spirit blue	Aniline blue, alcohol soluble; Gentiana blue 6B; Light blue; Lyon blue; Paris blue	155
690	42563	Victoria blue 4R	Fat blue 4R	156
692	42685	**Fuchsin, acid**	Fuchsin S, SN, SS, ST, or S III; Acid magenta; Acid rubin	143
706	42780	Methyl blue	Cotton blue; Helvetia blue	159
707	42755	**Aniline blue, water soluble**	China blue; Soluble blue 3M or 2R; Marine blue V; Cotton blue; Water blue	156

* The dyes printed in bold face type are the most commonly used stains.

† At least three different dyes are apparently sold to biologists as basic fuchsin.

‡ Nearly synonymous with methyl violet; various mixtures of methyl and crystal violet are sold under this name.

TABLE 1—*Continued*

Colour Index No.		Preferred Designation	Synonyms, and Slightly Varying Shades	Page Reference
1 Ed.	2 Ed.			
710	42700	Isamine blue		159
712	42051	Patent blue V	Alphazurine 2G; Patent blue VF; Pontacyl brilliant blue V	160
715	43535	Xylene Cyanol FF	Cyanol FF	160
724	43800	Rosolic acid	Aurin; (Yellow corallin is its sodium salt)	162
726	—	Red corallin	Aurin R	162
727	43810	Chrome violet CG		162
728	44040	Victoria blue R	New Victoria blue B or R; Corn blue B	163
729	44045	Victoria blue B	Fat blue B; Corn blue BN	163
731	44085	Night blue		164
737	44090	Wool green S	Wool green BS, BSNA or C; Lissamine green B, BS; Pontacyl green S; Acid green S; Cyanol green B; Fast light green; Calcoid green S extra	164
739	45005	Pyronin Y	Pyronin G	166
740	45000	Acridine red 3B		166
741	45010	Pyronin B		168
749	45170	Rhodamine B	Rhodamine O; Brilliant pink	169
752	45160	Rhodamine 6G	Rhodamine 6GX and 6GDN extra; Calcozine red 6G extra	169
758	45190	Violamine R	Acid violet 4R; Fast acid violet 3RL, A2R and R	170
760	45205	Fast acid blue R	(Almost the same as Violamine 3B)	170
766	45350	Fluorescein	(Uranin is its sodium salt)	174
768	45380	**Eosin, yellowish***	Eosin, water soluble; Bromo acid, J, TS, XL or XX; Bromo fluorescein; Bronze bromo ES; Various shades denoted: Eosin B extra, BP, BS, DH, G, GGF, J extra, 3J, 4J, JJF, KS, S extra, Y extra and YS	175
769	45385	Methyl eosin	Eosin, alcohol soluble	177
770	45386	Ethyl eosin	Eosin, alcohol soluble; Eosin S	178
771	45400	Eosin B (i.e., bluish)	Eosin BN, BA, BS, BW, DHV; Saffrosin; Eosin scarlet; Scarlet J, JJ, V; Nopalin G; Imperial red; Eosin scarlet B	178
—		Mercurochrome 220		179
772	45425	Erythrosin, yellowish	Erythrosin R or G; Pyrosin J; Iodeosin G; Dianthine G	180

773	45430	Erythrosin, bluish	Erythrosin B, N or JN; Pyrosin B; Eosin J; Iodeosin; Dianthine B; (Slightly different shades: Erythrosin D, J, JNV, W)	180
774	45405	Phloxine	Erythrosin BB, or B extra; New pink	182
777	45435	Rose bengal G	Rose SA; (Various shades denoted: Rose bengal N, AT, NT, NTO, and B)	184
778	45410	Phloxine B	Phloxine TA, N, BP super, RB, TB, or BB; Cyanosine; Eosin 10B	182
779	45440	Rose bengal	(Various shades denoted as: Rose bengal extra, B, 2B, 3B conc., DY, N extra)	184
785	46025	Acridine yellow		195
787	46020	Coriphosphine O		195
788	46005	Acridine orange NO	Basic orange 3RN; Euchrysine 3RXA	195
		Rivanol		196
790	46000	Acriflavine	Trypaflavine; Flavine	196
790	46000	Neutral acriflavine	Neutral trypaflavine; Euflavine; Neutroflavine; Gonocrin	197
790	46000	Proflavine		197
—		Atabrine		197
793	46045	Phosphine	Leather yellow; Xanthene	198
795	46075	Rheonine A	Rheonine AL, G or N; Fast phosphine NAL	198
808	—	Pinacyanol	Sensitol red	206
812	49000	Primulin	Primulin yellow	205
813	19540	Titan yellow G	Thiazol yellow	205
815	49005	Thioflavine T	Thioflavine TG	206
816	49010	Thioflavine S		206
819	49405	Bindschedler's green		91
820	49410	Toluylene blue		91
821	49700	Indophenol blue	Indophenol	92
825	50040	Neutral red	Toluylene red	116
826	50030	Neutral violet		117
828	50085	Azocarmine G	Azocarmine GX; Rosazine; Rosinduline GXF	122
840	50200	Phenosafranin	Safranin B extra	118
841	50240	**Safranin O**	Gossypimine; Cotton red; Safranin Y or A; (Slightly different shades: Safranin AG, T, MP, and G)	119
847	50225	Amethyst violet	Heliotrope B; Iris violet	122
857	50375	Magdala red	Naphthalene red; Naphthalene pink; Naphthylamine pink; Sudan red	123

* The dyes printed in bold face type are the most commonly used stains.

TABLE 1—*Concluded*

Colour Index No. 1 Ed.	Colour Index No. 2 Ed.	Preferred Designation	Synonyms, and Slightly Varying Shades	Page Reference
860	50400	Indulin, spirit soluble	Indulin (with various shade designations); Spirit indulin; Spirit nigrosin R	124
861	50405	Indulin, water soluble	Indulin (with various shade designations); Soluble indulin 3B; Fast blue B, OB, R, 2R, etc.	125
865	50420	Nigrosin, water soluble	Nigrosin W, WL, etc.; Gray R, B, BB; Silver gray; Steel gray; Indulin black	125
877	51010	Brilliant cresyl blue	Cresyl blue 2RN or BBS; Brilliant blue C	106
883	51030	Gallocyanin	Alizarin blue RBN; Chrome blue GCB; Fast violet	108
894	51045	Gallamin blue		108
900	51050	Celestin blue B	Coreine 2R	109
908	51400	Resorcin blue	Fluorescent blue; Iris blue; Often called lacmoid	109
909	51175	New blue R	Naphthol blue R; Fast blue 3R; Phenylene blue; Meldola's blue; Indin blue 2RD	114
913	51180	Nile blue sulfate	Nile blue A	110
—	—	Cresyl violet acetate	Cresyl fast violet	111
—	—	Darrow red		113
—		Resazurin		114
920	52000	Thionin	Lauth's violet; (Not thionin blue, which is Schultz No. 661)	93
922	52015	**Methylene blue***	Swiss blue; (Slightly different grades: Methylene blue BX, B, BG and BB; Grade preferred for staining: Methylene blue chloride)	100
923	52010	Azure C	Methylene azure; Azure I	96
923	52010	Azure A	Methylene azure; Azure I	98
923	52010	Azure B	Methylene azure; Azure I	99
—		Methylene violet, Bernthsen	(Not methylene violet RRA or 3RA, Schultz No. 680)	103
924	52020	Methylene green		104

925	52040	Toluidine blue O	Methylene blue T50 or T extra	104
927	52030	New methylene blue N	Methylene blue NN	104
1027	58000	Alizarin	(Various grades denoted as: Alizarin P, VI, Ie)	199
1034	58005	Alizarin red S	Sodium alizarin monosulfonate; Alizarin red water soluble; Alizarin carmine	200
1037	58205	Purpurin	Alizarin No. 6; Alizarin purpurin	201
1045	58500	Quinalizarin	Alizarin Bordeaux BA	202
—	—	Oil blue NA		203
1240 (note)	—	Alkanet		204
1048	53015	Acid alizarin blue GR		203
1063	58610	Acid alizarin blue BB		203

(b) Natural Dyes

—	(75100)	Saffron		236
1177	73000	Indigo	Indigo blue	237
1180	73015	Indigo carmine	Indigotine Ia	237
—	74240	Alcian blue 8GX	Ingrain blue I	207
1237	75160	Berberine		238
1239	75470	**Cochineal**	(The aqueous extract of the cochineal insect)	239
		Carmine	(The lake prepared by adding alum to cochineal)	239
		Carminic acid	(The active dye purified from cochineal)	240
1242	—	Orcein		241
		Litmus		242
1243	75280	Brazilin		244
1246	75290	**Hematoxylin**	(The ether extract of logwood)	244
		Hematein	(The dye formed on oxidation of hematoxylin)	246
1286	77368	Sky blue	Coelestin blue; Coeline; Coeruleum; ($CoOSnO_2$)	208
—	—	Ruthenium red	($RuCl_3$)	208
1288	77510	Prussian blue	Berlin blue; Chinese blue; Milori blue; Steel blue; $[Fe_4(FeC_6N_6)_3]$	208

* The dyes printed in bold face type are the most commonly used stains.

TABLE 2

Colour Index Numbers of Biological Stains in Both Editions of the Index
(Arranged in Order Adopted in Second Edition)

2nd Edition	1st Edition	Page Ref. to This Book	2nd Edition	1st Edition	Page Ref. to This Book	2nd Edition	1st Edition	Page Ref. to This Book
10005	2	53	26670	284	78	45430	773	180
10020	5	53	26905	280	77	45435	777	184
10305	7	54	27195	282	78	45440	779	184
10315	9	57	27290	252	73	46000	790	196
10360	12	56	30235	581	87	46005	788	195
11020	19	58	37025		210	46020	787	195
11050?	(133)*	66	to ?	—	to	46025	785	195
11270	20	58	37275		235	46045	793	198
11350	—	59	41000	655	128	46075	795	198
11825?	(134)*	67	42000	657	130	49000	812	205
12020	81	65	42040	662	132	49005	815	206
12140	73	63	42045	672	160	49010	816	206
12150	113	65	42053	—	134	49405	819	91
13015	16	57	42095	670	133	49410	820	91
13020	211	72	42500	676	136	49700	821	92
13025	142	68	42510	677	137	50030	826	117
13065	138	68	42520	678	137	50040	825	116
13080	143	69	42530	679	145	50085	828	122
13085	144	70	42535	680	146	50200	840	118
14600	150	70	42555	681	149	50225	847	122
14780	225	73	42556	686	154	50240	841	119
14890	—	63	42563	690	156	50375	857	123
14895	54	62	42585	684	151	50400	860	124
14930?	127	204	42590	685	153	50405	861	125
15510	151	70	42600	682	151	50420	865	125
15511	152	71	42685	692	143	51010	877	106
16150	79	64	42700	710	159	51030	883	108
16180	88	65	42755	707	156	51045	894	108
16185	184	72	42775	689	155	51050	900	109
16230	27	59	42780	706	159	51175	909	114
16545	59	62	43535	715	160	51180	913	110
16570	29	60	43800	724	162	51400	908	109
18050	31	61	43810	727	162	52000	920	93
19540	813	205	44040	728	163	52010	923	96
20470	246	73	44045	729	163	52015	922	100
21000	331	79	44085	731	164	52020	924	104
21010	332	80	44090	737	164	52030	927	105
22120	370	81	45000	740	166	52040	925	104
22145	375	81	45005	739	166	58000	1027	199
22850	438	82	45010	741	168	58005	1034	200
23500	448	82	45160	752	169	58205	1037	201
23510	454	83	45170	749	169	58500	1045	202
23570	456	83	45190	758	170	58610	1063	203

TABLE 2—Continued

2nd Edition	1st Edition	Page Ref. to This Book	2nd Edition	1st Edition	Page Ref. to This Book	2nd Edition	1st Edition	Page Ref. to This Book
23680	463	84	45205	760	170	63015	1048	203
23690	465	84	45350	766	174	73000	1177	237
23850	477	84	45380	768	175	73015	1180	237
24400	520	86	45385	769	177	74240	—	207
26050	—	76	45386	770	178	75100	—	236
26100	248	73	45400	771	178	75160	1237	238
26105	258	75	45405	774	182	75280	1243	244
26125	—	76	45410	778	182	75290	1246	244
26150	—	87	45425	772	180	75470	1239	239

* See footnote, pg. 66.

TABLE 3

List of Biological Stains on Certification Basis, January 1, 1961

Alizarin red S
Aniline blue, water soluble
Auramine O
Azocarmine G
Azure A
Azure B
Azure C
Bismarck brown Y
Brilliant cresyl blue
Brilliant green
Carmine
Chlorazol black E
Congo red
Cresyl violet acetate
Crystal violet
Darrow red
Eosin, bluish
Eosin, yellowish
Erythrosin B
Ethyl eosin
Fast green FCF
Fuchsin, acid
Fuchsin, basic
    Id. *special for flagella*
Giemsa stain
Hematoxylin
Indigo carmine
Janus green B
Jenner's stain

Light green SF yellowish
Malachite green
Martius yellow
Methyl green
Methyl orange
Methyl violet 2B
Methylene blue
Methylene blue thiocyanate tablets
Methylene violet
Neutral red
Nigrosin
Nile blue A
Orange G
Orange II
Orcein
Phloxine B
Protargol S
Pyronin B
Pyronin Y
Resazurin tablets
Rose bengal
Safranin O
Sudan III
Sudan IV
Sudan black B
Tetrachrome stain (MacNeal)
Thionin
Toluidine blue O
Wright's stain

TABLE 4
Dye Solubilities at 26°C (Purified Samples)
Based on data obtained by Holmes (1927, 1928, 1929)

Note: With a few exceptions (the iodides, the magnesium and calcium salts) these figures are for commercial dyes recrystalized from water or aqueous-alcoholic mixtures. Commercial dyes are often considerably less soluble; see Table 7.

Name of Dye	Percent soluble in	
	Water	95 percent alcohol
Alizarin	nil	0.125
Alizarin red S	7.69	0.15
Alizarol orange G	0.40	0.57
Alizarol yellow GW	25.84	0.04
Amaranth	7.20	0.01
Amethyst violet	3.12	3.66
Auramin O	0.74	4.49
Aurantia	nil	0.33
Azo acid yellow	2.17	0.81
Azo Bordeaux	3.83	0.19
Benzopurpurin 4B	—	0.13
Biebrich scarlet	—	0.05
Bismarck brown R	1.10	0.98
Bismarck brown Y	1.36	1.08
Brilliant crocein	5.04	0.06
Chromotrope 2R	19.30	0.17
Chrysoidin R	0.23	0.99
Chrysoidin Y	0.86	2.21
Congo red	—	0.19
Crystal ponceau	0.80	0.06
Crystal violet (chloride) ⎱ gentian	1.68	13.87
Crystal violet (iodide) ⎰ violets	0.035	1.78
Cresyl violet (N. A. Co.)	0.38	0.25
Cyanol extra	1.38	0.44
Eosin B (Na salt)	39.11	0.75
Eosin Y* (Na salt)	44.20	2.18
Eosin Y* (Mg salt)	1.43	0.28
Eosin Y* (Ca salt)	0.24	0.09
Eosin Y* (Ba salt)	0.18	0.06
Erika B	0.64	0.17
Erythrin X	6.41	0.06
Erythrosin* (Na salt)	11.10	1.87
Erythrosin* (Mg salt)	0.38	0.52
Erythrosin* (Ca salt)	0.15	0.35
Erythrosin* (Ba salt)	0.17	0.04
Ethyl eosin	0.03	1.13
Fast green FCF	16.04	0.35
Fast red A	1.67	0.42
Fast Yellow	18.40	0.24

TABLE 4—*Continued*

Name of Dye	Percent soluble in	
	Water	95 per cent alcohol
Fluorescein (color acid).........................	0.03	2.21
Fluorescein (Na salt)...........................	50.20	7.19
Fluorescein (Mg salt)...........................	4.51	0.35
Fluorescein (Ca salt)...........................	1.13	0.41
Fluorescein (Ba salt)...........................	6.54	0.56
Fuchsin, basic:		
Pararosanilin (chloride).....................	0.26	5.93
Pararosanilin (acetate).....................	4.15	13.63
Rosanilin (chloride)........................	0.39	8.16
New fuchsin (chloride)......................	1.13	3.20
Gentian violet (see crystal or methyl violet)		
Guinea green B................................	28.40†	7.30
Indigo carmine................................	1.68	0.01
Janus green...................................	5.18	1.12
Light green SF yellowish.......................	20.35	0.82
Malachite green (oxalate)......................	7.60	7.52
Martius yellow, Na salt........................	4.57	0.16
Martius yellow, Ca salt........................	0.05	1.90
Metanil yellow................................	5.36	1.45
Methyl orange.................................	0.52	0.08
Methyl orange (acid)..........................	0.015	0.015
Methyl violet (Gentian violet).................	2.93	15.21†
Methylene blue ($ZnCl_2$ double salt)...........	2.75	0.05
Methylene blue (chloride)......................	3.55	1.48
Methylene blue (iodide)........................	0.09	0.13
Methylene green...............................	1.46	0.12
Naphthol yellow G.............................	8.96	0.025
Narcein.......................................	10.02	0.06
Neutral red (chloride).........................	5.64	2.45
Neutral red (iodide)..........................	0.15	0.16
Neutral violet................................	3.27	2.22
New methylene blue N..........................	13.32†	1.65
New Victoria blue R...........................	0.54	3.98
Niagara blue 4B...............................	13.51	nil
Nile blue 2B..................................	0.16	0.62
Oil red O.....................................	nil	0.39
Orange I......................................	5.17	0.64
Orange II.....................................	11.37	0.15
Orange G......................................	10.86	0.22
Patent blue A.................................	8.40	5.23
Phloxine* (Na salt)...........................	50.90†	9.02
Phloxine* (Mg salt)...........................	20.84	29.10
Phloxine* (Ca salt)...........................	3.57	0.45
Phloxine* (Ba salt)...........................	6.01	1.17

TABLE 4—*Concluded*

Name of Dye	Percent Soluble in	
	Water	95 percent alcohol
Picric acid	1.18	8.96
Ponceau 2G	1.75	0.21
Ponceau 6R	12.98	0.01
Pyronin B (iodide)	0.07	1.08
Pyronin Y	8.96	0.60
Resorcin yellow	0.37	0.19
Rhodamine B	0.78	1.47
Rhodamine G	1.34	6.31
Rose bengal* (Na salt)	36.25	7.53
Rose bengal* (Mg salt)	0.48	1.59
Rose bengal* (Ca salt)	0.20	0.07
Rose bengal* (Ba salt)	0.17	0.05
Safranin	5.45	3.41
Spirit blue	nil	1.10
Sudan I	nil	0.37
Sudan III	nil	0.15
Sudan IV	nil	0.09
Thionin	0.25	0.25
Toluidine blue O	3.82	0.57
Victoria blue 4R	3.23	20.49
Victoria green 3B	0.04	2.24
Victoria yellow	1.66	1.18

* The color acids of these dyes (not listed here) are practically insoluble in water
† These figures are grams per hundred grams of saturated solution (the other being grams per hundred milliliters).

TABLE 5
Solubilities of Certain Certified Commercial Stains

Data obtained in the laboratory of the American Pharmaceutical Association, and published with the permission of the Association

Percent Soluble in

Dye	Water					95 percent alcohol				
	Pure* dye	Commercial samples†				Pure* dye	Commercial samples†			
		A	B	C	D		A	B	C	D
Alizarin red S.	7.69	4.8	4.25	4.15	—	0.15	0.5	0.26	0.26	—
Aniline blue W.S.	—	3.7	4.8	4.8	—	—	0.48	0.17	0.31	—
Azure A.	—	4.15	—	—	—	—	0.68	—	—	—
Bismarck Brown Y.	1.36	1.23	3.13	2.44	—	1.08	0.39	0.55	0.57	—
Brilliant Cresyl Blue.	—	3.22	—	—	—	—	0.13	—	—	—
Brilliant Green.	—	3.45	4.8	4.8	6.25	—	3.22	4.8	5.0	6.25
Chrysoidin Y (not certified).	0.86	0.66	—	0.61	—	2.21	1.65	—	1.30	—
Congo Red.	—	5.6	—	—	—	0.19	0.033	0.022	0.027	—
Crystal Violet.	1.68	0.22	0.62	0.94	1.05	13.87	9.8	10.00	8.35	10.00
Eosin Y (Na salt).	44.2	33.3	37.00	37.00	28.00	2.18	2.44	1.95	3.03	1.85
Ethyl eosin.	0.03	0.053	—	—	—	1.13	1.21	—	—	—
Fuchsin, acid.	—	12.00	12.5	—	—	—	0.3	0.15	—	—
Fuchsin basic { Pararosanilin chloride.	0.26				{0.31	5.93				{3.70
Fuchsin basic { Pararosanilin acetate.	4.15	2.40				13.63	9.1			
Fuchsin basic { Rosanilin chloride.	0.39		0.59	0.37		8.16		6.25	6.25	
Hematoxylin.	3.55	1.0	1.2	—	—	—	30.00	39.00	6.25	—
Methylene blue (chloride).	—	3.03	4.5	4.35	3.21	1.48	1.70	1.88	1.82	1.75
Methyl green.	—	4.8	4.8	—	—	—	0.75	0.38	—	—
Neutral red.	5.64	2.70	2.85	—	—	2.45	2.40	2.18	—	—
Orange G.	10.86	15.5	18.00	17.00	—	0.22	0.19	0.195	0.22	—
Pyronin Y.	8.96	6.25	7.7	—	—	0.60	0.67	0.43	—	—
Rosolic acid (not certified).	—	0.15	—	0.067	—	—	26.00	—	33.00	—
Rose bengal.	36.25	23.00	—	—	—	7.53	4.8	—	—	—
Safranin O.	5.45	4.35	2.95	2.17	—	3.41	2.56	2.70	2.13	—
Sudan III.	0	0	?	?	—	0.15	0.095	0.095	0.12	—
Toluidine blue O.	3.82	5.9	3.4	—	—	0.57	0.41	0.34	—	—
Wright stain.	—	0.091	—	—	—	—	0.23	—	—	—

* Data in this column taken from Table 4.

† The letters A, B, C, and D refer to American stain companies.

APPENDIX II

METHODS FOR TESTING BIOLOGICAL STAINS*

In the examination of stains submitted to the Biological Stain Commission for certification, procedures for testing them have been worked out for the most common stains and were originally published by Pederson, Conn and Melin (1933–1934). They may be regarded as assay methods used in evaluating dyes as biological stains.

The original methods included determinations of light absorption by means of a visual spectrophotometer; using that instrument, it proved most practical to express the color characteristics of a sample by a simple ratio of color densities at two selected wave lengths. Later, the availability of a photoelectric spectrophotometer made it possible to characterize stains by complete absorption spectra and by exact location of the absorption maximum. The same type of ratio has been retained, however, as additional characterization.

It has proved possible to assay (as to actual dye content) by spectrophotometry those stains whose manufacture is apparently sufficiently standardized to result in quite identical spectral characteristics. The color density at the maximum absorption of such stains is easily related to the dye content as determined by other methods. In the case of stains in which various samples show considerable variation in the position of the absorption peak, it is impossible to establish the spectrometric assay, and it has proved necessary to re-evaluate the titanous chloride method, in which some changes have been made.

The following pages give the methods in use at the time the present edition of this book is going to press. See Stotz *et al.* (1950), from which much of the following is quoted.

GENERAL

SPECTRAL CHARACTERISTICS

A 50-mg sample of the homogenous (powdered if necessary) stain is weighed to the nearest 0.5 mg on a Roller-Smith torsion balance. The sample is transferred quantitatively to a 250-ml volumetric flask and approximately 225 ml of the appropriate solvent added. The flask is then vibrated on a Boerner shaker† for 20 min to insure complete solution of the dye. The solution is made up to the mark

* Revised for this edition by V. M. Emmel, Mary A. Darrow and Nicholas Parente.
† Arthur H. Thomas Co.

with solvent, thoroughly mixed, and an appropriate aliquot taken for further dilution to provide a satisfactory dye concentration for spectrophotometric work.

Maximum accuracy of weighing and insured complete solution of the dye is of course dispensable if the spectrophotometric assay is not employed.

Matched Corex cells of 1 cm light path are employed in the Beckman DU spectrophotometer, the reference cell containing the same solvent as the dye solution. Spectrophotometric readings are taken at least every 5 mμ and usually at smaller intervals in the area of the absorption maximum. An actual reading at the exact peak is of course desirable for spectrophotometric assay.

The older method of expressing the shape of the curve by the ratio of color densities at two predetermined wave lengths loses its significance if the exact peak is known, since any differences in the position of the peak necessarily cause a change in the ratio. More elaborate methods have been used to express the shape of the curve independently of the peak position (Lillie and Roe, 1942) but we have chosen the simple ratio of the color densities at minus and plus 15 mμ of the peak wave length found with the given sample. These densities can be estimated from the plotted spectrum or an absolute figure actually measured after location of the peak.

Titanous Chloride Assay

A study of the titanous chloride standardization, use of the solution, and the dye titration itself led to various modifications. Titanous chloride solutions are standardized against ceric sulfate, which in turn is standardized against arsenious oxide. Both titrations employ ferrous-o-phenanthroline indicator which gives sharp end points.

Sodium Arsenite. Dissolve 4.947 gm of Mallinckrodt "Primary Standard" arsenious oxide (As_2O_3) in a 600 ml beaker containing 200 ml of distilled water and 5 gm of sodium hydroxide pellets. After complete solution add 13 ml of concentrated hydrochloric acid, mix, and then add 10 gm of sodium bicarbonate slowly to prevent loss by spray. Transfer the solution quantitatively to a 1-liter volumetric flask, dilute to the mark, and mix. The resulting solution is 0.1 N.

Ceric Sulfate. Weigh 66.5 gm of anhydrous ceric sulfate [$Ce(SO_4)_2$] into a 600 ml beaker and add 28 ml of concentrated sulfuric acid. Add cautiously about 30 ml of distilled water with stirring. Heat the solution, stir, and add successive portions of water until the salt is completely dissolved. Cool, transfer the solution to a 1-liter volumetric flask and dilute to the mark. This approximately 0.1 N ceric sulfate solution is completely stable.

Iodine Monochloride Catalyst. Dissolve 10 gm of potassium iodide (KI) and 6.74 gm of potassium iodate (KIO$_3$) in 90 ml of distilled water. Add 90 ml of concentrated hydrochloric acid and mix. This solution is 0.5 molar in iodine monochloride. It should be stored in the dark.

Standardization of Ceric Sulfate. Pipette exactly 25.0 ml of 0.1 N sodium arsenite into a 200-ml Erlenmeyer flask, add 20 ml of concentrated hydrochloric acid, and 2.5 ml of 0.005 M iodine chloride (dilute above stock). Dilute the mixture to about 100 ml, add 1 drop of ferrous-o-phenanthroline indicator,* and titrate with the

---

* "Ortho-Phenanthroline Ferrous Complex (Ferroin) 0.025 M." Purchased from the G. Frederick Smith Chemical Co., Columbus, Ohio.

ceric sulfate until the orange color of the indicator returns only slowly after drop-wise addition of the ceric solution. At this stage warm the solution to 50° C, add another drop of indicator, and continue the titration dropwise until a single drop produces a light green solution with no return of the orange color for at least one minute. The end point is sharp and reproducible. The normality of the ceric sulfate solution is calculated as follows:

$$N \text{ ceric} = \frac{25 \times 0.1}{\text{ml ceric}}$$

Titanous Chloride Solution. The stock solution is 20 percent titanous chloride sta-bilized with hydrochloric acid.* An approximately 0.05 N solution is prepared by diluting 8.0 to 8.5 ml of the stock solution to 200 ml with distilled water. Storage experiments with this diluted titanium solution showed that it could be stored under mineral oil for a normal working day without change, and for 20 hr with approxi-mately a 1 to 2 percent decrease in strength. In practice the solution was placed in a burette equipped with a side reservoir, and both surfaces of the solution were covered with ½ in of mineral oil. A fresh solution was made daily and the solution standardized against ceric sulfate as follows: Exactly 5 ml of standard ceric sulfate was placed in a 50-ml Erlenmeyer flask, and 5 ml of concentrated sulfuric acid added. After adding a drop of ferrous-o-phenanthroline indicator, the solution was titrated with the stored titanium solution. The initial yellow color of the solution passes through a green stage, then nearly colorless, and finally a single drop of Ti^{+++} produces the orange color of the reduced indicator. The titration is rapid and the end point exceedingly sharp.

DYE TITRATION WITH TITANOUS CHLORIDE

Minor changes have been made in the dye titration procedure. Smaller amounts of dye are used and a more dilute titanous chloride solution is employed than has been recommended in "Biological Stains, 5th Ed." In the case of most dyes we have preferred a strong acetate buffer to maintain a more constant pH during the titration, although in some cases the tartrate or bitartrate buffer has been retained. We also prefer to use nitrogen gas washed through two titanium-chloride-safranin bottles to maintain more anaerobic conditions and minimize autoxidation of re-duced dyes during the titration. Following is a general description of the titanous chloride assay as carried out in the Stain Commissions laboratory. Specific varia-tions will be noted under the individual dyes.

The titration is carried out in an ordinary "Mason" jar of about 350 ml capacity and a 2½ in diameter mouth. A tight-fitting rubber stopper contains five holes for the accommodation of a gas inlet, gas outlet, the burette extension tip, a thermome-ter and a ground glass sleeve for the shaft of a stirring propeller. The titration jar is mounted on an asbestos covered hot-plate. Water-pumped tank nitrogen is led through two successive gas-washing bottles containing titanous chloride safranin. The latter solution is made by diluting 40 ml of 20 percent titanous chloride and 40 ml of concentrated hydrochloric acid to 500 ml with distilled water. After filling

* LaMotte Chemical Products Co., Baltimore, Md.

the gas-washing bottles, approximately 10 mg of safranin is added to each bottle. This mixture is replaced by fresh solution every 2 or 3 days depending on amount of use.

The weighed dye sample is dissolved in the appropriate solvent in the titration jar, and buffer added. The total volume of dye mixture is usually 200 ml. The solution is stirred, heated if necessary, and the nitrogen passed through the jar for at least 15 minutes before the titration is started. Like most titrations, the first run locates the approximate end point so that a second trial can be rapid and the type of end point color change familiar.

The percentage of dye is calculated by the general formula:

$$\text{percentage of dye} = \frac{\text{ml TiCl}_3 \text{ used} \times \text{normality of TiCl}_3 \times \text{mol. wt. of dye} \times 100}{\text{Wt. of sample} \times \text{No. of hydrogen equivalents} \times 1000}$$

General Approach to Examination of Individual Stains. Study of the individual stains by the general methods described consisted of measuring the spectra of a series of samples of recent origin and of satisfactory staining quality. Ratios of the color density at the peak (D-peak) to previously recorded assay values were then calculated and compared. If these ratios (Assay/D-peak) were reasonably constant, the chemical assays were carefully repeated, the ratios recalculated, and the average value used to serve as the necessary factor for spectrophotometric assay of the stain. If the ratios proved not to be reasonably constant, either the spectrophotometric data or the chemical assay was considered to be at fault. Spectrophotometric assay was obviously unsuitable when representative samples of the stain showed great variation in the position of the peak or other spectral characteristics. In such cases the chemical assay proved to be the method of choice.

In a few cases the titanous chloride assay was not entirely satisfactory, and it was difficult to establish a figure for percentage of purity. In such cases nitrogen analyses were made and the percentage of dye calculated on this basis. This figure in turn served to standardize the spectrophotometric assay of the dye.

It should be noted that the methods here reported are designed to provide a quick chemical and spectrophotometric evaluation of commercial stains as they are received for certification. As such, the standards set are based primarily on past commercial samples and their satisfactory use in staining procedure. From the strictly chemical standpoint it is recognized that "percentage of dye" as determined by titanous chloride, spectrophotometry, or color base precipitation cannot adequately describe the true content of the dye specifically named.

CERTAIN NITRO AND AZO DYES

Qualitative and quantitative determinations of the dyes in this group and of the ones following are, for the most part, the same as the general methods outlined at the beginning of the chapter. Where special treatment is required it will be found under the individual dye.

MARTIUS YELLOW   c. i. no. 10315

Martius yellow is the monosodium or calcium salt of 2:4-dinitro-1-naphthol. $C_{10}H_5N_2O_5Na$ or $(C_{10}H_5N_2O_5)_2Ca$.

Absorption Characteristics: Dissolve 50 mg of martius yellow in 250 ml of distilled water. Dilute 10 ml of this solution to 200 ml with distilled water. Read in a spectrophotometer in a 1-cm cell. Absorption maximum 431–440 mμ; ratio P − 15/ P + 15 is from 1.00 to 1.12.

A marked distinction is observed in the solubilities of the two salts in water, the sodium salt being soluble to the extent of 4.5 parts in 100 parts of water at 26° C, whereas only 0.05 parts of the calcium salt are soluble in 100 parts of water at the same temperature.

Assay: Dissolve 100 mg of dye in 200 ml of distilled water, add 10 gm of sodium bitartrate, heat to boiling, and titrate with 0.05 N TiCl$_3$. A change from orange to a straw yellow indicates the end point. The following data are used in calculating the percentage of anhydrous dye in the original sample:

(1) Molecular weight, $C_{10}H_5N_2O_5Na$ 256.153
    Hydrogen equivalents per mole of dye 12
    Milliliters of N/10 TiCl$_3$ per gm of dye 468.467
(2) Molecular weight, $(C_{10}H_5N_2O_5)_2Ca$ 506.392
    Hydrogen equivalents per mole of dye 24
    Milliliters of N/10 TiCl$_3$ per gm of dye 473.944

Biological Test: Martius yellow is tested as a counterstain to resorcin blue for staining pollen tubes in the style. Slender styles and ovaries, while still moist, are crushed between two slides; while larger ones are treated similarly after sectioning longitudinally by hand. The material is either stained on the slide or immersed in the stain in pieces in a small dish, for 2 to 5 min. The staining solution consists of 5 mg resorcin blue (often called lacmoid) and 5 mg of martius yellow in 10 to 15 ml of water, with a few drops of 1 percent aqueous ammonia added to bring the reaction to about pH 8, as shown by the solution assuming an olive color. The material is mounted in the stain or else in water of the same reaction, and examined with a powerful light. A good sample is one with which the pollen tubes show blue on a light yellowish green background.

ORANGE G   C. I. NO. 16230

Orange G is the disodium salt of benzene-azo-2-naphthol-6:8-disulfonic acid $C_{16}H_{10}N_2O_7S_2Na_2$.

Absorption Characteristics: Dissolve 50 mg of orange G in 250 ml of distilled water. Dilute 15 ml of this solution to 200 ml with distilled water. Read in a spectrophotometer in a 1-cm cell. Absorption maximum 476–481 mμ; ratio P − 15/P + 15 is from 0.88 to 0.94.

Assay: Dissolve 100 mg of dye in 200 ml of distilled water, add 10 gm of sodium bitartrate, heat to boiling, and titrate with 0.05 N TiCl$_3$ to a sharp change from brownish-yellow to a pale yellowish-green. The following data are used in calculating the percentage of anhydrous dye:

Molecular weight 452.382
Hydrogen equivalents per mole of dye 4
Milliliters of N/10 TiCl$_3$ per gm of dye 88.424

For certification, samples of this stain must contain not less than 80 percent anhydrous dye.

Biological Test: Orange G is tested (1) in Mallory's connective tissue stain and (2) as a counterstain in histology, and (3) in cytology.

It is tested in Mallory's connective tissue stain on animal tissue fixed in Zenker's fluid and embedded in paraffin. The procedure followed is the one given under acid fuchsin, p. 304. With a good sample, the red blood corpuscles and myelin sheaths are yellow and elastic fibers pale pink or yellow or unstained.

For its histological use it is tested on animal tissue fixed in Bouin's or Zenker's solution and embedded in paraffin. A 0.5 percent solution in 95 percent alcohol is employed and applied for 15 sec or more as a counterstain after Heidenhain's hematoxylin. (See hematoxylin, p. 311.)

For cytological work, it is tested as a counterstain on root tip material, fixed in Navashin's or Flemming's fluid. (See test with iodine under crystal violet, p. 301.) In both of these procedures a stain is required which gives a good contrast to the nuclear dye.

JANUS GREEN B* c. i. no. 11050

Janus green B is diethylsafranin-azo-dimethylanilin, $C_{30}H_{31}N_6Cl$.

Absorption Characteristics: Dissolve 50 mg of Janus green B in 125 ml of 95 percent alcohol and then dilute to 250 ml with distilled water. Dilute 10 ml of this solution to 200 ml with 50 percent alcohol. Read in a spectrophotometer in a 1-cm cell. Absorption maximum 610–666 mμ; ratio $P - 15/P + 15$ is from 0.98 to 1.03.

Assay: Dissolve 100 mg of dye in 50 ml of 95 percent alcohol, add 150 ml of distilled water and 10 gm of sodium titartrate, heat to boiling, and titrate with 0.05 N TiCl$_3$.

The dye solution undergoes several color changes on reduction, but the final end point, usually yellow or orange-yellow is easy to recognize. The following data are used to calculate the percentage of anhydrous dye in the original sample:

Molecular weight. 511.053
Hydrogen equivalents per mole of dye. 6
Milliliters of N/10 TiCl$_3$ per gm of dye. 117.405

Samples of this stain should contain not less than 50 percent anhydrous dye.

Biological Test: Janus green B is tested, mixed with neutral red, for the supravital staining of blood. Neutral absolute alcohol is distilled over CaO. Saturated stock solutions of the two dyes are prepared by adding 300 mg of neutral red to 100 ml of neutral absolute alcohol and 50 mg of Janus green B to 25 ml of neutral absolute alcohol. Both of these solutions are stable. Just before using, a dilute stock solution is prepared by adding 35 to 40 drops (Wright's capillary pipette) of neutral red stock to 5 ml neutral absolute alcohol and 5 drops (Wright's capillary pipette)

---

* The formula given in the Colour Index (*1.ed*) for Janus green B was found incorrect for all samples furnished in this country. The dye usually encountered as a biological stain has the formula given here. However, German samples of the dye, although similar, are not identical with the usual stain sample.

of Janus green B stock solution. Occasionally a few more drops of Janus green B are necessary (up to 8 to 10).

New slides are placed for 48 hr in cleaning solution, washed 48 hr in running tap water, rinsed 3 times with distilled water and may be stored in alcohol. Wipe dry, avoiding lint. The slides are flamed, cooled until slightly warm, and flooded with stain rapidly. Drain and air-dry. Place a drop of fresh blood on a cover slip which is inverted on top of the slide. Seal edges of cover slip with Vaseline. Let preparation stand for at least 5 min before placing on microscope. Study at room temperature (optimum for cellular motility is 98.8° F).

By this technic, with good samples of both dyes, the basophilic granules becomes deep brick red; the eosinophilic granules, yellow or light orange; neutrophilic granules, pale pink; vacuoles of monocytes, salmon. Vacuoles of clasmatocytes or macrophages reflect the full pH range of neutral red stain (6.8 to 8.0, red-yellow). Mitochondria are green. All the areas that stain with neutral red take up the dye quickly except in the case of monocytes, which require about 10 min. The mitochondria show up after about 15 min as small green dots or rods. The cells should remain in good condition for at least an hour.

METHYL ORANGE   C. I. NO. 13025

Methyl orange is the sodium salt of p-sulfobenzene-azo-dimethyl-aniline, $C_{14}H_{14}N_3O_3SNa$.

Absorption Characteristics: Dissolve 50 mg of methyl orange in 250 ml of distilled water. Dilute 5 ml of this solution and 1 ml of 1 N HCl to 200 ml with distilled water. Read in a spectrophotometer in a 1-cm cell. Absorption maximum 506–508 $m\mu$; ratio P $-$ 15/P $+$ 15 is from 0.95 to 0.97.

Assay: Dissolve 100 mg of dye in 200 ml of distilled water, add 15 gm of sodium bitartrate, heat to boiling, and titrate with 0.05 N TiCl$_3$. The end point is sharp, giving a colorless solution. The following data are used in calculating the percentage of anhydrous dye in the original sample:

Molecular weight. 327.339
Hydrogen equivalents per mole of dye. 4
Milliliters of N/10 TiCl$_3$ required per gm of dye. 122.200

Samples of this stain should contain not less than 85 percent anhydrous dye.

Biological Test: Methyl orange is tested in saturated alcoholic solution as a counterstain, applied for 15 min following crystal violet, or 1 or 2 min following Harris' or Heidenhain's hematoxylin, on paraffin sections of animal tissue fixed in Bouin's or of plant tissue fixed in Flemming's fluid. A good sample is one which shows a good contrast to the nuclear stain.

ORANGE II   C. I. NO. 15510

Orange II is the sodium salt of p-sulfobenzene-azo-2-naphthol, $C_{16}H_{11}N_2O_4SNa$.

Absorption Characteristics: Dissolve 50 mg of orange II in 250 ml of distilled water. Dilute 10 ml of this solution to 200 ml with distilled water. Read in a spectrophotometer in a 1-cm cell. Absorption maximum 484–485 $m\mu$; ratio P $-$ 15/P $+$ 15 is from 0.93 to 0.96.

Assay: Dissolve 100 mg of dye in 200 ml of distilled water, add 10 gm of sodium bitartrate, heat to boiling and titrate with 0.05 N TiCl$_3$. Reduce to a practically colorless solution. The following data are used in calculating the percentage of anhydrous dye in the original sample:

Molecular weight. 350.327
Hydrogen equivalents per mole of dye. 4
Milliliters of N/10 TiCl$_3$ per gm of dye. 114.179

Samples of this stain should contain not less than 85 percent anhydrous dye.
Biological Test: Orange II is tested by the same procedure as for methyl orange.

SUDAN III   C. I. NO. 26100

Sudan III is benzene-azo-benzene-azo-2-naphthol, $C_{22}H_{16}N_4O$.
Absorption Characteristics: Dissolve 50 mg of Sudan III in 250 ml of benzene. Dilute 2 ml of this solution to 50 ml with benzene. Read in a spectrophotometer in a 1-cm cell. Absorption maximum 508–510 mμ; ratio P − 15/P + 15 is from 0.96 to 1.01.
Assay: Due to its low solubility, Sudan III is sulfonated before titration. Weigh 200 mg of Sudan III into a 200 ml volumetric flask, add 5 ml of 30–33 percent fuming H$_2$SO$_4$, mix, and heat for about a minute in a boiling water bath. Let stand for about an hour with occasional shaking. *Carefully* add a small amount of distilled water. Allow to cool to room temperature and bring up to mark.* Pipet a 100 ml aliquot of the sulfonated solution into the titration flask, add 100 ml of distilled water and 30 gm of sodium bitartrate, heat to boiling, and titrate with 0.05 N TiCl$_3$ to a yellow end point. The following data are used in calculating the percentage of anhydrous dye:

Molecular weight. 352.380
Hydrogen equivalents per mole of dye. 8
Milliliters of N/10 TiCl$_3$ per gm of dye. 227.026

Samples of this stain should contain not less than 75 percent anhydrous dye.
Biological Test: Sudan III is tested as a fat stain. The method employed is the same as that given under the following dye. Sudan III, however, is not expected to give as intense a coloration as Sudan IV.

SUDAN IV   C. I. NO. 26105

Sudan IV is o-toluene-azo-o-toluene-azo-2-naphthol, $C_{24}H_{20}N_4O$.
Absorption Characteristics: Dissolve 50 mg of Sudan IV in 250 ml of benzene. Dilute 2 ml of this solution to 50 ml with benzene. Read in a spectrophotometer in a 1-cm cell. Absorption maximum 513–522 mμ; ratio P − 15/P + 15 is from 0.97 to 1.00.
Assay: The low solubility of this dye interferes with its determination, and it is therefore sulfonated before titration, by the same procedure as that outlined for

---

* The red solution obtained on the dilution of the blue sulfonation product should be clear. If the sulfonation has been incomplete, the solution is cloudy.

Sudan III. The percentage of dye in the original sample is calculated from the following data:

Molecular weight.. 380.432
Hydrogen equivalents per mole of dye...................... 8
Milliliters of N/10 TiCl₃ per gm of dye................... 210.286

For certification, samples must contain not less than 80 percent anhydrous dye.

Biological Test: Sudan IV is tested on thin frozen sections of formalin-fixed tissue in Lillie and Ashburn's supersaturated isopropanol method. Prepare a stock saturated solution of Sudan IV in 99 percent isopropanol. Dilute 6 ml of stock solution with 4 ml water. Let stand 5 to 10 min and then filter. (Filtrate can be used for several hours.) The sections are stained 10 min, washed in tap water and stained 5 min in an acid alum hematoxylin of about 0.1 percent strength (e.g., Mayer's undiluted, Lillie's diluted 1 to 4 in 2 percent acetic acid, or Ehrlich's diluted 1 to 5 in 2 percent acetic acid). Then place in 1 percent aqueous Na_2HPO_4 or in tap water, until blue, float out in water and take up on a slide. Sections are mounted in a suitable aqueous medium such as Apathy's syrup, Zwemer's glycogel or Maiser's mounting medium. A good sample should give an orange-red color to the fat globules; nuclei, blue; erythrocytes, sometimes green and the cytoplasm, a lighter green.

BISMARCK BROWN Y   c. i. no. 21000

Bismarck brown Y is the dihydrochloride of benzene-m-disazo-bis-m-phenylene-diamine, $C_{18}H_{20}N_8Cl_2$.

Absorption Characteristics: Dissolve 50 mg of Bismarck brown Y in 125 ml of 95 per cent alcohol, then dilute to 250 ml with distilled water. Dilute 10 ml of this solution and 1 ml 1 N HCl to 200 ml with 50 percent alcohol. Read in a spectrophotometer in a 1-cm cell. Absorption maximum 455–458 mμ; ratio P − 15/P + 15 is from 0.98 to 1.02.

Assay: Dissolve 100 mg of dye in 100 ml of alcohol and 100 ml of distilled water, add about 10 gr of sodium bitartrate, heat to boiling, and titrate with 0.05 N TiCl₃. The end point, which is not always sharp, ranges from pale yellow to brownish-yellow. The following data are used for calculating the percentage of anhydrous dye:

Molecular weight.. 419.318
Hydrogen equivalents per mole of dye...................... 8
Milliliters of N/10 TiCl₃ per gm of dye................... 190.787

For certification, samples of this stain must not contain less than 45 percent anhydrous dye.

Biological Test: Bismarck brown Y is tested in a 1 percent aqueous solution for staining mucus in goblet cells of the intestine, or cartilage in the trachea or in embryonic material, fixed in one of the usual fixatives and embedded in paraffin. The sections are stained for about 5 to 10 min, rinsed in 95 percent alcohol, and transferred to the 0.5 percent aqueous methyl green solution until they appear dark green, after which they are dehydrated, cleared and mounted. A good Bismarck brown should show light brown mucus and deep brown cartilage.

Congo Red

Congo red is the disodium salt of diphenyl-disazo-bis-l-naphthyl-amine-4-sulfonic acid, $C_{32}H_{22}N_6O_6S_2Na_2$.

Absorption Characteristics: Dissolve 50 mg of Congo red in 250 ml of distilled water. Dilute 10 ml of this solution and 2 ml of 1 percent Na_2CO_3 to 200 ml with distilled water. Read in a spectrophotometer in a 1-cm cell. Absorption maximum 497–500 mμ; ratio P − 15/P + 15 is from 0.99 to 1.04.

Assay: Dissolve 100 mg of the dye in 170 ml of distilled water, add 30 ml of 30 percent sodium tartrate solution, heat to boiling, and titrate with 0.05 N $TiCl_3$. Titrate rapidly until near the end point, then slowly. The end point is sharp, a practically colorless solution resulting. The following data are used in calculating the percentage of anhydrous dye:

Molecular weight 696.670
Hydrogen equivalents per mole of dye 8
Milliliters of N/10 $TiCl_3$ per gm of dye 114.834

For certification, samples of this stain must contain not less than 75 percent anhydrous dye.

Biological Test: Congo red is tested on paraffin sections of animal tissue fixed in Bouin's fluid. The sections are stained 5 min in Mayer's hemalum, dipped in tap water once or twice, and transferred directly into 0.5 percent aqueous solution of Congo red and left therein for 1 min. They are then rinsed in tap water, run up through the alcohols, cleared and mounted. The criteria by which the sample is judged are as follows: Congo red should give a bright cytoplasmic stain with a certain amount of differentiation from orange to reddish. Erythrocytes, for instance, should be light orange and the spindle fibers in mitotic figures should be deep orange to light red.

Chlorazol Black E

Chlorazol black E has the empirical formula $C_{34}H_{25}N_9O_7S_2Na_2$.

Absorption Characteristics: Dissolve 50 mg of chlorazol black E in 250 ml of 50 percent alcohol. Dilute 5 ml of this solution to 200 ml with 50 percent alcohol. Read in a spectrophotometer in a 1-cm cell. Absorption maximum 597–602 mμ; ratio P − 15/P + 15 is from 0.97 to 1.00.

Method of Analysis: No method of analysis has been devised for chlorazol black E.

Biological Test: Chlorazol black E is tested on paraffin sections of animal tissue fixed in Zenker's fluid, and on plant tissue fixed in Flemming's or Bouin's. The sections are stained 5 to 10 min in a 1 percent solution in 70 percent ethyl alcohol. The excess dye is drained off and the sections are dehydrated, cleared and mounted in balsam. No mordant and no differentiation are necessary. The tissue elements should stain varying shades of green, gray and black, and sharp differentiation should be evident. Too general appearance of green is regarded as undesirable.

In using this as an auxiliary stain in making chromosome counts on plants, the above staining solution is applied 5 to 25 min to the dissected tissue, fixed in acetic acid (1 vol. to 3 vol. of alcohol), preferably 12 to 24 hr, though 10 to 15 min can be used, rinsed in three changes of 70 percent alcohol and the material is then transferred to a slide. A drop of aceto-carmine (boiling 45 percent acetic acid saturated with carmine and filtered) is added and then covered with a cover glass, heated, flattened and sealed. The chromosomes should stain deep reddish black with a fairly clear cytoplasm.

ALIZARIN RED S   C. I. NO. 58005

Alizarin red S has the empirical formula $C_{14}H_7O_7SNa$.

Absorption Characteristics: Dissolve 50 mg of alizarin red S in 250 ml of 0.1 N NaOH. Dilute 15 ml of this solution to 200 ml with 0.1 N NaOH. Read in a spectrophotometer in a 1-cm cell. Absorption maxima 554–558 mμ, 594–599 mμ; ratio $P - 15/P + 15$ is from 0.98 to 1.05 for the first maximum.

Assay: No assay method for alizarin red S is known.

Biological Test: Alizarin red S is tested on small vertebrates, completely eviscerated and fixed 2 to 4 days or longer in 95 percent alcohol, by the following technic: Place specimen in 1 percent aqueous KOH until the bones are clearly visible through the surrounding tissues, transfer to dilute (0.0025–0.01 percent) alizarin red S in 1 percent aqueous KOH and allow to stand until desired degree of staining is obtained (the smaller the animal, the more dilute the stain may be); complete the clearing by placing in a mixture of 1 vol. glycerin to 4 vol. of 1.25 percent aqueous KOH (glycerin 20 ml, KOH 1 gm, water 79 ml) and continue through increasing concentrations of glycerin. Store in glycerin alone. The bones should be red, soft tissue transparent and unstained.

SUDAN BLACK B   C. I. NO. 26150

The empirical formula for Sudan black B is $C_{29}H_{24}N_6$.

Absorption Characteristics: Dissolve 50 mg of Sudan black B in 250 ml of 95 percent alcohol. Dilute 10 ml of this solution to 200 ml with 95 percent alcohol. Read in a spectrophotometer in a 1-cm cell. Absorption maximum 596–605 mμ; ratio $P - 15/P + 15$ is from 0.98 to 1.02.

Assay: A method for determinating dye content has not yet been perfected.

Biological Test: Sudan black B is tested for fatty material in bacteria in Burdon's technic. Culture *Bacillus cereus* is grown at room temperature for 18 to 24 hr on agar slants. Prepare smear and air dry. Flood entire slide with Sudan black B solution (Sudan black B, 0.3 gm; 70 percent alcohol, 100 ml). After bulk of dye has been dissolved, shake thoroughly at intervals during the day and allow to stand overnight. Flood slide with the stain and allow it to remain undisturbed 10 to 20 min, drain off excess stain, blot dry, clear with xylene, blot dry. Counterstain with 0.5 percent aqueous safranin 5 to 10 sec, wash in tap water, blot and dry. A satisfactory sample should stain intracellular fat dark blue-black.

AZOCARMINE G   C. I. NO. 50085

Azocarmine G is the sodium salt of a disulfonic acid of phenylrosinduline, $C_{28}H_{18}N_3O_6S_2Na$.

Absorption Characteristics: Dissolve 50 mg of azocarmine G in 250 ml of distilled water. Dilute 20 ml of this solution to 200 ml with distilled water. Read in a spectrophotometer in a 1-cm cell. Absorption maximum 510–514 mμ; ratio P $-$ 15/ P + 15 is from 0.93 to 0.95.

Assay: Dissolve 200 mg of dye in 200 ml of distilled water. Add 10 gm of sodium bitartrate, heat to boiling, and titrate with 0.05 N TiCl$_3$ to an orange end point. The following data are used to calculate the percentage of anhydrous dye in the sample:

Molecular weight 579.577
Hydrogen equivalents per mole of dye 2
Milliliters of N/10 TiCl$_3$ per gm of dye 34.508

Biological Test: It is tested in Heidenhain's "Azan" modification of the Mallory trichrome stain on paraffin sections of animal tissue fixed in Zenker, Helly, Bouin or Carnoy. Prepare a staining solution as follows: boil 1 gm of azocarmine G in 100 ml distilled water, cool and acidify with 1 ml glacial acetic acid. The paraffin is removed and the sections hydrated in the usual manner. Sections are stained 30 to 60 min in a covered dish at 50 to 55° C and then 1 to 2 hr at 37° C, washed in distilled water, differentiated in 0.1 percent aniline in 95 percent alcohol, rinsed in 1 percent acetic acid in 95 percent alcohol, mordanted 30 min to 3 hr in 5 percent aqueous phosphotungstic acid and rinsed in distilled water. The sections are then stained 1 to 3 hr in a 1:1 or 1:2 dilution of a stock solution consisting of: aniline blue, 0.5 gm; orange G, 2 gm; glacial acetic acid, 8 ml; distilled water, 100 ml. Then the sections are rinsed in distilled water, differentiated and dehydrated in 95 percent alcohol followed by absolute, cleared in xylene and mounted. A satisfactory stain shows nuclei, red; muscle, orange; mucin, blue; reticulum and collagen, dark blue.

THE QUINONE-IMIDE DYES

THIONIN (LAUTH'S VIOLET)   c. i. no. 52000

Thionin is diaminodiphenazthionium chloride, C$_{12}$H$_{10}$N$_3$SCl.

Absorption Characteristics: Dissolve 50 mg of thionin in 250 ml of distilled water. Dilute 5 ml of this solution to 200 ml with distilled water. Read in a spectrophotometer in a 1-cm cell. Absorption maximum 598–600 mμ; ratio P $-$ 15/P + 15 is from 1.15 to 1.30.

Assay: Spectrophotometric. Percentage of dye = D-peak $\times$ 97. D-peak (color density at peak) is measured on dye solution as described under "Absorption characteristics."

Samples of this stain should contain not less than 85 percent anhydrous dye.

Biological Test: Thionin is tested as a stain in the end point buffered staining method for Nissl substance in nervous tissue, and also in Stoughton's method for sections of plant pathological material. For nervous tissue, paraffin sections of brain or spinal cord fixed in 10 percent formalin or Carnoy's fluid are decerated, hydrated and stained for 20 min or longer in a 0.025 percent solution of thionin in M/10 acetate buffer at pH 3.7 to 4.5, then dehydrated through alcohol, cleared in xylene and covered. A satisfactory sample should show the Nissl granules stained purplish blue. In the Stoughton method, plant pathological material is fixed in one of the usual botanical fixatives, paraffin sections are stained for 1 hr in 0.1 percent thionin in 5 percent aqueous phenol, dehydrated in successively stronger alcohols and differentiated in a saturated solution of orange G in absolute alcohol for 1 min. They are then washed in absolute alcohol, cleared in xylene and mounted in balsam. Fungal parasites should be violet to purple; cell walls, yellowish or green; lignified tissue, blue; host nuclei, blue with purple nucleoli; chromosomes, deep blue; and nuclei of the fungal hyphae or spores, deep purple.

METHYLENE BLUE   C. I. NO. 52015

Methylene blue is tetramethyldiaminodiphenazthionium chloride (tetramethyl thionin), $C_{16}H_{18}N_3SCl$. This dye is sometimes marketed for textile purposes as the zinc chloride double salt, but the dye in this form is not recommended for use as a biological stain.

Absorption Characteristics: Dissolve 50 mg of methylene blue in 250 ml of distilled water. Dilute 3 ml of this solution to 200 ml with distilled water. Read in a spectrophotometer in a 1-cm cell. Absorption maximum 664–666 mμ; ratio P $-$ 15/ P $+$ 15 is from 1.21 to 1.70.

Assay: Spectrophotometric. Percentage of dye = D-peak $\times$ 127. D-peak (color density at peak) is measured on dye solution as described under "Absorption characteristics."

For certification, samples of this stain must contain not less than 82 percent anhydrous dye.

Biological Test: Methylene blue is tested for histological and bacteriological staining and as a constituent of Wright's blood stain. As a histological stain it is tested on paraffin sections of tissue fixed in Zenker's fluid, with phloxine as a counterstain, (see phloxine B, p. 308). A good sample should show good nuclear staining without removing the phloxine from the cytoplasm.

As a bacteriological stain it is tested for staining the diphtheria organism and for staining bacteria in milk. For the former purpose smears from a throat culture of a case of diphtheria are stained in three different solutions of the sample under examination; namely Loeffler's formula (methylene blue, 0.3 gm; 95 percent ethyl alcohol, 30 ml; 0.01 percent KOH, 100 ml), alcoholic aqueous methylene blue (same, but with distilled water in place of 0.01 percent KOH), and also in a 1 percent aqueous solution of the dye. The solutions are applied to the preparation for a few seconds which is then washed in tap water and examined under the microscope to see if the typical barred or granular structure shows. A good sample should show this typical staining with all three solutions.

For staining bacteria in milk, 0.01 ml is placed on a microscopic slide and smeared over an area of 1 sq cm with a stiff needle, dried with gentle heat on a level surface, dipped in xylene a few minutes to remove the fat, immersed in 90–95 percent ethyl alcohol a few minutes to fix the smear to the slide. It is then dipped 2 to 4 times in methylene blue solution (methylene blue, 0.3 gm; 95 percent ethyl alcohol, 30 ml; after dissolving, mixed with 100 ml distilled water), washed briefly in 90 to 95 percent ethyl alcohol until the intense blue color changes to a faint tinge. (This decolorizing may be omitted if the staining period has been made briefer, 10 to 15 sec, or if a more dilute staining fluid has been employed). The slide is then dried and examined. A good sample should not remove the milk smear from the slide and should show deeply stained bacteria in a light blue background.

In testing as a constituent of Wright's stain, the same procedure is followed as in the case of eosin Y (see p. 305).

Azure A

Azure A is dimethyldiaminodiphenazthionium chloride (dimethyl thionin) $C_{14}H_{14}N_3SCl$.

Absorption Characteristics: Dissolve 50 mg of azure A in 250 ml of distilled water. Dilute 3 ml of this solution to 200 ml with distilled water. Read in a spectrophotometer in a 1-cm cell. Absorption maximum is 620–634 mμ; ratio P − 15/P + 15 is from 1 02 to 1.20.

Assay: Dissolve 100 mg of dye in 175 ml of distilled water, add 25 ml pH 4.0 acetate buffer (6 vol. of 50 percent NaAc·3H₃O + 4 vol. of glacial acetic acid), heat to boiling and titrate with 0.05 N TiCl₃ to a yellow end point. The following data are used in calculating the percentage of anhydrous dye:

Molecular weight...291.799
Hydrogen equivalents per mole of dye......................2
Milliliters of N/10 TiCl₃ per gm of dye...................68.541

For certification, samples of this stain must contain not less than 55 percent anhydrous dye.

Biological Test: Azure A is tested in Lillie's modified Nocht's method on Zenker or formalin-fixed tissue. Bring paraffin sections to water in the usual manner, using 0.5 percent iodine, 5 percent sodium thiosulfate sequence for mercuric chloride fixed material. Stain 1 hr in Coplin jar containing 0.1 percent aqueous azure A, 4 ml; 0.1 percent aqueous eosin B, 4 ml; C. P. acetone, 5 ml; distilled water, 25 ml; and buffered at pH 4.1 with M/10 citric acid, 1.2 ml; M/5 disodium phosphate, 0.8 ml. Dehydrate in 2 to 3 changes of acetone, clear in a 1:1 acetone-xylene mixture, 2 changes of xylene, and mount in synthetic resin. A good sample should show nuclei stained blue; mast cell granules, blue-violet; cartilage matrix, reddish-violet; cytoplasm, light blue to violet or lavender; muscle fibers, bright pink; erythrocytes, orange-pink.

Azure B   C. I. NO. 52010

Azure B is trimethyldiaminodiphenazthionium chloride (trimethyl thionin) $C_{15}H_{16}N_3SCl$.

Absorption Characteristics: Dissolve 50 mg of azure B in 250 ml of distilled water. Dilute 3 ml of this solution to 200 ml with distilled water. Read in a spectrophotometer in a 1-cm cell. Absorption maximum 648–655 mμ; ratio P − 15/P + 15 is from 1.06 to 1.11.

Assay: Dissolve 100 mg of dye in 175 ml of distilled water, add 25 ml of pH 4.0 acetate buffer (6 vol. of 50 percent NaAc·3H₂O + 4 vol. of glacial acetic acid), heat to boiling and titrate with 0.05 N TiCl₃ to a yellow end point. The following data are used in calculating the percentage of anhydrous dye:

Molecular weight. 305.825
Hydrogen equivalents per mole of dye. 2
Milliliters of N/10 TiCl₃ per gm of dye. 65.398

Biological Test: Azure B is tested in the same way as azure A (p. 289).

It is also tested as a constituent of the tetrachrome stain (See Tetrachrome Stain, p. 313). With a good azure A this compound stain should color the platelets, the lobes of the polymorphonuclear cells and the nuclei of the lymphocytes a distinct purple.

AZURE C

Azure C is monomethyldiaminodiphenazthionium chloride (monomethyl thionin), $C_{13}H_{12}N_3SCl$.

Absorption Characteristics: Dissolve 50 mg of azure C in 250 ml of distilled water. Dilute 3 ml of this solution to 200 ml with distilled water. Read in a spectrophotometer in a 1-cm cell. Absorption maximum 608–612 mμ; ratio P − 15/P + 15 is from 0.98 to 1.03.

Assay: Dissolve 100 mg of dye in 175 ml of distilled water, add 25 ml of pH 4.0 acetate buffer (6 vol. of 50 percent $NaAc \cdot 3H_2O$ + 4 vol. of glacial acetic acid), heat to boiling and titrate with 0.05 N TiCl₃ to a yellow end point. The following data are used in calculating the percentage of anhydrous dye in the sample:

Molecular weight. 277.773
Hydrogen equivalents per mole of dye. 2
Milliliters of N/10 TiCl₃ per gm of dye. 72.003

Biological Test: Azure C is tested in the same way as azure A (see p. 289).

METHYLENE VIOLET

Absorption Characteristics: Dissolve 25 mg of methylene violet in 125 ml of 95 percent alcohol, add 10 ml of 0.1 N HCl and dilute to 250 ml with distilled water. Dilute 10 ml of this solution and 20 ml of 0.1 N HCl to 200 ml with 50 percent alcohol. Read in a spectrophotometer in a 1-cm cell. Absorption maximum 579–584 mμ; ratio P − 15/P + 15 is from 0.99 to 1.06.

Assay: Spectrophotometric. Percentage of dye = D-peak × 181. D-peak (color density at peak) is measured on dye solution described under "Absorption characteristics."

Biological Test: It is tested as a constituent of the tetrachrome stain (see Tetrachrome Stain, p. 313). A blood smear stained with this mixture, containing a satisfactory methylene violet, shows a pure blue in the cytoplasm of the lymphocytes and a deeper blue in the granules of this cytoplasm.

TOLUIDINE BLUE O   C. I. NO. 52040

Toluidine blue O is usually the zinc chloride double salt of aminodimethylaminotoluphenazthionium chloride, $C_{15}H_{16}N_3SCl$ + $ZnCl_2$, but may also be prepared as the chloride.

Absorption Characteristics: Dissolve 50 mg of toluidine blue O in 250 ml of distilled water. Dilute 5 ml of this solution to 200 ml with distilled water. Read in a spectrophotometer in a 1-cm cell. Absorption maximum 620–638 mμ; ratio P − 15/ P + 15 is from 1.00 to 1.20.

Assay: Dissolve 100 mg of dye in 175 ml distilled water, add 25 ml of pH 4.0 acetate buffer (6 vol. of 50 percent NaAc·$3H_2O$ + 4 vol. glacial acetic acid), heat to boiling and titrate with 0.05 N $TiCl_3$ to a yellow end point. The following data are used in calculating the percentage of anhydrous dye in the sample:

Molecular weight.. 305.825
Hydrogen equivalents per mole of dye...................... 2
Milliliters of N/10 $TiCl_3$ per gm of dye.................... 65.398

For certification, samples of this stain must contain not less than 50 percent anhydrous dye.

Biological Tests: Toluidine blue O is tested as a metachromatic stain. Paraffin sections of animal tissue are fixed in 10 percent neutral formalin, cold absolute alcohol or Carnoy (absolute alcohol-glacial acetic, 3:1). The paraffin is removed in the usual manner and the sections are stained 1 to 2 min in a fresh 0.1 percent aqueous toluidine blue O (or for 5 to 10 min in a 0.01 percent solution), rinsed in distilled water and a coverslip applied directly from distilled water, blotted around edges of coverslip and sealed with Vaseline or fingernail polish. A satisfactory sample should show metachromatic staining (pink to red to violet) of connective tissue mucins, ground substance of cartilage, mast cell granules and epithelial mucins; and orthochromatic staining (blue) of nuclei and cytoplasm.

It is also tested as a constituent of Albert's diphtheria stain, using the following method: Smears are made and fixed with gentle heat. They are stained 5 min in the following solution: toluidine blue, 0.15 gm; methyl green, 0.02 gm; glacial acetic acid, 1 ml; 95 percent ethyl alcohol, 2 ml; and distilled water, 100 ml. The stain is drained off without washing, and Lugol's iodine solution is applied for 1 min; the smears are then washed briefly in tap water, blotted with filter paper and examined. A good stain shows the granules of the diphtheria bacilli black, the bars of bacilli dark green to black, the body of the cells and other bacteria light green.

Brilliant Cresyl Blue   C. I. NO. 51010

In general, samples of this stain are aminodimethylaminomethyldiphenazonium chlorides, $C_{15}H_{16}N_3OCl$, although the dye is given in the Colour Index as the diethyl derivative.

Absorption Characteristics: Dissolve 50 mg of brilliant cresyl blue in 125 ml of distilled water and then dilute to 250 ml with 95 percent alcohol. Dilute 5 ml of this solution to 200 ml with 50 percent alcohol. Read in a spectrophotometer in a 1-cm cell. Absorption maximum 626–630 mμ; ratio P − 15/P + 15 is from 1.05 to 1.24.

Assay: Dissolve 100 mg of dye in 100 ml 95 percent alcohol, add 100 ml of distilled water and 10 gm of sodium bitartrate, heat to boiling and titrate with 0.05 N $TiCl_3$ to the first appearance of a lighter reddish-brown color. The following data are used in calculating the percentage of anhydrous dye.

Molecular weight.. 289.759
Hydrogen equivalents per mole of dye...................... 2
Milliliters of N/10 TiCl₃ per gm of dye.................... 69.023

For certification, samples of this stain must contain not less than 50 percent anhydrous dye.

Biological Test: In testing brilliant cresyl blue, fresh blood is examined under a cover glass on which a filtered 0.3 percent ethyl or methyl alcoholic solution of brilliant cresyl blue has been dried, or blood films are made on similar cover glasses, dried and counterstained with Wright's or similar stain. The reticulum of immature red cells should be a clear-cut blue on a very pale blue (fresh) or eosin colored (stained) background. Blood platelets should stain a pale blue or lilac and be discrete, with only a minimum of precipitate or debris.

NILE BLUE SULFATE (NILE BLUE A)   C. I. NO. 51180

Nile blue A is aminodiethylaminonaphthophenazonium sulfate $(C_{20}H_{20}N_3O)_2SO_4$.

Absorption Characteristics: Dissolve 50 mg of Nile blue sulfate in 125 ml of 95 percent alcohol and then dilute to 250 ml with distilled water. Dilute 3 ml of this solution to 200 ml with 50 percent alcohol. Read in a spectrophotometer in a 1-cm cell. Absorption maximum 635–646 mμ; ratio P − 15/P + 15 is from 1.02 to 1.16.

Assay: Dissolve 100 mg of dye in 100 ml of 95 percent alcohol, add 75 ml of distilled water and 25 ml of 30 percent sodium tartrate solution, heat to boiling and titrate with 0.05 N TiCl₃. It is necessary to keep the solution boiling throughout the reduction, otherwise the reaction is very slow, especially near the end point. The final color change is from reddish brown to yellow. The following data are used in calculating the percentage of anhydrous dye in the original sample:

Molecular weight.. 732.834
Hydrogen equivalents per mole of dye...................... 4
Milliliters of N/10 TiCl₃ per gm of dye.................... 54.584

Samples of this stain should contain not less than 70 percent anhydrous dye.

Biological Test: Nile blue A is tested for differentiation of melanins and lipofuscins in animal tissue. Paraffin sections are fixed in formalin or other appropriate fixatives. Paraffin is removed in the usual manner and the sections are stained 20 min in a solution consisting of 0.05 percent Nile blue A in 1 percent H_2SO_4 (H_2SO_4 98.5 percent, 1 ml; water, 99 ml), washed 10 to 20 min in running water and mounted in glycerol-gelatin. A satisfactory sample shows lipofuscins dark blue or green-blue; melanins dark green; cytoplasm, muscle pale green; red corpuscles greenish yellow to greenish blue; and myelin green to deep blue.

CRESYL VIOLET ACETATE

Cresyl violet acetate is aminonaphthoaminophenazonium acetate, $C_{18}H_{15}N_3O_3$.

Absorption Characteristics: Dissolve 50 mg of cresyl violet acetate in 125 ml of 95 percent alcohol and then dilute to 250 ml with distilled water. Dilute 5 ml of this solution to 200 ml with 50 percent alcohol. Read in a spectrophotometer in a 1-cm cell. Absorption maximum 596–598 mμ; ratio P − 15/P + 15 is from 0.94 to 1.06.

Assay: Dissolve 100 mg of dye in 300 ml of 50 percent alcohol, add 10 gm of sodium bitartrate, heat to boiling and titrate with 0.05 N TiCl$_3$ to a yellow end point. The following data are used in calculating the percentage of anhydrous dye in the sample:

Molecular weight... 321.324
Hydrogen equivalents per mole of dye....................... 2
Milliliters of N/10 TiCl$_3$ per gm of dye................... 62.242

Biological Test: Cresyl violet acetate is tested on formalin or Bouin's fixed spinal cord and brain. Remove paraffin with xylene, hydrate through *n*-butyl alcohol, 95 percent and 70 percent alcohol, wash in distilled water. Stain 20 min in cresyl violet acetate solution, (prepare a stock solution of 100 mg of cresyl violet acetate in 75 ml distilled water then dilute 0.5 ml, 3 ml and 6 ml with 50 ml 0.1 M acetate buffer at pH 3.5. The desired intensity of staining should be obtained in one of these solutions). Rinse very briefly (in and out) in 70 percent alcohol, then with 95 percent alcohol. Complete dehydration in *n*-butyl alcohol with 2 changes for a total of 4 minutes. Clear in xylene and cover in Permount. A satisfactory stain shows nuclei (DNA), blue; Nissl bodies (RNA), purplish blue and background, unstained.

DARROW RED

Darrow red is aminonaphthoacetylaminophenazonium chloride, C$_{18}$H$_{14}$N$_3$O$_2$Cl.

Absorption Characteristics: Dissolve 50 mg of Darrow red in 125 ml of 95 percent alcohol and then dilute to 250 ml with distilled water. Dilute 5 ml of this solution to 200 ml with 50 percent alcohol. Read in a spectrophotometer in a 1-cm cell. Absorption maximum 504 mμ; ratio P − 15/P + 15 is 1.01.

Assay: Dissolve 100 mg of dye in 300 ml of 50 percent alcohol. Add 10 gm of sodium bitartrate, heat to boiling, and titrate with 0.05 N TiCl$_3$ to a yellow end point. The following data are used to calculate the percentage of anhydrous dye in the sample:

Molecular weight... 339.773
Hydrogen equivalents per mole of dye....................... 2
Milliliters of N/10 TiCl$_3$ per gm of dye................... 58.863

Biological Test: Darrow red is tested for the staining of nerve cell bodies in paraffin or frozen sections of formalin-fixed brain and spinal cord. Prepare a staining solution by dissolving 50 mg of Darrow red in 200 ml of 0.2 M acetic acid (pH 2.7), boiling gently for 10 min, then cooling to room temperature and filtering. Stain frozen or decerated and hydrated paraffin sections for 20 to 30 min in the above solution. Rinse in distilled water, and differentiate and dehydrate through 50, 70 and 95 percent alcohols. Complete dehydration in *n*-butyl alcohol, clear in xylene and mount in synthetic resin. A satisfactory stain should show Nissl bodies and nuclear chromatin stained red.

NEUTRAL RED   c. i. no. 50040

Neutral red is aminodimethylaminotoluphenazonium chloride, C$_{15}$H$_{17}$N$_4$Cl.

Absorption Characteristics: Dissolve 50 mg of neutral red in 250 ml of 50 percent alcohol containing 1.25 ml of glacial acetic acid. Dilute 5 ml of this solution to 200 ml with 50 percent alcohol containing 1 ml of glacial acetic acid. Read in a spectrophotometer in a 1-cm cell. Absorption maximum 539–542 mμ; ratio P − 15/P + 15 is from 1.00 to 1.10.

Assay: Spectrophotometric. Percentage of dye = D-peak × 132. D-peak (color density at peak) is measured on dye solution described under "Absorption characteristics."

For certification, samples of this stain must contain not less than 50 percent anhydrous dye.

Biological Test: Neutral red is tested for supravital staining of living blood cells, in the same procedure used for Janus green B, p. 281.

SAFRANIN O   C. I. NO. 50240

Safranin is a mixture of diaminophenylditolazonium chloride, $C_{20}H_{19}N_4Cl$ and diamino-o-tolylditolazonium chloride, $C_{21}H_{21}N_4Cl$.

Absorption Characteristics: Dissolve 50 mg of safranin O in 250 ml of 50 percent alcohol. Dilute 3 ml of this solution to 200 ml with 50 percent alcohol. Read in a spectrophotometer in a 1-cm cell. Absorption maximum 530–533 mμ; ratio P − 15/P + 15 is from 1.10 to 1.32.

Assay: Spectrophotometric. Percentage of dye = D-peak × 231. D-peak (color density at peak) is measured on dye solution described under "Absorption characteristics."

For certification, samples of this stain must contain not less than 80 percent anhydrous dye.

Biological Test: Safranin is tested as a chromosome stain in the Flemming triple stain and in combination with light green SF yellowish or fast green FCF, also the Gram stain. The procedures for the Flemming stain are the same as described below under crystal violet (p. 302). The procedure with fast green or light green as a stain is given on p. 298.

NIGROSIN, WATER SOLUBLE   C. I. NO. 50420

Nigrosin water soluble is the sodium salt of the product resulting from the sulfonation of spirit soluble nigrosin which is obtained by the interaction of aniline, aniline hydrochloride and nitrophenol (or nitrobenzene and iron).

Absorption characteristics: Dissolve 50 mg of nigrosin in 250 ml of 50 percent alcohol. Dilute 25 ml of this solution to 200 ml with 50 percent alcohol. Read in a spectrophotometer in a 1-cm cell. Absorption maximum 575–600 mμ; ratio P − 15/P + 15 is from 0.94 to 1.00.

Assay: Since this dye is a variable mixture of complex compounds of unknown constitution, quantitative determination of the dye content is impossible.

Biological Test: Nigrosin is tested in Dorner's spore stain, using a 2- to 4-day-old culture of some rapid spore-former such as *Bacillus cereus*.

A heavy suspension of the organism is made in 2 to 3 drops of distilled water in a small test tube, and an equal quantity of freshly filtered Ziehl's carbol fuchsin is added. This mixture is allowed to stand in a boiling water bath 10 min or longer. On a cover slip or slide, one loopful of the stained preparation is mixed with a loopful of a 5 to 10 percent aqueous nigrosin. (This solution must be filtered before use, and may be kept indefinitely if preserved with a few drops of formalin.) It is smeared as thinly as possible and allowed to dry fairly rapidly. A good sample shows the spores red, the vegetative cells unstained, and the background dark gray.

THE DIPHENYL METHANE DERIVATIVES

AURAMINE O   C. I. NO. 41000

Auramine O has the empirical formula $C_{17}H_{22}N_3Cl$.

Absorption Characteristics: Dissolve 50 mg of auramine O in 250 ml of distilled water. Dilute 5 ml of this solution to 200 ml with distilled water. Read in a spectrophotometer in a 1-cm cell. Absorption maximum 431–432 mμ; ratio P $-$ 15/ P $+$ 15 is from 1.02 to 1.09.

Assay: Spectrophotometric. Percentage of dye = D-peak $\times$ 131. D-peak (color density at peak) is measured on dye solution described under "Absorption characteristics."

Samples of this stain must contain not less than 80 percent anhydrous dye.

Biological Test: Auramine O is tested for acid-fast bacteria in sputum. Smears from sputum are air-dried and are stained 2 to 3 min in the staining solution (auramine O, 0.1 gm; liquified phenol, 3 ml; distilled water, 97 ml), washed in tap water, destained 3 to 5 min in freshly prepared solution containing 100 ml 70 percent ethyl alcohol, 0.5 ml conc. HCl, 0.5 gm NaCl and dried. The smears are examined under a monocular microscope, using 8 mm dry objective and a 20× ocular. Illumination should be a low voltage, high amperage microscope lamp, or a mercury arc (AH3, AH4 or HBo-200) supplied with a blue (ultraviolet transmitting) filter (Corning #5-58, or equivalent), and a complementary yellow filter (Corning #3-75, or equivalent) for the ocular. Acid-fast bacteria should be bright yellow, fluorescent, other organisms not visible and background nearly black.

THE TRIPHENYL METHANE DERIVATIVES

MALACHITE GREEN   C. I. NO. 42000

Malachite green is the chloride or oxalate of p,p'-tetramethyldiamino-triphenyl-carbinol anhydride, $C_{23}H_{25}N_2Cl$ or $2C_{23}H_{25}N_2 + 3C_2H_2O_4$.

Absorption Characteristics: Dissolve 50 mg of malachite green in 250 ml of distilled water. Dilute 3 ml of this solution to 200 ml with distilled water. Read in a spectrophotometer in a 1-cm cell. Absorption maximum 617–620 mμ; ratio P $-$ 15/P $+$ 15 is from 1.01 to 1.11. To differentiate between the chloride and the oxalate, dissolve approximately 0.1 gm of the dye in 50 ml of cold water and precipitate the dye base by the addition of a slight excess of dilute NaOH. Filter off the base and divide the filtrate into two parts. Heat one part to boiling and add dilute $Ca(OH)_2$ solution. A fine white crystalline precipitate indicates that the original dye was the oxalate. Make the other portion of the filtrate slightly acid with dilute HNO_3 and if a copious white precipitate is obtained upon addition of dilute $AgNO_3$, the original dye contained chloride.

Assay: Dissolve 200 mg of dye in 120 ml of distilled water, add 50 ml alcohol, 10 ml of glacial acetic acid and 30 ml of 30 percent sodium tartrate solution, heat to boiling and titrate slowly with 0.05 N TiCl$_3$ to a light straw color. The following data are used in calculating the percentage of anhydrous dye in the sample:

(1) Molecular weight, C$_{23}$H$_{25}$N$_2$Cl................................ 364.903
    Hydrogen equivalents per mole of dye.................... 2
    Milliliters of N/10 TiCl$_3$ per gm of dye.................... 54.810
(2) Molecular weight, 2C$_{23}$H$_{25}$N$_2$ + 3C$_2$H$_2$O$_4$................ 929.000
    Hydrogen equivalents per mole of dye.................... 4
    Milliliters of N/10 TiCl$_3$ per gm of dye.................... 43.057

Samples of this stain should contain not less than 75 percent anhydrous dye (if the chloride) or not less than 90 percent dye (if the oxalate).

Biological Test: Malachite green is tested as a counterstain on botanical material (preferably plant pathological material) after fixation in a suitable fixative (e.g., Flemming's, Carnoy's or Farmer's fluid) and embedding in paraffin. The paraffin is removed in the usual manner, and sections are stained 20 min in 1 percent aqueous safranin O, washed in distilled water. Apply a few drops of 0.5 percent malachite green in 95 percent alcohol for 20 sec, pour off stain, rinse quickly with 1 drop of 100 percent alcohol, clear in xylene and mount. When used on plant pathological material, the nuclei, xylem, cutinized walls and the nuclei of infecting fungus should appear red. The cytoplasm and cellulose walls of the host should appear green.

It is also tested in the Schaeffer and Fulton spore stain for bacteria and in Conklin's modification of the method. For the former, bacterial smears are fixed in a flame and flooded with 5 percent aqueous malachite green for 30 to 60 sec, then heated to steaming three or four times. They are washed in water 30 sec and 0.5 percent aqueous safranin is added for 30 sec; they are then washed and blotted dry. The spores should be green, the rest of the cells red.

For the latter method, bacterial smears are fixed in a flame and flooded with 5 percent aqueous malachite green and allowed to steam 10 min. The slides are washed in running water 30 sec and counterstained 1 min with 5 percent aqueous mercurochrome, washed in tap water and blotted dry. The spores should be green, the rest of the cells red.

BRILLIANT GREEN   C. I. NO. 42040

Brilliant green is the acid sulfate of p,p'-tetraethyldiaminotriphenylcarbinol anhydride, C$_{27}$H$_{33}$N$_2$SO$_4$H.

Absorption Characteristics: Dissolve 50 mg of brilliant green in 250 ml of 50 percent alcohol. Dilute 3 ml of this solution to 200 ml with 50 percent alcohol. Read in a spectrophotometer in a 1-cm cell. Absorption maximum 628–632 mμ; ratio P − 15/P + 15 is from 0.94 to 1.12.

Assay: Dissolve 100 mg of dye in 100 ml of 95 percent alcohol, add 100 ml of distilled water and 15 gm of sodium bitartrate, heat to boiling and titrate with 0.05 N TiCl$_3$ to a pale yellow end point. The following data are used in calculating the percentage of anhydrous dye:

Molecular weight... 482.618
Hydrogen equivalents per mole of dye...................... 2
Milliliters of N/10 TiCl$_3$ per gm of dye...................... 41.440

For certification, samples of this stain must contain not less than 85 percent anhydrous dye.

Biological Test: Brilliant green is tested as to its suitability for determining the presence of the colon organism in drinking water. The object of the dye is to prevent formation of gas by the bacillus of gas gangrene, *Bacillus welchii*. For this purpose standard methods prescribe a medium containing 2 percent dried oxgall with a 1/75,000 dilution of brilliant green after addition to the water to be tested. In testing a dye sample, varying amounts of brilliant green are added to the bile medium for one series of tests, using a sufficient variety of solutions to be certain of growth in the most dilute and absence of growth in the most concentrated. A second series of tests is set up with varying dilutions of pure cultures of the colon organism (*Escherichia coli*) on the standard medium as above mentioned, while another comparison is made in standard lactose broth. A satisfactory sample should allow 10 percent gas production in 1 to 3 days by the colon organism, but not by *Bacillus welchii* at the dilution called for in the standard medium. The object of the long series of tests is to check up on the delicacy of the medium as used, and on the effect of varying the quantities of brilliant green.

It is also tested as a bacteriostatic agent by the following technic:

Make three daily transfers at 37° C of a spore-former (e.g., *Bacillus cereus*) and of two members of the colon-typhoid group (including *Escherichia coli*) into a broth containing 1 percent peptone and 1 percent lactose. As soon as distinct turbidity appears in the third transfer (3 to 6 hr incubation), make a microscopic count of the organisms, with the use of a hemocytometer; (it is desirable to have the count between 4 and 20 million per ml). Dilute with the above-mentioned broth so that the concentration of bacteria is approximately 200 per ml. Meanwhile make a 0.01 percent solution of the sample to be tested and of a check batch of brilliant green (known to have the correct bacteriostatic titer) by adding 10 mg dye to a 100 ml volumetric flask not quite full of distilled water and bringing up to the volume mark. Allow to stand over night. From this flask prepare 0.001 percent, 0.0001 percent and 0.00001 percent solutions. Fill a series of test tubes with 7.5 ml of a broth containing 1.33 percent peptone and 1.33 percent lactose, and divide into three lots, one intended for each of the three test organisms. To each of these three series of tubes add varying quantities of the dye by introducing, with a pipet, 0.2 to 2.0 ml of the four above-mentioned dilutions; then bring the total volume in each tube up to 9.5 ml by adding distilled water and mixing thoroughly. (In this way final dilutions from 1:50,000 to 1:500,000,000 may be obtained, although a partial set of them can be selected for each particular organism, from 1:5,000,000 to 1:100,000,000 for the spore-former and from 1:50,000 to 1:2,000,000 for the others.) Sterilize the tubes in the autoclave and cool to room temperature. Inoculate each set of the tubes containing broth and diluted dye with the proper culture, using 0.5 ml of the diluted culture (i.e., approximately 100 organisms) per tube. Mix each tube well and incubate at 37° C. Examine for growth on the 1st, 2nd and 4th days.

A satisfactory sample should show bacteriostatic action on all three organisms sufficiently like that of the check sample so that the first dilution permitting growth will not be more than two stages apart from it in the above series of final dilutions.

Fast Green FCF   c. i. no. 42053

Fast green FCF is the disodium salt of p,p'-dibenzyldiethyldiamino-p''-hydroxy-triphenylcarbinol trisulfonic acid anhydride, $C_{37}H_{34}O_{10}N_2S_3Na_2$.

Absorption Characteristics: Dissolve 50 mg of fast green in 250 ml of 50 percent alcohol. Dilute 3 ml of this solution to 200 ml with 50 percent alcohol. Read in a spectrophotometer in a 1-cm cell. Absorption maximum 624–626 mμ; ratio P − 15/ P + 15 is from 1.00 to 1.16.

Assay: Dissolve 200 mg of dye in 200 ml of distilled water, add 3 gm of sodium bitartrate, heat on a hotplate to 90° C and turn off hotplate. When the temperature reaches 95° C titrate with 0.05 N $TiCl_3$. The end point varies in color from yellow to reddish brown. The following data are used in calculating the percentage of anhydrous dye in the original sample:

Molecular weight. 808.850
Hydrogen equivalents per mole of dye.   2
Milliliters of N/10 $TiCl_3$ per gm of dye. 24.727

Samples of this stain should contain not less than 85 percent anhydrous dye.

Biological Test: Fast green is tested for use as a cytological counterstain. Sections of root tips or buds are fixed in Flemming's fluid or in craf and are stained in 1 percent aqueous safranin for from 30 to 50 minutes, rinsed in distilled water and differentiated with 0.2 percent fast green in 95 percent alcohol until the chromatin and nucleoli remain red. The slides are then passed through absolute alcohol to xylene and mounted in balsam. Chromosomes and other chromatin bodies as well as nucleoli and lignified walls should appear bright red, while the spindles, cellulose walls, and cytoplasm are green.

Light Green SF Yellowish   c. i. no. 42095

Light green SF yellowish is the disodium salt of p,p'-dibenzyldiethyldiamino-triphenylcarbinol trisulfonic acid anhydride, $C_{37}H_{34}N_2O_9S_3Na_2$.

Absorption Characteristics: Dissolve 50 mg of light green in 250 ml of distilled water. Dilute 5 ml of this solution to 200 ml with distilled water. Read in a spectrophotometer in a 1-cm cell. Absorption maximum 629–634 mμ; ratio P − 15/ P + 15 is from 0.96 to 1.10.

Assay: Dissolve 200 mg of dye in 200 ml of distilled water, add 10 gm of sodium bitartrate, heat on a hotplate to 60° C and turn off hotplate. When the temperature reaches 65° C titrate with 0.05 N $TiCl_3$. The end point is a sharp change from light green to yellow. The following data are used in calculating the percentage of anhydrous dye in the original sample:

Molecular weight. 792.850
Hydrogen equivalents per mole of dye.   2
Milliliters of N/10 $TiCl_3$ per gm of dye. 25.226

Samples of this stain should contain not less than 65 percent anhydrous dye.

Biological Test: Light green is tested by the same procedure as fast green (above).

Basic Fuchsin

c. i. no. 42500 (pararosanilin); 42510 (rosanilin)

Stains marketed under the name of basic fuchsin may be either the chloride or acetate of pure* pararosanilin, or mixtures of it with the higher homologs. Rosanilin (the base) is triaminodiphenyltolylcarbinol. Its chloride has the formula, $C_{20}H_{20} \cdot N_3Cl$, its acetate is $C_{20}H_{20}N_3 \cdot C_2H_3O_2$. Pararosanilin (the base) is triaminotriphenylcarbinol. Its chloride has the formula, $C_{19}H_{18}N_3Cl$, and its acetate is $C_{19}H_{18}N_3 \cdot C_2H_3O_2$. To test for acetate, add 1 ml of 6 N H_2SO_4 to 2.0 gm of the dye dissolved in 5 ml of distilled water, and heat. The odor of acetic acid escaping from the hot mixture indicates the presence of acetate in the original sample; if not present the sample can be assumed to be the chloride.

Absorption Characteristics: Dissolve 50 mg of basic fuchsin in 125 ml of 95 percent alcohol and dilute to 250 ml with distilled water. Dilute 3 ml of this solution to 200 ml with 50 percent alcohol. Read in a spectrophotometer in a 1-cm cell. Absorption maxima; pararosanilin 545–546 mμ; rosanilin 549–550 mμ; ratio P − 15/P + 15 for pararosanilin is 1.21 to 1.34, for rosanilin 1.16 to 1.35.

Assay: Spectrophotometric. Percentage of dye (pararosanilin acetate) = D-peak × 129. Percentage of dye (rosanilin chloride) = D-peak × 122. D-peak (color density at peak) is measured on dye solution described under "Absorption characteristics."

For certification, samples of this stain should contain not less than 88 percent anhydrous dye.

Decolorization Test: Dissolve 0.5 gm of the dye in 100 ml of boiling distilled water, cool to 50° C, filter into a small flask and add 10 ml of N hydrochloric acid to the filtrate. Add 0.5 gm of potassium metabisulfite, $K_2S_2O_5$, shake until dissolved, stopper tightly and allow to stand in the dark for 12 to 18 hr. The solution is colorless, or not more than pale yellow. (A yellowish orange, yellowish brown or brown solution, especially in the presence of a dark sediment, indicates the poorer grades of fuchsin.)

Biological Test: Basic fuchsin is tested for several purposes: (1) For use as a stain for the tubercle organism; (2) for use in the Endo medium for distinguishing between the coli and aerogenes types of bacteria; (3) for use in the periodic acid-Schiff (PAS) method; (4) for use in the Feulgen stain.

(1) In testing as a stain for the tubercle organism, smears are covered with carbol fuchsin (1 part of 3 percent alcoholic fuchsin to 9 parts of 5 percent aqueous phenol) and heated on a water bath for 3 to 5 min. They are then rinsed in tap water and differentiated in 70 percent alcohol containing 3 percent hydrochloric acid until practically no red color remains visible to the naked eye. They are again rinsed in tap water; rinsed once more and counterstained with dilute (i.e., about 0.1 percent) aqueous methylene blue for 1 min. The slides are then rinsed in tap water and dried and examined under the microscope. The tubercle organisms should be distinctly red, while other bacteria, leucocytes and debris appear blue.

* "Pure" is used here in the sense of freedom from homologous dyes, and not in the sense of freedom from such impurities as inorganic salts, colorless organic substances, and sometimes subsidiary dyes.

(2) In testing for use in the Endo medium, three separate solutions of the sample to be tested are prepared: saturated alcoholic; 1 percent alcoholic; and 3 percent alcoholic. Of these solutions, 0.5 ml of the first and 1 ml of each of the others are mixed separately with 0.125 gm of anhydrous sodium sulfite dissolved in 5 ml of hot distilled water. The tests are carried out separately with each of these three solutions; good results must be obtained with at least one of them. The solution should be a faint pink or straw color, or sometimes light brown, but without noticeable precipitate. This decolorized solution is added to 100 ml of melted lactose agar of the standard formula. The color of this medium should then be a light pink, which fades almost entirely upon cooling. Before cooling it is poured into a Petri dish and allowed to harden. The surface is then streaked in parallel lines with *Escherichia coli* and *Aerobacter aerogenes* and allowed to incubate for 24 hr. A good sample should show red growth with a strong metallic sheen for the former organism, pink growth without metallic sheen for the latter, and no reddening of the medium except where growth has occurred.

(3) It is also tested in the periodic acid leucofuchsin (PAS) method on Zenker, formalin, or Bouin-fixed animal tissues. Paraffin sections are decerated and hydrated as usual, then rinsed in tap water and oxidized 10 min in 1 percent periodic acid, washed 5 min in running tap water and stained 10 min in Schiff's reagent (basic fuchsin, 1 gm; distilled water, 80 ml; $NaHSO_3$, 2 gm (or $Na_2S_2O_5$, 1.9 gm); N HCl, 20 ml. After shaking at intervals for 2 hr, 500 mg finely powdered fresh charcoal are added, the mixture shaken 1 min and filtered. The filtrate should be clear and colorless. Sections are then passed directly to 3 successive baths of 2 min each in $M/20$ (0.52 percent) $NaHSO_3$, washed 10 min in running water, stained 1 to 2 min in acid hemalum and washed in tap water. The sections are then dehydrated in 2 changes each of 95 percent and 100 percent alcohol and cleared through 100 percent alcohol-xylene (1:1) and 2 changes of xylene and mounted in clarite. A satisfactory stain should show collagen, pink to red; basement membranes, purplish red; epithelial mucin, red-purple to violet; glycogen, dark purplish red; nuclei, blue; cytoplasm, gray.

(4) In testing for its behavior in the Feulgen stain, the procedure followed is to test the stain on properly prepared sections from which the paraffin has been removed in the usual manner; these sections are rinsed in cold N HCl, placed 4 to 5 min in N HCl at 60° C, and then rinsed in cold N HCl, and finally in distilled water. If the sections are of animal tissue they are then stained 2 hr, or if plant tissue 3 to 5 hr, in the above Schiff's reagent. The sections, after remaining for the specified time in this solution, are drained and passed for 10 min each into three successive baths containing N HCl, 10 percent $K_2S_2O_5$, and distilled water in the proportion of 5:5:100 by volume (carrying out this step in closed jars); they are then put in tap water for 10 min, rinsed in distilled water and counterstained in 1 percent aqueous orange G for $1\frac{1}{2}$ to 2 min (for animal tissue) or 0.1 percent alcoholic light green for 30 to 60 sec (for plant tissue), dehydrated, cleared and mounted. A good sample should show nuclei stained magenta, and cytoplasm green or orange depending on counterstain.

"SPECIAL" BASIC FUCHSIN FOR FLAGELLA STAINING

Samples sold under this designation are presumed to be mixtures of pararosanilin acetate and chloride in the proportion of 3:1 by weight, as recommended by Leifson (1951).

Biological Test: They are tested by Leifson's method: Treat slides 1 week in K_2CrO_4 in conc. H_2SO_4, washed thoroughly with final rinsing in distilled water, drained dry, held in colorless flame for few seconds, cooled, making a heavy wax line across middle and along margin to distal half. A loopful of sediment from a centrifuged 24-hr broth culture of a motile species of bacteria is placed at end of slide; tilted, causing liquid to flow to opposite wax line; and air dried. There is quickly added 1 ml of stain mixture (equal proportions of the following 3 solutions mixed together: 1.5 percent NaCl in distilled water; 3 percent tannic acid in distilled water; 1.2 percent of sample in 95 percent alcohol). After 5 to 15 min at room temperature, slide is rinsed with tap water under faucet, but without pouring stain off before rinsing. Drain dry. Satisfactory sample should show the flagella bright red.

METHYL VIOLET 2B   c. i. no. 42535

Methyl violet 2B is a mixture of the more highly methylated fuchsins, principally pentamethylpararosanilin chloride, that is, the chloride of pentamethyltriamino-triphenylcarbinol anhydride. For purposes of estimation the formula $C_{24}H_{28}N_3Cl$ is employed.

Absorption Characteristics: Dissolve 50 mg of methyl violet 2B in 250 ml of 50 percent alcohol. Dilute 2 ml of this solution to 200 ml with 50 percent alcohol. Read in a spectrophotometer in a 1-cm cell. Absorption maximum 583–587 mμ; ratio P $-$ 15/P $+$ 15 is from 1.07 to 1.18.

Assay: Spectrophotometric. Percentage of dye = D-peak $\times$ 207. D-peak (color density at peak) is measured on dye solution described under "Absorption characteristics."

Samples of this stain should contain not less than 75 percent anhydrous dye.

Biological Test: Methyl violet 2B is tested by the same procedures as crystal violet, C. I. No. 42555, but omitting the Gram stain. Results should be the same except that the violet color obtained is of a redder hue.

CRYSTAL VIOLET   c. i. no. 42555

Crystal violet is the chloride of hexamethylpararosanilin, that is, hexamethyl-triaminotriphenylcarbinol anhydride, $C_{25}H_{30}N_3Cl$.

Absorption Characteristics: Dissolve 50 mg of crystal violet in 250 ml of distilled water. Dilute 2 ml of this solution to 200 ml with distilled water. Read in a spectrophotometer in a 1-cm cell. Absorption maximum 589–593 mμ; ratio P $-$ 15/ P $+$ 15 is from 0.98 to 1.19.

Assay: Spectrophotometric. Percentage of dye = D-peak $\times$ 209. D-peak (color density at peak) is measured on dye solution described under "Absorption characteristics."

For certification, samples of this stain must contain not less than 88 percent anhydrous dye.

Biological Test: Crystal violet is tested in three procedures: (1) the Gram stain; (2) the Flemming triple stain; (3) followed by iodine in the staining of cytological preparations.

(1) In testing crystal violet for staining bacteria by the Gram technic, the sample is made up in an ammonium oxalate solution consisting of 2 gm of crystal violet in 20 ml 95 percent alcohol, and mixed with 80 ml of 1 percent aqueous ammonium oxalate. Bacterial smears are stained by the following procedure: Crystal violet 1 min, wash in tap water 1 to 5 sec, Lugol's iodine (1 gm of iodine, 2 gm of KI in 300 ml of distilled water) solution 1 min, wash in tap water and blot dry, 95 percent alcohol 30 sec, blot dry, safranin O (0.25 gm of safranin O in 10 ml of 95 percent alcohol and 100 ml of distilled water) 10 sec, tap water 1 to 5 sec, and dry. A satisfactory sample should show Gram-positive organisms, purple and Gram-negative organisms, red.

(2) In testing the sample in the Flemming stain, the following procedure is followed: Root tips or buds, fixed in Flemming's fluid or CRAF, are embedded in paraffin and sectioned. Sections are stained for 20 min to 1 hr in 1 percent aqueous safranin, rinsed in distilled water, stained from 2 to 30 min in a 1 percent solution of the sample being tested, again rinsed in distilled water, dehydrated in 95 percent and absolute alcohol, differentiated in a 0.25 percent solution of orange G in clove oil about 15 min, cleared in xylene and mounted in Canada balsam. A good stain should show red chromosomes and nucleoli, while metabolic chromatin should stain a deep purple on an orange cytoplasm.

(3) In the test with iodine, paraffin sections of root tips or buds (fixed in Navashin's fluid or one of its modifications) are stained for 5 min in a 1 percent aqueous solution of the dye, rinsed in distilled water, and treated for 15 to 50 sec in equal parts of 1 percent iodine in 80 percent alcohol and 1 percent potassium iodide in 80 percent alcohol. They are next rinsed in absolute alcohol and differentiated in a saturated solution of orange G in clove oil for 1 to 2 min and cleared in xylene and mounted. By this technic, chromatin and nucleoli should stand out a deep violet on a light orange protoplasm.

METHYL GREEN, (ETHYL GREEN)   C. I. NO. 42590

This methyl green is the zinc chloride double salt of ethylhexamethylpararosanilin chlorobromide, $C_{27}H_{35}N_3ClBr + ZnCl_2$.

Absorption Characteristics: Dissolve 50 mg of methyl green in 250 ml of distilled water. Dilute 10 ml of this solution to 200 ml with distilled water. Read in a spectrophotometer in a 1-cm cell. Absorption maximum 630–634 mμ; ratio $P - 15/P + 15$ is from 0.86 to 1.01. Dilute solution just prior to reading because of instability of solution. Take peak readings first then ratio points as rapidly as possible.

Assay: Dissolve 200 mg of dye in 100 ml of 95 percent alcohol. Add 75 ml of distilled water and 25 ml of 30 percent sodium tartrate solution, heat to boiling and titrate with 0.05 N TiCl$_3$ to a greenish-yellow end point. The following data are used to calculate the percentage of anhydrous dye:

Molecular weight.. 653.241

Hydrogen equivalents per mole of dye...................... 2

Milliliters of N/10 TiCl₃ per gm of dye.................... 30.617

For certification, samples of this stain must contain not less than 65 percent anhydrous dye.

Biological Test: Methyl green is tested as a counterstain in Altmann's aniline acid fuchsin technique for mitochondria after fixation in Regaud's or formalin followed by potassium dichromate. The staining solution is prepared as follows: To 25 ml of distilled water, add a few drops of aniline oil, shake vigorously and filter. Dissolve 1 gm acid fuchsin in 10 ml of aniline water and filter into dropping bottle. The paraffin is removed from sections in the usual manner. The sections are covered with a few drops of the stain, heated to steaming, then allowed to cool and staining continued 4 to 6 min, draining and washing for 3 min in distilled water; counterstained about 5 to 60 sec with 1 percent aqueous methyl green (time in methyl green must be adjusted to give adequate counterstaining without excessive extraction of acid fuchsin). Slides are drained and plunged into 95 percent alcohol for 1 sec, rinsed in absolute alcohol, cleared in toluene and mounted in balsam. A satisfactory sample should show mitochondria and zymogen granules, red; nuclei, green.

It is also tested in Taft's methyl green-pyronin stain. See Pyronin Y, p. 309.

ACID FUCHSIN
C. I. NO. 42685

Acid fuchsin should be the disodium salt of the trisulfonic acid of rosanilin or pararosanilin or mixtures of these two. Some samples may contain the mono or disodium salts of the disulfonic acid or the trisodium salt of the trisulfonic acid, but if such is the case they are not nearly as satisfactory as those which contain only the disodium trisulfonate. Samples of acid fuchsin are considered for analytical purposes as a mixture of equal parts of trisulfonated rosanilin and pararosanilin, unless specific information concerning the character of the fuchsin used for the starting material has been obtained from the dye manufacturer.

Andrade Indicator: Acid fuchsin is tested as to its behavior in the Andrade indicator as follows: A 0.2 percent solution of the dye in 100 ml of distilled water is decolorized by adding normal NaOH a little at a time. Complete decolorization should be brought about without the use of more than 25 ml of the sodium hydroxide.

Absorption Characteristics: Dissolve 50 mg of acid fuchsin in 250 ml of distilled water. Dilute 5 ml of this solution and 5 ml of 0.1 N HCl to 200 mμ with distilled water. Read in a spectrophotometer in a 1-cm cell. Absorption maximum for pararosanilin 540–544 mμ, for rosanilin 545–548 mμ; ratio P $-$ 15/P $+$ 15 if from 1.13 to 1.26 for pararosanilin, from 1.12 to 1.26 for rosanilin.

Assay: Spectrophotometric. Percentage of dye (for pararosanilin) = D-peak $\times$ 142. Percentage of dye (for rosanilin) = D-peak $\times$ 151. D-peak (color density at peak) is measured on dye solution described under "Absorption characteristics."

For certification, samples of this stain must contain not less than 55 percent anhydrous dye.

Biological Test: Acid fuchsin is tested in the Van Gieson connective tissue stain on animal tissue fixed in formalin or other suitable fixing fluid and embedded in paraffin. The paraffin is removed in the usual manner: the sections are stained deeply in alum-hematoxylin or Weigert's iron-hematoxylin (Zenker-fixed, 1 hr; formalin-fixed, 1 to 5 min), washed in tap water and stained 3 to 5 min in Van Gieson's solution, (5 ml of 1 percent aqueous acid fuchsin and 100 ml of saturated aqueous picric acid). They are then quickly washed in tap water, differentiated in 95 percent alcohol, dehydrated, cleared and mounted in balsam. The tissue elements stained by the acid fuchsin should show a clear red, contrasting well with hematoxylin and picric acid. A good sample does not show great tendency to fade.

Acid fuchsin is also tested in the aniline blue connective tissue stain on animal tissue fixed in Zenker's fluid and embedded in paraffin. The paraffin is removed in the usual manner and the sections are stained in a 0.5 percent aqueous acid fuchsin for 1 to 5 min or longer, depending on the freshness of the tissue. The sections are transferred directly to the following solution (aniline blue W.S., 0.5 gm; orange G, 2.0 gm; 1 percent aqueous phosphotungstic acid, 100 ml) for 20 min or longer, dehydrated in several changes of 95 percent alcohol, then absolute alcohol, cleared in xylene and mounted in balsam. A satisfactory sample shows: nuclei, red; cytoplasm, pink; collagen and mucin, blue.

ANILINE BLUE, WATER SOLUBLE   C. I. NO. 42755

Aniline blue consists of mixtures of the various sulfonation products of variable mixtures of phenylated rosanilin and pararosanilin, usually the latter.

Absorption Characteristics: Dissolve 50 mg of aniline blue in 250 ml of distilled water. Dilute 10 ml of this solution and 10 ml of 0.1 N HCl to 200 ml with distilled water. Read in a spectrophotometer in a 1-cm cell. Absorption maximum 595–610 mμ; ratio P $-$ 15/P $+$ 15 is from 0.98 to 1.09.

Assay: Dissolve 200 mg of dye in 175 ml of distilled water, add 25 ml of pH 4.5 acetate buffer, heat to boiling and titrate with 0.05 N TiCl$_3$. The end point will vary from yellow to dark yellow-green. Specifications have been made which place the minimum TiCl$_3$ consumption per gm of dye at 12.0 ml of 0.1 N solution.

Decolorization Test: To 100 ml of a 0.01 percent solution of the dye add 2 ml of N NaOH. The color should turn red immediately, fading after 10 minutes to a straw color, and after 20 min should become almost colorless. (Some good samples become colorless in 10 min.) Addition of a few drops of normal acid should restore the blue color almost instantly.

Biological Test: Aniline blue is tested in Mallory's connective tissue stain on animal tissue fixed in Zenker's fluid and embedded in celloidin or paraffin. The procedure followed is the one given under acid fuchsin (above). With a good sample, the collagen fibrils, reticulum, amyloid, and mucus stain blue.

THE FLUORAN DERIVATIVES

The fluoran derivatives are readily reduced by titanous chloride and excellent checks are obtained in duplicate reductions, but due to the heterogeneous character of some of the commercial samples of the halogenated dyes of this group, large errors in the indicated dye content are encountered. It has been found that the dye content of these samples may be determined more accurately and conveniently by the conversion of the dye into the form of the insoluble color acid.

Certain members of this group are used as biological stains, but as there is considerable difference in the purpose for which the various members of the group are employed, different biological tests are necessary for each of the dyes listed. The biological tests employed at the present time are given for all these dyes, with the single exception of fluorescein.

The following methods, employed for the standardization of the fluorans, include (1) the identification or qualitative examination; (2) the quantitative analysis; and (3) the biological tests for each individual dye.

Eosin Yellowish c. i. no. 45380

Eosin yellowish (eosin Y) is the sodium salt of tetrabromofluorescein, $C_{20}H_6O_5Br_4Na_2$.

Absorption Characteristics: Dissolve 50 mg of eosin Y in 250 ml of distilled water. Dilute 5 ml of this solution and 2 ml of 1 percent Na_2CO_3 solution to 200 ml with distilled water. Read in a spectrophotometer in a 1-cm cell. Absorption maximum 515–517 mμ; ratio P − 15/P + 15 is from 1.21 to 1.77.

Assay: Spectrophotometric. Percentage of dye = D-peak × 147. D-peak (color density at peak) is measured on dye solution described under "Absorption characteristics."

For certification, samples must contain not less than 80 percent anhydrous dye.

Biological Test: Eosin Y is tested for four biological purposes: as a counterstain against hematoxylin, as a constituent of Wright's stain, in a modified Nocht's method (see Azure A, p. 289) and in the eosin-methylene-blue medium.

As a counterstain to Delafield's hematoxylin, Zenker's fixed material is used and embedded in paraffin (see Hematoxylin, p. 311, for details).

In the preparation of Wright's stain, add 0.5 gm of sodium bicarbonate to 100 ml of distilled water in a flask, heat gently and add 0.9 gm of methylene blue. Put in a steamer 1½ hours, shaking occasionally, then cool. Dissolve 0.5 gm of eosin Y in 500 ml of distilled water and filter the methylene blue solution into it. Shake several times during the day and let stand at room temperature over night. The following day, without shaking the flask (till toward the end), filter. Let precipitate dry on paper in 37° C incubator. The staining procedure to be followed is given under Wright's stain, p. 313. In judging a good Wright's stain, special attention is given to the question of whether the red cells show the desired yellow pink and whether all the granules of the various leucocytes are differentially stained.

The eosin-methylene-blue medium is prepared as follows: 1 gm of peptone, 0.2 gm of K_2HPO_4, 1½ gm of agar and 100 ml of distilled water. Dissolve by heat and add 2 ml of 2 percent aqueous eosin Y and 1.3 ml of 0.5 percent aqueous methylene blue. After sterilizing, add 5 ml of sterilized 20 percent aqueous lactose, pour into Petri dishes and inoculate with *Escherichia coli* and *Aerobacter aerogenes* and allow to incubate for 24 hr. A good sample should show red growth with a strong metallic sheen for the former organism, pink growth without metallic sheen for the latter and no reddening of the medium except where growth has occurred.

ETHYL EOSIN   C. I. NO. 45386

Ethyl eosin is the potassium (or sodium) salt of the ethyl ester of tetrabromofluorescein, $C_{22}H_{11}O_5Br_4K$ (or Na).

Absorption Characteristics: Dissolve 50 mg of ethyl eosin in 250 ml of 50 percent alcohol. Dilute 5 ml of this solution and 2 ml of 1 percent Na_2CO_3 solution to 200 ml with 50 percent alcohol. Read in a spectrophotometer in a 1-cm cell. Absorption maximum 531–533 mμ; ratio P − 15/P + 15 is from 1.27 to 1.92.

Assay: Spectrophotometric. Percentage of dye = D-peak × 130. D-peak (color density at peak) is measured on dye solution described under "Absorption characteristics."

For certification, samples must contain not less than 78 percent anhydrous dye.

Biological Test: Ethyl eosin is tested for the demonstration of Negri bodies in the central nervous system of rabid animals. Pieces of the hippocampus major, cortex of cerebrum and cerebellum 3 to 5 mm in thickness, are placed between squares of ordinary writing paper (cut end next to the paper) and are immersed in acetone 2½ to 6 hr. The paper is removed and the fixed tissue is placed in fresh paraffin at 60 to 62° C for 4 hr or overnight. Sections are cut 5 μ thick, floated onto albuminized glass slides and fixed by gentle heat over Bunsen burner, and placed in oven for 1 hr at 60 to 62° C. They are washed in two changes of xylene and passed through two changes of absolute alcohol and two changes of 95 percent, then to distilled water; then stained 1 min in 1 percent ethyl eosin in 95 percent alcohol adjusted to pH 4.6 with 1 ml acetate-acetic acid buffer (sodium acetate, 25 gm; glacial acetic, 5 ml; distilled water, 250 ml). They are then washed in distilled water, stained 1 min in a solution of 0.3 gm of methylene blue in 30 ml of 95 percent alcohol and mixed with 90 ml of distilled water, adjusted to pH 4.6 by adding 1 ml of acetate-acetic acid buffer to 60 ml of staining fluid, washed in distilled water and treated in water acidulated with acetic acid (3 drops of glacial acetic acid to 60 ml of distilled water) until the sections become brownish red, rinsed in distilled water, differentiated by passing slowly through 95 percent alcohol, dehydrated in absolute alcohol, cleared in xylene and mounted. By this technic, the Negri bodies are stained terra cotta to cardinal red, nucleoli are dark blue and the cytoplasm, pale blue with majority of tissue pink.

EOSIN BLUISH   C. I. NO. 45400

Eosin bluish (eosin B) is the sodium salt of dibromodinitrofluorescein,
$$C_{20}H_6N_2O_9Br_2Na_2.$$

Absorption Characteristics: Dissolve 50 mg of eosin B in 250 ml of distilled water. Dilute 5 ml of this solution and 2 ml of 1 percent Na_2CO_3 solution to 200 ml with distilled water. Read in a spectrophotometer in a 1-cm cell. Absorption maximum 512–519 mμ; ratio P − 15/P + 15 is from 1.00 to 1.13.

Assay: Spectrophotometric. Percentage of dye = D-peak × 226. D-peak (color density at peak) is measured on dye solution described under "Absorption characteristics."

Samples of this stain should contain not less than 85 percent anhydrous dye.

Biological Test: Eosin B is tested as a counterstain for hematoxylin by the following technic: Material fixed in either Bouin's fluid or Zenker-formol is embedded in paraffin and cut 10 μ in thickness. Sections are mounted on slides with Mayer's albumin fixative. They are then run down to distilled water, stained for from 5 to 10 min in Mayer's hemalum, dipped once or twice in tap water, then holding them in forceps dipped into the solution of eosin once, twice or three times, dehydrated and mounted.

The solution of eosin is 0.5 percent solution of the stain in 20 percent alcohol. If it overstains, dilute with 2 vol. of distilled water. In going quickly from Mayer's hemalum into the eosin a precipitate is formed in the latter and the color is also precipitated into the tissue so that it does not wash out readily.

Eosin B is also tested in Mallory's phloxine-methylene blue, substituting 2 percent aqueous eosin B for phloxine in this technic. (See phloxine B, p. 308) and in Lillie's modified Nocht's method. (See azure A, p. 289.)

ERYTHROSIN B   C. I. NO. 45430

Erythrosin is the sodium salt of tetraiodofluorescein, $C_{20}H_6O_5I_4Na_2$.

Absorption Characteristics: Dissolve 50 mg of erythrosin B in 250 ml of distilled water. Dilute 5 ml of this solution and 2 ml of 1 percent Na_2CO_3 solution to 200 ml with distilled water. Read in a spectrophotometer in a 1-cm cell. Absorption maximum 524–527 mμ; ratio P $-$ 15/P $+$ 15 is from 1.15 to 1.51.

Assay: Dissolve an accurately weighed sample of about 0.5 gm of the dye to be examined in approximately 500 ml of water, heat to boiling and add slowly with constant stirring, 2 or 3 ml of 6 N hydrochloric acid. Cool the hot solution to room temperature and allow to stand at least 1 or 2 hr. Filter the precipitated color acid on a weighed Gooch crucible, thoroughly wash with a 0.2 percent solution of hydrochloric acid, dry at 110° C, and weigh. Calculate the dye content of the original sample from the weight of the color acid by means of the following formula:

$$\frac{\text{Wt. of color acid} \times 879.922 \times 100}{835.944 \times \text{Wt. of original sample}} = \text{percentage of anhydrous dye.}$$

Note: 879.922 = Molecular weight of erythrosin.
      835.944 = Molecular weight of the color acid of erythrosin.

Samples of this stain should not contain less than 80 percent anhydrous dye.

Biological Test: Erythrosin is tested in the Jackson stain (1926) for plant anatomy. In employing this procedure as a test for erythrosin, plant buds or other botanical material containing both lignified and non-lignified cell walls are fixed in one of the usual fixatives, embedded in paraffin and sectioned. After removing the paraffin they are rinsed with absolute alcohol, then 95 percent alcohol, and stained 15 min in 1 percent aqueous crystal violet. Then, after quickly rinsing in distilled water and dehydrating, they are differentiated 1 to 5 min in a saturated solution of erythrosin in clove oil, cleared in xylene in absolute alcohol, 1:1, passed through xylene and mounted. By this method the non-lignified tissues should stain with erythrosin and the lignified walls with crystal violet.

PHLOXINE B   C. I. NO. 45410

Phloxine B is the sodium salt of tetrabromotetrachlorofluorescein,
$$C_{20}H_2O_5Cl_4Br_4Na_2 .$$

Absorption Characteristics: Dissolve 50 mg of phloxine B in 250 ml of 50 percent alcohol. Dilute 5 ml of this solution and 2 ml of 1 percent Na_2CO_3 solution to 200 ml with 50 percent alcohol. Read in a spectrophotometer in a 1-cm cell. Absorption maximum 546–548 mμ; ratio P $-$ 15/P $+$ 15 is from 1.38 to 2.00.

Assay: Precipitate the color acid of a weighed sample of the dye to be tested by the method outlined for the analysis of erythrosin B. From the weight of the color acid, the dye content of the original sample is calculated by means of the following formula:

$$\frac{\text{Wt. of color acid} \times 829.702 \times 100}{\text{Wt. of the original sample} \times 785.724} = \text{percentage of anhydrous dye.}$$

Note: 829.702 = Molecular weight of phloxine B.
      785.724 = Molecular weight of the color acid of phloxine B.

Samples of this stain should not contain less than 80 percent anhydrous dye.

Biological Test: Phloxine B is tested in Mallory's phloxine-methylene blue stain on paraffin sections of animal tissue fixed in Zenker's. The paraffin is removed in the usual manner and the sections are stained 20 min or longer in a 5 percent aqueous phloxine B, washed in distilled water, stained 30 min in borax methylene blue (methylene blue, 1 gm; borax, 1 gm; distilled water, 100 ml; diluted in proportions of 10 ml to 90 ml distilled water) by pouring the solution on and off several times, washed in distilled water, differentiated and dehydrated in a dish of 95 percent alcohol containing a few drops of 10 percent alcoholic collophonium (rosin). The sections are kept in constant motion so that the decolorization is uniform. Staining is controlled under the microscope; when the pink color has returned to the section and the nuclei are still a deep blue, the dehydration is finished quickly with absolute alcohol, cleared and mounted. The cytoplasm should stain pink in contrast to the blue of the nuclei.

ROSE BENGAL   C. I. NO. 45440

Rose bengal is the sodium salt of tetraiodotetrachlorofluorescein,
$$C_{20}H_2O_5I_4Cl_4Na_2 .$$

Absorption Characteristics: Dissolve 50 mg of rose bengal in 250 ml of distilled water. Dilute 5 ml of this solution and 2 ml of 1 percent Na_2CO_3 solution to 200 ml with distilled water. Read in a spectrophotometer in a 1-cm cell. Absorption maximum 544–550 mμ; ratio P $-$ 15/P $+$ 15 is from 1.21 to 1.74.

Assay: The method for the determination of rose bengal is identical with that of erythrosin B, except that in the calculation of the dye content of the original sample, the following formula is to be used in place of the one given for the after dye.

$$\frac{\text{Wt. of color acid} \times 1017.718 \times 100}{\text{Wt. of original sample} \times 973.740} = \text{percentage of anhydrous dye.}$$

Note: 1017.718 = Molecular weight of rose bengal.

973.740 = Molecular weight of the color acid of rose bengal.

For certification, samples of this stain should contain not less than 80 percent anhydrous dye

Biological Test: Rose bengal is tested in Conn's technic for staining bacteria in soil. The procedure is to stain a dried drop of soil suspension made by mixing soil with 5 to 10 times its weight of 0.015 percent gelatin in distilled water. While on a flat surface over boiling water this film is stained 1 min with 1 percent rose bengal in 5 percent aqueous phenol, containing 0.01 percent, more or less, of $CaCl_2$. The amount of $CaCl_2$ is varied if unsatisfactory results are obtained with 0.01 percent, on the theory that increasing its concentration intensifies the action of the stain. A sample is judged satisfactory which permits a deep staining of the bacteria without sufficient coloring of the soil or dead organic matter to obscure the microorganisms. In making the test, soil known to have an unusually large number of bacteria is employed.

MISCELLANEOUS DYES

PYRONIN Y   C. I. NO. 45005

Pyronin Y is tetramethyldiaminoxanthenyl chloride, $C_{17}H_{19}N_2OCl$.

Absorption Characteristics: Dissolve 50 mg of pyronin Y in 250 ml of 50 percent alcohol. Dilute 5 ml of this solution to 200 ml with 50 percent alcohol. Read in a spectrophotometer in a 1-cm cell. Absorption maximum 546–550 mμ; ratio P − 15/P + 15 is from 1.23 to 1.64.

Assay: Spectrophotometric. Percentage of dye = (D-peak × 100)/1.58. D-peak (color density at peak) is measured on dye solution described under "Absorption characteristics."

For certification, samples of this stain must contain not less than 45 percent anhydrous dye.

Biological Test: Pyronin Y is tested in Taft's methyl green-pyronin stain on liver cells fixed in Carnoy's fluid. Prepare the staining solution as follows: To 100 ml of hot distilled water add an amount of methyl green representing 0.5 gm of pure dye (e.g. if dye content is 80 percent, add 0.625 gm). When cool, extract the solution in separatory funnel with successive 20 to 30 ml aliquots of chloroform until the latter remains colorless or is only slightly tinged with green. Add to the above aqueous solution an amount of pyronin Y representing 0.05 gm of pure dye and shake to dissolve. Store in amber glass stoppered bottle. Solution need not be filtered prior to use. Remove paraffin from sections in the usual manner, stain 3 to 5 min, rinse in distilled water and blot with smooth filter paper. Before completely dry, differentiate at least 2 min in tertiary butyl alcohol-absolute alcohol, 3:1, clear in 2 changes of xylene (5 min each) and mount in synthetic resin. With a good sample the chromatin is blue-green; nucleoli, rose; cytoplasmic granules, dark rose; cytoplasma of plasma cells, dark rose occasionally almost purple; cartilage matrix and mast cell granules, refractile, orange red.

PYRONIN B   C. I. NO. 45010

Pyronin B is tetraethyldiaminoxanthenyl chloride, $C_{21}H_{27}N_2OCl$.

Absorption Characteristics: Dissolve 50 mg of pyronin B in 250 ml of 50 percent alcohol. Dilute 5 ml of this solution to 200 ml with 50 percent alcohol. Read in a spectrophotometer in a 1-cm cell. Absorption maximum 554–556 mμ; ratio P − 15/P + 15 is from 1.40 to 1.61.

Assay: Spectrophotometric. Percentage of dye = (D-peak × 100)/1.74. D-peak (color density at peak) is measured on dye solution described under "Absorption characteristics."

For certification, samples of this stain must contain not less than 30 percent anhydrous dye.

Biological Test: Pyronin B is tested by the same procedure as pyronin Y, except that the initial methyl green solution is prepared in 100 ml M/10 acetate buffer at pH 4.4, and the amount of pyronin B should be equivalent to 0.06 gm of pure dye. Pyronin B gives slight differences in hue.

INDIGO CARMINE (INDIGOTINE)   C. I. NO. 73015

Indigo carmine is the disodium salt of indigotin-5,5′-disulfonic acid,
$$C_{16}H_8N_2O_8S_2Na_2 .$$

Absorption Characteristics: Dissolve 50 mg of indigo carmine in 250 ml of distilled water. Dilute 10 ml of this solution to 200 ml with distilled water. Read in a spectrophotometer in a 1-cm cell. Absorption maximum 608–612 mμ; ratio P − 15/P + 15 is from 1.04 to 1.07.

Assay: Dissolve 200 mg of dye in 200 ml of distilled water, add 15 gm of sodium bitartrate, heat to boiling and titrate with 0.05 N TiCl₃ solution. The color change at the end point is from blue to reddish brown. The following data are used in calculating the percentage of anhydrous dye in the original sample:

Molecular weight 466.366
Hydrogen equivalents per mole of dye 2
Milliliters of N/10 TiCl₃ per gm of dye 42.895

Samples of this stain should contain not less than 80 percent anhydrous dye.

Biological Test: Indigo carmine is tested in Shumways' modification (1926) of the Cajal stain. Young amphibian larvae fixed in Bouin's picro-formol-acetic are embedded in paraffin and sectioned. Sections are stained 20 min in basic fuchsin (sat. aq. sol.) after which they are rinsed in distilled water and placed in an equal mixture of the indigo carmine to be tested and picric acid (each in sat. aq. sol.) for 5 min. They are passed rapidly through 70 percent alcohol (when the sections appear red), 95 percent and absolute alcohol (until the sections appear green) and cleared in xylene. With a satisfactory sample muscle tissue is green and connective tissue blue, contrasting sharply with the red of the nuclei.

CARMINE   C. I. NO. 75470

Absorption Characteristics: Carmine is a cochineal product, usually furnished as the aluminum-calcium salt of carminic acid. The exact structure for carminic acid is somewhat uncertain; the molecular formula is $C_{22}H_{20}O_{13}$. It is a strong dibasic acid with a side chain which contains four hydroxyl groups and possibly possesses a sugar-like structure, although carminic acid is not a glucoside. It contains at least one asymmetric carbon.

Assay: Due to the uncertainty of its constitution, no dye content is determined for samples of this stain.

Biological Test: Carmine is tested in Orth's lithium carmine technique on paraffin sections of animal tissue for nuclear staining following any good fixative. The paraffin is removed in the usual manner and the sections are stained 2 to 5 min in a carmine solution (2.5 to 5 gm of carmine dissolved in 100 ml saturated aqueous lithium carbonate (approx. 1.25 percent) and boiled 10 to 15 min, cooled, 1 gm of thymol added and then filtered). Transfer directly to acid alcohol (1 percent conc. HCl in 70 percent alcohol) 1 or more changes for several minutes, wash in tap water, dehydrate, clear and mount. A satisfactory sample should show the nuclei red and the cytoplasm light pink or unstained.

Carmine is also tested in Schneider's aceto-carmine formula (saturated solution in boiling 45 percent glacial acetic acid) for staining chromosomes in smears of anthers. The anthers are squeezed out gently onto the slide. A small drop of carmine is quickly put on the anthers, and a coverslip is placed on it. It is heated gently and then examined. The result should be a dark translucent red stain, selective for chromatin, with uncolored cytoplasm.

HEMATOXYLIN

Absorption Characteristics: Hematoxylin is a logwood product whose exact chemistry is not entirely understood, although its formula is assumed to be as given on p. 245. Because of this uncertainty, reliable chemical methods for its identification and analysis have not yet been devised.

Biological Test: It is tested on paraffin sections of animal tissue fixed in any general fixative by Delafield's, Heidenhain's, and Ehrlich's technics, as follows.

Delafield's hematoxylin is made up as follows: 4 gm of hematoxylin are dissolved in 25 ml 95 percent alcohol, and 400 ml of saturated aqueous $AlNH_4(SO_4)_2 \cdot 12H_2O$, 100 ml of glycerin and 100 ml of methyl alcohol are added. The solution at this time is usually light brown. It is then ripened (partially oxidized) by adding 0.4 gm of $NaIO_3$. The solution then becomes a deep reddish purple and is ready for use. The paraffin is removed in the usual manner, and the sections are stained for 15 min in this solution diluted with equal parts of water; they are then rinsed in tap water and immersed in fresh tap water for about 10 min. If the sections are still very blue, 2 drops of acidulated 35 percent alcohol (containing 3 drops conc. HCl to 50 ml) are added to them on the slides and they are returned to the water. Then a few drops of eosin Y (0.1 percent in 25 percent alcohol) is applied for 2 to 5 min, quickly washed in distilled water, passed through 95 percent alcohol and absolute alcohol into xylene and mounted. A satisfactory sample should show blue nuclei and pink cytoplasm.

Heidenhain's technic is as follows: The paraffin is removed from the sections in the usual manner. The sections are mordanted in 1.5 to 4 percent aqueous $NH_4 \cdot Fe(SO_4)_2 \cdot 12H_2O$ for 30 min to 3 hr, rinsed in tap water, stained 1 to 3 hr in 0.5

percent aqueous solution of hematoxylin, rinsed in tap water, differentiated in the above iron alum solution, controlling the differentiation by microscopic examination, washed in running water about 5 to 10 min, counterstained with 0.1 percent eosin Y in 25 percent alcohol 2 to 5 min, dehydrated, cleared and mounted in balsam. The criterion of a satisfactory sample is that the nuclei should appear black.

Ehrlich's method is as follows: Dissolve 2 gm hematoxylin in 100 ml of 95 percent ethyl alcohol, and add 100 ml of distilled water, 3 gm of $AlNH_4(SO_4)_2 \cdot 12H_2O$, 100 ml of glycerin, and 10 ml glacial acetic acid. Ripen immediately by addition of 0.2 gm $NaIO_3$. The paraffin is removed in the usual manner and the sections are stained 2 to 5 min in this solution, washed in tap water until section appears blue, stained 1 min in 0.5 percent aqueous eosin Y, rinsed in distilled water, dehydrated in 2 changes each of 95 percent and 100 percent alcohol, cleared and mounted in balsam. A satisfactory sample should show dark purple nuclei.

ORCEIN (SYNTHETIC)

The exact formula of orcein is unknown.

Absorption Characteristics: Dissolve 50 mg of orcein in 250 ml of 0.01 N NaOH. Dilute 10 ml of this solution to 200 ml with 0.01 N NaOH. Read in a spectrophotometer in a 1-cm cell. Absorption maximum 575–582 mμ; ratio P − 15/P + 15 is from 0.98 to 1.18.

Assay: Since the exact formula of orcein is unknown, determination of dye content is impossible.

Biological Test: Orcein is tested as an elastic tissue stain on Zenker's, acetone, formalin, or Bouin's fixed tissue. The paraffin is removed in the usual manner. The sections are stained 30 min in orcein (orcein, 0.4 gm in 70 percent alcohol + 1 ml conc. HCl), rinsed briefly in 70 percent alcohol, then in distilled water, stained 5 min in diluted methylene blue solution (methylene blue, 1 gm; borax, 1 gm; distilled water, 100 ml; for use, dilute 1 vol. with 9 vol. of distilled water), rinsed in distilled water differentiated and dehydrated in a dish of 95 percent alcohol to which has been added a few drops of 10 percent alcoholic rosin, keeping the section in constant motion about 2 min; dehydration is quickly completed with absolute alcohol, followed by clearing in xylene and mounting in balsam. A satisfactory sample should show even the finest elastic fibers either a dark purple or reddish purple.

It is also tested for staining chromosomes in salivary-gland cells of *Drosphilia* (and other *Diptera*) and meristematic cells of root tips. A stock solution is prepared by boiling 1 gm of orcein in 50 ml of 45 percent acetic acid, refluxing for 2 hr, cooling and filtering. Dissect salivary glands using a slide resting on a piece of ice. Transfer glands into drop of acetic orcein on albuminized slide and stain 3 to 6 min. Half-strength is usually satisfactory (1 part stock solution to 1 part 45 percent acetic acid). Add coverslip and flatten glands by pressing on cover with fingers, then tapping or stroking cover with a blunt instrument. Transfer slides to 95 percent alcohol vapor chamber (a covered dish lined with paper toweling saturated with alcohol and containing rack in which slides have been placed). Allow to remain few hours to overnight, and then transfer to alcohol until covers drop off, or can be removed easily, and mount in euparal.

Fix root tips in glacial acetic acid and 100 percent alcohol (1:3) and transfer to mixture of equal parts alcohol and conc. HCl for 5 min, then rinse thoroughly in alcohol alone. Full strength acetic orcein may be required and allowed to stain 6 to 9 min. Add coverslip and flatten. Transfer slides to 95 percent alcohol-vapor chamber a few hours or overnight and then transfer to alcohol until covers drop off, and mount in euparal. The result should show chromosomes, purplish to brownish red and the cytoplasm and nucleoli, little coloration.

WRIGHT STAIN

Absorption Characteristics: Wright stain is a compound of eosin with an oxidized and partly demethylated methylene blue. Because of its complexity no satisfactory chemical methods have been yet worked out for its identification or analysis.

Biological Test: The dye is dissolved in methyl alcohol (1 to 600) and allowed to stand for 5 to 7 days. The stain is applied with a medicine dropper to a dried blood film for 1 to 3 min. An equal volume of distilled water is then added. After standing twice as long as the undiluted stain, this solution is flooded off and the slide is washed with distilled water, until the thin portions of the stained film are pink. The smear is dried by blotting carefully. A satisfactory sample should show the following picture: erythrocytes, yellowish red; polymorphonuclear neutrophilic leucocytes, with dark blue nucleus, reddish lilac granules, and pale pink cytoplasm; eosinophilic leucocytes, with blue nuclei, red to orange-red granules and blue cytoplasm; basophilic leucocytes, with purple or dark blue nucleus and granules dark purple (almost black); lymphocytes with nuclei dark purple and cytoplasm sky blue; platelets, with violet to purple granules.

To be accepted for certification, Wright stain must also prove satisfactory for the staining of malarial parasites in thick and thin films of blood.

JENNER'S STAIN

Absorption Characteristics: Jenner's Stain is a methylene blue eosinate and is obtained as the precipitate formed on mixing solutions of methylene blue and eosin Y. It thus resembles Wright's stain, but differs from the latter in not using polychromed methylene blue, and for this reason is generally considered inferior to Wright's stain.

Biological Test: A solution of 0.25 gm of Jenner's stain is made up in 100 ml of methyl alcohol. This is applied to the staining of blood smears as described under Wright's stain (above).

TETRACHROME STAIN (MacNEAL)

Absorption Characteristics: Tetrachrome stain is a mixture containing methylene blue chloride, 1.0 gm; azure A, 0.6 gm; methylene violet, 0.2 gm; eosin Y, 1 gm. No satisfactory methods for the identification or analysis of this stain have yet been devised.

Biological Test: Dissolve 0.15 to 0.3 gm in 100 ml of methyl alcohol (neutral, acetone free) by heating to 50° C, shake thoroughly and leave 2 days at 37° C with occasional shaking. It is then filtered, after which it is tested by the same procedure as Wright's stain (above). A satisfactory stain should give results very similar to those secured with a good Wright stain.

GIEMSA STAIN

Absorption Characteristics: As in the case of Wright stain, no chemical methods for the identification or analysis of this stain have yet been devised. Like Wright stain it is a compound of eosin with methylene blue and its oxidation products.

Biological Test: It is tested on dried thin films of blood which have been treated 5 to 7 minutes in methyl alcohol. The staining fluid is prepared according to the directions on the label, if such directions are furnished by the manufacturer; otherwise 0.5 gm of the powdered dye is dissolved in 33 ml of glycerin by standing at 55 to 60° C for $1\frac{1}{2}$ to 2 hr, then 33 ml of methyl alcohol is added and the solution allowed to stand 24 hr. The dried blood films are immersed in a staining fluid containing 30 drops of the above solution in 30 ml of distilled water. As different lots of stain vary in rapidity of action it is best to test a sample with three or four slides stained at varying periods from 15 to 40 min; it is not condemned if good results are obtained on any one of the slides. Results should be very similar to those secured with a good Wright stain, the chief difference being that the nuclei of the leucocytes are reddish purple instead of a dark violet.

To be accepted for certification, Giemsa stain must also prove satisfactory for the staining of malarial parasites in thick and thin films of blood.

PROTARGOL-S (AND SIMILAR TYPES OF SILVER PROTEINATES)

Silver proteinates are reaction products of silver nitrate and protein that has been partially hydrolized. They are pharmaceutically equivalent to "strong silver protein" and contain about 8 percent Ag. Such a compound is a powder or finely granular material, tan to light brown in color, freely soluble in water, precipitated from aqueous solutions by alcohol or acetone. A 1 percent aqueous solution has a pH of 7.5 to 8.5. There is no precipitate when such a solution is mixed with a solution of Na_2CrO_4 of similar concentration (i.e., no Ag ions are present).

Assay: No satisfactory chemical tests are available because those ordinarily used (Ag content, absence of free Ag ions, etc.) do not correlate with staining performance. Hence performance of a given sample under actual staining conditions is the only dependable criterion.

Biological Test: Silver proteinates are tested in Bodian's Protargol-S method for selective staining of nerve fibers in mammalian brain and spinal cord. Specimens may be fixed in Bouin's fluid or alcoholic formalin-acetic acid (formalin, 5 ml; glacial acetic acid, 5 ml; 80 percent alcohol, 90 ml). Paraffin sections are run to water in the usual manner and stained for 12 to 48 hr at 37° C in a 1 percent aqueous solution of Protargol-S previously prepared by dusting the required amount of material on the surface of distilled water and allowing the Protargol to dissolve (without shaking) from the surface downward. Just before placing slides in Coplin jar for staining, about 5 gm of bright clean granular copper is placed in the bottom of the jar. Duplicate slides are also stained in Protargol without the addition of copper. After staining, the slides are rinsed for a few seconds in distilled water, placed for 2 to 10 min in a reducing solution (hydroquinone, 1 gm; anhydrous Na_2SO_3, 5 gm; water, 100 ml) washed thoroughly in running water and toned for 5 to 10 min in a 1 percent solution of gold chloride to which 3 drops of glacial acetic acid per 100 ml have been added. Slides are then rinsed in distilled water, placed for 2 to 5 min in 1 to 2 percent aqueous oxalic acid solution until sections have a faint purple or blue color, rinsed again in water and transferred for 5 to 10 min to 5 percent aqueous solutions of $Na_2S_2O_3 \cdot 5H_2O$. They are then washed thoroughly in tap water, dehydrated, cleared and covered. A satisfactory stain shows axis cylinders of nerve fibers and neurofibrils of cells black or purplish black.

Silver proteinates are also tested in the 2-hour Protargol method of Davenport, McArthur and Bruesch. Specimens of nervous tissue are fixed in a solution containing formalin (conc.), 15 ml; 1.5 percent picric acid in 80 percent alcohol, 85 ml; trichloracetic acid 0.3 to 0.5 gm. Paraffin sections are run down to water in the usual manner, and placed for 1 hr in 10 percent $AgNO_3$ at about 37° C, washed through 3 changes of distilled water (3 sec each), placed for 1 hr in 0.2 to 0.3 percent Protargol-S at room temperature, rinsed quickly (2 sec) in distilled water and placed for 1 to 2 min in Bodian's reducing solution (see above). They are then washed well in running tap water, toned in 0.2 percent gold chloride until sections are gray, washed and cautiously intensified in 0.1 to 0.2 percent oxalic acid or 0.2 to 0.3 percent aniline in 50 percent alcohol, washed, fixed in 5 percent hypo, washed, dehydrated, cleared and covered. A satisfactory sample shows staining similar to that obtained with Bodian's method.

BIBLIOGRAPHY

(Matter in parenthesis indicates the purpose for which each reference is cited in the preceding pages, not necessarily the main subject matter of the article in question.)

ADAMS, A. ELIZABETH 1928 Paraffin sections of tissue supra-vitally stained. Science, **68**, 303–304. (Employs Nile blue sulfate.)

ADDICOTT, F. T. 1944 A differential stain for rubber in Guayule. Stain Technol., **19**, 99–102.

ALCORN, G. D., and YEAGER C. C. 1937 Orseillin BB for staining fungal elements in Sartory's fluid. Stain Technol., **12**, 157–158.

ALBERT, H. 1921 Modification of stain for diphtheria bacilli. J. Am. Med. Assoc., **76**, 240. (Toluidine blue and methyl green for staining diphtheria preparations.)

AMBLER, J. A., and HOLMES, W. C. 1924 The investigation of biological stains in the Color Laboratory of the Bureau of Chemistry. Science, **60**, 501–502.

ANDRADE-PENNY, E. 1895 Acid fuchsin as an agent for the differentiation of bacteria. U. S. Marine Hosp. Serv. Ann. Rept. for 1895, 335–339.

ANONYMOUS 1865 Injectionsmassen von Thiersch und Müller. Arch. mikroskop. Anat. u. Entwicklungsmech., **1**, 148. (Use of carminates with oxalic acid.)

ANTHONY, E. E., JR. 1931 A note on capsule staining. Science, **73**, 319.

ANTOPOL, W., GLAUBACH, S., and GOLDMAN, L. 1948 Effects of a new tetrazolium derivative on tissue, bacteria and onion root tips. U. S. Public Health Repts., **61**, 1231–1238.

APATHY, S. 1888 Nachträge zur Cellodintechnik. Z. wiss. Mikroskop., **5**, 45–49.

ARTSCHWAGER, E. 1943 Contributions to the morphology and anatomy of Guayule. U. S. Dept. Agr. Tech. Bull. No. 842, 1–33.

ASTBURY, W. T., and PRESTON, R. D. 1940 The structure of the cell wall in some species of the filamentous green alga *Cladophora*. Proc. Roy. Soc. (London) (B), **129**, 54–76.

ATKINSON, E., MELVIN, S., and FOX, S. W. 1950 Some properties of 2,3,5-triphenyl tetrazolium chloride and several iodo derivatives. Science, **111**, 385–387.

BACKMAN, ELSA 1935 A rapid combined fixing and staining method for plant chromosome counts. Stain Technol., **10**, 83–86. (Alizarin red S in plant cytology.)

BAILEY, P. 1921 Cytological observations on the pars buccalis of the hypophysis cerebri of man, normal and pathological. J. Med. Research, **42**, 349–381. (Employs acid violet as a counterstain to Altmann's aniline fuchsin, also alone, and in neutral combination with safranin.)

BAKER, W., *et al.* 1942 The synthesis and standardization of sodium resazurate for testing the hygienic quality of milk. Biochem. J., **36**, No. 1–2, Proc. Biochem. Soc., pp. i–ii.

BALDWIN, WESLEY MANNING 1928 Mercurochrome-220 soluble as a histologic stain. Anat. Record, **39**, 229.

BALL, J., AND JACKSON, D. S. 1953 Histological, chromatographic and spectrophotometric studies of toluidine blue. Stain Technol., **28**, 33–40.

BALL, G. H. 1926 Studies on Paramecium: III. The effects of vital dyes on *Paramedium caudatum*. Biol. Bull., **52**, 68–78.

BANK, O. 1938 Die Vitalfärbung des Zellkernes mit basischen Farbstoffen. Protoplasma, **29**, 587–594.

BANNY, THERESA M., and CLARK, GEORGE 1950 New domestic cresyl echt violet. Stain Technol., **25**, 195–196.

BARROLLIER, J., and SUCHOWSKY, G. 1950 Betrachtungen über Lipoid-Farbstoffe und eine neue Methode einer Sudan-Färbung. Acta. Histochem., **5**, 294–296.

BAYLISS, W. M. 1906 On some aspects of adsorption phenomena with especial reference to the action of electrolytes and to the ash-constituents of proteins. Biochem. J., **1**, 175–232.

BEAN, R. J. 1927 Stain technic for Nissl's granules following alcohol-formol fixation. Stain Technol., **2**, 56–59. (Nigrosin as counterstain to neutral red.)

BELLING, JOHN 1921 On counting chromosomes in pollen mother cells. Am. Naturalist, **55**, 573–574. (Stains with iron-aceto-carmine.)

BELLING, JOHN 1928 A method for the study of chromosomes in pollen mother cells. Univ. of Calif. Publ. in Botany, **14**, No. 9, 293–299. (Use of brazilin for staining chromosomes in pollen mother cells.)

BENDA, CARL 1886 Über eine neue Färbemethode des Centralnervensystems, und theoretisches über Haematoxylinfärbungen. Arch. Anat. u. Physiol. Anat. Abt. (Physiol. Abt.) **1886**, 562–564.

BENDA, CARL 1891 Neue Mittheilungen über die Entwickelung der Genitaldrüsen and über die Metamorphose der Samenzellen. Arch. Anat. u. Physiol. Anat. (Physiol. Abt.), 1891, 549–552. (Safranin with light green for staining spermatozoa.)

BENDA, CARL 1893 Zellstructuren und Zellteilungen des Salamanderhodens. Anat. Anz., Ergänzhft., **8**, 161–165.

BENDA, CARL 1899 Weitere Mittheilungen über die Mitochondria. Arch. Anat. u. Physiol. Anat. Abt. (Physiol. Abt.) 1899, 376–383. (Proposes crystal-violet-alizarin method for chondriosomes.)

BENDA, CARL 1901 Die Mitochondriafärbung und andere Methoden zur untersuchung der Zellsubstanzen. Anat. Anz., Ergänzhft. **19**, 155–174. (Describes the crystal-violet-alizarin method.)

BENEKE 1862 Correspbl. d., Ver. f. gemeinsch. Arbeiten, No. 59, 980. (A note without title, being first reference to use of aniline dyes in histology.)

BENIANS, T. H. C. 1916 Relief staining for bacteria and spirochaetes. Brit. Med. J., **1916** (2), 722.

BENSLEY, R. R. 1911 Studies on the pancreas of the guinea pig. Am. J. Anat., **12**, 297–388. (Acid fuchsin and Janus green for chondriosomes. Describes "neutral gentian.")

BENSLEY, SYLVIA E. 1952 Pinacyanol erythrosinate as a stain for mast cells. Stain Technol., **27**, 269–273.

BERGONZINI, C. 1891 Über das Vorkommen von granulierten basophilen und acidophilen Zellen im Bindegewebe und über die Art sie sichtbar zu machen. Anat. Anz., **6**, 595–600. (Methyl orange in place of orange G in Ehrlich-Biondi stain.)

BERNTHSEN, A. 1885 Studien in der Methylenblaugruppe. Liebig's Ann. Chem., **230**, 73–136, 137–211. (Chemistry of azure I, etc.)

BERNTHSEN, A. 1906 Ueber die chemische Natur des Methylenazurs. Ber. deut. chem. Ges., **39**, II, 1804–1809.

BEST, F. 1906. Ueber Karminfärbung des Glycogens und der Kerne. Z. wiss. Mikroskop., **23**, 319–322.

BLACK, E. 1938 The staining reactions of fats after the use of various dyes and fixing agents. J. Lab. Clin. Med., **23**, 1027–1036.

BLACKMAN, V. H. 1905 Congo red as a stain for Uredineae. New Phytologist, **4**, 173–174.

BLAYDES, G. W. 1939 The use of Bismarck brown Y in some new stain schedules. Stain Technol., **14**, 105–110.

BLOCH, F., and GODIN, M. R. 1936 Technique de coloration du foie sur coupes à la paraffine pour le diagnostic histologique de la fièvre jaune. Bull. histol. appl. physiol. et pathol. et tech. microscop., **13**, 343–345. (An application of the Masson trichrome stain.)

BLUMENTHAL, J. M., and LIPSKEROW, M. 1905 Vergleichende Bewertung der differentielen Methode zur Färbung des Diphtheriebacillus. Cent. Bakteriol., Parasitenk I Abt., Orig., **38**, 359–366. (Describes Lujbinsky stain for the diphtheria organism.)

BÖHMER, F. 1865 Zur pathologischen anatomie der Meningitis cerebromedullaris epidemica. Aerztl. Intelligenzb. (Munich), **12**, 539–550. (First use of alum hematoxylin.)

BÖTTCHER, A. 1869 Ueber Entwicklung und Bau des Gehörlabyrinths nach untersuchungen an Säugethieren. I Theil. Verh. Kais. Leop.-Carol. deut. Akad. Naturf., Dresden, **35**, Abh. No. 5, 203 pp. (First use of alcohol for differentiation after staining.)

BOWIE, D. J. 1924 Cytological studies of the islets of Langerhans in a teleost, *Meomaenis griseus*. Anat. Record, **29**, 57. (Uses ethyl violet in a neutral stain combination with biebrich scarlet.)

BRASIL, LOUIS 1905 Sur la reproduction des Grégarines monocystidées. Arch. zool. exptl. et gén., 4 Ser., **4**, 69–100. (Light green with hematoxylin for sections of seminal vesicles.)

BRECHER, GEORGE 1949 New methylene blue as a reticulocyte stain. Am. J. Clin. Pathol., **19**, 895–896.

BREED, R. S., and BREW, J. D. 1916 Counting bacteria under the microscope. N. Y. State Agr. Exp. Sta., Bull. 49.

BRODA, B. 1939 Über die Verwendbarkeit von Chinalizarin, Titangelb, und Azoblau zum mikro- und histochemischen Magnesiumnachweis in Pflanzengeweben. Mikrokosmos, **32**, 184.

BRODE, W. R. 1943 *Chemical spectroscopy*. 2nd. Ed. John Wiley and Sons, New York.

BROWNING, C. H., GILMORE, M., and MACKLE, T. J. 1913 The isolation of typhoid bacilli from feces by means of brilliant green in fluid media. J. Hyg., **13**, 335–342.

BRUNSCHWIG, A., SCHMITZ, R. L., and JENNINGS, S. 1940 Selective localization of Evans Blue in subplacental portions of entoderm in the rat. Proc. Soc. Exptl. Biol. Med., **44**, 64–66.

BUCHHOLZ, JOHN T. 1931 The dissection, staining and mounting of styles in the study of pollen-tube distribution. Stain Technol., **6**, 13–24.

BUCKMAN, T. E., and HALLISEY, J. E. 1921 Studies in the properties of blood platelets. J. Am. Med. Assoc., **76**, 427. (Crystal violet as a substitute for brilliant cresyl blue in staining platelets.)

BUGNON, M. P. 1919 Sur une nouvelle méthode de coloration élective des membranes végétales lignifiées. Compt. rend. acad. sci., **168**, 62–64. (Light green and Sudan III for the staining of lignified tissue in distinction from suberized and cutinized tissue.)

BURDON, K. L., STOKES, JULIA C., and KIMBROUGH, C. E. 1942 Studies of the common aerobic spore-forming bacilli. I. Staining for fat with Sudan black B safranin. J. Bacteriol. 43, 717–724.

BURSTONE, M. S., and FOLK, J. B. 1956 Histochemical demonstration of aminopeptidase. J. Histochem. Cytochem., 4, 217–220.

BURSTONE, M. S. 1957a The cytochemical localization of esterase. J. Natl. Cancer Inst., 18, 167–173.

BURSTONE, M. S. 1957b Studies on calcification. I. The effect of inhibition of enzyme activity on developing bone and dentine. Am. J. Pathol., 33, 1229–1236.

BURSTONE, M. S. 1958a Histochemical comparison of naphthol AS-phosphates for the demonstration of phosphatases. J. Natl. Cancer Inst., 20, 601–615.

BURSTONE, M. S. 1958b Histochemical demonstration of acid phosphatases with naphthol AS-phosphates. J. Natl. Cancer Inst., 21, 523–529.

BURSTONE, M. S. 1958c The relationship between fixation and techniques for the histochemical localization of hydrolytic enzymes. J. Histochem. Cytochem., 6, 322–340.

BURTNER, H. J., BAHN, R. C., and LONGLEY, J. B. 1957 Observations on the reduction and quantitation of neotetrazolium. J. Histochem. Cytochem., 5, 127–134.

BUTT, E. M., BONYNGE, C. W., and JOYCE, R. L. 1936 The demonstration of capsules about hemolytic streptococci with India ink or azo blue. J. Infectious Diseases, 58, 5–9.

BUZAGLO, J. H. 1934 Une coloration pouvant remplacer celle de Van Gieson. Bull. histol. appl., 11, 40–43. Abs. in Stain Technol., 9, 109. (A tissue stain using gallocyanine, acid alizarin blue, and orcein.)

CANNON, H. G. 1937 A new biological stain for general purposes. Nature, 1937, 549. (Suggests use of chlorazol black E.)

CANNON, H. G. 1941 On chlorazol black E and some other new stains. J. Roy. Microscop. Soc., 61, 88–94.

CARNOY, J. B., and LEBRUN, H. 1897 La fecondation chez l'Ascaris megalocephala. La Cellule, 13, 63–195. (Congo red with hematoxylin and other nuclear stains.)

CARTER, J. S. 1933 Reactions of Stenostomum to vital staining. J. Exptl. Zoology, 65, 159–179. Abs. in Stain Technol., 9, 75.

CARTER, W. 1939 The use of prontosil as a vital dye for insects and plants. Science, 90, 394.

CHAMBERLAIN, C. J. 1932 Methods in plant histology. 5th ed. xiv and 416 pp. Univ. of Chicago Press.

CHAMBERLAIN, C. J. 1927 Staining with phloxine. Stain Technol. 2, 91–93. (Recommends phloxine, rather than magdala red, for staining algae.)

CHAMBERS, R. 1935 Disposal of dyes by proximal tubule cells of chick mesonephros in tissue culture. Proc. Soc. Exptl. Biol. Med., 32, 1199–1200.

CHAPMAN, G. H., and LIEB, C. W. 1937 The use of leuco triphenylmethanes as reagents for bacterial polysaccharides. Stain Technol., 12, 15–19.

CHRISTMAN, J. F., and TRUBEY, R. H. 1952 Chromatography and biological stains. Stain Technol., 27, 53–60.

CHURCHMAN, J. W. 1927 The structure of B. anthracis and reversal of the Gram reaction. J. Exptl. Med., 46, 1009–1029. (Employs gentian violet mixed with acriflavine—"acri-violet"—for its bacteriostatic properties.)

CHURCHMAN, J. W. 1933 The tinctorial behavior of the capsule in *Clostridium tetani* during sporulation. Stain Technol., 8, 111–116.

CIACCIO, C. 1906 Rapporti istogenetici tra il simpatico e le cellule cromaffini. Arch. ital. anat. e. embriol., 5, 256–267. (Iodine green with acid fuchsin and picric acid for nervous tissue.)

CLARA, M., and CANAL, F. 1932 Histochemische Untersuchungen an den Kornchen in den basalgekörnten Zellen des Darmepithels. Z. Zellfrosch., u. mikroscop. Anat., 15, 801–808.

CLARA, M. 1934 Über die Entwickelung der basalgekörnten Zellen beim Menschen. Z. Anat. Entwicklungsgeschichte, 103, 131–139.

CLARA, M. 1935 Über die Diazokuppelungsreaktion zum Nachweis der ortho- und para-Phenole in der histologischen Technik. Z. wiss. Mikroskop., 51, 316–337.

CLARK, W. M., and LUBS, H. A. 1917 The colorimetric determination of hydrogen-ion concentration. J. Bacteriol. 2, 1–34, 109–136, 191–236.

CLAUSER, F., and STRANI, M. 1930 Primäre Färbung durch Chloroform und saure Farbstoffe. Z. wiss. Mikroskop., 47, 58–63. Abs. in Stain Technol., 5, 109.

COHEN, B. 1923 Some new sulfonphthalein indicators. A preliminary note. Public Health Repts., 38, 199.

COHEN, B. 1926 Indicator properties of some new sulfonphthaleins. Public Health Repts., 41, 3051–3074.

COHEN, ISADORE, and DOAK, K. D. 1935 The fixing and staining of *Liriodendron tulipifera* root tips and their mycorrhizal fungus. Stain Technol., 10, 25–32. (Orseillin BB and crystal violet for fungi in root tips.)

COLE, E. C. 1931 Isohematein as a biological stain. Stain Technol., 6, 93–96.

COLEMAN, I. C. 1938 Preparation of leuco basic fuchsin for use in the Feulgen Reaction. Stain Technol., 13, 123–124.

COLOUR INDEX. See Society of Dyers and Colourists.

COMMISSION ON STANDARDIZATION OF BIOL. STAINS, H. J. CONN, CHAIRMAN. 1923b The preparation of staining solutions. Science, 57, 15–16.

COMMISSION ON STANDARDIZATION OF BIOL. STAINS, H. J. CONN, CHAIRMAN. 1923e Dye solubility in relation to staining solutions. Science, 57, 638–639.

COMMISSION ON STANDARDIZATION OF BIOL. STAINS, H. J. CONN, CHAIRMAN. 1923f Standardized nomenclatures of biological stains. Science, 57, 743–746.

CONKLIN, MARIE E. 1934 Mercurochrome as a bacteriological stain. J. Bacteriol. 27, 30–31.

CONN, H. J. 1918 The microscopic study of bacteria in soil. N. Y. State Agr. Exptl. Sta., Tech. Bull. 64.

CONN, H. J. 1921 Rose bengal as a general bacterial stain. J. Bacteriol., 6, 253–254.

CONN, H. J. 1927 The hematoxylin problem. Stain Technol., 2, 1–3.

CONN, H. J. 1929 Note on Loeffler's methylene blue: Stain Technol., 4, 27.

CONN, H. J., et al. 1933 *History of staining.* Commission on Standardization of Biological Stains, Geneva, N. Y. 1948. 2nd Edition.

CONN, H. J., and DARROW, MARY A. 1934 Can the Endo medium be standardized? Stain Technol., 9, 61.

CONN, H. J., and DARROW, MARY A. (Compilers and editors.) 1943–1944. Staining Procedures used by the Biological Stain Commission. A loose-leaf publication, prepared with the assistance of numerous members of the Stain Commission. *Biotech Publications, Geneva, N. Y.*

CONN, H. J., DARROW, MARY A., and EMMEL, V. M. 1960 Id. *2nd Ed.* Williams & Wilkins, Baltimore, Md.

CONN, H. J., and HOLMES, W. C. 1926 Fluorescein dyes as bacterial stains: with special reference to their use for soil preparations. Stain Technol., 1, 87–95.

CONN, H. J. AND HOLMES, W. C. 1928 Certain factors influencing the staining properties of fluorescein derivatives. Stain Technol., 3, 94–104.

COOK, E. A. 1879 Note on logwood staining solution. J. Anat. Physiol., 14, 140–142.

COONS, A. H., and KAPLAN, M. H. 1950 Localization of antigen in tissue cells. II. Improvements in a method for the detection of antigen by means of fluorescent antibody. J. Exptl. Med., 91, 1–14 (Fluorescein to demonstrate "virus-tagged" antibodies.)

CORDIER, R., and LISON, L. 1930 Étude histochimique de la substance chromoargentaffine de la cellule de Kultschitzky. Bull. histol. appl. et tech. microscop., 7, 140–146.

CORNER, G. W., and HURNI, F. H. 1918 The non-effect of corpus luteum preparations on the ovulation cycle of the rat. Am. J. Physiol., 46, 483–486. (Use of dianil blue 2R as vital stain.)

CORTI, A. 1851 Recherches sur l'organe de l'ouïe des mammifères. Z. wiss. Zool., 3, 109–169. (An early use of carmine in histology, see note 10, pp. 143–144.)

CROSSMON, G. 1940 The selective staining of red blood cells. Stain Technol., 15, 155–158.

CUMLEY, RUSSELL, W. 1935 Negative stains in the demonstration of bacteria. Stain Technol., 10, 53–56.

CUNNINGHAM, J. H. 1920 A method for the permanent staining of reticulated red cells. Arch. Internal Med., 26, 405–409.

CURTIS, F. 1905 Méthode de coloration elective du tissu conjunctif. Compt. rend. soc. biol., 58, 1038–1040.

CUSTER, R. P. 1933. Studies on the structure and function of bone marrow. III. Bone marrow biopsy. Am. J. Med. Sci., N. S. 185, 617–624.

CUYLER, W. K. 1932 A differential stain for dried, unfixed vaginal smears. J. Lab. Clin. Med., 18, 314–315. (Use of indigo carmine with eosin Y as counterstain to hematoxylin.)

CYON, E. 1868 Ueber die Nerven des Peritoneum. Ber. d. k. Sächs Gessel, d. wiss. zu Leipzig., 20, 121–127. (Gives technic of carmine staining.)

CZOKOR, J. 1880 Die Cochenille-Carmin lösung. Arch. mikroskop. Anat. u. Entwicklungsmech., 18, 412–414. (Uses alum cochineal.)

DADDI, L. 1896 Nouvelle méthode pour colorer la graisse dans les tissus. Arch. ital. biol., 26, 143–146. (Proposes Sudan III.)

DARROW, MARY A. 1940 A simple staining method for histology and cytology. Stain Technol., 15, 67–68. (Use of chlorazol black E.)

DAVENPORT, H. A. 1960 Histological and histochemical technics. W. B. Saunders, Co., Philadelphia.

DAVIS, B. J., and ORNSTEIN, L. 1959 High resolution enzyme localization with a new diazo reagent "hexazonium pararosaniline." J. Histochem. Cytochem., 7, 297–298.

DAWSON, A. B. 1926 A note on the staining of the skeleton of cleared specimens with alizarin red S. Stain Technol., 1, 123–124.

DAWSON, A. B., EVANS, H. M., and WHIPPLE, G. H. 1920 Blood volume studies: III. Behavior of a large series of dyes introduced into the circulating blood. Am. J. Physiol., 51, 232–256. (Information as to the value of 62 dyes for vital staining.)

DEAN, H. R. 1937 The reaction of isamine blue with serum. J. Pathol. Bacteriol., 45, 745–771.

DeGALANTHA, ELENA 1936 A new stain for connective tissue, mucin and allied substances. Am. J. Clin. Path., 6, 196–197.

DEHN, W. M., and BALL, ALICE, A. 1917 Colorimetric studies of picrate solutions. J. Am. Chem. Soc., 39, 1381–1392.

DELPRAT, G. D., and STOWE, W. P. 1931 The rose bengal test for liver function. J. Lab. Clin. Med., 16, 923–925.

DE TOMASI, J. A. 1936a A new procedure for the Feulgen reaction; a preliminary note. Stain Technol., 11, 70.

DE TOMASI, J. A. 1936b Improving the technic of the Feulgen stain. Stain Technol., 11, 137–144.

DETWILER, S. R. 1917 On the use of Nile blue sulfate in embryonic tissue transplantation. Anat. Record, 13, 493. (Nile blue sulfate as vital stain for embryos.)

DETWILER, S. R., and McKENNON, G. E. 1929 Mercurochrome (di-brom oxy mercuri fluorescein) as a fungicidal agent in the growth of amphibian embryos. Anat. Record, 41, 205.

v. DIGRALSKI, W., and CONRADI, H. 1902 Ueber ein Verfahren zum Nachweis der typhus Bazillen. Z. f. Hyg. Infectionshrankh., 39, 283. (Uses crystal violet in agar.)

DIXON, B. T. 1920 The differential staining of plant pathogen and host. Science, 52, 63–64. (The use of "magdala red" with light green.)

DOGLIO, P. 1932 Rapid staining of tubercle bacilli in sputum. Giorn. batteriol. immunol., 8, 243. Abs. in Stain Technol., 8, 76. (Brilliant yellow as counterstain to basic fuchsin.)

DORNER, W. 1926 Un procédé simple pour la coloration des spores. Lait, 6, 8–12.

DOUGLAS, M. G. 1932 Cooper's modification of the Ziehl-Neelsen staining method as applied to tubercle bacilli in tissue. J. Lab. Clin. Med., 17, 1131–1132. Abs. in Stain Technol., 8, 77.

DUBLIN, W. B. 1943 Combined stains method for neurologic tissue. J. Neuropathol. Exptl. Neurol., 2, 205–206.

DUNN, R. C. 1946 A simplified stain for hemoglobin in tissues or smears using patent blue. Stain Technol., 21, 65–67.

DURAN-REYNALS, F. 1937 Localization of foreign proteins and dyes in neoplastic growth. Proc. Soc. Exptl. Biol. Med., 36, 369–370.

DUTTON, L. O. 1928 Wright's as a differential spore stain. Stain Technol., 3, 140–142.

EBBINGHAUS, HEINR. 1902 Eine neue Method zur Färbung von Hornsubstanzen. Centr. allgem. Pathol. u. pathol. Anat., 13, 422–425. (Methyl orange for keratin.)

EHRENBERG, C. G. 1838 Die Infusionsthierchen als volkommene Organismen, 548 pp. Leopold Voss, Leipsig.

EHRLICH, P. 1910 Enzyklopädie der Mikroskopischen Technik, Vol. 1, 800 pp.; 2, 680 pp. 2nd Ed. Urban & Schwartzenberg, Berlin.

EHRLICH, P., and LAZARUS, A. 1898 Die Anaemie. I Abt. In Nothnagel's Spec. Path. u. Ther., Bd. 8, Vienna. (Describes various "neutral" stain mixtures; the "triacid" mixture; also pyronin and narcein with methyl green or methylene blue; and narcein with acid fuchsin and methyl green.)

ELLIOTT, K. A. C., and BAKER, Z. 1935 The effects of oxidation-reduction potential indicator dyes on the metabolism of tumor and normal tissues. Biochem. J., 29, 2396–2404. Abs. in Stain Technol., 11, 78.

EMERY, A. J., JR., HAZEN, FRANCES KNAPP, and STOTZ, ELMER 1950 Spectrophotometric characteristics and assay of biological stains. III. The xanthenes. Stain Technol., 15, 201–208.

EMERY, A. J., and STOTZ, ELMER 1952 Paper chromatography for analysis of a dye mixture. Stain Technol., 27, 21–28.

ENDO, S. 1904 Ueber ein Verhaften zum Nachweiss der Typhusbacillen. Centr. Bakteriol. Parasitenk., I Abt., Orig., 35, 109–110. (Proposes the fuchsin agar known as "Endo medium.")

EVANS, H. M., and SCOTT, KATHARINE J. 1921 On the differential reaction to vital dyes exhibited by the two great groups of connective-tissue cells. Carnegie Inst. Publ., No. 273.

EVANS, E. E., and WALLS, K. W. 1952 The separation of biological stains by filter paper electrophoresis. J. Bacteriol., 63, 422–423.

FARBER, E., STERNBERG, W. H., and DUNLAP, C. E. 1956a Histochemical localization of specific oxidative enzymes. I. Tetrazolium stains for diphosphopyridine nucleotide diaphorase and triphosphopyridine nucleotide diaphorase. J. Histochem. Cytochem., 4, 254–265.

FARBER, E., STERNBERG, W. H., and DUNLAP, C. E. 1956b Histochemical localization of specific oxidative enzymes. III. Evaluation studies of tetrazolium staining methods for diphosphopyridine nucleotide diaphorase, triphosphopyridine nucleotide diaphorase and the succindehydrogenase system. J. Histochem. Cytochem., 4, 284–294.

FARIS, H. A. 1924 Neutral red and Janus green as histological stains. Anat. Record, 27, 241–244.

FAUTREZ, J. 1936 Sur le point isoélectrique des cellules du système réticulo-endothélial des vertébrés. Bull. histol. appl. et tech. microscop., 13, 202–206.

FAVORSKY, M. V. 1939 New polyploid-inducing chemicals. Compt. rend. acad. sci. U.S.S.R., 25, 71–74.

FEIGL, FRITZ. 1958 Spot Tests in Inorganic Analysis. Elsevier Publ. Co.. New York.

FEULGEN, R., and ROSSENBECK, H. 1924 Mikroskopisch-chemischer Nachweis einer Nucleinsäure von Typus der Thymonucleinsäure und auf die darauf beruhende elektive Färbung von Zellkernen in mikroskopischen Präparaten. Z. Physiol. Chem., 135, 203–248.

FEULGEN, R., and VOIT, K. 1924 Über den Mechanismus der Nuclealfärbung. Z. Physiol. Chem., 135, 249–252; 136, 57–61.

FISCHEL, ALFRED 1901 Untersuchungen über Vitale Färbung. Anat. Hefte. I Abt. Bd. 16, No. 3/4 (Hfte. 52/3) 417–519. (Auramin for salamander larvae.)

FLEMMING, W. 1881 Ueber das E. Hermann'sche Kernfärbungs verfahren. Arch. mikroskop. Anat. u. Entwicklungsmech., 19, 317–330. (Magdala red as a nuclear stain. Investigated principle of differentiation with alcohol.)

FLEMMING, W. 1884 Mittheilungen zur Färbetechnik. Z. wiss. Mikroscop., 1, 349–361.

FLEMMING, W. 1891 Ueber Theilung und Kernformen bei Leukocyten, und über denen Attractionssphären. Arch. Mikroscop. Anat. u. Entwicklungsmech., 37, 249–298. (Triple staining technic—gentian violet, safranin and orange G—described on p. 296.)

FOLEY, J. O. 1943 A protargol method for staining nerve fibers in frozen or celloidin sections. Stain Technol., 18, 27–33.

FOOT, KATHERINE, and STROBELL, ELLA CHURCH 1905 Prophases and metaphases of the first maturation spindle of *Allolobophora foetida*. Am. J. Anat., **4,** 199–243. (Use of Bismarck brown for staining chromosomes in smear preparations of eggs.)

FOOT, N. C. 1933 The Masson trichrome staining methods in routine laboratory use. Stain Technol., **8,** 101–110.

FOSHAY, LEE 1931 A new method for staining *Bacterium tularense* in tissue sections. J. Lab. Clin. Med., **17,** 193–5. (Employs Nile blue A with safranin.)

FREDERICK, W. G. 1941 Estimation of small amounts of antimony with rhodamine B. Ind. Eng. Chem., Anal. Ed., **13,** 922.

FRENCH, R. W. 1926a Standardization of biological stains as a problem of Medical Department of the Army. Stain Technol., **1,** 11–16.

FRENCH, R. W. 1926b Azure C tissue stain. Stain Technol., **1,** 79. Fat stains. Id.

FRENCH, R. W. 1926c Basic fuchsin for the Endo medium. J. Lab. Clin. Med., **11,** 571.

FREY 1868 Die Hämatoxylinfärbung. Arch. Mikroscop. Anat. u. Entwicklungsmech., **4,** 345–346.

FROST, W. D. 1916 Comparison of a rapid method of counting bacteria in milk with the standard plate method. J. Infectious Diseases, **19,** 273–287. (Use of thionin for staining young bacterial colonies.)

GALIGHER, A. E. 1934 The Essentials of Practical Microtechnique in Animal Biology. Albert E. Galigher, Inc., Berkeley, Calif.

GARRETT, S. D. 1937 Brom thymol blue in aqueous sodium hydroxide as a clearing and staining agent for fungus-infected roots. Ann. Botany, **1,** 563.

GELLHORN, E. 1931 Vital staining and permeability. II. Communication. Protoplasma **12,** 66–78. Abs. in Stain Technol., **7,** 70.

GERARD, P. 1935 Sur l'emploi du noire soudane B pour reconnaître les inclusions de Vaseline liquide. Bull. histol. appl. et tech. microscop., **12,** 92–93.

GERLACH, J. 1858 Mikroskopische Studien aus dem Gebiet der menschlichen Morphologie. Erlangen, 1858. 72 pp. (Shows the advantage of dilute carmine solutions.)

GESCHICKTER, CHAS. F. 1930a The application of dyes in the cancer problem. Stain Technol., **5,** 49–64. (A modified Giemsa stain; see note 14, p. 62.)

GESCHICKTER, CHAS. F. 1930b Fresh tissue diagnosis in the operating room. Stain Technol., **5,** 81–86. (Staining frozen sections with a mixture of azure A and Erie garnet B.)

GEYER, EDMUND. 1932 Emulsion als Unterscheidungsmittel zwischen Kuhmilch und Ziegenmilch. Z. Fleisch- Milchhyg., **42,** 480–481. Abs. in Stain Technol., **8,** 37. (Alizarin as indicator of difference between cows' and goats' milk.)

GIBB, T. R. P. 1942. *Optical methods of chemical analysis.* McGraw-Hill Book Co., New York.

GIEMSA, G. 1902 Färbemethoden für Malariaparasiten. Centr. Bakteriol. Parasitenk., I Abt., **31,** 429–430. (Showing the value of preparing blood| stains with eosin and azure I alone.)

GIEMSA, G. 1902 Färbemethoden für Malariaparasiten. Centr. Bakteriol. Parasitenk., I Abt., **32,** 307–313. (Describes use of azure I and azure II.)

GIEMSA, G. 1904 Eine Vereinfachung und Vervollkommnung meiner Methylenazur-Methelenblau-eosin Färbemethode zur Erzielung der Romanowsky-Nochtschen Chromatinfärbung. Centr. Bakteriol. Parasitenk., I Abt., **37,** 308–311.

GIERKE, H. 1884, 1885 Färberei zu mikroskopischen Zwecken. Z. wiss. mikroskop., **1**, 62–100, 372–408, 497–557; **2**, 13–36, 164–221. (Discussion of history of staining.)

GLENNER, G. G., BURTNER, H. J., and BROWN, G. W. JR. 1957 The histochemical demonstration of monoamine oxidase activity by tetrazolium salts. J. Histochem. Cytochem., **5**, 591–600.

GÖMÖRI, G. 1936 Microtechnical demonstration of iron. Am. J. Pathol., **12**, 655–663.

GÖMÖRI, G. 1943 Calcification and phosphatase. Am. J. Pathol., **19**, 197–209. (Methyl green and acridine red 3B for staining calcium deposits in tissue.)

GÖMÖRI, G. 1952 *Microscopic histochemistry*, University of Chicago Press, Chicago, Ill.

GÖMÖRI, G. 1954 Histochemistry of the enterochromaffin substance. J. Histochem. Cytochem. **2**, 50–53.

GÖPPERT, H. R., and COHN, F. 1849 Ueber die Rotation des Zellinhaltes von Nitella flexilis. Botan. Zeitg., **7**, 665–673, 681–91, 697–705, 713–719. (An early use of carmine for microscopic staining purposes.)

GÖSSNER, W. 1958 Histochemischer Nachweis hydrolytisches Enzyme mit Helfe der Azofarbstoffmethode. Histochemie, **1**, 48–96.

GRAM, C. 1884 Ueber die isolierte Färbung der Schizomyceten in Schnitt und Trochenpraparaten. Fortschr. Med., **2**, 185–189.

GRENACHER, H. 1879 Einige Notizen zur Tinctionstechnik, besondes zur Kernfärbung. Arch. mikroskop. Anat. u. Entwicklungsmech. **16**, 463–471. (Uses alum carmine.)

GRIESBACH, H. 1882 Ein neues Tinctionsmittel für menschliche und thierische Gewebe. Zool. Anz., **5**, 406–10. (Iodine green as a nuclear stain.)

GRIESBACH, H. 1886 Weitere Untersuchungen über Azofarbstoffe behufs Tinction menschlicher und thierischer Gewebe. Z. wiss. Mikroskop., **3**, 358–385. (Congo red and amaranth for staining axis cylinders.)

GROAT, R. A. 1949 Initial and persisting staining power of solutions of iron-hematoxylin lake. Stain Technol., **24**, 157–163.

GURR, EDWARD 1959 *Methods of analytical histology and histochemistry*. Williams & Wilkins Co., Baltimore.

GURR, EDWARD 1960 *Encyclopoedia of microscopic stains*. Williams & Wilkins Co., Baltimore.

GUTSTEIN, M. 1932 Zur Theorie der Vitalfärbung. Z. ges. exptl. Med., **82**, 479–524; Abs. in Stain Technol., **8**, 78.

GUTSTEIN, M. 1937 New direct staining methods for elementary bodies. J. Pathol. Bacteriol., **45**, 313.

GUYER, M. F. 1936 *Animal micrology*. 4th Ed. 331 pp. University of Chicago Press.

HALLBERG, W. 1946 (A new method for staining tubercle bacilli, applicable also to the microörganism of leprosy and other acid-fast germs.) Acta Med. Scand., Suppl. **180**.

HALBERT, V. A. 1935 A study in the differentiation of *Escherichia coli* and *Aerobacter aerogenes* by the bacteriostatic action of organic dyes. J. Bacteriol., **30**, 653–654.

HAMMER, B. W., and COLLINS, M. A. 1934 The number of lipolytic bacteria in various dairy products, as determined with Nile blue sulfate. Iowa Res. Bulletin **169**.

HANSEN, F. C. C. 1905 Ueber Eisenhämatein, Chromalaumhämatein, Tonerdealaunhämatein Hämateinlösungen und einige Cochenille farblösungen. Z. wiss. Mikroskop., 22, 45–90.

HARRIS, D. L. 1908 A method for the staining of Negri bodies. J. Infectious Diseases, 5, 566–569. (Use of alcohol soluble eosin followed by Unna's alkaline methylene blue.)

HARTIG, TH. 1854 Ueber die Functionen des Zellenkerns. Botan. Zeitz., 12, 574–584. (Includes an investigation of the ability of various parts of plant protoplasm to take carmine.)

HARTIG, TH. 1854 Ueber das Verhalten des Zellkerns beider Zellentheilung. Botan. Zeitg., 12, 893–902. (An early use of carmine.)

HARTIG, TH. 1858 Entwickelungsgeschichte des Pflanzenkeims, dessen stoffbildung während der Vorgänge des Reifens und des Keimens. Leipsig, 1858, 164 pp. (Uses carmine.)

HARTMAN, T. L. 1940 The use of sudan black B as a bacterial fat stain. Stain Technol., 15, 23–28.

HASTINGS, T. W. 1905 A method of preparing a permanent Nocht's stain (Nocht-Jenner stain). J. Exptl. Med., 7, 265–279.

HAUSDORF, G. 1927 Färbung zur Darstellung reifer Samenzellen im Hodenschnittpräparat. Z. wiss. Mikroskop., 44, 327–328. Abs. in Stain Technol., 4, 62.

HAYNES, R. 1926a Modification of the French azure C tissue stain. Stain Technol., 1, 68–69.

HAYNES, R. 1926b Azure stains. Stain Technol., 1, 107–111.

HAYNES, R. 1927 Investigations of thiazin dyes as biological stains: I. The staining properties of thionin and its derivatives as compared with their chemical formulae. Stain Technol., 2, 8–16.

HAYNES, R. 1928 Fast green, a new substitute for light green SF yellowish. Stain Technol., 3, 40.

HEIDENHAIN, M. 1892 Ueber Kern und protoplasma. Festschr. A.v. Kolliker, Leipsig, p. 109–165. (Iron hematoxylin described, p. 118.) Abstr. in Z. wiss. Mikroskop., 9, 198–206.

HEIDENHAIN, M. 1896 Nach einmal über die Darstellung der Centralkörper durch Eisenhämatoxylin nebst einigen allgemeinen Bemerkungen über die Hämatoxylinfärben. Z. wiss. Mikroscop., 13, 186–199.

HEIDENHAIN, M. 1903 Über die zweckmässige Verwendung des Congo und anderer Amidoazokörper, sowie über neue Neutralfärben. Z. wiss. Mikroskop., 20, 179–186. (Suggests the use of thiazine red R.)

HEIDENHAIN, M. 1915 Über die Mallorysche Bindegewebsfärbung mit Karmin und Azokarmin als Vorfarben. Z. wiss. Mikroskop., 32, 361–372.

HEIDENHAIN, R. 1885 Eine neue Verwendung des Haematoxylin. Arch. mikroskop. Anat. u. Entwicklungsmech., 24, 468.

HEIDENHAIN, R. 1886 Eine Abänderung der Färbung mit Haematoxylin und chromsauren Salzen. Arch. mikroskop. Anat. u. Entwicklungsmech., 27, 383.

HEIDENHAIN, R. 1888 Beiträge zur Histologie und Physiologie der Dünndarmschleimhaut. Pflüger's Arch. ges. Physiol., 43, Suppl., 103 pp.

HELD, HANS 1895 Beiträge zur Structur der Nervenzellen und ihrer Fortsätze. Arch. Anat. u. Physiol., Anat. Abt., 1895, 396–414. See p. 399. (For nervous tissues uses a double stain of erythrosin and methylene blue.)

HENDRICKSON, A. A., BALDWIN, I. L., and RIKER, A. J. 1934 Studies on certain physiological characters of Phytomonas tumefaciens, Phytomonas rhizogenes and Bacillus radiobacter. Part II. J. Bacteriol., 28, 597–618. (Bacteriological media containing aniline blue W.S.)

HERCIK, F. 1939 Die Fluoreszenzmikroskopische Analyse der α-Strahlenwirkung. Protoplasma, **32**, 527–535.

HERMANN, E. 1875 Ueber eine neue Tinctionsmethode. Tagbl. d. 48 Versaml. deut. Naturf. u. Aerzte, Graz 1875, 105 pp. (Early use of alcohol differentiation to bring out nuclei.)

HERXHEIMER, GOTTHOLD 1901 Über Fettstoffe. Deut. med. Wochsch., **27**, 607–609.

HERZBERG, K. 1934 Viktoriablau zur Färbung von filtreierbarem Virus (pocken-, Barizellen-, Ektromelia- und Kanarenvogelvirus). Zentbr. Bakteriol., Parasitenk., I. Abt., Orig., **131**, 358–366. Abs. in Stain Technol., **10**, 67.

HETHERINGTON, D. C. 1936 Pinacyanol as a supra-vital mitochondrial stain for blood. Stain Technol., **11**, 153–154.

HICKSON, S. J. 1901 Staining with brazilin. Quart. J. Microscop. Sci., N. S. **44**, 469–471. (Brazilin after iron alum.)

HILL, J. 1770 The construction of timber, from its early growth: explained by the microscope, etc. London, 1770. (Use of carmine in studying the ascent of sap.) Original not seen; cited from Woodruff, 1926.

HISS, P. H., JR. 1905 A contribution to the physiological differentiation of Pneumococcus and Streptococcus. J. Exptl. Med., **6**, 317–345.

HOLLISTER, GLORIA 1934 Clearing and dyeing fish for bone study. *Zoologica*, **12**, No. 10, 89–101. Abs. in Stain Technol., **10**, 37.

HOLMES, W. C. 1924 The influence of variation in concentration on the absorption spectra of dye solutions. J. Ind. Eng. Chem., **16**, 35.

HOLMES, W. C. 1927 Stain Solubilities. Part II. Stain Technol., **2**, 68–70.

HOLMES, W. C. 1928 Stain Solubilities. Part III. Stain Technol., **3**, 12–13.

HOLMES, W. C. 1929a Stain Solubilities. Part IV. Stain Technol., **4**, 73–4.

HOLMES, W. C. 1929b The mechanism of staining. Stain Technol., **4**, 75–80.

HOLMES, W. C., and FRENCH, R. W. 1926 The oxidation products of methylene blue. Stain Technol., **1**, 17–26. (Contains technic of French azure C tissue stain.)

HOLMES, W. C., MELIN, C. G., and PETERSON, A. R. 1932 Eosin B. Stain Technol., **7**, 121.

HOLMES, W. C., and PETERSON, ANIS R. 1930 The analysis of neutral red and of the pyronins. Stain Technol., **5**, 91–96.

HOUCKE, E. 1928 Emploi du mélange rhodamine-bleu de méthylène dans la coloration des tissus splénique et lymphoïde. Compt. rend. soc. biol., **99**, 788.

HRUBY, K. 1933 Double staining by the Cajal-Brozek method. Science, **77**, 352–353. (Indigo carmine with picric acid in contrast to basic fuchsin.)

HUCKER, G. J., and CONN, H. J. 1923 Methods of Gram staining. N. Y. State Agr. Expt. Sta., Tech. Bul. 93.

HUDDLESON, I. F. 1931 Differentiation of the species of the genus Brucella. Am. J. Public Health, **21**, 491–498.

IMPERIAL CHEMICAL INDUSTRY 1951 *The dyeing of cotton with brenthol dyestuffs.* See pp. 69–121. Kynoch Press, Birmingham.

IRWIN, MARIAN 1927 On the nature of the dye penetrating the vacuole of Valonia from solutions of methylene blue. J. Gen. Physiol., **10**, 927–947.

ISADA, M. 1938 Geisselfärbung aus alter Bakterienkultur. Zentbr. Bakteriol., Parasitenk., I Abt., Orig., **142**, 480–483.

IVANOV, M. F., and BRAUN, A. A. 1938 On the problem of permeability of tissue membranes. Arch. Russ. Anat. Hist. Embriol., **19**, 161–74.

JACKSON, GEMMA 1926 Crystal violet and erythrosin in plant anatomy. Stain Technol., 1, 33–34.

JACOBSON, W. 1939 The argentaffine cells and pernicious anaemia. J. Pathol. Bacteriol., 49, 1–19. (The use of diazonium salts for histochemical demonstration of phenolic compounds.)

JENKINS, R. 1937 Microscopy with fluorescent light. Stain Technol., 12, 167–173.

JENNER, LOUIS 1899 A new preparation for rapidly fixing and staining blood. Lancet, 1899, Pt. 1, 370.

JERCHEL, D., and MOHLE, W. 1944 Die Bestimmung des Reduktionspotentials von Tetrazoliumverbindungen. Ber. deut. chem. Ges., 77, 591–601.

JOHANSEN, D. A. 1939 A quadruple stain combination for plant tissues. Stain Technol., 14, 125–128.

JOHNS, C. K., and HOWSON, R. K. 1940 Potentiometric studies with resazurin and methylene blue in milk. J. Dairy Science, 23, 295–302.

JOHNSON, H., and STAUB, P. 1927 A proposed new food dye. Ind. Eng. Chem., 19, 497–498. (Discusses fast green FCF.)

JORDAN, J. H., and HEATHER, A. H. 1929 Staining of Negri bodies. Stain Technol., 4, 121–126.

KALTER, S. S. 1943 A quadruple staining method for tissues. J. Lab. Clin. Med., 28, 995–997. (A staining procedure employing Orange II, fast green FCF, safranin O, and crystal violet.)

KASSANIS, B. 1939 Intranuclear inclusions in virus infected plants. Ann. Appl. Biol., 26, 705–709.

KEENER, P. D. 1951 Mycoflora of buds. II. Results of histological studies of non-irradiated buds of certain woody plants. Am. J. Botany, 38, 105–110.

KEHRMANN, F. 1906 Ueber Methylen-azur. Ber. deut. chem. Ges., 39, II, 1403–1408.

KEMPTON, R. T., BOTT, P. A., and RICHARDS, A. N. 1937 The glomerular elimination of indigo carmine in rabbits. Am. J. Anat., 61, 505–521.

KERNOHAN, JAMES W. 1931 A new modification of Mallory-Heidenhain's differential staining method and adaptation of formalin-fixed material for Mallory's stains. Am. J. Clin. Pathol., 1, 399–403. Abs. in Stain Technol., 7, 70.

KISSER, J. 1931 Eine neue Farbstoffkombination, das Kallichrom nach Dr. Gross. Mikroskopie f. Naturfreunde, 9, 95. Abs. in Stain Technol., 7, 30.

KLEBS, G. 1886 Ueber die Organisation der Gallerte bei einige Algen und Flagellaten. Unter Botan. Inst. Tübingen, 2, No. 2, 333–418. (Congo red as reagent for cellulose; see p. 369).

KLINE, EDMUND K. 1935 Toxicity of brilliant green for certain bacteria. Am. J. Public Health, 25, 314–318. Abs. in Stain Technol., 10, 110.

KNAYSI, G. 1941 On the use of basic dyes for the demonstration of hydrolysis of fat. J. Bacteriol., 42, 587–589.

KNAYSI, G. 1942 Further studies on the use of basic dyes for measuring hydrolysis of fats. J. Dairy Science, 25, 585–588.

KONEFF, A. A. 1936 An iron-hematoxylin-aniline-blue staining method for routine laboratory use. Anat. Record, 66, 173–179.

KORNHAUSER, S. I. 1930 Hematein—Its advantages for general laboratory usage. Stain Technol., 5, 13–15.

KORNHAUSER, S. I. 1943 A quadruple tissue stain for strong color contrasts. Stain Technol., 18, 95–97.

KRAJIAN, A. A. 1941 A new staining method for Gram-positive and Gram-negative organisms in frozen sections. Arch. Pathol., 32, 825.

KRAUSE, R. 1926–1927 *Enzyklopädie der mikroskopischen technik*, 2444 pp. in 3 vols. Urban & Schwarzenberg, Berlin.

KULTSCHITZKY, N. 1895 Zur Frage über den Bau der Milz. Arch. mikroskop. Anat. u. Entwicklungsmech. 46, 673–695. (Magdala red for elastic tissues.)

KURNICK, N. B. 1952 Histological staining with methyl-green-pyronin. Stain Technol., 27, 233–242.

KURNICK, N. B. 1955 Pyronin Y in the methyl-green-pyronin histological stain. Stain Technol., 30, 213–230.

LAKON, G. 1942 Topographischer Nachweis der Keimfähigkeit des Mais durch Tetrazoliumsalze. Ber. deut. botan. Ges., 60, 434.

LANDAU, E. 1934 Coloration des fragments entiers pour les études cytoarchitectoniques. Bull. histol. appl. physiol. et pathol. et tech. microscop. 11, 44–46. Abs. in Stain Technol., 9, 109.

LANGERON, M. 1934 *Précis de microscopie*. 5th Ed. Masson et Cie., Paris.

LACOUR, L. 1941 Acetic-orcein: a new stain-fixative for chromosomes. Stain Technol., 16, 169–74.

LEACH, E. H. 1946 Curtis' substitute for Van Gieson stain. Stain Technol., 21, 107–109.

LEE, A. B. 1937 *The microtomists vade-mecum*. 10th Ed., edited by J. B. Gatenby. Blakistons, Philadelphia.

LEE, A. B., and MAYER, P. 1907 *Grundzüge der mikroskopischen Technik*. 3rd Ed. Berlin.

LEIFSON, EINAR 1951 Staining, shape, and arrangement of bacterial flagella. J. Bacteriol., 62, 377–389.

LEISHMAN, W. B. 1901 A simple and rapid method of producing Romanowsky staining in malarial and other blood films. Brit. Med. J., 1901, Pt. 2, 757–758. (Redissolved precipiate of Nocht stain in methyl alcohol.)

LENDRUM, A. C. 1935 Celestin blue as a nuclear stain. J. Pathol. Bacteriol., 40, 415–415. Abs. in Stain Technol., 10, 110.

LENDRUM, A. C., and McFARLANE, D. 1940 A controllable modification of Mallory's trichromic staining method. J. Pathol. Bacteriol., 50, 381–384.

LEVINE, M. 1921 Bacteria fermenting lactose and their significance in water analysis. Iowa State College Eng. Expt. Sta. Bull. 62. (Use of eosin-methylene-blue agar; see p. 62–64).

LEWIS, F. T. 1942 The introduction of biological stains: Employment of saffron by Vieussens and Leeuwenhoek. Anat. Record, 83, 229–253.

LEWIS, I. M. 1938 Cell inclusions and the life cycle of Rhizobia. J. Bacteriol., 35, 573–587.

LEWIS, MARGARET REED, and GOLAND, P. G. 1948 *In vivo* staining and retardation of tumors in mice by acridine compounds. Am. J. Med. Sci., 215, 282–289.

LEWIS, MARGARET REED, SLOVITER, H. A., and GOLAND, P. G. 1946 *In vivo* staining and retardation of growth of sarcomata in mice. Anat. Record, 95, 89–96.

LEWIS, P. R. 1958 A simultaneous coupling azo dye technique suitable for whole mounts. Quart. J. Microscop. Sci., 99, 67–71.

LEVADITI, C., REINIÉ, L., STAMATIN, L., and BEQUIGNON, R. 1940 Ultravirus et fluorescence. Le virus vaccinal. Ann. inst. Pasteur. 64, 359–414.

LILLIE, R. D. 1928 The Gram stain. I. A quick method for staining Gram positive organisms in the tissues. Arch. Pathol., 5, 828.

LILLIE, R. D. 1940 Further experiments with the Masson trichrome modification of Mallory's connective tissue stain. Stain Technol., 15, 17–22.

LILLIE, R. D. 1941 Romanowsky staining with buffered solutions. III. Extension of the method to Romanowsky stains in general. Stain Technol., 16, 1–6.

LILLIE, R. D. 1942 Studies on polychrome methylene blue. I. Eosinates, their spectra and staining capacity. Stain Technol., 17, 57–63.

LILLIE, R. D. 1944a Factors influencing the Romanovsky staining of blood films and the role of methylene violet. J. Lab. Clin. Med., 29, 1181–1197.

LILLIE, R. D. 1944b The deterioration of Romanovsky stain solutions in various organic solvents. Public Health Repts., Suppl. No. 178.

LILLIE, R. D. 1944c Various oil soluble dyes as fat stains in the supersaturated isopropanol technic. Stain Technol., 19, 55–58.

LILLIE, R. D. 1944d Various thiazin and fluorane dyes in paired combinations as neutral stains for tissues. J. Tech. Methods, 24, 43–45.

LILLIE, R. D. 1945a Oil blue N or NA as a fat stain for animal histology. Stain Technol., 20, 7–9.

LILLIE, R. D. 1945b Carycinel red and coccinel red, oil soluble anthraquinone dyes, as fat stains in animal histology. Stain Technol., 20, 73–75.

LILLIE, R. D. 1945c Studies on selective staining of collagen with acid anilin dyes. J. Tech. Methods, 25, 1–47.

LILLIE, R. D. 1948 Histopathological technic. Blakiston, Philadelphia.

LILLIE, R. D. 1950 Further exploration of the HIO₄-Schiff reaction with remarks on its significance. Anat. Record, 108, 239–253.

LILLIE, R. D. 1951 Simplification of the manufacture of Schiff reagent for use in histochemical procedures. Stain Technol., 26, 163–165.

LILLIE, R. D. 1954 Histopathologic technic and practical histochemistry. Blakiston, New York.

LILLIE, R. D. 1956 Phenolic oxidative activities of the skin: Some reactions of keratohyalin and trichohyalin. J. Histochem. Cytochem., 4, 318–336.

LILLIE, R. D., BURTNER, H. J., and HENSON, J. G. 1953 Diazosafranin for staining enterochromaffin cells. J. Histochem. Cytochem., 1, 154–159.

LILLIE, R. D., HENSEN, J. P. G., and CASON, J. C. 1961 Azocoupling rate of enterochromaffin with various diazonium salts. J. Histochem. Cytochem., 9, 11–21.

LILLIE, R. D., and PASTERNACK, J. G. 1932 Romanowsky staining with buffered solutions. Arch. Pathol., 14, 515.

LILLIE, R. D., and PASTERNACK, J. G. 1936 Id. II. Current modification. J. Tech. Methods, 14, 65–70.

LIPMAN, HARRY J. 1935 Staining the skeleton of cleared embryos with alizarin red S. Stain Technol., 10, 61–63.

LIPP, HANS 1940 Ersparnisse bei der Gonokokken- und Spirochätenfärbung. Münch. med. Wochschr., 87, 888. (Victoria blue 4R, either alone or with methyl green and pyronin, as a stain for Spirochaetes.)

LISON, L. 1931 Recherches histochimiques sur les phénols et leurs dérivés. Arch. biol., 41, 343–346.

LISON, L. 1938 Etudes histophysiologiques sur les tubes de Malpighi des insects. III. L'élimination des colorants basiques chez les Orthopteres. Z. Zellforsch. mikroscop. Anat., 28, 179–209.

LISON, L. 1953 Histochimie et cytochimie animales. Gauthier-Villars, Paris.

LISON, L. 1954 Alcian blue 8G with chlorantine fast red 5B. A technic for selective staining of mucopolysaccharides. Stain Technol., 29, 131–138.

LISON, L. and DAGNELIE, J. 1935 Méthodes nouvelles de coloration de la myéline. Bull. histol. appl. physiol. et pathol. et tech. microscop., 12, 85–91.

LIST, J. H.   1885   Zur Färbetechnic.   Z. wiss. Mikroskop., **2**, 145–156. (Uses eosin preceding methyl green.)

LOOSANOFF, V. L.   1937   Use of Nile blue sulfate in marking starfish.   Science, **85**, 2208.

LOWENSTEIN, E.   1930   Die Methodik der Reinkulture von Tuberkelbazillen aus dem Blute.   Deut. med. Wochschr., **56**, 1010. (Malachite green in culture media.)

LUBS, H. A.   1955   *The chemistry of synthetic dyes and pigments.* Reinhold Book Publishing Co., New York.

LYNCH, J. E.   1930   Eine neue Karminmethode für Totalpräparate.   Z. wiss. Mikroskop., **46**, 465–469. Abs. in Stain Technol., **5**, 111.

MACCALLUM, W. G.   1919   A stain for influenza bacilli in tissue.   J. Am. Med. Assoc., **72**, 193. (Basic fuchsin followed by picric acid and gentian violet.)

MACNEAL, W. J.   1906   Methylene violet and methylene azur.   J. Infectious Diseases, **3**, 412–433. (The history of blood stains and the chemistry of its ingredients.)

MACNEAL, W. J.   1922   Tetrachrome blood stain; an economical and satisfactory imitation of Leishman's stain.   J. Am. Med. Assoc., **78**, 1122.

MACNEAL, W. J.   1925   Methylene violet and methylene azure A and B.   J. Infectious Diseases, **36**, 538–546.

MACNEAL, W. J., and KILLIAN, J. A.   1926*a*   Chemical studies on polychrome methylene blue.   J. Am. Chem. Soc., **48**, 740–747. (Method of preparation of azures A and B and of methylene violet from methylene blue.)

MACNEAL, W. J., and KILLIAN, J. A.   1926*b*   Methylene azure B (tri-methyl thionin).   Proc. N. Y. Pathol. Soc., **26**, 20–23.

MAHESHWARI, P., and WULFF, H. D.   1937   Recent advances in microtechnic. I. Methods of studying the development of the male gametophyte in Angiosperms.   Stain Technol., **12**, 61–70.

MALLORY, F. B.   1891   Phospho-molybdic acid haematoxylon.   Anat. Anz., **6**, 375–376. (Use of hematoxylin with molybdic acid.)

MALLORY, F. B.   1897   On certain improvements in histological technic.   J. Exptl. Med., **2**, 529–533. (Proposes formula for phosphotungstic acid hematoxylin.)

MALLORY, F. B.   1900   A contribution to staining methods.   J. Exptl. Med., **5**, 15–20. (Anilin blue connective tissue stain described.)

MALLORY, F. B.   1904   Scarlet fever. Protozoan-like bodies found in four cases.   J. Med. Research, **10**, 483–492. (Eosin preceding methylene blue for staining, especially in pathology.)

MALLORY, F. B.   1938   *Pathological technic.* W. B. Saunders Co., Philadelphia.

MALLORY, F. B., and WRIGHT, J. H.   1924   *Pathological technic.* 8th Ed. W. B. Saunders Co., Philadelphia.

MANEVAL, W. E.   1934   Rapid staining methods.   Science, **80**, 292–294. Abs. in Stain Technol., **10**, 38.

MANEVAL, W. E.   1941   Staining bacteria and yeasts with acid dyes.   Stain Technol., **16**, 13–19.

MANHEIMER, L. H., and SELIGMAN, A. M.   1948   Improvement in the method for the histochemical demonstration of alkaline phosphatase and its use in a study of normal and neoplastic tissue.   J. Natl. Cancer Inst., **9**, 181–197.

MANN, GUSTAV   1894   Ueber die Behandlung der Nervenzellen für experimentell-histologische Untersuchungen.   Z. wiss. Mikroskop., **11**, 479–494. See p. 490. (Employs methyl blue with eosin.)

MANN, GUSTAV   1902   *Physiological Histology.* Clarendon Press, Oxford.

Margolena, L. A. 1933a Concerning fast green. Stain Technol., 8, 73.

Margolena, L. A. 1933b Notes on the staining of tubercle bacilli in sputum. Stain Technol., 8, 73.

Margolena, L. A., and Hansen, P. A. 1933 The nature of the reaction of the colon organism on Endo's medium. Stain Technol., 8, 131.

Maschke, O. 1859 Pigmentlösung als Reagenz bei Mikroskopisch physiologisch Untersuchungen. Botan. Zeitg., 17, 21–27. J. prakt Chem. v. Erdmann u. Wether, 76, 37. (First use of indigo.)

Masson, P. 1929 Some histological methods. Trichrome stainings and their preliminary technique. J. Tech. Methods and Bul. Intern. Assoc. Med. Museum, 12, 75.

Matsuura, S. 1925 Ueber die Färbung mit Kongorot. Folia Anat. Japon., 3, 107–110. (Congo red for staining elastic tissue.)

Maurer, S., and Lewis, D. 1922 The cellular structure and differentiation of the specific cellular elements of the pars intermedia of the hypophysis of the domestic pig. J. Exptl. Med., 36, 141–156. (In staining sections of the hypophysis, employs a mixture of acid violet and acid fuchsin, also a neutral stain combination of acid violet with safranin.)

Mayer, Paul 1878 Die Verwendbarkeit der Cochenille in der microscopischen Technic. Zool. Anz., 1, 345–346. (Uses cochineal with alum.)

Mayer, Paul 1891 Ueber das Färben mit Hämatoxylin. Mitt Zool. Stat. z. Neapel, 10, 170–186. (Hemalum, hemacalcium, etc.)

Mayer, Paul 1892 Ueber das Färben mit Carmin, Cochenille und Hämatein Thonerde. Mitt. Zool. Stat. z. Neapel, 10, 480–504.

Mayer, Paul 1896 Ueber Schleimfärbung. Mitt. Zool. Stat. z. Neapel, 12, 303–330. (Describes muci-carmine, muc-hematin and gluc-hematin.)

Mayer, Paul 1899 Ueber Hämatoxylin, Carmin, und verwandte Materien. Z. wiss. Mikroskop., 16, 196–220.

McClung, C. E. 1923 Haematoxylin. Science, 58, 515.

McClung, C. E. 1950 Handbook of Microscopical Technique. 3rd Ed., revised by Ruth McClung Jones. Hoeber, New York.

McFarlane, D. 1944 Picro-Mallory. Stain Technol., 19, 29–37.

McGregor, Leone 1929 The finer histology of the normal glomerulus. Am. J. Pathol., 5, 545–558. (A modification of the Mallory-Heidenhain azocarmine-anilin-blue stain.)

McLean, R. S., and Ireland, E. J. 1940 Rapid staining methods in plant histology. J. Am. Pharm. Assoc., 29, 318–321.

McManus, J. F. A. 1946 Histological demonstration of mucin after periodic acid. Nature, 158, 202.

McMaster, P. D., and Parsons, R. J. 1938 Path of escape of vital dyes from the lymphatics into the tissues. Proc. Soc. Exptl. Biol. Med., 37, 707–709.

Menner, E. 1935 Ganglienzellen-Präparate für Kurszwecke. Zool. Anz., 110, 200–202.

Merton, Hugo 1932 Die Verwendung von Kupfersalzen zur Herstellung von Paramaecium Präparate. Arch. Protistenk., 76, 171–187. Abs. in Stain Technol., 8, 39.

Metcalf, R. L., and Patton, R. L. 1944 Fluorescence microscopy applied to entomology and allied fields. Stain Technol., 19, 11–27.

Meves, F., and Duesberg, J. 1908 Die Spermatozytenteilungen bei der Hornisse. (Vespa crabro L.). Arch. Mikroskop. Anat. u. Entwicklungsmech., 71, 571–587.

MICHAELIS, L. 1900 Die vitale Färbung, eine Darstellungsmethode der Zellgra-
nula. Arch. Mikroskop. Anat. u. Entwicklungsmech., 55, 558. (Uses Janus
green for chondriosomes.)

MICHAELIS, L. 1901 Ueber Fett Farbstoffe. Virchow's Arch. pathol. Anat. u.
Physiol., 164, 263. (Proposes Sudan IV).

MOLLIER, G. 1938 Eine Vierfachfärbung zur Darstellung glatter und quergestreif-
ter Muskulature und ihrer Beziehung zum Bindegewebe. Z. wiss. Mikroskop.,
55, 472–473. (Use of orcein and naphthol green B in a quadruple stain.)

MONNÉ, L. 1935 Permeability of the nuclear membrane to vital stains. Proc.
Soc. Exptl. Biol. Med., 32, 1197–1199. (Use of azo blue.)

MONNÉ, L. 1938 Über experimentell hervorgerufene strukturelle Veränderungen
der Golgiapparats und der Mitochondrien sowie über Bildung von Myelinfi-
guren in Spermatocyten und Spermatiden von Helix lutescens. Protoplasma,
30, 582–591.

MONNÉ, L. 1939 Polarisationsoptische Untersuchungen über den Golgi-Apparat
und die Mitochondrien männlicher Geschlechtszellen einiger Pulmonaten-
Arten. Protoplasma, 32, 184–192.

MOORE, E. J. 1933 The use of phenosafranin for staining fungi on culture media or
in host tissue. Science, 77, 23–24. Abs. in Stain Technol., 8, 79.

MOWRY, R. W. 1956 Alcian blue techniques for the histochemical study of acidic
carbohydrates. J. Histochem., 4, 407.

MÜLLER, H. A. C. 1912 Kernstudien an Pflanzen. Arch. Zellforsch., 8, Hft. 1,
1–51. (Applies to plant pathology the stain mixture of Pianese—malachite
green, acid fuchsin and martius yellow.)

NACHLAS, M. M., GOLDSTEIN, T. P., ROSENBLATT, D. E., KIRCH, M., and SELIGMAN,
A. M. 1959 Influence of chemical structure on the rate of azo coupling and
its significance in histochemical methodology. J. Histochem. Cytochem., 7,
50–65.

NACHLAS, M. N., and SELIGMAN, A. M. 1949 The chemical demonstration of esterase. J. Natl. Cancer Inst., 9, 415–425.

NACHLAS, M. M., TSOU, K-C., SOUZA, E. DE, CHENG, C-S., and SELIGMAN, A. M.
1957 Cytochemical demonstration of succinic dehydrogenase by the use of a
new p-nitrophenyl substituted ditetrazole. J. Histochem. Cytochem., 5, 420–
436.

NACHLAS, M. M., WALKER, D. G., and SELIGMAN, A. M. 1958 A histochemical
method for the demonstration of diphophosphopyridine nucleotide diaphorase.
J. Biophys. Biochem. Cytol., 4, 29–38.

NACHLAS, M. M., WALKER, D. G., AND SELIGMAN, A. M. 1958 The histochemical
localization of triphosphopyridine nucleotide diaphorase. J. Biophys. Biochem. Cytol., 4, 467–474.

NEBEL, B. R. 1931 Lacmoid-martius-yellow for staining pollen-tubes in the style.
Stain Technol., 6, 27–29.

NEBEL, B. R. 1940 Chlorazol black E as an aceto-carmine auxiliary stain. Stain
Technol., 15, 69–72.

NEUBERG, C., and NORD, F. F. 1919 Anwendungen der Abfangmethode auf die
Bakteriengärungen. I. Acetaldehyd als Zwischenstufe bei der Vergärung von
Zucker, Mannit und Glycerin durch Bacterium coli, durch Erreger der Ruhr
und des Gasbrandes. Biochem. Z., 96, 133–157.

NEWCOMER, E. H. 1938 A procedure for growing, staining, and making permanent
slides of pollen tubes. Stain Technol., 13, 89–91.

NEWTON, W. C. F. 1925 Chromosome studies in Tulipa and some related genera.

J. Linnean Soc., London, Botany, 47, 339–354. (Crystal violet iodine technic in plant cytology.)

NINEHAM, A. W. 1955 The chemistry of formazans and tetrazolium salts. Chem. Rev., 55, 355–483.

NOCHT. 1898 Zur Färbung der Malariaparasiten. Centr. Bakteriol. Parasitenk., I Abt., 24, 839–843. (First to polychromize methylene blue intentionally in preparing blood stains.)

NOVIKOFF, A. B., SHIN, W-Y., AND DRUCKER, J. 1961 Mitochondrial localization of oxidative enzymes: staining results with two tetrazolium salts. J. Biophys. Biochem. Cytol., 9, 47–61.

ODA, T., SEKI, S., and OKAZAKI, H. 1958 New colorimetric methods for the estimation of cytochrome c oxidase and of cytochrome c-cytochrome oxidase system. Acta Med. Okayama, 12, 293–301.

ÖKLAND, F. 1939 Untersuchungen über Osteoblasten in Schliffen und Ausstrichen. Z. wiss. Mikroskop., 56, 345. (Nile blue sulfate for staining bone sections.)

ONO, K. 1934 Studien über die Färbung der Rekurrensspirochäten, insbesondere über den Zusammenhang der Färbung mit den Vorbehandlungen. Acta dermatol. (Kyoto), 23, 1–14, 39–55. Abs. in Stain Technol., 10, 112.

ORTH, J. 1883 Notizen zur Färbetechnik. Berlin. klin. Wochschr., 20, 421–422 (Proposes lithium carmine.)

OSBORNE, S. G. 1857 Vegetable cell structure and its formation as seen in the early stages of the growth of the wheat plant. Trans. Micro. Soc., 5, 104–122. (Observes coloring of cell contents in plants grown in colored solutions—carmine, indigo, or vermilion.)

PALADINO, GIOVANNI 1895 Della nessuna partecipazione dell' epitelio della mucosa uterina e della relative glandole alla formazione della decidua vera e riflessa nella donna. Rend. accad. sci. fis. mat. e nat. soc. reale. Napoli, 34, 208–215. (Biebrich scarlet with alum hematoxylin.)

PAPANICOLAOU, GEORGE N. 1941 Some improved methods for staining vaginal smears. J. Lab. Clin. Med., 26, 1200–1205.

PAPPENHEIM, A. 1898 Befund von Smegmabacillen im menschlichen Lungenswurf. Berlin. klin. Wochschr., 37, 809. (Rosolic acid with methylene blue in the decolorizing solution following carbol-fuchsin in staining the tubercle organism.)

PAPPENHEIM, A. 1899 Vergleichende Untersuchungen über die elementare Zuzammensetzung des rothen Knochenmarkes einige Säugethiere. Virchow's Arch. f. pathol. Anat. u. Physiol., 157, 19–76. (Uses mixture of methyl green and pyronin.)

PARKS, L. R., and BARTLETT, P. G. 1935a Principles of dyeing with acid dyes. Am. Dyestuff Repr., 24, 476–478.

PARKS, L. R., and BARTLETT, P. G. 1935b Principles of dyeing with basic dyes. Am. Dyestuff Repr., 24, 523–532.

PEARSE, A. G. E. 1953 Histochemistry, Theoretical and Applied. Little, Brown & Co., Boston.

PEARSE, A. G. E. 1953 The histochemical demonstration of cystine-containing structures by methods involving alkaline hydrolysis. The alkaline tetrazolium method. J. Histochem. Cytochem., 1, 460–468.

PEARSE, A. G. E. 1957 Intracellular localization of dehydrogenase systems using monotetrazolium salts and metal chelation of their formazans. J. Histochem. Cytochem., 5, 515–527.

PEARSE, A. G. E. 1958 Cytochemical localization of pyridine nucleotide-linked dehydrogenases. Nature, 181, 1531–1532.

PEARSE, A. G. E. 1960 *Histochemistry, Theoretical and Applied.* Little, Brown & Co., Boston.

PEARSON, B. 1957 Improvement in the histochemical localization of succinic dehydrogenase by the use of nitroneotetrazolium chloride. J. Histochem. Cytochem., 6, 112–121.

v. PECHMANN, H., and RUNGE, P. 1894 Oxydation der Formazylverbindungen. Ber. deut. chem. Ges., 27, 2920–2930.

PELAGETTI, M. 1904 Ueber einige neue Färbungsmethoden mit Anwendung der Zenkerschen Fixierungsflüssigkeit in der histologischen Technik der Haut. Monatsch. prak. Dermat., 38, 532–536. (Biebrich scarlet after polychrome methylene blue or after Unna's hematein. Rose bengal following hematoxylin.)

PETER, KARL 1899 Die Bedeutung der Nährzelle im Hoden. Arch. mikroskop. Anat. u. Entwicklungsmech., 53, 180–211. (Light green with hematoxylin.)

PETERSEN, HANS 1924 Färben mit Säurealizarinblau. Z. wiss. Mikroskop., 41, 363–365.

PETERSON, A. R., CONN, H. J., and MELIN, C. G. 1933–1934. Methods for the standardization of biological stains:

Part I. General considerations. Stain Technol., 8, 87.

Part II. The fluorane derivatives. Stain Technol., 8, 95.

Part III. Certain nitro and azo dyes. Stain Technol., 8, 121.

Part IV. The triphenylmethane derivatives. Stain Technol., 9, 41.

Part V. Miscellaneous dyes. Stain Technol., 9, 147.

PETRAGNANI, G. 1928 Metodi rapidi di colorazione dei corpi del Negri. Boll. ist. sieroterap. milan., 7, 557–561. Abs. in Stain Technol., 5, 34.

PETROFF, S. A. 1915 A new and rapid method for the isolation and cultivation of tubercle bacilli directly from the sputum and feces. J. Exptl. Med., 21, 38–42. (Use of a gentian-violet-egg medium.)

PFITZER, E. 1883 Ueber ein Härtung und Färbung vereinigts Verfahren für die Untersuchung des plasmatischen Zelleibs. Ber. deut. botan. Ges., 1, 44–47. (Picro-nigrosin for chromatin.)

PHILLIPS, M., and COHEN, B. 1927 The preparation of vital neutral red. Stain Technol., 2, 74–79.

PIANESE, G. 1896 Beitrag zur Histologie und Aetiologie des Carcinoms. Beitr. pathol. Anat. u. allgem. Pathol., Suppl. I, 193 pp. (Malachite green and martius yellow with acid fuchsin.)

PICK, J. 1935 Einige Vitalfärbungen am Frosch mit neuen fluoreszierenden Farbstoffen. Z. wiss. Mikroskop., 51, 338–351.

POWERS, M. M., and CLARK, G. 1955 An evaluation of cresyl echt violet acetate as a Nissl stain. Stain Technol., 30, 83–88.

POWERS, M. M., CLARK, G., DARROW, M. A., and EMMEL, V. M. 1960 Darrow Red, a new basic dye. Stain Technol., 35, 19–21.

PRATT, ROBERTSON, DUFRENOY, JEAN, and PICKERING, VIRGINIA L. 1948 Tetrazolium chloride, a valuable reagent in stain technology. Stain Technol., 23, 137–141.

PRENANT, A. 1902 Contribution à l'étude de la ciliation. Arch. Anat. Microskop., 5. (Light green with hematoxylin.)

PROESCHER, F. 1927 Oil red O pyridin, a rapid fat stain. Stain Technol., 2, 60–61.

PROESCHER, F. 1933 Pinacyanol as a histological stain. Proc. Soc. Exptl. Biol. Med., 31, 79–81. Abs. in Stain Technol., 9, 78.

PROESCHER, F. 1934 Contribution to the staining of neuroglia. Stain Technol., 9, 33–38.

PROESCHER, F., and ARKUSH, A. S. 1928 Metallic lakes of the oxazines (gallimin blue, gallocyanin, and coelestin blue) as nuclear stain substitutes for hematoxylin. Stain Technol., 3, 28–38.

PRUDDEN, J. M. 1885 (A note without title). Z. wiss. Mikroskop., 2, 288. (In answer to a question by Flemming, gives formula of Delafield's hematoxylin.)

RAKIETEN, M. L., and RETTGER, L. F. 1927 Brilliant green and its use in an enrichment medium in the isolation of typhoid and paratyphoid organisms. J. Infectious Diseases, 41, 93.

RAMSDELL, G. A., JOHNSON, W. T. and EVANS, F. R. 1935 Investigation of resazurin as an indicator of the sanitary condition of milk. J. Dairy Science, 18, 705–717.

RANVIER 1868 Technique microscopique. Arch. phys. biol. 1, No. 2, 319–21; No. 5, 666–670. (First use of picro-carmine in a single procedure.)

RAWITZ, B. 1899 Bemerkungen über Karminsäure und Hämatein. Anat. Anz., 15, 437–444.

REUTER, KARL 1901 Über den färbenden Bestandteil der Romanowsky-Nochtschen Malaria-plasmodienfärbung, seine Reindarstellung und praktische Verwendung. Centr. Bakteriol. Parasitenk. I Abt., 30, 248–256. (Dissolves precipitate of Nocht stain in absolute alcohol plus aniline oil.)

REYNOLDS, B. D. 1936 Alum cochineal-hematoxylin stain. Stain Technol., 11, 166–167.

RICHARDS, O. W. 1943 Actinomyces of potato scab demonstrated by fluorescence microscopy. Stain Technol., 18, 91–94.

RICHARDS, O. W., and MILLER, D. K. 1941 An efficient method for the identification of M. tuberculosis with a simple fluorescence microscope. J. Clin. Pathol., 11, 1–8.

ROBERTSON, O. H. 1917 The effects of experimental plethora on blood production. J. Exptl. Med., 26, 221–237. (Use of brilliant cresyl blue for staining reticulated blood cells.)

ROBINSON, H. C., and RETTGER, L. F. 1916 Studies on the use of brilliant green and a modified Endo's medium in the isolation of Bacillus typhosus from feces. J. Med. Research, N.S., 29, 363–376.

ROE, M. A., LILLIE, R. D., and WILCOX, A. 1940 American azures in the preparation of satisfactory Giemsa stains for malaria parasites. Public Health Repts., 55, 1272–1278.

ROGERS, T. H. 1940 The inhibition of sulphate-reducing bacteria by dyestuffs. J. Soc. Chem. Ind., 59, 34–39.

ROMANOVSKI, D. L. 1891 On the question of parasitology and therapy of malaria. (In Russian.) Imp. Med. Military Acad., Dissert. No. 38, St. Petersburg, 1891. (Proposes combination of eosin and methylene blue for staining blood.)

ROMANOVSKI, D. L. 1891 Zur Frage der Parisitologie und Therapie der Malaria. St Petersburg Med. Wochschr., 16, 297–302, 307–315. A slightly condensed version of the above.

ROMEIS, B. 1928 Taschenbuch der mikroskopischen Technik. 12th Ed. Oldenbourg, Munich.

ROMELL, L. G. 1934 A blue stain for microörganisms in humus and in soil. Stain Technol., 9, 141–145.

ROTHBERGER, C. J. 1898 Differential diagnostische Untersuchungen mit gefärbten

Nährböden. Centr. Bakteriol. Parasitenk. Bakt. I Abt., **24**, 513–518. (Neutral red as indicator in media for differentiating typhoid and colon bacilli.)

RUTENBERG, A. M., GOFSTEIN, R., and SELIGMAN, A. M. 1950 Preparation of a new tetrazolium salt which yields a blue pigment on reduction, and its use in the demonstration of enzymes in normal and neoplastic tissues. Cancer Research, **10**, 113–121.

RUTH, E. B. 1946 Demonstration of the ground substance of cartilage, bone and teeth. Stain Technol., **21**, 27–30.

SABIN, FLORENCE R. 1929 Chemical Agents: Supravital Stains. *In* McClungs' Handbook of Microscopical Technique, Paul B. Hoeber, New York.

SANDIFORD, B. R. 1938 A new contrast stain for gonococci and meningococci in smears. Brit. Med. J., **1**, 1155.

SCALES, F. M. 1922 A new method for differential staining of bacteria. J. Infectious Diseases, **31**, 494–498.

SCANLAN, J. T., FRENCH, R. W., and HOLMES, W. C. 1927 Acid fuchsin as a stain—a refinement in manufacture. Stain Technol., **2**, 50–55.

SCANLAN, J. T., and MELIN, C. G. 1937 The production of basic fuchsin suitable for the Feulgen technic. Stain Technol., **12**, 1–8.

SCHAFFER 1888 Die Färberei zum Studium der Knochenentwicklung. Z. wiss. Mikroskop., **5**, 1–19. (Fast yellow for bone; Congo red for embryo sections.)

SCHMORL, G. 1899 Darstellung feinere Knochenstructuren. Centr. allgem. Pathol. u. pathol. Anat., **10**, 745–749.

SCHOOR, E. 1941 A new technic for staining vaginal smears: III. A single differential stain. Science, **94**, 545.

SCHULTZ, G. 1928–1934 Farbstofftabellen. 7 Aufl. Leipzig. Bd. 1, 764 pp.; Bd. 2, 444 pp.; Erganzbd. 1, 182 pp.

SCHUMACHER, J. 1922 Welche chemische Substanz baut die Pollkörnchen des Diphtheriebazillus auf? Zentr. Bakteriol., Parasitenk., I Abt., Orig., **88**, 362–366. (Phosphine as a microchemical reagent.)

SCHWARTZ, E. 1867 Ueber eine Methode doppelter Färbung mikroskopischer Objecte und ihre Anwendung, etc. Sitzber. Acad. Wiss: Wien, **55**, Hft. 1, 671–689. (First double staining.)

SCHWEIGER-SEIDEL, F., and DOGIEL, J. 1866 Ueber die peritoneal Hülle bei Fröschen und ihren zusammenhang mit dem Lymphgefässysteme. Ber. Sachs. Gessel. Wiss. zu Leipzig, **18**, 247–254. (Use of carminates with acetic acid.)

SCHWIND, J. L. 1950 The supravital method in the study of the cytology of blood and marrow cells. Blood, **7**, 597–622.

SCOTT, R. E., and FRENCH, R. W. 1924a Standardization of biological stains. Military Surgeon, Aug. 1924, 15 pp.

SCOTT, R. E., and FRENCH, R. W. 1924b Standardization of biological stains. II. Methylen blue. Military Surgeon, Sept. 1924, 16 pp.

SCOTT, R. E., and FRENCH, R. W. 1924c Standardization of biological stains. III. Eosin and haematoxylin. Military Surgeon, Nov. 1924, 8 pp.

SCUDDER, SARA A. 1931 A differential stain favorable to the diagnosis of Neisserian infection. Stain Technol., **6**, 99–105.

SCUDDER, SARA A., and LISA, J. R. 1931 A preliminary report on a combined Gram-Pappenheim stain for formalin fixed tissues. Stain Technol., **6**, 51–52.

SELIGMAN, A. M., and MANNHEIMER, L. H. 1949 A new method for the histochemical demonstration of acid phosphatase. J. Natl. Cancer Inst., **9**, 427–437.

SELIGMAN, A. M., and RUTENBURG, A. M. 1951 The histochemical demonstration succinic dehydrogenase. Science, 113, 317–320.

SHAEFFER, ALICE B., and FULTON, MACDONALD 1933 A simplified method of staining endospores. Science, 77, 194. Abs. in Stain Technol., 8, 80.

SHAFFER, R. W. 1933 A rapid method for distinguishing bleached sulfate from bleached sulfite. Ind. Eng. Chem., 5, 35. (Brazilin for the microscopic differentiation of fibers.)

SHELTON, E. and SCHNEIDER, W. C. 1952 On the usefulness of tetrazolium salts as histochemical indicators of dehydrogenase activity. Anat. Record, 112, 61–81.

SHUMWAY, WALDO 1926 Fuchsin and picro-indigo-carmine, a polychromatic stain for vetebrate organogeny. Stain Technol., 1, 37–38.

SINGER, MARCUS 1952 Factors which control the staining of tissue sections with acid and basic dyes. Intern. Rev. of Cytol., 1952, 211–255.

SMITH, F. E. 1951 Tetrazolium salt. Science, 113, 751–754.

SMITH, G. M. 1915 The development of botanical microtechnique. Trans. Am. Microscop. Soc., 34, 71–129. (Includes discussion of early history of staining.)

SMITH, H. A. 1939 A technic for making photomicrographic prints in color. J. Tech. Methods, 19, 45–51.

SMITH, J. LORRAIN 1907 On the simultaneous staining of neutral fat and fatty acid by oxazine dyes. J. Pathol. Bacteriol., 12, 1–4. (Shows the possibility of differentiating fat and fatty acids in tissue by means of Nile blue sulfate.)

SMITH, J. LORRAIN, and MAIR, W. 1911 Fats and lipoids in relation to methods of staining. Skand. Arch. Physiol., 25, 245–255. (Describes the Nile blue sulfate technic for staining fat in sections, as well as other methods for fat staining.)

SMITH, LOUISE 1920 The hypobranchial apparatus of Spelerpes bislineatus. J. Morphol., 33, 527–583. (Use of methylene blue in staining cartilage by the Van Wijhe technic.)

SMITH, N. R., and DAWSON, VIRGINIA T. 1944 The bacteriostatic action of rose bengal in media used for plate counts of soil fungi. Soil Sci., 58, 467–471.

SOCIETY OF AMERICAN BACTERIOLOGISTS 1957 Manual of microbiological methods. McGraw-Hill Book Co., New York.

SOCIETY OF DYERS AND COLOURISTS 1924 Colour Index. Edited by F. M. Rowe. Published by the Society, Bradford, Yorkshire, England.

SOCIETY OF DYERS AND COLOURISTS 1956 Id. 2nd Ed. Published by the Society of Dyers and Colourists, England, and the American Association of Textile Chemists, Lowell, Mass.

SOEP, LEO 1927 Le vert Janus en face du bleu de méthylène dans l'essai a la réductase selon Barthel. Lait, 7, 927–935. (Janus green as substitute for methylene blue in reductase test of milk.)

SPIRIDONOVITCH, R. 1924 Vital staining of white blood cells with cresylecht violet. Anat. Record, 27, 367–373.

SPULER, A. 1901 Ueber eine neue Stückfärbemethode. Deut. med. Wochschr., 27, Vereine-Beilage No. 14, 116. (Iron alum cochineal.)

STEARN, A. E., and STEARN, ESTHER W. 1928 The effect of the chemical nature of a decolorizer on its functioning. I. The Gram classification. Stain Technol. 3, 81–93; II. The apparent isoelectric point. Stain Technol., 3, 87–93.

STEARN, A. E., and STEARN, ESTHER W. 1929 The mechanism of staining explained on a chemical basis. I. The reaction between dyes, proteins, and nucleic acid. Stain Technol., 4, 111–119.

STEARN, A. E., and STEARN, ESTHER W. 1930 The mechanism of staining explained on a chemical basis. II. General presentation. Stain Technol., **5**, 17–24.

STEEDMAN, H. F. 1950 Alcian blue 8GS; a new stain for mucin. Quart. J. Microscop. Sci., **91**, 477–479.

STILLING, H. 1886 Fragmente zur Pathologie der Milz. Virchow's Arch. pathol. Anat. u. Physiol., **103**, 15–38. (Iodine green for amyloid.)

STIRLING, W. 1890 Some recent and some new histological methods. J. Anat. Physiol., **24** (n. s., Vol. 4), 601.

STITT, E. R. 1923 *Practical bacteriology, blood work, and animal parasitology.* 7th Ed. Blakistons, Philadelphia.

STOCK, ALEXANDER 1944 The determination of calcium in histological sections. J. Roy. Microscop. Soc., **69**, 20–24.

STOTZ, ELMER, CONN, H. J., KNAPP, FRANCES, and EMERY, A. J. 1950 Spectrophotometric characteristics and assay of biological stains. Stain Technol., **25**, 57–68.

STOUGHTON, R. H. 1930 Thionin and orange G for the differential staining of bacteria and fungi in plant tissues. Ann Appl. Biol., **17**, 162–164. Abs. in Stain Technol., **6**, 72.

STOVALL, W. D., and BLACK, C. E. 1940 The influence of pH on the eosin methylene blue method for demonstrating Negri bodies. Am. J. Clin. Pathol., **10**, 1–8.

STRAUS, F. H., CHERONIS, N. D., and STRAUS, E. 1948 Demonstration of reducing systems in neoplasms and living mammalian tissues by triphenyltetrazolium chloride. Science, **108**, 113.

STRUGGER, S. 1938 Die Vitalfärbung des Protoplasms mit Rhodamine B und 6G. Protoplasma, **30**, 85–100.

STRUGGER, S. 1948 Fluorescence microscope in examination of bacteria in soil. Can. J. Research, **C26**, 188–193.

SUTTER, M. 1919 On the behavior of the mammary epithelial cell toward vital dyes in various functional epochs of its life cycle. Anat. Record, **16**, 164–165, (abstract). (Use of dianil blue 2 R as vital stain.)

TAFT, E. B. 1951 The problem of a standardized technic for the methyl green-pyronin stain. Stain Technol., **26**, 205–212.

TARAO, S. 1940 Microchemical studies on the Golgi apparatus using protease Nile blue sulfate technique. II Golgi apparatus of pancreatic acinar cells in the mouse in fixed and living conditions. Cytologia, **11**, 261–281.

TEICHMÜLLER, W. 1899 Die eosinophile Bronchitis. Deut. Arch. klin. Med., **63**, 444–456.

TEICHMÜLLER, W. 1887 Über eine neue Methode zur Färbung von Fibrin und von Microorganismen. Forts. d. Med., **5**, 228–232.

TERRY, B. T. 1928 A new and rapid method of examining tissue microscopically for malignancy. J. Lab. Clin. Med., **13**, No. 6.

THORNTON, H. R., and SANDIN, R. B. 1935 Standardization of the methylene blue reduction test by the use of methylene blue thiocyanate. Am. J. Public Health, **25**, 1114–1117.

TOLSTOOUHOV, A. V. 1926 Some practical applications of the physico-chemical theory of differential staining: Blood, tissue, and bacteria staining. Methylene blue eosin water-soluble mixtures as a universal dye mixture. Proc. N. Y. Pathol. Soc., **26**, 147–159.

TOLSTOOUHOV, A. V. 1928 The effect of preliminary treatment (fixing fluids) on staining properties of the tissues. Stain Technol., **3**, 49–56.

TOLSTOOUHOV, A. V. 1929 Detailed differentiation of bacteria by means of a mixture of acid and basic dyes at different pH-values. Stain Technol., 4, 81–89.

TORREY, J. C. 1913 Brilliant green broth as a specific enrichment medium for the paratyphoid-interiditis group of bacteria. J. Infectious Diseases, 13, 263–272.

TORREY, J. C., and BUCKELL, G. T. 1922 Cultural methods for the gonococcus. J. Infectious Diseases, 31, 125–147. (Iodine green in a culture medium.)

TSUCHIYA, H. 1936 The effects of dyes on Endameba histolytica in vitro. J. Lab. Clin. Med., 21, 1028–1035.

TSVETT 1911 Sur un nouveau réactif colorant de la callose. Compt. rend. acad. sci., 153, 503–505. (Use of resorcin blue—or lacmoid—as a micro-chemical reagent for callose in vegetable tissue.)

TWORT, F. W. 1924a An improved neutral red light green double stain for staining animal parasites, microorganisms and tissues. J. State Med., 32, 351–355.

TWORT, F. W. 1924b Further modifications in the preparation of neutral red, light-green, double stain, and an improved method of embedding tissues in paraffin. Brit. J. Exptl. Pathol., 5, 350–351.

UNNA, P. G. 1891 Ueber die Reifung unserer Farbstoffe. Z. wiss. Mikroscop., 8, 475–487. (Polychrome methylene blue).

UNNA, P. G. 1921 Chromolyse. Abderhalden's Handb. der Biol. Arbeitsmethoden. Abt. 5, Teil 2, Hft. 1, (Lief'ng. 17) 1–62.

VAN GIESON, J. 1889 Laboratory notes of technical methods for the nervous system. N. Y. Med. J., 50, 57–60. (Hematoxylin, acid fuchsin and picric acid as nervous tissue stain.)

VARCO, R. L., and VISSCHER, M. B. 1941 Further studies in the elimination of certain dyes by gastric mucosa. Proc. Soc. Exptl. Biol. Med., 46, 295–298.

VARRELMAN, F. A. 1938 Technic in the study of vascular systems in plants. Stain Technol., 13, 115–119. (Niagara sky blue to demonstrate location of vessels in twigs.)

VAUGHAN, R. E. 1914 A method for the differential staining of fungus and host cells. Ann Missouri Botan. Garden, 1, 241–242. (An adaptation for botanical purposes of Pianese's stain: malachite green, acid fuchsin and martius yellow.)

VENKATARAMAN, K. 1952 The chemistry of synthetic dyes. Academic Press, New York.

VERDCOURT, BERNARD 1947 Chlorazol paper brown B as a stain for plant tissues. Stain Technol., 22, 155–156.

VERONA, O. 1935 Manière de se comporter des microörganismes vis-à-vis de certaines substances colorantes. Étude particulière sur le vert malachite sur son application éventuelle en phytothérapie. Boll. sez. ital. soc. intern. microbiol., 7, 426–428.

VINASSA, E. 1891 Beiträge zur pharmakognostischen Mikroskopie. Z. wiss. Mikroskop., 8, 34–50. (Auramin for plant sections.)

v. VOLKMANN, R., and STRAUSS, F. 1934 Ein Ersatz für die Hornowskysche Kombination zur Darstellung von Elastin, Muskulatur und Kollagen auf der Basis der Azanmethode. Z. wiss. Mikroskop., 51, 244–249. Abs. in Stain Technol., 10, 70.

WALDEYER 1863 Untersuchungen über den Ursprung und den Verlauf des Axsencylinders bei Wirbellosen und Wirbelthieren sowie über dessen Endverhalten in der quergestreiften Muskelfaser. Henle & Pfeifer's Z. rationelle. Med., 3 Reihe, Bd. 20, 193–256. (First attempt to stain with logwood extract. Early use of aniline dyes.)

WALLART, J., and HOUETTE, C. 1934 Une coloration trichromique rapid à l'héma-toxyline, la fuchsine acide et le jaune solide. Bull. histol. appl. et tech. mi-croscop., 11, 404–407. Abs. in Stain Technol., 10, 71.

WEICHHERZ, E. 1934 Die Kahnsche Reaktion mit Färbung nach Hecht. Časopis. lékáru českých, 1934, p. 1096. Abs. in Stain Technol., 10, 145.

WEIGERT, CARL 1884 Ausführliche Beschreibung der in No. 2 dieser Zeitschrift erwähnten Färbungsmethode für das Centralnervensystem. Ertsch. Med., 2, 190–191. (Chrom-hematoxylin for medullary sheaths.)

WEIGERT, CARL 1898 Ueber eine Methode zur Färbung elastischer Fasern. Centr. allgem. Pathol. u. pathol. Anat., 9, 289–292. (Fuchsin for elastic tissue.)

WEIMER, B. R. 1927 The use of Nile blue sulfate as a vital stain on Hydra. Biol. Bull., 52, 219–222.

WEISS, E. 1928 Method of staining flagella. J. Infectious Diseases, 43, 228–231. Abs. in Stain Technol., 4, 32.

WEISS, E. 1929 A simple method for staining spirochetes. J. Lab. Clin. Med., 14, 1191–1193. Abs. in Stain Technol., 5, 35.

WHITBY, G. S. 1942 Dyes and dye chemistry fight disease. Textile Colorist, 64, 119.

WHITTENBERGER, R. T. 1944 Oil blue NA as a stain for rubber in sectioned or ground plant tissues. Stain Technol., 19, 93–98.

WILKINSON, G. R., and BARKSDALE, I. S. 1928 Effect of bismuth violet (hexa-methyl-para-rosanilin-bismuth) on certain pathogenic organisms. South. Med. J., 21, 914–917.

WILLIAMS, B. G. R. 1923 Cresylecht violet, a rare dye. J. Lab. Clin. Med., 8, No. 4, Jan., 4 pp.

WILLIAMS, B. G. R. 1925 Further studies with cresylecht violet, including a report of my six-second method for staining tissue. J. Lab. Clin. Med., 10, 312–315.

WILLIAMS, J. W., and GREEN, L. 1935 Effect of dyes on colonies of certain patho-genic fungi. Proc. Soc. Exptl. Biol. Med., 32, 625–628.

WINDLE, W. F., RHINES, RUTH, and RANKIN, JAMES 1943 A Nissl method using buffered solutions of thionin. Stain Technol., 18, 77–86.

WINOGRADSKY 1924 Sur l'étude microscopique du sol. Compt. rend. acad. sci., 179, 367. (Erythrosin for staining bacteria in soil.)

WINTREBERT, P. 1932 La conservation dans les coupes de paraffin des marques vi-tales au brun Bismarck et au sulfate de bleu de Nil, faites sur les oeufs vivants d'Amphibiens. Compt. rend. acad. sci. Paris, 194, 1013–1015. Abs. in Stain Technol., 8, 161.

WOLF, F. T. 1938 Cytological observations on gametogenesis and fertilization of Achlya flagellata. Mycologia, 30, 456–467. (Picric acid as a counterstain to crystal violet.)

WOODRUFF, L. L. 1926 The versatile Sir John Hill, M.D. Am. Naturalist, 60, 417–442.

WRIGHT, J. H. 1902 A rapid method for the differential staining of blood films and malarial parasites. J. Med. Research, 7, 138–144.

YEGIAN, D., and PORTER, K. R. 1944 Some artifacts encountered in stained prepa-rations of tubercle bacilli. I. Non-acid-fast forms arising from mechanical treatment. J. Bacteriol., 48, 83–90.

YOE, J. H., and BOYD, G. R. 1939 Patent blue V as a pH and redox indicator. Ind. Eng. Chem., Anal. Ed., 11, 492–493.

ZAHL, P. A., and WATERS, L. L. 1941 Localization of colloidal dyes in animal tumors. Proc. Soc. Exptl. Biol. Med., 48, 304–310.

ZIMMERMANN, A. 1893 Beiträge zur Morphologie und Physiologie der Pflanzenzelle. Bd. II. Tübingen, 1893. 35 pp. (Iodine green as chromatin stain for plant cells.)

ZSCOKKE, E. 1888 Ueber einige neue Farbstoffe bezüglich ihrer Verwendung zu histologischen Zwecken. Z. wiss. Mikroscop., 5, 465–470. (Benzopurpurin in contrast to hematoxylin.)

INDEX

In this index the preferred designations of dyes are printed in bold face type, synonyms in italics. Figures in bold face type indicate the prinicipal references.

Acid alizarin blue BB, 203
Acid alizarin blue GR, 203
Acid and basic dyes, nature of, 19–21
Acid Bordeaux, 65
Acid Congo R., 83
Acid fuchsin (see Fuchsin, acid)
Acid green, 133
Acid green O, 53
Acid green S., 164
Acid magenta, 143
Acid orange II, Y or A., 70
Acid phloxine GR, 60
Acid rubin, 143
Acid violet, 154
Acid violet 4R, 170
Acid yellow, 57
Acid yellow D, 69
Acid yellow R, 68
Acme yellow, 88
Acridine dyes, 194–198
Acridine orange NO, 195
Acridine red 3B, 166
Acridine yellow, 195
Acriflavine, 27, 196
Acriviolet, 197
Alcian blue 8GX, 27A, 207
Algae, staining of, 183
Alizarin, 27, 199
Alizarin blue RBN, 108
Alizarin bordeaux BA, 202
Alizarin carmine, 200
Alizarin No. 6, 201
Alizarin orange, 89
Alizarin P, VI, Ie, 199
Alizarin purpurin, 201
Alizarin red, water soluble, 200
Alizarin red S, 27, 200
  absorption curve of, 201
  assay of, 286

Alizarin yellow GG or *R*, 89
Alkanet, 204
Alphazurin 2G, 160
Amaranth, 72
Amethyst violet, 122
Amidonaphthal red G, 61
Amanil garnet II, 81
Amino-azins, 115–118
1-Aminonaphthalene, 228
Analysis of dyes, spectrophotometric, 41–51
Andrade indicator, 144
Aniline blue, alcohol soluble, 155
Aniline blue WS (water soluble), 27, 123, 134, **156**
  absorption curve of, 157
  assay of, 304
  in Mallory connective tissue stain, 4
Aniline red, 136
Anthracene blue SWX, SWX extra, 203
Anthracene yellow GG or RN, 89
Anthraquinone dyes, 199–204
Archelline 2B, 65
Assay methods, 32–33, 276–315
Atabrine, 197
Atebrine, 197
Auramine O, 27, 128
  absorption curve of, 129
  assay of, 295
Aurantia, 56
Aurin, 27, 162
Aurin R, 162
Auxochromes, 18
"Azan carmine", 123
Azidine blue 3B, 84
Azidine scarlet R, 83
Azins, 115–125
Azo acid blue B, 62
Azo acid red L, 62

343

Azo blue, 84, 202
Azo-Bordeaux, 65
Azocarmine B, 123
Azocarmine G, 122, 242
    absorption curve of, 117
    assay of, 286
Azocarmine GX, 122
Azo dyes, 56–88
Azo fuchsin, 62, 83
Azofuchsin 3B, 62
Azophloxine GA, 61
Azo rhodine 3G, 62
Azo rubin, 72
Azure I, 96, 255
Azure II, 96, 255
Azure II-eosin, 255
Azure A, 97, 103, 255–258
    absorption curve of, 98
    assay of, 289
Azure A eosinate, 256
Azure B, 99, 103, 255–258
    absorption curve of, 98
    assay of, 289
Azure B eosinate, 256
Azure C, 71, 96
    absorption curve of, 98
    assay of, 290

Bacteria, negative staining of, 81, 125
    staining of, 79, 94, 110, 121
        by Gram technic, 149–151
        in soil, 171, 185
        with auramine O, 128
        with crystal violet, 149–151
        with methylene blue, 101–102
Bacterial capsules, staining of, 84
Bacterial fat, staining of, 88
Bacterial flagella, staining of, 156
Bacterial spores, staining of, 125, 131, 180
Bacteriostatic dyes, 131–133, 149–150,
    196–197
Basic brown BR or BXN, 80
Basic brown G, GX or GXP, 79
Basic fuchsin (see Fuchsin, basic)
Basic orange, 3RN, 195
Basic rubin, 136
Basilene fast blue B, 89
Benzamine blue 3B, 84
Benzene, 16
Benzene-d-naphthylamine (BAN), 59
Benzo blue 3B, 84

Benzo new blue 2B, 84
Benzo sky blue, 86
Benzoin blue R, 84
Benzopurpurin 4B, 82
Benzyl violet, 155
Berberine, 238
Berlin blue, 208
Biebrich scarlet R (footnote), 75
Biebrich scarlet, W. S. (water solu-
    ble), 77
Bindschedler's green, 91
Biological stains, in time of war, 8
Bismarck brown G, 79
Bismarck brown GOOO, 80
Bismarck brown R, 80
Bismarck brown Y, 21, 26, 79
    absorption curve of, 80
    assay of, 284
"Bismuth violet", 151
Black BS salt, 227
Blood, staining of, 60, 96–104, 107, 116,
    144, 151–152, 207
Blue tetrazolium, 233
Bone, staining of, 110, 200
Bordeaux, 72
Bordeaux B, BL, G, R, R extra, 65
Bordeaux red, 65
Bordeaux SF, 72
Brazilin, 244
Brilliant blue C, 106
Brilliant Congo R, 83
Brilliant Congo red R, 83
Brilliant cresyl blue, 26, 106
    absorption curve of, 107
    assay of, 291
Brilliant croceine, 73
Brilliant fat brown B, 65
Brilliant fat scarlet B, 65
Brilliant green, 27, 132
    absorption curve of, 131
    assay of, 296
Brilliant pink B, 169
Brilliant ponceau G, 64
"Brilliant purpur R", 83
Brilliant purpurin R, 83
Brilliant vital red, 83
Brilliant yellow S, 70
Brom chlor phenol blue, 188, 190
Brom cresol green, 188, 191
Brom cresol purple, 188, 192
Brom phenol blue, 188, 190

Brom thymol blue, 188, 193
Brom phenol red, 188, 192
Bromo acid J, TS, XL, or XX, 175
Bromofluorescein, 175
Bronze bromo ES, 175
Brown R, AT, C or N, 80
Buffalo black NBR, 73
Buffalo garnet R, 81
Bulk staining, 239–240
Butter yellow, 58

Calcoid green S extra, 164
Calcozine red 6G extra, 169
Canary yellow, 128
Capri blue, 115
Carbol fuchsin, (*see Fuchsin, carbol*)
Cardinal red, 89
Carmalum, 240
Carmein, 241
Carmine, 156, 159, **239**
  assay of, 310
  first use of, 3
  in plant histology, 6
Carmine naptha, 89
Carminic acid, 240
Carycinel red, 202
Celestin blue B, 109
Cerasin, 89
Cerasin R, 65
Cerasin red, 74
Cerotin orange, 89
Cerotine ponceau 3B, 75
Certified stains, list of, 271
Chelating tetrazole MTT, 232
Chemical theory of staining, 36
China blue, 156
Chinese blue, 208
Chlor cresol green, 188, 191
Chlor phenol red, 188, 191
Chlorazol black E, 87
  absorption curve of, 80
  assay of, 285
Chlorazol blue 3B, 84
Chlorazol paper brown B, 89
Chlorazol pink Y, 73
Chlorazol violet N, 89
Chromatography, 48–51
Chrom blue GCB, 108
Chrome black J or F, 89
Chrome violet CG, 162
Chromogens, 18–19

Chromophores, 21–22
Chromotrope 2R, 60
Chromotrope blue 2R, 60
Chromotrope N2R, 60
Chrysoidin R, 89
Chrysoidin Y, 58
Chrysoin, 88
C. I. Acid black 1, 73
C. I. Acid black 2, 125
C. I. Acid blue 1, 160
C. I. Acid blue 19, 170
C. I. Acid blue 20, 125
C. I. Acid blue 22, 156
C. I. Acid blue 74, 237
C. I. Acid blue 93, 159
C. I. Acid green 1, 53
C. I. Acid green 3, 136
C. I. Acid green 5, 133
C. I. Acid green 50, 164
C. I. Acid orange 10, 59
C. I. Acid orange 5, 69
C. I. Acid orange 7, 70
C. I. Acid orange 20, 70
C. I. Acid orange 52, 68
C. I. Acid red 2, 27, 72
C. I. Acid red 7, 62
C. I. Acid red 1 and 29, 60–61
C. I. Acid red 17, 65
C. I. Acid red 26, 64
C. I. Acid red 51 and 95, 180
C. I. Acid red 66, 77
C. I. Acid red 73, 73
C. I. Acid red 87, 175
C. I. Acid red 91, 178
C. I. Acid red 92 and 98, 182
C. I. Acid red 93 and 94, 184
C. I. Acid red 101, 122
C. I. Acid violet 9, 170
C. I. Acid violet 19, 143
C. I. Acid yellow 9, 57
C. I. Acid yellow 16, 70
C. I. Acid yellow 24, 55
C. I. Acid yellow 36, 68
C. I. Acid yellow 73, 174
C. I. Azoic Diazo
  No. 1, 215
  No. 3, 212
  No. 4 and 21, 225
  No. 5, 214
  No. 6, 216
  No. 8 and 42, 220

No. 9 and 11, 218
No. 10, 213
No. 13, 214
No. 20, 223
No. 24 and 43, 221
No. 27, 226
No. 34, 219
No. 35, 227
No. 36, 229
No. 37, 217
No. 38, 223
No. 41, 222
No. 48, 226
No. 51, 224
C. I. Azoic Diazo component, 228
C. I. Basic black 2, 67
C. I. Basic blue 6, 114
C. I. Basic blue 8, 156
C. I. Basic blue 9, 100
C. I. Basic blue 11 and 26, 163
C. I. Basic blue 12, 110
C. I. Basic blue 15, 164
C. I. Basic blue 17 and 24, 105
C. I. Basic blue 20, 151
C. I. Basic brown 1, 79
C. I. Basic brown 4, 80
C. I. Basic green 1, 132
C. I. Basic green 4, 130
C. I. Basic green 5, 104
C. I. Basic orange 2, 58
C. I. Basic orange 14, 195
C. I. Basic orange 15 and 23, 198
C. I. Basic red 1, 169
C. I. Basic red 2, 119
C. I. Basic red 5, 116
C. I. Basic red 6, 123
C. I. Basic red 9, 136
C. I. Basic violet 1, 146
C. I. Basic violet 2 and 14, 137
C. I. Basic violet 3, 149
C. I. Basic violet 4, 151
C. I. Basic violet 10, 169
C. I. Basic yellow 1, 206
C. I. Basic yellow 2, 128
C. I. Basic yellow 7, 195
C. I. Direct black 38, 87
C. I. Direct blue 14, 84
C. I. Direct blue 15, 86
C. I. Direct blue 31, 84
C. I. Direct blue 41, 159

C. I. Direct blue 53, 85
C. I. Direct red 2, 82
C. I. Direct red 10 and 28, 81
C. I. Direct red 15 and 34, 83
C. I. Direct red 45, 73
C. I. Direct red 48, 204
C. I. Direct violet 39, 84
C. I. Direct yellow 7, 206
C. I. Direct yellow 9 and 59, 205
C. I. Food green 3, 134
C. I. Ingrain blue 1, 207
C. I. Mordant blue 10 and 45, 108
C. I. Mordant blue 14, 109
C. I. Mordant blue 23, 203
C. I. Mordant green 4, 53
C. I. Mordant red 3, 200
C. I. Mordant red 11, 199
C. I. Mordant violet 39, 162
C. I. Natural black 1 and 2, 244
C. I. Natural red 4, 238
C. I. Natural red 24, 244
C. I. Natural red 28, 241
C. I. Natural yellow 6, 236
C. I. Natural yellow 18, 238
C. I. Solvent black 3, 87
C. I. Solvent blue 3, 155
C. I. Solvent blue 7, 124
C. I. Solvent brown 5, 65
C. I. Solvent orange 7, 63
C. I. Solvent red 1, 65
C. I. Solvent red 1A, 76
C. I. Solvent red 23, 74
C. I. Solvent red 24, 75
C. I. Solvent red 27, 76
C. I. Solvent red 44, 177
C. I. Solvent red 45, 178
C. I. Solvent yellow 2, 58
C. I. Solvent yellow 4, 59
C. I. Vat blue 1, 237
Classification of dyes, 24–27
Coccinel red, 202
Cochineal, 239
Coelestin blue, 208
Coeline, 208
Coeruleum, 208
Colour index numbers, 28, 262–271
Commercial sources of stains, 8–10
Congo, 81
Congo blue 3B, 84

Congo corinth G or GW, 81
Congo red, 4, 26, 81
  absorption curve of, 67
  assay of, 285
Connective tissue, staining of, 123, 144,
  158, 242
Coreine 2R, 109
Corinth brown G, 81
Coriphosphine O, 195
Corn blue B and BN, 163
Cotton blue, 156, 159
Cotton corinth G, 81
Cotton orange, 89
Cotton red, 119
Cotton red 4B, 82
Cotton red B or C, 81
Cresol red, 188, 193
Cresolphthalein, 188, 194
Cresyl blue 2RN or BBS, 106
Cresyl echt violet, 111
Cresyl fast violet, 111
Croceine scarlet, 77
Croceine scarlet 3B, MOO, 73
Crystal orange GG, 59
Crystal ponceau 6R, 89
Cresyl violet acetate, 111
  absorption curves of, 113
  assay of, 292
Crystal violet, 79, 148, 149
  absorption curves of, 48, 148
  assay of, 301
  in Flemming triple stain, 6, 149
  in Kalter's quadruple stain, 71
  in staining pollen tubes, 69
Curcumine, 70
Cyanol FF, 160
Cyanol green B, 164
Cyanosine, 182
Cytological staining, 121, 133–135, 149–
  150, 242–244, 247

Dahlia, 145
Dahlia B, 146
Darrow red, 113
  absorption curve of, 113
  assay of, 293
Delta dye indicator, 63
Diamine Bordeaux CGN, 81
Diamine red 4B, 82
Diamine violet N, 89

Di-amino-tri-phenyl methanes, 130–136
Diamond black F, 89
Diamond flavine G, 89
Diamond green B, BX or P extra, 130
Diamond green G, 132
Dianil blue H3G, 84
Dianil blue 2R, 84
Dianil red 4B, 82
Dianthine B and G, 180
Diazin green S, 66
Diazine black, 67
Diazonium and Tetrazonium salts, 210–
  229
2,6-Dichloroindophenol, 92
Dimethoxy neotetrazolium, 233
Diphenyl methanes, 128
Diphenyl-naphthyl methanes, 163–164
*Direct black MS, RL, E, GX, EE, 2V, F
  or A*, 87
*Direct deep black EW extra, E, EA, EAD
  extra*, 87
Direct garnet R, 81
Direct red 4B, 82
Direct red C, R or Y, 81
Direct sky blue, 86
Direct steel blue BB, 84
Direct violet B, 84
Direct violet C, 81
Direct violet K, N or R, 89
Dis-azo and poly-azo dyes, 73–89
Ditetrazolium chloride, 233
Ditetrazolium salts, 233–235
Double green SF, 151
Double scarlet BSF, 77
Dye indexes, 28–29
Dye nomenclature, 262–269
Dye solubilities, 29–31, 272–275

Ehrlich - Biondi - Heidenhain staining
  method, 71, 144, 152
Ehrlich's tri-acid stain, 60, 252
Elastin, staining of, 81, 242
Embryos, staining of, 81, 110, 156
Emerald green, 208
Emerald green crystals, 132
Endo medium, 140–141
Eosin 10B, 182
Eosin B (i.e. Bluish), 172, 173, **178**
  absorption curve of, 176
  assay of, 306

Eosin B extra, BP, BS, DH, G, GGF, J extra, 3J, 4J, JJF, KS, S extra, Y extra, or YS, 175
Eosin BN, BA, BW or DJV, 178
Eosin J, 180
Eosin S, 178
Eosin alcohol soluble (See also Ethyl eosin), 177, 178
"Eosin, bluish blend", 179
Eosin-methylene-blue medium, 101
Eosin scarlet, 178
Eosin scarlet B, 178
Eosin water soluble, 175
Eosin(s), 175–185
Eosin Y, 101, 103, 172, 173, 175
  absorption curve of, 176
  assay of, 305
  in chromatography, 51
  with hematoxylin, (H-E stain), 4, 176 248
  with thiazin dyes, 253–259
Erie black GXOO, B, BF, 87
Erie garnet B, 81
Erie violet 3R, 89
Eriorubine G, 62
Erythrosin B, 27, 172, 173, 180
  absorption curve of, 183
  assay of, 307
  in chromatography, 51
Erythrosin BB, or B extra, 182
Erythrosin B, N, or JN, 180
Erythrosin R or G, 180
Erythrosin Y, 27 173, 177, 180
Ethyl eosin, 172, 178
  absorption curve of, 176
  assay of, 306
Ethyl green, 132, 153
Ethyl purple 6B, 151
Ethyl violet, 78, 151
Euchrysine 3RXA, 195
Euflavine, 197
Eurhodins, 115–118
Evans blue, 85
Excelsior brown, 79

Fast acid blue R, 170
Fast acid green N, 133
Fast acid violet 3RL, A2R and R, 170
Fast black B, 227
Fast black K, 223

Fast blue B, 226
Fast blue BB, 223
Fast blue B, OB, R, 2R, etc., 125
Fast blue 3R, 114
Fast blue 4R, 156
Fast blue RR, 221
Fast brown III, 65
Fast brown RR, 213
Fast brown V, 225
Fast Bordeaux GP, 215
Fast Corinth LB, 221
Fast crimson GR, 61
Fast dark blue R, 224
Fast fuchsin G, 60
Fast garnet GBC, 225
Fast garnet GC, 226
Fast green FCF, 153, 134
  absorption curve of, 135
  assay of, 298
  for staining vaginal smears, 78
  in Kalter's quadruple stain, 71
  in Kornhausler "Quad" stain, 242
  in Masson's stain, 164
Fast light green, 164
Fast oil brown S, 65
Fast oil orange II, 63
Fast oil yellow B, 58
Fast orange GR, 216
Fast phosphine NAL, 198
Fast ponceau 2B, 78
Fast printing green, 65
Fast red, 72
Fast red, A, AV, AL, BX, S or O, 89
Fast red AL, 229
Fast red B, 214
Fast red B, BN or P, 65
Fast red GG, 217
Fast red GL and ITR, 220
Fast red 3GL and TR, 218
Fast red RC, 213
Fast red RL, 219
Fast red violet LB, 216
Fast scarlet CG, 212
Fast scarlet R, 214
Fast violet, 108
Fast violet B, 222
Fast yellow, 57
Fast yellow FY, G, GG, S, BG, etc., 57
Fat blue B, 163
Fat ponceau, 63, 75

Fat ponceau G, 74
Fat ponceau R or LB, 75
Fat, staining of, 64, 65, 74–77, 87, 93, 110, 114, 202–203
Feulgen stain, 24, 33, 139–141
Flavine, 196
Flemming triple stain, 6, 120, 149, 150
Fluoran derivatives, 171–185
Fluorescein, 174
Fluorescence microscopy, 128, 169, 175, 185, 195–198, 204–205
Fluorescent blue, 109
Frozen sections, staining of, 94, 207
Fuchsia, 122
Fuchsin, acid, 27, **143–145,** 152, 154
  absorption curve of, 139
  assay of, 303
  in Ehrlich's "Tri-acid stain", 251, 252
  in Mallory connective tissue stain, 4, 60, 158
  in Masson's stain, 68, 248
  in Pianese stain, 55, 131
  in plant histology, 6
Fuchsin, basic, 27, 79, **136–143,** 146, 162
  absorption curve of, 48, 139
  assay of, 299
  in plant microtechnic, 6
  reduction of, 23–24
Fuchsin, carbol (see Fuchsin basic)
Fuchsin NB, 137
Fuchsin RFN, 136
Fuchsin S, SN, SS, ST, or SIII, 143
Fuchsin, sulphurous acid, 40
Fungi staining of, 79, 96

Gallamin blue, 108
Gallo blue E, 109
Gallocyanin, 108
Gambine, 53
Gentian violet, 38, 146, **147**
  in Flemming stain, 121
Gentiana blue 6B, 155
Geranine G, 204
Giemsa stain, 96, 255–259
  assay of, 314
Glycogen, staining of, 241
Gold orange, 70
Gold orange MP, 68
Gold yellow, 88
Gonacrin, 197

Gossypimine, 119
Gram stain, 79, 121, 149–151, 168
Gray, R, P, BB, 125
Green PL, 53

Helianthin, 68
Heliotrope B, 122
Helvetia blue, 159
Hematein, 246
Hematoxylin, 27, 243, **244**
  assay of, 311
  in Masson's stain, 68
  with aniline blue WS, 158
  with carmine, 240
  with eosin and related dyes, 4, 176, 179, 181, 185
Hexamethyl violet, 149
Histochemistry, 5, 33, 40, 84, 131, 168, **210–235**
  rhodamine B in, 169
Hickson purple, 86
History of staining, 1–4
Hofmann's violet, 145
Hydrogen-ion indicators, 186–194
Hydroresorufin, 114
Hydroxy tri-phenylmethanes (Rosolic acids), 161–162

Imperial red, 178
Imperial yellow, 56
Impurities, influence of on intensity of staining, 31–32
Indamin dyes, 91
Indexes, dye, 28, 261, 262–271
Indicators, dyes as, 92, 160, 180–194
  acid fuchsin as, 144–145
  aniline blue as, 158
  resazurin as, 114
Indigo, 3, **237**
Indigo blue, 237
Indigo-carmine, 3, **237**
  assay of, 310
Indigotine Ia, 237
Indin blue, 2RD, 114
Indoine blue BR, R or BR, 89
Indole blue B or R, 89
Indophene blue, 89
Indophenol, 92
Indophenols, 91–93
Indophenol blue, 92

Indulin, 125
Indulins, 124–125
Indulin black, 125
Indulin, spirit soluble 124
Indulin, water soluble, 125
Influence of impurities on intensity of staining, 31–32
Insects, staining of, 69, 104
Iodeosin B and G, 180
Iodine green, 154
Iodine violet, 145
Iodo-nitro tetrazolium (INT), 232
Iris blue, 109
Iris violet, 122
Isamine blue, 159
Isohematein, 249
Isorubin, 137

Janus black, 67
Janus blue G or R, 89
Janus green B, 66, 116
  absorption curve of, 67
  assay of, 281
Janus red, 88
Jenner stain, 254
  assay of, 313

Kiton red S, 62
Kornhauser's "Quad" stain, 60, 135, 242

Lacmoid, 6, 55, 110
Lake ponceau, 64
Lauth's violet, 93
Leather brown, 79
Leather yellow, 198
Leishman stain, 254
Leuco compounds, 23–24
Leuco-fuchsin, 23
Leuco-methylene-blue, 23
Light blue, 155
Light green, 151
Light green 2G, S or 2GN, 133
Light green N, 130
Light green FS yellowish, 27, 133–134, 153
  absorption curve of, 135
  assay of, 298
  in Flemming stain, 121
Lissamine green B, BS, 164
Litmus, 242
Lyon blue, 155

"*Lyons blue*", 156
MacNeal's tetrachrome stain, 256
Madder, 3
Magdala red, 26, 123, 181, 183
"Magdala Rot der Handels", 124
"Magdala Rot echt", 124
Magenta O, 136
Magenta, 136
Magenta I, 137
Magenta II, 137
Magenta III, 137
Malachite green, 27, 70, 130
  absorption curve of, 49, 131
  assay of, 295
  in bacterial spore stain, 180
  in Pianese stain, 55
  in plant histology, 6
Malachite green A, B, BX, 4B, J3E, J3ES, NB, NH, or NJ, 130
Malachite green G, 132
Malarial parasites, staining of, 253, 255–256, 258
Manchester brown, 79
Manchester brown EE, 80
Manchester yellow, 55
Mandarin G, 70
Marine blue V, 156
Marshall red, 86
Martius yellow, 6, 55, 131
  assay of, 279
Masson's trichrome stain, 61–65, 68, 74, 78, 164, 236
Media, dyes in, 101, 116, 132, 140–142, 150, 158
Meldola's blue, 114
Mercurochrome, 179
Meta-cresol purple, 188, 189
Metanil yellow, 68
Methods for testing biological stains, 276–315
Methyl blue, 159
Methyl eosin, 177
Methyl green, 27, 151–153, 168
  absorption curve of, 135
  assay of, 302
  in Ehrlich's "tri-acid" stain, 60, 251, 252
  in plant histology, 6
Methyl orange, 68
  absorption curve of, 61
  assay of, 282

Methyl red, 72, 188
Methyl violet(s), 27, 79, 134, 146–149, 301
Methyl violet 2B, 146
  absorption curve of, 148
  assay of, 301
Methyl violet 10B, 149
Methylene azure, 96
Methylene blue, 22, 26, 47, 100, 162, 181
  absorption curve of, 50, 95
  assay of, 288
  polychrome, 102
  with eosin and related dyes, 178, 181, 183, 253–259
Methylene blue BX, B, BG, BB, 100
Methylene blue chloride, 100, 102
Methylene blue NN, 105
Methylene blue T 50 or T extra, 104
Methylene blue thiocyanate, 102
Methylene green, 104
Methylene violet (Bernthsen), 103, 256
  absorption curve of, 95
  assay of, 290
Methylene violet RRA or 3RA, 104
Michrome black salt 296, 227
Milori blue, 208
Mineral pigments, 207–209
Mitochondria, staining of, 144, 151, 168
Modern standardization of stains, 10–14
Mono-azo dyes, 57–73
Monotetrazolium salts, 231–233
Mordant yellow 2GT and PN, 89
Muci-carmine, 240

Naphthalene pink, 123
Naphthalene red, 123
Naphthamene blue 3BX, 84
Naphthamene brilliant blue 2R, 84
Naphthol blue R, 114
Naphthol blue black, 73, 83
Naphthol green B, 26, 53, 242
Naphthol green Y, 53
Naphthol orange, 70
Naphthol red S, C or O, 72
Naphthol yellow, 55
α-**Naphthylamine,** 228
Naphthylamine pink, 123
Narcein, 71
Natural dyes, 236–249
Nature of dyes and their classification, 15–33

Negri bodies, staining of, 99, 102, 178, 182, 238
Neotetrazolium, 233
Neptune blue BG, absorption curve of, 48
Nervous tissue, staining of, 81, 101, 108, 112, 159
  in small invertebrates, 200
Neutral acriflavine, 197
"Neutral gentian", 60
Neutral red, 21, 26, 116
  absorption curve of, 117
  assay of, 293
Neutral stains, 250–260
Neutral trypaflavine, 197
Neutral violet, 117
Neutroflavine, 197
New blue R, 114
New fuchsin, 25, 137
New methylene blue N, 105
New pink, 182
New ponceau 4R, 64
New victoria blue B or R, 163
New victorica green extra, O, I, or II, 130
Niagara blue 3B, 84
Niagara blue 4B, 86
Niagara sky blue 6B, 86
Night blue, 164
Nigrosin W, WL, etc., 125
Nigrosin, water soluble, 26, 125
  assay of, 294
Nile blue A, 110, 292
Nile blue sulfate, 26, 110
  absorption curve of, 107
  assay of, 292
Nitrazine, 63
Nitrazine yellow, 63
Nitro dyes, 53–56
Nitro BT, NBT, 234
Nitro blue tetrazolium, 234
Nitroneotetrazolium, 234
Nitroso dyes, 52–53
Nocht's stain, 253
Nomenclature and synonyms of dyes, 262–269
Napolin G, 178

Oil blue NA, 81, 203
Oil brown D, 65
Oil red IV, 75
Oil red AS, O, B or 3B, 74

Oil red 4B, 64, 77
Oil red O, 64, 76
Oil scarlet, 63
Oil vermillion, 65
Oil yellow, 89
Oil yellow D, 58
Oil yellow II, 58
Orange I, 70
Orange II, 70
  absorption curve of, 61
  assay of, 282
Orange III, 68
Orange IV, 69
Orange A, P or R, 70
Orange extra, 70
Orange G, 4, 6, 26, **59**
  absorption curve of, 48, 61
  assay of, 280
  for staining vaginal smears, 78
  in chromatography, 51
  in Ehrlich's "Tri-acid stain", 252
  in Flemming stain, 121, 158
  in Kornhauser's "Quad" stain, 272
Orange GG, GMP, 59
Orange MNO or MN, 68
Orange N, 69
Orange R, 89
Orange RR, 63
Orange S, 88
Orcein, 53, 158, **241**
  assay of, 312
Orseillin BB, 78
Oxazins, 106–115

Parafuchsin, 136
Paraleucanilin, 130
Paramagenta, 136
Pararosanilin, 136
Paris blue, 155, 208
Paris violet, 146
Patent blue V, 160
Patent blue, VF, 160
Phenazines, 21, 115
Pheno-safranin, 118
Phenolphthalein, 186, 188, **194**
Phenolphthalein and the sulfonphtha-
    leins, 185–194
Phenol red, 188, 193
Phenyl-methane dyes, 126–164
Phenylene blue, 114

Phenylene brown, 79
Phloxine, 124, 172, 173, **182**
Phloxine B, 182
  absorption curve of, 183
  assay of, 308
*Phloxine BB, BP super, N, RB, TA or
  TB,* 182
Phosphine, 198
Phosphine 3R, 198
Physical theory of staining, 35
Phthalocyanine dyes, 207
Phytolacca, 3
Picric acid, 22, 26, 54, 152, 154, 159
  with carmine, 240
  with hematoxylin, 248
Pigments, mineral, 207–208
Pinacyanol, 27, **206**
Pollen tubes, staining of, 55, 58, 68–69,
  110, 133
Polychrome methylene blue, 102
Ponceau B, 77
"Ponceau de xylidine", 61, 62, 64
Ponceau S, 78
Ponceau 2R, 64
Ponceau 6R, 89
*Ponceau FR, G, 4R, GR, J, NR, R, RG,
  2RE,* 64
Pontacyl blue black SX, 73
Pontacyl brilliant blue V, 160
Pontacyl green S, 164
Pontamine black E, EX, or EXX, 87
Pontamine sky blue 5BX, 86
Pontamine sky blue 6BX, 86
Pontamine violet N, 89
Primula R water soluble, 145
Primulin, 205
Primulin yellow, 205
Proflavine, 197
Prontosil, 69
Prontisil red, 69
Protargol S, 209
  assay of, 314
Protozoa, staining of, 81, 84, 200
Prune pure, 108
Purpurin, 201
Prussian blue, 208
Pyoktanin yellow, 128
Pyoktaninum aureum, 128
Pyoktanium coeruleum, 146
Pyronin(s), 165–168

Pyronin B, 27, 156, **168**
 absorption curve of, 167
 assay of, 310
Pyronin G, 166
Pyronin Y, 27, **166**
 absorption curve of, 167
 assay of, 309
Pyrosin B, 180
Pyrosin J, 180

Quinalizarin, 202
Quinoline dyes, 206–207
Quinone-imine dyes, 90–125

Red B, 63
Red corallin, 162
Red violet, 145
Relation of molecular structure to color,
 17–19
Renol black G, 87
Resazurin, 114
 absorption curve of, 107
Resorcin blue, 109
Resorufin, 114
Rheonine A, 198
Rheonine AL, G or N, 198
Rhodamine B, 27, **169**
Rhodamine 6G, 169
Rhodamine 6GX and 6GDN extra, 169
Rhodamine O, 169
Rhodamine S, 170
Rhodamines, 168–171
Ribonucleic acid, detection of, 40
Rivanol, 196
Roccellin, 89
Romanovsky stain, 253
Rosanilin, 137
Rosanilin picrate, 260
Rosanilins, 136–161
Rosazine, 122
Rose bengal, 27, 32, 172, 173, **184**
 absorption curve of, 183
 assay of, 308
Rose bengal AT, B, N, NT or NTO, 184
Rose bengal extra, 3B conc., N extra, DY,
 B or 2B, 184
Rose bengal G, 184
Rose SA, 184
Rosinduline GXF, 122
Rosolic acid, 27, **162**

Rosolic acid dyes, 161–162
Rosophenine 10B, 73
Ruthenium red, 208
Rubidin, 89

Saffron, 3, **236**
Saffrosin, 178
Safranin(s), 118–124
Safranin AG, T, MP, and G, 119
Safranin B extra, 118
Safranin blue R, 89
Safranin extra bluish, 122
Safranin O, 26, **119,** 134
 absorption curve of, 120
 assay of, 294
 in Kalter's quadruple stain, 71
 in plant microtechnic, 6
 with methyl blue, 159
 "Safranin pur", 122
Safranin Y or A, 119
Salacin black D, 89
Scarlet B or EC, 77
Scarlet B, fat soluble, 74
Scarlet, J, JJ, V, 178
Scarlet R, 64, 75
Scarlet red, 75
"Scharlach R", 75
Schiff's reagent, 24, 139–140
Sensitol red, 206
Silver gray, 125
Silver protienates, 209
Sky blue, 208
Solid green JJO, 132
Solid green O, 130
Solubilities of dyes, 29, 31, 272–275
Soluble blue 3M or 2R, 156
Soluble indulin 3B, 125
Soluble yellow OL, 68
Sorbine red, 62
Spectrophotometer, diagram of, 44, 45, 46
Spectrophotometric analysis of dyes,
 41–51
Spectrum, table of, 42
Spirit blue, 155, 240
Spirit indulin, 124
Spirit nigrosin R, 124
Spirochaetes, staining of, 156, 163, 185
Standardization of biological stains,
 10–14
Steel blue, 208

Steel gray, 125
Sudan II, 63
Sudan III, 26, 57, **74**
  absorption curve of, 75
  assay of, 283
Sudan IV, 26, 57, **75**
  absorption curve of, 75
  assay of, 283
Sudan black B, 87
  absorption curve of, 75
  assay of, 286
Sudan brown, 65
Sudan brown AN and 5B, 65
Sudan G, 74, 89
Sudan R, 65
Sudan R III, 66
Sudan red, 123
Sudan red 4B, 64
Sudan red 7B, 76
Sulphonphthaleins, 185–194
Sultan 4B, 82
Swiss blue, 100
Synonymy and nomenclature of stains,
  262–269

Tables relating to stains, 261–271
Tartrazine, absorption curve of, 48
Testing biological stains, methods for,
  276–315
Tetrachrome blood stain, MacNeal's, 256
  assay of, 313
Tetrazolium salts, 230–235
Tetrazolium violet, 232
Tetrazonium and Diazonium salts, 210–
  229
Theories of staining, 34–40
Thiazin eosinates, 253–259
Thiazine red R, 73
Thiazins, 93–106
Thiazol dyes, 204–206
Thiazol yellow, 205
Thioflavine S, 206
Thioflavine T, 206
Thioflavine TG, 206
Thionin, 6, 26, 50, **93**
  absorption curve of, 50, 95
  assay of, 287
Thionin blue, 94
Thymol blue, 188, 189
Titan yellow G, 27, **205**
Toluidine blue O, 26, **104, 185**

  absorption curve of, 98
  assay of, 290
Toluylene blue, 91
Toluylene red, 116
Tony red, 74
Tri-acid stain, Ehrlich's, 252
  Pappenheim panoptic, 260
Tri-amino-tri-phenyl methanes, 136–161
"Triosin", 176
Tri-phenyl methanes, 129–162
**Triphenyl   tetrazolium   chloride
  (TTC), 231**
Tropaeolin D, 68
Tropaeolin G, 68, 70
Tropaeolin O, 88
Tropaeolin OO, 69
Tropaeolin OOO No. 1, 70
Tropaeolin OOO No. 2, 70
Tropaeolin Y, 88
Trypaflavine, 196
Trypan blue, 84
Trypan red, 82
TTC, 231
Tubercle organism, staining of, 70, 142,
  162, 164
Tumor tissue, staining of, 55, 112, 131, 144

Union green B, 66
Uranin, 174
Uses and standardization of biological
  stains, 1–14
Uses of stains, 4–7

Vaginal smears, staining of, 78, 238
Van Gieson's connective tissue stain, 54,
  78, 135, 144, 248
Variamine blue B, 227
Vesuvin, 79
Vesuvin NR, B, R, 80
Victoria blue B, 27, **163**
Victoria blue R, 27, **163**
Victoria blue 4R, 156
Victoria green B or WB, 130
Victoria green G, 88
Victoria rubin O, 72
Violamine 3B, 170
Violamine R, 170
Violet C, G, or 7B, 149
Violet PDH, 108
Violet R, RR or 4RN, 145
Vital new red, 85

Vital red, 83
Vital staining, 82–86, 107, 200

War, biological stains in time of, 8
Water blue, 156
Wool green BS, BSN A or C, 164
Wool green S, 164
Wool orange 2G, 59
Wool red, 72
Wright's stain, 254–259
  assay of, 313

Xanthin, 198
Xanthene dyes, 165–198
XL Carmoisene 6R, 60
Xylene cyanol FF, 160
"Xylidine ponceau", 61, 62, 64
Xylidine ponceau 3RS, 64

Yeast, staining of, 81, 83, 163
Yellow corrallin, 162
Yellow M, 68
Yellow WR, 70